D1269208

WILDLIFE MANAGEMENT

Fur Bearers, Waterfowl, and Fish

The American Forestry Series

HENRY J. VAUX, *Consulting Editor*

ALLEN AND SHARPE · An Introduction to American Forestry
BAKER · Principles of Silviculture
BOYCE · Forest Pathology
BROCKMAN · Recreational Use of Wild Lands
BROWN, PANSHIN, AND FORSAITH · Textbook of Wood Technology
Volume I—Structure, Identification, Defects, and Uses of the Commercial Woods of the United States
Volume II—The Physical, Mechanical, and Chemical Properties of the Commercial Woods of the United States
BRUCE AND SCHUMACHER · Forest Mensuration
CHAPMAN AND MEYER · Forest Mensuration
CHAPMAN AND MEYER · Forest Valuation
DANA · Forest and Range Policy
DAVIS · American Forest Management
DAVIS · Forest Fire: Control and Use
DUERR · Fundamentals of Forestry Economics
GRAHAM · Forest Entomology
GREELEY · Forest Policy
GUISE · The Management of Farm Woodlands
HARLOW AND HARRAR · Textbook of Dendrology
HUNT AND GARRATT · Wood Preservation
PANSHIN, HARRAR, BAKER, AND PROCTOR · Forest Products
PRESTON · Farm Wood Crops
SHIRLEY · Forestry and Its Career Opportunities
STODDART AND SMITH · Range Management
TRIPPENSEE · Wildlife Management
Volume I—Upland Game and General Principles
Volume II—Fur Bearers, Waterfowl, and Fish
WACKERMAN · Harvesting Timber Crops

Walter Mulford was Consulting Editor of this series from its inception in 1931 until January 1, 1952.

Sketch of rainbow trout jumping for fly.

WILDLIFE MANAGEMENT

Fur Bearers, Waterfowl, and Fish

Volume II

REUBEN EDWIN TRIPPENSEE
Professor of Wildlife Management
Department of Forestry and Wildlife Management
University of Massachusetts

New York Toronto London
McGRAW-HILL BOOK COMPANY
1953

WILDLIFE MANAGEMENT: FUR BEARERS, WATERFOWL, AND FISH

Library of Congress Catalog Card Number: Agr. 48-285

9 10 11 12 13 14 15 16 - MPMM - 1 0 9

65196

Preface

The importance of managing wild lands on a sound scientific basis is becoming increasingly evident as the human population and its needs increase. As our population grows from its present 150 million to 200 million and probably more, we have no choice but to conserve our soil and water and to manage each acre for its greatest productiveness. This concept applies not only to the better soils but also to the neglected areas now generally regarded as wasteland, such as swamps, marshes, and ocean borders, and the drier lands ill-suited in their present state to produce plentiful plant growth. Many such areas may never become especially productive of domesticated plants, but for the production of wild animal crops they may be excellent, particularly the wetter situations which, if properly managed, will yield fish, birds, and mammals in abundance, and by so doing will provide food, clothing, and healthful recreation for our growing millions of people.

Good land management, however, entails more than making neglected areas productive. It concerns the wise use of *all* lands, much of which can be made to serve several purposes simultaneously without seriously jeopardizing the success of any one type. Fortunately, wildlife management often fits admirably into such a plan of multiple use. This is not only true in conjunction with the practice of forestry, but applies also in the science of agriculture. That wildlife management in one form or another may be adapted to nearly all programs of land use is a fact deserving major emphasis.

At present we know too little about the value of our natural land resources or the techniques of managing them, and no concerted effort to use our resources well is evident over extensive land areas. Basic resources like surface water are allowed to deteriorate or are wasted while at the same time we seek new sources of the same materials. By allowing the waste or deterioration of some resources, we destroy the value of others, a good example being the effect of water pollution and poor watershed management on fish and other aquatic life. Until we as a nation regard all land resources—the soil, water, vegetation, and wildlife—as a natural heritage to be conserved against waste and managed for maximum productivity, only then can it be said we have fulfilled our responsibilities.

There remains to be mentioned the recreational values of wildlife. In a highly organized society, and particularly a highly industrialized one such as ours, the need for clean, healthful recreation is readily apparent. No better form of relaxation exists than the quiet peacefulness associated with fishing and hunting. The money spent each year on this kind of activity is eloquent testimony to the important place it holds in the lives of many millions of people. The monetary value of such recreation is important in itself, but the social values, though not susceptible of measurement, are unquestionably of vastly greater worth to the nation in terms of better health, happier outlook, and longer years of service.

This volume of *Wildlife Management* is the second and last in the series. The first, which was published in 1948, discussed the general principles of wildlife management, and the life histories, ecology, and management of upland game species. The present book includes four parts. Section I relates to water, its conservation, and the management of swamp and marsh habitats. The remaining three sections are concerned with the life histories, ecology, and management of fur bearers, waterfowl, and game fish.

REUBEN EDWIN TRIPPENSEE

AMHERST, MASS.
June, 1953

Acknowledgments

It is with great pleasure that I thank those who so willingly helped to make this book possible. Unfortunately, not all who have given assistance can be acknowledged by name, but their contributions are nonetheless appreciated.

A number of people have contributed entire parts of the manuscript relating to special phases of the subject. These men include Dr. Ira N. Gabrielson of the Wildlife Management Institute; Stanley P. Young, U.S. Fish and Wildlife Service; Dr. Clarence M. Tarzwell, U.S. Public Health Service; Dr. R. W. Eschmeyer, Sports Fishing Institute; and Dr. Louis A. Krumholz, Tennessee Valley Authority. Special thanks are due these contributors.

Descriptions of waterfowl habitats in many parts of North America were written by Dr. Clarence C. Cottam, U.S. Fish and Wildlife Service; Fred G. Evenden, Jr., of the same organization; Joseph A. Hagar, Massachusetts State Ornithologist; and W. G. Leitch, Ducks Unlimited, Canada. These descriptions have added materially to the value of the chapters on waterfowl.

Contributions in the form of compilations and suggestions have been made by the following men in or attached to the Department of Forestry and Wildlife Management at the University of Massachusetts: Prof. Robert P. Holdsworth; Prof. Arnold D. Rhodes; Dr. William G. Sheldon, leader of the Massachusetts Cooperative Wildlife Research Unit; and Donald R. Progulske, a student at the University. Special appreciation is due Prof. Paul W. Stickel for his valuable assistance.

Reading of special sections of the manuscript with suggestions for its improvement was done by Frank G. Ashbrook, U.S. Fish and Wildlife Service; Dr. William R. Hamilton, Jr., Cornell University; Richard H. Stroud, Massachusetts Department of Conservation; Harry Everhart, University of Maine; and Joseph Hagar, Massachusetts Conservation Department. Edward N. Munns, U.S. Forest Service, assisted with the chapter on water. Dr. Neil W. Hosley gave excellent suggestions on the entire volume.

Diagrams and sketches were produced by the skilled pens and brushes of Herb Chidley, Peter Ward, Wilma Cashin, Barbara Johnson, and

Clayt Seagears. Able assistance on illustrations was given by the U.S. Fish and Wildlife Service, U.S. Soil Conservation Service, Michigan, New York, Virginia, Massachusetts, and Wisconsin Conservation Departments. Preparation of the manuscript for submission to the publishers was the painstaking work of Mrs. Edward Cooley and Mary O'Brien.

It is fitting also to acknowledge the indirect contributions of the many research workers in the wildlife field whose findings serve as the basis for books of this type. To this large group of scientists, some anonymous, I am greatly indebted.

To my wife, Gertrude Fox Trippensee, I owe a special debt of gratitude. Her helpful suggestions and unfailing faith were pillars of strength that made completion of the task possible. To her I give both thanks and affection.

REUBEN EDWIN TRIPPENSEE

Contents

FISH

SECTION ONE

Foundations of Wildlife Production

CHAPTER 1

Water and Its Conservation

A man rests briefly beside a rocky ledge. Nearby, his pack animal stands with its head down and feet wide apart in a posture of total fatigue. Man and beast have walked twenty miles to reach this spot, but there is no joy of accomplishment in the arrival. The whole attitude of both is one of disappointment and despair. It shows in the dull look of the man's eyes and the dejected posture of the tired burro. No sound of water has rewarded the travelers for their long journey. No reflection of light has come from the old spring bed.

The spring has dried up; the water has gone.

A businessman sits down to breakfast in his country home. The view through the window shows a riot of color in the fall foliage, with maple trees that are a glory of brilliant red and golden yellow. A look of despair passes over the man's face as he sees the headline in the morning paper. For the headline spells disaster: silent factory wheels, men out of work, and hungry women and children. The headline reads: WATER SUPPLY OF WEAVERVILLE FAILS!

A farmer is standing in a pleasant farmyard beside a wooden pump. The handle is worn smooth, and there are small depressions in the wood where fingers have grasped the handle in years past. The pump gives forth a hollow cough as the plunger moves up and down in a waterless cylinder. The horses rattle their harness impatiently as they press their muzzles along the bottom of the mossy watering trough. A terrifying thought passes through the farmer's mind as he pumps the handle faster and faster.

The well has gone dry!

A fisherman brushes the perspiration from his forehead as he rests on a boulder beside a stream. The surroundings are wild but familiar. The spot is far from the highway, and few creatures have been here except the deer and raccoons in their nightly wanderings. He has always found the brook at this point deep and dark, running swiftly under the shade of green hemlocks, and with trout that disappear swiftly in the pools and along the riffles as he approaches. It has been a hard two hours' walk, but the effort has usually paid big dividends in a singing reel and a full creel.

Now all is changed. Last winter the watershed had been logged, and this summer the forest burned. Now in place of a deep, cool stream the boulders are dry and bleached. The water no longer fills the bank cavities and rock-strewn stream bed.

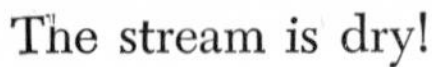

The stream is dry!

PROPERTIES OF WATER

Fresh water is vital to life. It is one of the four items basic to our existence, along with soil, air, and solar radiation. The importance of fresh water for drinking far exceeds its utility for bathing, recreation, or commercial uses. Man is so dependent on an abundant supply of fresh, cool water that most of his activities are found in the humid regions of the earth (12, 28).[1] There are cases, however, where other factors of the environment, such as high or low air temperatures, may restrict the highest development of civilization and so nullify the significance of abundant water supplies. In such areas there may be either too much water or water in a form unavailable to plants and animals.

At this time, when shortages are bringing the water question to the foreground, it is apparent that under the present standard of living everyone needs water in prodigious amounts (31).

> Even the man who drinks no water is in trouble! It takes fifteen gallons of water to produce a gallon of beer and seven to ten gallons to produce a gallon of gasoline. Manufacturers of steel, rubber, and even ice need lots of water to operate (30). People living in the West need as much water as those in the East, although the average rainfall is much less in the former locality. Intensive industry in the East, as well as greater human population densities, creates a greater overall water problem there (52 *g.r.*, 4).

The sea is our greatest reservoir of water, but sea water is not suitable for use by most animals or plants because of its high mineral content. With the energy of the sun, sea water is transferred to the land and is transformed from unusable to usable supplies by natural means. All of our supply of fresh water comes from rain or snow. Some of this is held in lakes and ponds, but more is stored in the soil where it moves into underground reservoirs or emerges later to replenish and sustain rivers, springs, and wells. The average rainfall for the United States is 30 inches, but this is greater in the East and Northwest and less in the West and Southwest. About half of our daily supply of water comes from underground supplies, and the remainder is taken from surface supplies (23, 30). Although the highest use of water by man and animals is for drinking purposes, water is also needed to provide sufficient moisture in the soil to produce agricultural and forage crops and forests, and to maintain the ground water which is sometimes pumped many miles for domestic and industrial uses.

Water, like many other gifts of God, is endowed with both beneficial

[1] Numbers in parentheses refer to references at the end of the chapter unless accompanied by the notation *g.r.*, which refers to general references at the end of the book.

and harmful attributes, depending on its stability. Rapidly flowing water moves soil, destroys stream banks, and when carrying abrasive materials, prevents the development and growth of aquatic life. Soil carried by moving water may be transported from its place of origin to locations where it may cover other fertile soils elsewhere, thus destroying additional productive capacity, or it may silt in water reservoirs (1, 24). Water clouded by silt is less productive of plant and animal life than is clear water.

Water may or may not be useful to man, animals, and plants, depend-

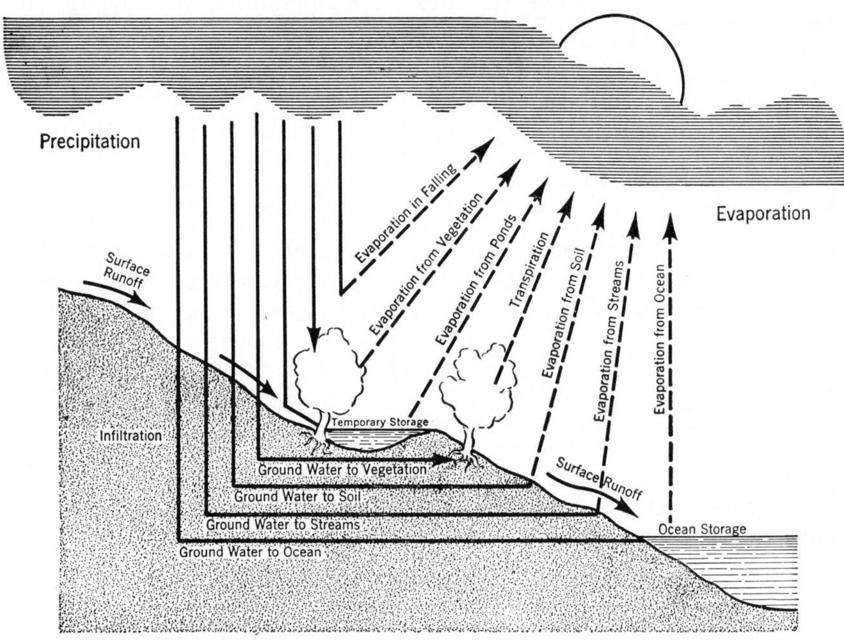

FIG. 1-1. The hydrologic cycle. The cycle in which moisture is received by the earth and returns to the atmosphere. (*From Little Waters*, 24.)

ing on its physical and chemical condition. Physically, water may be too warm or too cold as a habitat for aquatic animals, for the growth of aquatic plants, and for human or industrial uses. For drinking purposes, temperatures between 40 and 50°F. are desirable. Different species of fish have optimum water temperatures for spawning, hatching of eggs, and for other life processes.

The oxygen content of water is vital to animals living in it. This gaseous ingredient is likewise somewhat dependent on water temperature, cold water being capable of containing more oxygen than warm water, although the need for oxygen is greater in warmer than colder waters. A lack of sufficient oxygen may exclude some forms of aquatic animal life altogether (25).

The chemical content of water is also important. Water containing too much mineral—sea water, for example—or chemical compounds having objectionable tastes or odors is unsuitable for use by human beings and lower animals. A balance between oxygen and carbon may determine the fertility of water, as will also its content of various nitrogenous compounds. Where much plant or animal matter is decomposing in water, the amount of free oxygen may not be sufficient for supporting any but a few low animal forms.

Slightly acid waters, as against alkaline waters, are very desirable from the standpoint of bathing and for use for laundry purposes but are less productive of life forms than are those containing more nitrogen and carbon.

Under natural conditions in humid regions water has both beauty and utility. Both still and moving water can be pure, attractive, and productive. Radiation of the sun, exposure to oxygen in the air, and the presence of living plants and animals produce this kind of water. The balance between plants and animals is one of the wonders of nature and in part accounts for the beauty and high productiveness of primeval waters. As part of this system, trees and other plants prevent erosion on the higher hillsides, and aquatic vegetation, both floating and anchored, prevents soils and other materials in the water from covering submerged plants and animals and provides an anchorage for lower forms of animal life. Carnivores, always present in limited numbers, consume and convert dead bodies of animals to living flesh, and higher animals constantly consume the lower forms, which in turn live on plants of various kinds. Low water temperatures are usually maintained in temperate climates where shade is available along the shores of rivers and ponds (34).

Primeval waters, like those found under conditions of high human populations, vary greatly in conditions of temperature, kinds and numbers of plants and animals present, and the basins which contain them. Lakes may be clear or murky, have sand or mud bottoms, be clear of vegetation or choked with plant life, depending on altitude, latitude, and the geological age of the country in which they are found. Likewise, the fish and other animals found in water will be those suited to the quality of both the water and the surrounding lands. Cool rapid streams contain trout, while warm sluggish streams contain bass or other warm-water fish. Some deep, cold lakes will support lake trout, while others support bass and pond fishes.

Biologically, water may be fertile or sterile depending on the degree to which its properties meet the needs of these various organisms. Warm, fertile waters, providing they carry sufficient oxygen, will contain a wider variety of species and more individuals per unit of volume than will colder waters. However, with all animal life there is a basic dependence on plants for synthesizing simple inorganic elements into more complex organic compounds before they are edible. In general, then, abundant plant growth in waters is an indicator of fertility and therefore also indicates the amount of animal life present. Some animals live directly on plants, while others live on lower animal forms. Concerning the populations of animals in water, Adams and Trippensee state (1 *g.r.*):

> Temperature, food, predators, parasites, natural barriers such as mountains, oceans, etc., are all factors limiting the population of animals and plants. Only the species capable of combatting environmental resistances are able to perpetuate themselves in their habitat. Some forms of life possess a wide natural tolerance to various climatic and biotic factors, while others are very exacting in their requirements and so are limited in distribution.

PROCESSES OF NATURE AND EFFECTS OF CIVILIZATION ON WATER QUANTITY AND QUALITY

It is probable that the activities of man have not changed to a great extent the amount of water that falls on the earth as rain. Even this is not an indisputable contention, because the removal of vegetation over large areas may affect the amount of rain that falls locally. Both nature and the works of man, however, have affected the amount of water that is available for human use and for the production of animals. These changes have come about through the processes of geology; lumbering; agriculture, including grazing, drainage, and impounding of waters; siltation; and pollution. Except geology, which is a natural process, all of these are legitimate activities if conducted properly and with consideration to their effect on the landscape. A most obvious injurious effect would be the destruction of a run of migrating fish by building a dam across a river for the purpose of producing electrical energy where the value of the resource destroyed is greater than the value of the energy created.

> Almost every human activity that has had an effect on our water supply has an alternate course that would have served as well without too much damage to other values. These alternate courses are just now beginning to receive attention and will help to solve some of the difficult problems in relation to water (21).

The discussion which follows is an attempt to point out some of the relationships between the various natural phenomena and the activities of man as they affect fish, birds, or other wildlife involved in the handling of water.

Land Changes. All our soils have in the past come under the influence of the action of ice, water, wind, or gravity. Soils slowly removed from highlands have built up in the lowlands or in the ocean along the continental shelves. Lakes in plateaus have been drained by the cutting action of rivers, and former water areas have been transformed into land habitats. Thus, former high, deep-soil vegetation, such as forests which sheltered deer, moose, bears, and grouse, have changed after the removal of the soil so that they produce only primitive plant forms, shrubby vegetation, and early-succession animal life such as snakes, pikas, and mountain goats.

High lakes which originally supported typical cold-water fishes changed after drainage first to barren exposed lake bottoms, then later to grass, and finally to beaver flowages or possibly deep-forest habitats. Any land will finally reach a forested condition if enough rainfall is present and nature is allowed to take its course. Soil and rocks are kept in place by plant roots, so waters in forested areas are clear and usually constant in flow. Decaying leaf mold has the effect of keeping soils porous and in place by preventing rain from striking the mineral soil directly.

Lumbering. Cutting of trees and logging may have a profound effect on the land on which a forest grows. Entire hillsides may move after a destructive timber-cutting operation, because of the effects of water and frost. Streams may become gouged by wood pulp, and ravines may be started by logging operations that a thousand years of time will not erase. After trees are removed, water may be warmed beyond the tolerance of one fish species and into the range of another. Springs may dry up, swamps disappear, and the water-holding capacity of the forest soil itself may be altered. All this because of the operation of removing the trees.

Cows and Corn. Agriculture and grazing may include many operations that affect the amount and movements of water in relation to animal life. The lower forms of animal life in soil are affected by changes in the moisture and organic materials in the soil. Good surfaces which are covered with vegetation and soil in which root tendrils are abundantly present tend to be porous and to act as host to many low forms of animals, including earthworms. Soils where leaching has occurred tend to have minerals concentrated at different levels. Water evaporation to a limited extent is determined by the wind velocity that passes over the surface, and this in turn is determined by the vegetation barriers which break the force of the wind. The soil-moisture content is affected by cultivation or packing of the soil, as well as by the amount of plant material on the surface. Handling of pastures to prevent gullies and keeping soil tied down in place help to keep land at the lower levels clear of silt and streams free from sediment. The number of cows on a distant hillside may determine whether a new crop of fish eggs hatch in a nearby stream or additional earthworms develop in the field below.

Drainage and Water Impoundments. Much has been written about the values of water bodies developed by dams or other barriers. Some of these values are real and some are fallacious. Frequently the same water caught downstream in impoundments, if kept at the place where it fell, would have cost less and would have been of greater value.

FIG. 1-2. Water in abundance is essential to life. Impoundment of water is especially important in arid climates. (*W. F. Kubichek, U.S. Fish and Wildlife Service.*)

Gabrielson (13) points out that river impoundments often change the fish life of a river from one of great value, as trout, bass, or other game fish, to species of less value, such as carp, suckers, and buffalo. Also, if a swamp or marsh is destroyed, a set of purely aquatic and low-value species like turtles, snakes, and fish, may replace the semiaquatic high-value species such as fur bearers, waterfowl, and shore birds. Gabrielson (13) also suggests that the initial production of fish is generally greater than that produced after the "bank account of fertility" has been used up. He also says that waters with fluctuating levels frequently do not produce beyond the area of minimum flowage. With all impoundments there are the hazards of destroying valuable migratory runs of fish. Also, the period of usefulness of the water may be affected by the silting in of the area back of the dam. Nearly all these aspects of impounding waters have been ignored by both private corporations and governmental agencies where engineering rather than biological skill has been the chief background of the builder. All these hazards can be eliminated and the permanence of the value of water arrived at, if the same thought and effort is applied to the water in the location where it falls.

Temporary Nature of Reservoirs. The problem of siltation has many headaches for other than the wildlife manager. Siltation is the process of a stream dropping its load of suspended materials as the rate of flow is reduced back of a dam. This process has cost the people of the United States billions of dollars in lost water and construction costs over a relatively short period of time. Hugh H. Bennett (11 *g.r.*), head of the U.S. Soil Conservation Service, says there are over 3,000 reservoirs in the United States and that more than one-third of these will have to be replaced or supplemented within the next 50 years because of excessive silting. This prospect is enough to cause water-company officials to develop ulcers, but it also involves the health, well-being, and pocketbooks of millions of citizens, in addition to heavy taxes for replacement of water-storage facilities.

Pollution, Our National Shame. An abundance of fish for food and sport, of furs for clothing, and of waterfowl for food and recreational purposes is dependent on a constant supply of clean water (3, 10). When water becomes polluted or varies too widely as to amount or quality, some or possibly all of the aquatic life disappears. Under adverse water conditions man loses not only the value of the animals that live in the water but also the use of the water itself. Where waters become badly polluted, man is forced to resort to expensive means to again make them usable.

> Pollution has been rightly termed our "national shame." One has only to view the streams flowing through the thickly settled parts of the United States to gather evidence of our national folly (37).

Eyes and nose will tell us how far we are from the outlet of a village sewer or the discharge of a canning factory or chemical plant. Nor are the larger corporations more guilty than the smaller communities or individuals. Tin cans, automobile tires, and discarded mattresses often meet the eye at every turn of a river or brook where these have been dumped by thoughtless individuals. Not only is pollution bad aesthetics, but it is also poor economics since much of the materials discarded has value for reconversion purposes.

Fundamentally, many of the causes of pollution are attributable to poor background training in neatness and good housekeeping. We need to train our youth and ourselves to be shocked and moved to action when someone dumps papers or tin cans along the roadside or throws garbage into a lake or a stream. We need to develop the same reaction toward a misused pond border or an abused stream that we have attempted to develop toward personal bad manners or national disloyalty. Certainly pollution of water is just as damaging to national strength as is any other act of vandalism. Wasting of materials that can be used for the support or preservation of a growing nation should be considered just as much of a menace to the public welfare as giving aid and comfort to an enemy. There seems to be no part of the country, however, that has done better than any other in the problem of keeping natural waters clean and free from misuse. The breweries of Missouri and Illinois have fouled the waters of their states with brewers' waste; the sawmills of New England and the Northwest have plugged the streams with sawdust; coal mines of Pennsylvania, West Virginia, and other states dumped coal wastes into their rivers and poisoned the waters for many miles with acids; chemical plants and dairies in Florida and Wisconsin have dumped chemicals and dairy wastes into the nearest stream. The populations of 3,400 cities and towns dump 2½ billion gallons of raw sewage into our waterways every day, according to Harvey (15). The economic loss of the materials discarded is enormous, but the loss through impaired health is still greater. When will these wasteful processes stop? Only as soon as the public understands what is happening and how a cure can be brought about. Events like dust storms in the Middle West and waterless days in New York City will help to dramatize the condition and indicate the need for action.

The problem of pollution appears so complex and diverse it seems wise to simplify it by classifying pollutants into a few broad categories.

Industrial Wastes. Practically all industrial wastes dumped into streams or ponds are detrimental in one way or another for humans, and many of the pollutants have a harmful effect on wildlife. A few examples of the losses through pollution are given below.

Industrial pollutants are so diverse in both kind and effect on wildlife that only a few examples can be given. The term "industrial waste" is a social rather than a substance classification, as it may include bacteria, organic matter (both plant and animal substances), acids, metals, milk, or hot water. The wastes may come from factories or groups of factories in which thousands of people earn their living, or they may come from a one-man shop. The harm done to water may vary from the extreme of poisoning it for all uses to making it only distasteful or giving it a bad odor. Some wastes use up all the oxygen in the water so that fish and other life smother, while other pollutants kill the food organisms, and still others destroy life by combining with materials in the water to produce a poison not present before the pollutant is dumped in. Substances like sawdust or milk products may blanket the stream bed and destroy fish eggs or may cover areas which produce insects or other aquatic life used as food by fish. Coal dust and other mineral wastes may completely fill the stream or pond and change the habitat from water to dry land, or at least something other than water.

Domestic Wastes. Domestic wastes include sewage and kitchen wastes. Considered from the health standpoint, these are very dangerous in terms of disease, particularly if they get into drinking-water sources. It is the prevention of disease caused by domestic wastes that results in the high-cost treatment of water which is to be used for human con-

FIG. 1-3. A river being polluted by industrial and domestic wastes. (*Hermann Postlethwaite, U.S. Soil Conservation Service.*)

sumption. Typhoid fever, diphtheria, gastroenteritis or diarrhea, cholera, and possibly poliomyelitis (infantile paralysis) may result if drinking water is not treated before use. The examples where time and life have been lost through sickness caused by polluted drinking water are almost too numerous to mention. Bill Davidson (8) lists dozens of cases where, through error, cities have had bad epidemics of gastroenteritis and other digestive disorders because drinking water has been contaminated and in fact says that mistakes of this kind occurred 327 times between 1938 and 1945.

Another detrimental effect of domestic sewage is the contamination of oyster and mussel beds and infection of fish with disease organisms so they cannot be used for human food. Millions of dollars worth of shellfish are lost each year because of the contamination of mussel beds with human waste. Other losses result from bathing beaches being contaminated with domestic waste. These losses are not easily reduced to dollar values, but nevertheless they are of considerable volume.

Domestic waste may not kill fish or other aquatic life if poured into streams in moderate amounts. In fact, mild doses of domestic sewage may stimulate the growth of aquatic organisms and in turn increase the production of fish. Few people, however, want to fish in a sewer, even if the fish are twice as large or twice as numerous, so this is no reason for allowing pollution in streams or ponds. The danger of fishing or eating fish products from polluted waters is so great that many people refuse to fish in such places.

Silt. Silt has been washing downhill and into our streams ever since the pioneers cut the first trees on a hillside on the Atlantic coast more than 300 years ago. It is natural and inevitable for soil particles to move downhill, but with natural vegetation growing on the slopes and hillsides the process is so slow that little harm is done. As an aftermath of destructive cutting of timberlands, forest fires, overgrazing of pastures and cultivation of farm lands up and down the slopes, fine particles of topsoil are carried downhill by rains and find their way into the water courses and ponds of the nation. This loss of soil is bad from an agricultural standpoint; it is also damaging to the waters which receive it. The present discussion is concerned with this damage.

The destruction of fish spawning beds by coverings of silt is well documented. Mud fills the crevices between the gravel, thus preventing the free flow of water around the pebbles, and kills the eggs and other aquatic life that seek protection among the gravel and rock particles of a stream bottom.

Muddy water destroys aquatic vegetation, both free and anchored. The vegetation may be a source of food for fish or waterfowl, or it may be only protection or "housing" for some of the lower forms of life. It is a most important link in the chain of the life of the waters, however, and anything that breaks this chain affects the whole life structure above it.

In many of the northern waters, shifting sand in streams, lakes, and ponds may limit practically all productivity of these waters. These sands, being constantly on the move, furnish no anchorage for plants nor protection for aquatic animals or fish eggs. Shifting aquatic sands are even more barren of aquatic life than are shifting desert sands.

Partial muddying of streams or ponds may not bar all aquatic life but nevertheless has the undesirable effect of allowing the less desirable forms—such as catfish, suckers, and carp—to increase. Once carp take over, they tend to stop natural succession by keeping the waters muddy with their foraging activities, even though no new sources of silt are added. Silt which covers meadows at high water may eventually produce fertile lands, but during the time the siltation is occurring, such areas are quite devoid of animal life.

Costs of Pollution and Pollution Abatement. The need for pollution abatement has been bandied around our legislative halls for the past 50 years, but little has been done to cure present conditions or prevent new sources of pollution from developing (32). A few ardent and hard-working groups like the Isaak Walton League have been trying to arouse the public to the cost of our present practices and the need for a change in attitude, but the cost of pollution as opposed to the cost of preventing it has thus far not been apparent to the public. Thus, we have gone on trying to get new sources of pure water and treating polluted water with chemicals when it would have been more economical to prevent the contamination in the first place. An additional angle of the pollution problem on the credit side of the ledger is that pollution prevention pays. Many of the items now dumped into the streams can and should be salvaged. We cannot afford to lose the resources now so disposed of nor the profit that can be made by salvaging them. The present process is not only dangerous and expensive but also economically unsound. At this date (1952) a start has been made to prevent the use of waterways as open gutters.

Losses from pollution may be classified as human losses, food losses, recreational losses, corrosion losses, water losses, material losses, and wildlife losses.

Human Losses. Human losses include loss of life, time lost because of sickness, and loss of efficiency due to unfavorable health conditions. Davidson (8) says 35,000 people were stricken in 1940 in Rochester, New York, from one error in turning river water into the drinking-water mains; 2,500 people in Henderson, Kentucky, in 1940; 1,500 were stricken from eating oysters contaminated with sewage in 1924; 30,000 from chlorine failure in Milwaukee, Wisconsin, in 1938, and so on. He indicates that these cases are the result of failures of one kind or another with purification of drinking water and that such failures occur once in each 10,000 cases. No doubt the losses in man-days because of contaminated drinking water run into millions of dollars each year, and the numbers that die from water-carried diseases are high (11).

Food Losses. The losses of food fishes and shellfish from contaminated water are high. Suckers and carp replace trout and bass; perch and pan fish become unfit for use because of phenol and other taints; seafoods are condemned resulting from polluted waters; waters are so contaminated that no fish can live in them or pass through the pollution block; mussel beds are destroyed by silt or sludge or condemned because of pollution. These all add up to a colossal total loss from this cause (29, 33).

Recreational Losses. What is lost when a million fishermen find their favorite trout brook no longer producing trout, or when natural reproduction of fish is halted because of silting (22)? Only a million disappointed people, you say! But isn't there more than this? How much is lost in work efficiency, tackle sales, gasoline and other sales which are based on suitable fishing waters (6, 9, 14, 18, 19)?

What value is lost when a million people find their nearby bathing beaches condemned? Multiply this by the thousands of beaches the length and breadth of this country, and it adds up to a high figure. Probably greater value is lost in the impaired health, both physical and mental, of city people who would otherwise have access to water, clean air, and relaxation for at least part of a summer season.

Corrosion Losses. Acid-laden waters will corrode metal at a rapid rate; thus, waters where acids are dumped cause shipping losses and untold damage to our most useful metals, iron and steel. The story is told that the Twenty-eighth Division of Pennsylvania was addressed by their ex-commander, Edward Martin, in the port of embarkation at New York because the Navy refused to send transports into the more highly polluted and smelly waters of the Delaware River (8). Additional losses are caused by the rusting of bridges, docks, and other metallic structures that must withstand the fumes and unusual corrosive action of acid-laden waters.

Water Losses. Few spots on earth had better original supplies of fresh, clean water than the southern half of the North American continent. Likewise, few places on earth have seen these water supplies destroyed so completely in so short a time. Surgeon General Parran states that the equivalent of 8 million dead and disintegrating mules is dumped into our waterways every year (8). Add to this the waste from mines, manufacturing plants, processing plants, sawmills, and paper mills, and you have a destructive force which has never been equalled (36). The water shortage in New York, the drying up of wells all over the land, the infiltration of salt water in many water supplies—all emphasize the importance and destructibility of water (16, 35).

Material Losses. All kinds of valuable resources are being lost every day because of their being dumped into the nearest watercourse. The actual loss in metals, wood fibers, acids, organic substances, and other valuable materials is enormous. Even a nation as wealthy as the United States cannot afford this loss. The loss does not stop with the substance discarded. The cost of recovering waste materials is often given by manufacturers as the reason for not conserving these valuable products, yet the recovered product can often be sold at a profit.

A host of examples of recovery successes is available, a few of which are given here. Cedar Rapids, Iowa, converts its sewage-treatment gas into electric power and uses and sells this power as a by-product of the sewage conversion. Hiram Walker & Sons, Inc., are converting their distilling wastes into livestock feed at a profit. Some steel plants are using their recovered acid over again rather than dumping it into the nearest river. Paper mills find the wood fibers from washings are just as valuable if recovered as those converted into paper in the first place. Milwaukee, Wisconsin, Toledo, Ohio, and Grand Rapids, Michigan, are converting their domestic sewage into plant fertilizers and have a ready sale for their products.

Wildlife Losses. The natural balance between some forms of wildlife and their habitat is a very delicate one. Trout of various kinds can live only in water of a limited range of temperatures and with an abundance of oxygen present. Some of the trout, like the lake trout, can withstand very heavy pressures, such as are found at great depths in large lakes, and require a specialized type of forage fish which is also conditioned to great depths. Changes of water quality by dumping of hot water, organic materials, acids, or inert matter of any kind may cause waters to become unsuited to these blue bloods of the finny tribe and forever prevent the presence of other desirable forms of life (15).

A manufacturing plant may discard a dye or some other chemical in a river and destroy a feeding ground for waterfowl in all of the lower reaches of that river (10). An abandoned coal mine may discharge acid into a stream and kill all animal life in those waters until the mine is sealed off and the pollution source removed. A tanker discharging water ballast along the ocean shore may kill a multitude of waterfowl by matting their feathers with oil and leaving them to die and decay along the beaches (14, 18). Oil which trickles into a stream or spreads out over a marsh or swamp appears harmless, yet it may smother the insect food of countless fishes and insect-eating animals.

Some types of pollution are so intricate and minute as to be difficult to detect. Many substances now handled and discarded by chemical manufacturing plants are difficult to remove and are fatal not only to fish life but also to lower forms on which the important fish species live. It is just as disastrous to destroy the basic food of an animal as it is to destroy the animal itself. The introduction of muddy water into a clear stream may seem of minor importance to an irrigation contractor, yet it may clog the breathing organs of hundreds of low forms of animals used for food by the fishes, birds, and mammals.

This is not intended as a complete summary of the effects of pollution on wildlife. It is intended, however, to bring to mind the intricate relationship of living organisms which involves man, plants, and animals.

No one group can be affected without affecting some other group and in the end affecting man.

ANSWERS TO OUR WATER PROBLEMS

Somewhere in the gloom of our water problems there should be a ray of sunshine. A cure for our troubles, wildlife and otherwise, will appear when people suffer enough and become conscious of the inadequate supply of so important a natural resource as water. When the turn of the spigot will not produce water, when people go unbathed and unshaven for the lack of water, only then will the problem begin to be understood and the answers to the problem be sought and found. Part of it will come through research, part through action of individuals and corporations, and part through legal and community action. It will cost money, but probably not so much as our present system of waste and destruction (17, 20).

Legal action on the Federal level has long been sought by members of Congress who have attempted to find laws to prevent new sources of pollution, correct or stop present sources, and assist in both know-how and finances to help both corporations and communities to solve their pollution problems. Such laws usually include the legal process of allowing several states to unite in interstate compacts to correct pollution abuses of waters beyond state lines. Federal Public Law 845 was passed in 1948 and involves three major courses of action: (1) development of programs of pollution abatement by the Federal Public Health Service and state and interstate organizations, (2) research on causes, means of prevention, and treatment of pollution, (3) construction of remedial works including Federal loans to states, municipalities, and corporations for pollution treatment and prevention activities (26). The weak spot in the Federal law is that its teeth are either nonharmful or nonexistent, in that action against a violation rests with the Surgeon General of the U.S. Health Service, who cannot bring court action without the consent of the state involved. Bill Davidson (8) points out that corporations who are nicely attuned to state governmental activities need have no fear of court action under this bill until further dental work is done on it. Perhaps this criticism is not so important after all. When once it appears popular to be sensible about pollution disposal, more action is likely to develop than where compulsion alone is depended upon. This has been in evidence in the handling of pollution in several states and is now evident in the program under way in Pennsylvania to clean up the Schuylkill River. This river, which runs for 130 miles north of Philadelphia, has been described as a river "too thick to navigate and too thin to cultivate." The solid material consists of 40 million tons of solids, mostly combustible materials from the anthracite mines. Through the determination of Pennsylvania state officials, this stream is getting a thorough cleaning and preventive operation which will keep it clean. This treatment came about through two legislative acts, the Desilting Act and the Clean Stream Act, both passed in 1945 under former Governors Martin and Duff. The cost will be a total of $55 million dollars, part of which will be borne by the Federal government. It is estimated that 4 billion dollars, less than a third of what we are spending annually on national defense, would go a long way toward cleaning up the rivers of the United States, and twice that would probably clean up our salt-water pollution troubles as well (17, 37).

Ohio has set an example in the conserving of water and flood in its Muskingum Watershed Conservancy District in eastern Ohio. Here, in an 8,000-square–mile area, flood waters once did 300 million dollars' worth of damage and killed more than 500 people in 1 year. Now in this same area repose 12 beautiful lakes, and elbow room is found for several million Ohioans to fish, swim, and enjoy themselves. The slopes are forested, some lands are farmed—soil-conservation style—and the whole region is a mecca for wildlife. At Muskingum the pattern is set to handle water properly for numerous human uses, and the investment is paying off big dividends in enjoyment and in human as well as material values (2, 7).

One bright spot in the pollution picture is the crusade that has been started by a group of hard-working sports writers, including Jack Van Coevering of the Detroit Free Press and Bill Wolf, a free-lance writer, to clean up pollution. Many of these writers began as hunting and fishing column writers, but have developed educational columns that reach a broad cross section of the reading public. Campaigns of education and action are being waged for decency and truth that are bringing results not even hoped for a decade ago. Where less courageous souls were depending on laws and local health officials to correct bad pollution situations, these intrepid newsmen have gathered the facts as they saw them and have named names in their campaign for cleaning up our polluted rivers (5).

Education and persuasion, as well as laws, are bringing about improvements in the pollution picture. Many industrialists are themselves sportsmen. Many others, not sportsmen, are decent citizens who see the folly of wasting raw materials and befouling the streams of our countryside. All are conscious of the value of favorable public opinion and the dangers of more bureaucracy so, as far as possible, are willing to correct past wasteful and harmful practices.

State pollution laws have also been strengthened during the past decade, so it is now not so easy to evade the issue and continue to dump waste materials into already overburdened waterways. Some of the worst offenders are the towns and cities which dump kitchen and toilet wastes into the streams and continue to allow the use of outdoor toilets. The city of Washington, D.C. is one of the world's showplaces, yet there are 2,000 outdoor toilets in Washington alone, and uncounted millions of gallons of untreated sewage are dumped into the Potomac River every day. What a disgraceful way to treat what was once a beautiful and productive river. And what a sad commentary on our national lawmakers who have and are appropriating millions of the taxpayers' money every year for development of backward regions of the world, yet are neglecting their own front door.

In conclusion, a few general statements are given as to the value of water and the importance of water conservation.

1. Water is a basic resource. Without an abundance of clean water there can be no abundant life, for either animals or plants. Without clean water there will be no water to drink, to bathe in, to grow crops, to support wildlife, or to run industries. Lack of water creates deserts and excludes or limits life itself.

2. Water must be kept in the soil or if moving at all, moving slowly, so as not to carry soil with it. Sound agricultural and forestry practices will keep it abundant and useful.

3. Swamps and marshes are sources of water for wells, springs, ponds, and streams. Drainage of swamps and marshes lowers the ground-water level and frequently reduces the amount of ground water without adding materially to the area of agricultural land or the volume of agricultural products. Where drainage programs have proved ineffective, efforts should be made to close the drainage ditches and bring the water table back to former levels.

4. Where land use has created a condition of flood hazard, flood-control dams should be handled in such a manner as to allow the water to flow through the watercourses in a sustained manner.

5. Water to be of the greatest use to the greatest number of people must be kept pure in quality and constant in amount.

Only clean water can be of the highest value for human consumption and for the production of abundant aquatic products. The fact that the value of the product from a factory using water from a particular stream is greater than the money value of fish caught by fishermen using the stream for fishing is no reason why the former has a more valid right to use the water than the latter.

Only when all the citizens of a community realize that pure water is a valuable community asset and that continued prosperity depends on keeping it pure and abundant can there be sound progress toward water conservation and better living.

REFERENCES

1. Anonymous. 1937. Headwaters control and use, Government Printing Office, Washington, D.C.
2. ———. 1941. A conservation story, Muskingum Watershed Conservancy District, New Philadelphia, Ohio.
3. ———. 1947. The pollution problem: A national menace, Wildlife Management Institute, Washington, D.C.
4. ———. 1950. A water policy for the American people, Government Printing Office, Washington, D.C.
5. ———. (No date). Ten rivers in America's future. No. 6. The Connecticut. *The Report of the President's Water Resources Policy Commission,* Government Printing Office, Washington, D.C., Vol. 2.
6. Beatty, Robert O. 1948. Wildlife's stake in pollution abatement. *Trans.* 13*th North Amer. Wildlife Conf.* Pp. 563–595.
7. Bromfield, Louis. 1950. I live on the edge of paradise. *The Saturday Evening Post.* **227**(37):22–23; 91, 93–94.
8. Davidson, Bill. 1948. Our poisoned waters. *Collier's.* **122**(16):20–21, 81.
9. Degani, John George. 1943. Studies of the toxicity of ammunition plant wastes to fishes. *Trans. Amer. Fisheries Soc.* **73**:45–51.
10. Ellis, M. M. 1937*a*. Pollution and aquatic life. *Trans.* 2*d North Amer. Wildlife Conf.* Pp. 653–657.
11. ———. 1937*b*. Detection and measurement of stream pollution. *U.S. Bur. Fisheries. Bul.* 22.
12. Frank, Bernard, and Anthony Netboy. 1950. Water, land and people, Alfred A. Knopf, Inc., New York.
13. Gabrielson, Ira N. 1947. Conservation of our public waters. *Trans. Amer. Fisheries Soc.* **77**:275–280.
14. Hadley, Alden H. 1930. Destruction of birds by oil pollution. *Trans.* 17*th Amer. Game Conf.* Pp. 64–69.
15. Harvey, Holman. 1945. America's dead and dying rivers. *The Reader's Digest.* **47**(282:75–78.
16. Heacox, Cecil E. 1950. Liquid assets. *N.Y. Conserv.* **4**(6):2–9.
17. Hollis, M. D. 1948. Nation-wide inventory of sanitation needs. *U.S. Pub. Health Serv. Rpts., Sup.* 204.
18. Lincoln, Frederick C. 1936. The effect of oil pollution on waterfowl. Wildlife restoration and conservation. *Proc. North Amer. Wildlife Conf.* Pp. 555–559.
19. Moffitt, James, and Robert T. Orr. 1938. Recent disastrous effects of oil pollution on birds in the San Francisco Bay region. *Calif. Fish and Game.* **24**(3):239–244.
20. Mundt, Karl E. 1949. What's needed in national water conservation?: Pollution control. *Trans.* 14*th North Amer. Wildlife Conf.* Pp. 118–123.
21. Munns, E. N. 1946. Water in wildland management. *Jour. Forestry.* **44**(11):799–804.
22. Nightingale, H. W. 1938. Concerning the effects of waste sulphite liquor upon fish life with special reference to early stages of the chinook salmon, The Argus Press, Seattle, Wash.
23. O'Byrne, Wilbur. 1950. Water: A forest product of increasing importance. *Va. Wildlife.* **11**(6):5–7.

24. Person, H. S. 1935. Little waters: A study of headwater streams and other little waters, their use and relations to the land, Government Printing Office, Washington, D.C.
25. Roach, Lee S. 1933. Some physical, chemical, and biological studies of impounded waters in Ohio. *Trans. Amer. Fisheries Soc.* **63**:265–270.
26. Scheele, Leonard A. 1949. Stream pollution program under public law 845. *Trans. 14th North Amer. Wildlife Conf.* Pp. 36–41.
27. Shaw, Paul A., and John A. Maga. 1943. The effect of mining silt on yield of fry from salmon spawning beds. *Calif. Fish and Game.* **29**(1):29–41.
28. Titus, Harold. 1944. Will there be enough water? *The Saturday Evening Post.* **216**(48):28–29, 105.
29. Trautman, Milton B. 1933. The general effects of pollution on Ohio fish life. *Trans. Amer. Fisheries Soc.* **63**:69–72.
30. Velie, Lester, 1948. Are we short of water? *Collier's.* **121**(20):14–15, 74–77.
31. Vogt, William. (No date). Thirst on the land. *Nat. Assoc. Audubon Socs. Cir.* 32.
32. Voigt, William, Jr. 1948. Does pollution go on forever? *Trans. 13th North Amer. Wildlife Conf.* Pp. 129–135.
33. Westman, J. R. 1949. Pollution: Case History. *N.Y. Conserv.* **3**(6):8–9.
34. Wickliff, R. L. 1944. Stream mistakes that should not be repeated. *Ohio State Univ. Engin. Expt. Sta. News.* April pp. 28–33.
35. Wiebe, A. H., J. G. Burr, and H. E. Faubion. 1934. The problem of stream pollution in Texas with special reference to salt water from the oil fields. *Trans. Amer. Fisheries Soc.* **64**:81–86.
36. Winget, Russell L. 1947. The pulp and paper industry's stream-improvement program. *Trans. Amer. Fisheries Soc.* **77**:262–270.
37. Wolf, Bill. 1948–1949. Running sores of our land. *Sports Afield.* **120**(3): 42–43, 81–87; **120**(4):36–37, 97, 99–106; **120**(5):48–49, 88, 91–96; **120**(6):40–41, 74–80; **121**(1):44–45, 71–77; **121**(2):48–49, 72–80; **121**(3):19–21, 60, 71–72, 74–75.

CHAPTER 2

Marsh and Swamp Management

In a text on wildlife management it would be out of place to go into great detail on natural laws. Fundamental natural processes are so basic as a preliminary to land management, however, as to demand at least partial definitions and explanations. It is the purpose of the first chapters of this book to give such definitions and explanations.

In the first chapter water and its conservation was discussed. In the second chapter the nature of vegetation on wet lands will be described, with suggestions for handling such lands productively. These discussions will attempt to keep in mind always the relationship of management to crops of wildlife.

DEFINITIONS[1]

A number of terms will be used in the following pages which need definition. Such definitions are hereby given.

Lake. Any body of water situated in a depression of land. A lake may include extensive bodies of water like the Great Lakes or smaller bodies of water 20 acres or more in area. The term "great pond" is usually used in New England for bodies of water more than 20 acres in size.

Pond. A small lake, in New England less than 20 acres in area.

Bog Lake. The remnant of a former lake which is being filled in by the remains of plant growth.

Mangrove.[2] Tropical lagoons, inlets, or estuaries where the land is flooded.

Marsh. Treeless swamps in which the vegetation is predominantly grassy or reedy. Marshes are often designated as wet marshes, hay marshes (cut for forage or packing materials), pastured marshes, cat-tail marshes, tidal marshes, salt marshes, etc.

[1] From Nichols (32).
[2] From Carpenter (11).

FIG. 2-1. An ideal marsh area on Lake Malheur Bird Refuge in Oregon. (*U.S. Fish and Wildlife Service.*)

Swamp.[3] An area where the soil is saturated with water throughout most of the year but not actually submerged. Swamps usually have a woody vegetation growing on them, but the intermixture of herbaceous and woody plants may vary greatly. Swamps are also designated according to the nature of their substratum, condition of the water, or nature of the vegetation. These include bog swamps, muck swamps, fresh or salt swamps, cedar swamps, red maple swamps, cypress swamps, etc.

Seepage Swamp.[3] An area where springs or seepage water keep the ground moist.

The nature of marshes and swamps cannot be understood until we know something of the natural laws that govern the growth of plants and their relation to one another. Each kind of plant has its own requirements of soil, soil moisture, acidity and alkalinity, and degree of shade it will tolerate. Plants will grow on rocks or in water and gradually change the environment so other plants can grow. This process is called "plant succession." Finally a condition is reached where the same plant persists. This is known as a "climax." All bodies of water have a tendency to fill in and shrink in area or to approach a land condition. This filling process comes about through the action of wind, waves, and streams in

[3] From Nichols (32).

bringing in soil, and from the bodies of plants and animals that live in the water and drop to the bottom after death. In limestone regions marl (nearly pure calcium carbonate) is formed by the action of plants and is deposited on the bottom as plants die and decay. Bogs form under conditions of short growing seasons where the plants decay slowly. Bog soils develop gradually into peat and then into muck as decomposition of the plants advances.

A lake or pond advances through various stages as the margins build up with soil and the encroachment of plants develops to a stage where enough soil and organic materials are present to afford anchorage to other than floating plants. Finally the entire former water area may become a wet mass of soil with marsh plants of various kinds and later woody plants gaining a foothold. As time passes, a forest will eventually develop. The action of fire, grazing of animals, and cutting of hay may prolong the marsh stage indefinitely. However, if environmental conditions are not disturbed, plant succession will gradually move along to the wet swamp condition and later to drier conditions similar to the nearby uplands.

Depending on the variety of conditions that prevail, not all wet lands arrive at the wooded climax stage. In fact, some salt tidal and alkaline marshes seem to remain in the grass or herbaceous stages indefinitely. Other marshes and swamps may intergrade anywhere between open water and an upland type of forest.

EXTENT AND DESCRIPTION OF MARSHES AND SWAMPS

Anyone who has traveled, trapped, or fished has had contact with numerous wet lands on the North American continent (15, 46). Even deserts have wet seepage areas. The trout fisherman often walks through a deep tangle of wet and springy soil and deep marsh vegetation to get to where large trout lurk. The duck hunter hides in the bulrushes to wait for a skein of waterfowl. The trapper makes his set in the edge of a cedar swamp or along a marsh watercourse, and the traveler passes many water holes, sloughs, and old lake beds as he travels across the continent.

The extent of this wet and overflow land is vast, reaching a total of 127 million acres, or an area equal to four times the size of Wisconsin (25 *g.r.*). These lands furnish suitable living room for a vast variety of fur bearers, waterfowl, and fishes and are part of the basic reservoir of water which is necessary for both wildlife and human needs. While drainage engineers, agricultural planners, and land promoters look upon these millions of acres of wet lands as possibilities for future developments, these lands have a high value in their present condition that should not be overlooked. The moisture in such lands helps to maintain water levels in wells, springs, and lakes and is the source of water for maintaining a constant flow in many brooks and rivers (19, 48). Soil water is the backlog on which we depend for drinking, bathing, manufacturing, and the production of fur bearers, waterfowl, and fish. In the South much valuable timber is grown in swamps, and in the North wet lands are used for the production of hay during the dry part of the season.

In the past much effort and money have been spent on attempting to convert marshes and swamps into suitable lands for traditional agricultural uses, with the near destruction of greater original values. A few examples where costly efforts have been expended on wet lands include Seney Marsh in Michigan, Horicon Marsh in Wisconsin, Mud and Thief Lakes in Minnesota, Lower Souris River flood plain in North Dakota, Lake Mattamuskeet in North Carolina, Lake Malheur and lower Klamath Lake in Oregon and California, and numerous swamps in Florida and along the Mississippi River. During periods of high prices of agricultural products many smaller wet lands on individual farms also have been drained to insure higher incomes for the owners. Sometimes this drainage goes on even where there are surpluses of the crops that are to be raised on them. Drainage of these small areas is probably more damaging than some of the extensive projects because it may lower the ground-water level on which the farmer depends for water for domestic uses, as well as destroy the last haven on the farm available for wildlife.

There are all degrees of variations in the conditions of wet lands of the continent because of differences of climate, soil, mineral content of the water, degree of wetness, and the treatment they have received from man. Also, the stage of plant succession will be different in each different location. Even with these variations, there is a similarity between all wet situations in the degree to which they prohibit conventional uses. Marshes and swamps are usually attractive to the amphibious and aquatic life forms, first because the latter are adapted by nature to a wet habitat and second because there is usually an abundance of food and cover in wet places.

There follows a brief description of some of the various types of marshes and swamps. These descriptions do not pretend to be complete nor do they expect to describe all possible forms of wet land habitats. They do, however, give a brief description of the places where fur bearers, waterfowl, and fish find suitable living conditions.

Salt-water Tidal Marshes. These outer marshes along the ocean shore are predominantly salty. They have a lush vegetation of great variety. Some minerals are being brought in by fresh-water streams, and the marsh is also being washed by the recurrence of salt water from the tides.

High and low tides follow each other at intervals of about 6 hours. The amount of fresh water brought in depends on the rainfall of the particular season of the year.

Tidal Marshes. Tidal marshes have some form of barrier protection along coasts of the ocean. Such barriers result from the dropping of the shore line, the forming of sand bars, or the deposition of soil brought in by fresh-water streams. There are several million acres of these wet lands that are under the influence of abundant moisture. Various conditions of water freshness or salinity exist because of water brought in by rivers, the action of tides, and the effectiveness of barriers. Wind, waves, soil, drift, and tides all influence the conditions of vegetation and animal life in these marshes. Conditions of moisture, especially water levels, are considered the controlling factor in relation to plants and animals of the marsh. The tides govern the vertical distribution of plants, and the drainage and salinity the horizontal distribution (8). Tides may vary in height from a few inches to 30 feet or more. There are two high and two low tides daily, with two high and two low tides monthly that may exceed the daily tide limits. The highest tides are those that occur twice a year in spring and autumn. Storms may cause the various tides to be higher or lower than normal. Waves pile up sand, and ocean drifts carry materials along and later deposit these so as to form barrier reefs. Soil of the marshes may be sand, silt, or fibrous material, depending on submergence or other effects. Usually there is a partial barrier between the marsh and the ocean which delimits the marsh and prevents the sea water at normal levels from entering the protected area.

The fresh water from rivers also has a marked influence on the animal and plant life of the tidal marshes. This influence may extend along the margins of the river and also out away from the river mouth. River water also tends to keep ponds in the marsh fresh or partly fresh rather than salt.

The vegetation of salt tidal marshes along the northeast coast is described by Bourn and Cottam (8) as consisting of three belts or associations of plants, progressing from offshore inland: (1) salt-water cord-grass (*Spartina alterniflora*),[4] (2) saltgrass (spike-grass) (*Distichlis spicata*), (3) salt-meadow cord-grass (*Spartina patens*), black grass (*Juncus gerardi*), three-square bulrush (*Scirpus* spp.), and numerous bordering shrubs, including groundsel-tree (*Baccharis halimifolia*), and marsh-elder (*Iva frutescens*).

The offshore group (salt-water cord-grass) is submerged by salt water

[4] Woody plant nomenclature according to William M. Harlow and Ellwood S. Harrar. 1950. Textbook of dendrology, 3d ed., McGraw-Hill Book Company, Inc., New York; while herbaceous plant names are taken from Merritt Lyndon Fernald, 1950. Gray's manual of botany, 8th (Centennial) ed., American Book Company, New York.

twice daily so is definitely a salt-water aquatic habitat. The salt-grass group grows in a drier site and is ordinarily flooded only twice during the monthly high tides or during storms. The salt-meadow cord-grass group is flooded twice a year in March and September and during unusually heavy storms, with its black grass rarely covered by standing water. Bulrush is often covered by either salt or fresh water and seems to get along very well under either condition (8). The zones between the various types of vegetation on these marshes are likely to be broad as the change of salinity of the water or the depth allows first one then another group of plants to develop dominance.

Where tidal marshes receive a large volume of fresh water, as for example from various rivers along the east coast, extensive beds of wild rice (*Zizania aquatica*) occur. According to Bourn and Cottam (8), wild rice holds the same relative place in fresh water as to submergence as salt-water cord-grass does in salt water. The wild rice marshes are bordered on higher levels by three-square bulrush (*Scirpus* spp.), smartweeds (*Polygonum* spp.), and wild millet (*Echinochloa* spp.). All of the above-named plants contribute heavily to the diet of waterfowl, as all are excellent food-producing plants. Farther south, spike-rush (*Eleocharis* spp.), water-hyssop (*Bacopa* spp.), and bull grasses are found in salt marshes. Rushes (*Juncus roemerianus*) may be found where the salt water is present only at high tide and cat-tails in water which is nearly free from salt (30 *g.r.*).

Fresh-water Marshes. Fresh-water northern marshes vary greatly in vegetation, depth of water, and condition of soil. The difference of length of growing season in northern and southern marshes also affects the condition of the vegetation. Marshes which develop from bog lakes are usually very acid. The most conspicuous plants in the early vegetation of bog marshes are sphagnum moss (*Sphagnum* spp.), cranberries (*Vaccinium* spp.), pitcher-plants (*Sarracenia* spp.), and sundew (*Drosera intermedia*). Other plants as cat-tail (*Typha* spp.), spike-rushes (*Eleocharis* spp.), and sedges (*Carex* spp.) appear as conditions become suitable.

Marshes frequently develop from the beds of fresh-water lakes and along the margins of lakes and rivers. Marshes along the upper Mississippi River Valley may consist of solid beds of wild rice (*Zizania aquatica*), cat-tails (*Typha* spp.), flags, and sedges (*Carex* spp.). Bulrushes (*Scirpus* spp.), reeds, and phragmites (*Phragmites* spp.) also grow in solid stands in northern marshes (7). Sharp (37) indicates there is a marked difference in the productiveness of marshes. In this case productiveness is defined as the capacity to produce an abundance of cover for muskrats and waterfowl. He states that highly productive marshes are underlaid with good soil and that marshes underlaid with clay, hardpan, or rocky soil are not first-class marshes. He also says that water in excess of 36 inches is not so productive a condition as less than this depth, even though dry conditions reduce the depth to less than 36 inches not more frequently than once each 5 years. Another somewhat unusual discovery by Sharp is that a gradual reduction of water levels during the June-August period is a normal and necessary condition for abundant fruiting of some of the marsh plants.

Southern Marshes. In the southern states several types of low or other than woody vegetation are often found in damp or wet situations. Some of these are called "canebreaks" because of the dominance of the canebreak (*Arundinaria* spp.) which develops dense stands.

Other openings in the swamp forests are dominated by chain-ferns (*Woodwardia* spp.), sphagnum moss (*Sphagnum cymbifolium*), and other lush growing plants. Magnolia trees (*Magnolia grandiflora*) may be present in many of the swamps. These may be extensions of open-water bays which are known locally as bay heads (30 *g.r.*).

Swamps. Swamps vary from north to south, having different species of woody plants present according to the climate and degree of wetness. The red maple (*Acer rubrum*) and American elm (*Ulmus americana*) are two of the hardwood trees found in many swamps from Canada to the Gulf Coast. Where conditions are likely to be very acid, southern white cedar (*Chamaecyparis thyoides*) occurs abundantly.

Hardwood Swamps. Hardwood swamps vary in degree of wetness, density, or types of vegetation. Many northern swamps are quite dry during all but the wettest part of the year and may have many of the upland types of trees present. Parts of swamps may show the remnants of marshes not yet developed to the swamp stage, while other higher and drier places may be present where the forest has been cleared and agricultural crops are grown. Frequently a variety of low bushes is found, including high and low bush blueberries (*Vaccinium* spp.), holly (*Ilex* spp.), and arrow-woods (*Viburnum* spp.). Some of the swamps in the Lake states are very wet and have a preponderance of black ash (*Fraxinus nigra*) in the overstory. Others may have thick stands of black spruce (*Picea mariana*), and others may be almost solid stands of northern white cedar (*Thuja occidentalis*) or larch (*Larix laricina*).

Black Gum Swamps. The swamps of the southland have great variety, both in the presence and distribution of different woody and herbaceous plant species. Many swamps are relatively wet with trees having "knees" showing above the water. Rotting logs are covered with ferns, and low-growing plants and Spanish moss hang from the branches of the trees.

Black gum (*Nyssa sylvatica*), a deciduous tree, and southern white cedar (*Chamaecyparis thyoides*) are often associated, with the deciduous trees predominating. Other trees found in associations are water tupelo (*Nyssa aquatica*), water ash (*Fraxinus caroliana*), and oak (*Quercus* spp.). Smaller trees are the sweetbay magnolia (*Magnolia virginiana*), ironwood (*Carpinus caroliniana*), willow (*Salix* spp.), alder (*Alnus* spp.), and swamp cottonwood (*Populus heterophylla*). Where the sand emerges above the water level, it gives solid footing for less mesophytic plants and animals. On these sandy islands other xerophytic trees and shrubs begin to appear (30 *g.r.*).

USE OF MARSHES AND SWAMPS BY WILDLIFE

Marshes and swamps are rich in the variety of plants which are useful for both food and cover to many fur bearers, waterfowl, and fish. This richness of fauna and flora is logical because of the nature of the environment. There is usually abundant water, although this varies somewhat with different parts of marshes and swamps and with the normal annual as well as the seasonal rainfall. The fertility of the soil and water is usually high. Soil nutrients are washed into low-lying areas, and drainage conditions frequently hold the soil from passing on to other localities. Dead bodies of plants and animals add organic matter. Also the loss of nutrients is slower than in higher locations.

The richness of animal life in salt and brackish marshes and swamps depends somewhat on the degree of freshness or salinity of the water. Where ocean water comes in with each tide, the habitat is less suitable and less productive than where the water is brackish or low in salt content.

Salt-water marshes along the eastern part of the continent are of the meadow type, with some low shrubbery along the banks of meandering streams. These salt meadows are feeding and nesting grounds for the black duck north of Long Island. The muskrat is the dominant fur bearer, with occasional otters, minks, and raccoons also being present. During the fall season, numerous ducks, geese, and swans may use the marshes for feeding and watering. Other migrants include black ducks, wood ducks, teal, and ring-necked ducks. South of Long Island the marshes are used for resting or feeding by many of the North American waterfowl. Fresh-water marshes north of the Missouri and Ohio Rivers are used for summering and nesting by a host of mid-Continent ducks, both the puddle ducks and the deep-water feeders. The snow and blue geese, old squaw ducks, brant, and whistling swans, nesting farther north, use the fresh-water marshes (except old squaw) for resting and feeding during migrations. The wood duck, hooded merganser, and bufflehead use wooded country rather than prairie-marsh habitats, because of the need for trees for nesting sites.

The wild rice marshes of the Great Lakes region and the fresh-water marshes to the south are the fattening grounds of a host of waterfowl that use the Mississippi and central flyways for the trip south. No better-flavored duck flesh is produced than from teal, mallards, and pintails that feed on wild rice beds in Alberta, Minnesota, and Wisconsin. Farther south along the coast of the Gulf of Mexico numerous geese winter and graze along the marshes of the Mississippi delta and Texas coasts.

Of the mammals, the muskrat is the dominant animal of the fresh-water marsh. From far north in Canada to the Gulf of Mexico this animal is found breeding in abundance wherever water and vegetation are combined to produce a marsh habitat (13). Minks, otters, and skunks are found in fresh-water marshes as well as on drier sites. Foxes and coyotes inhabit the drier margins of marshes. Fresh-water swamps are used by the tree ducks, including the wood ducks, buffleheads, hooded mergansers, and American goldeneyes. Raccoons, otters, minks, and wildcats prefer the wooded habitat, with the exception of the mink, which inhabits both marsh and swamp types of environment.

The western marshes are rich in animal life, which is likewise true of the wooded swamps found in the mountains and along the west coast. The Alaska and Canadian tundras are the nesting grounds for numerous geese and some of the ducks, such as the American pintails, old squaws, whistling swans, and black brant. The lake region of British Columbia is one of the few nesting spots for trumpeter swans. In Utah, the Bear River marshes, north of Great Salt Lake, are the summering and breeding ground for a host of both eastern and western ducks and geese, while the alkaline potholes and central valley of California furnish breeding sites for the cinnamon teal and wintering grounds for a host of waterfowl.

MARSH AND SWAMP MANAGEMENT

The management of a hundred million acres of land is important. It is more important at the present time because this class of land has been more or less neglected in the past except for drainage, a practice which has been and is in many cases proving to be "bad" rather than "good" management (21, 36). It is realized that many suggested details of management will apply only to a particular location and that many marshes are being managed efficiently at the present time. Even with these limitations, there is need for understanding the value of wet lands and for getting them into the highest possible use. Because of these variations, the suggestions that follow may not be complete or in all cases entirely correct, yet this chapter will at least be a starting point from which new directions and techniques may develop (1, 45).

The problem of mosquito control has had a profound effect on the productiveness of many marshes, especially those near centers of population where discomfort from mosquitoes and the pressure of human appeals have caused action to be taken which may have affected other interests. Drainage is another operation which, while legitimate and beneficial in the right location, may be detrimental if applied incorrectly. The use of fire in marshes certainly has limitations, but burning can result in much benefit if properly used as well as much damage if improperly used. Another technique is the use of dikes to keep out sea water or to prevent water-level fluctuations. Water levels if manipulated properly can be of benefit to wildlife. The cutting of marsh grass for hay and logging of swamps can usually be arranged so as to do a minimum of damage. The manipulation of marsh vegetation so as to keep useless plants out and encourage useful plants is another technique which may be used in the management of wet lands.

Mosquito Control. The operators of flying saucers—if there are such creatures—have probably noticed the regular lines or ditches which mark the low wet areas of our eastern and southern seaboards. These ditches are usually straight and connect with an outlet from onshore toward the sea. Much effort and money have been spent during the past 30 years in ditching marshes in the name of mosquito control or reduction of the mosquito nuisance (14). Other operations in relation to mosquito control are the use of larvicides as oils and poisons, physical or biological controls including the manipulation of water levels to destroy mosquito eggs and larvae and the encouragement of animals that consume the mosquito larvae.

Williams *et al.* (44) state there are 135 different species of mosquitoes in North America. These mosquitoes all have different life habits and are probably quite different with respect to their habits in relation to man. Certainly the mosquito that affects man most is the anopheles mosquito (*Anopheles quadrimaculatus*). At least this species is most frequently mentioned as the common carrier of malaria, although four additional mosquitoes may carry this disease.

The reason for a discussion of mosquito control is to suggest control measures that are the least harmful to wildlife but which will at the same time prevent discomfort and damage to man and his interests. Perhaps the only safe attitude toward this subject is that each case should be treated on its individual merits. The discussion that follows will consider only controls that affect lakes, streams, and marshes of value for the production and needs of fur bearers, waterfowl, and fish. It will relegate other processes in the relations of men to mosquitoes to the engineer and health departments, within whose legitimate province they fall.

Drainage or Ditching. In both fresh and salt marshes, the process of drainage has been a costly and usually ineffective method of mosquito control (10). Drainage has destroyed the biological enemies of mosquitoes, the food and habitat of wildlife, and has not, in most cases, reduced the mosquito nuisance. Its ineffectiveness results because it is likely to reduce the enemies of mosquitoes without eliminating suitable habitats for mosquitoes. Ditch maintenance is expensive and is usually neglected. After a time the side walls of ditches fall down, and vegetation so clogs the ditches that water is held in pools, a situation which creates as effective a breeding place for mosquitoes as the original marsh. Where ditching has been used extensively, marsh ponds have been lowered, and much habitat and food for waterfowl and fur bearers have been destroyed (8, 9). A sound method of both fresh- and salt-water mosquito control has been the joining of marsh ponds by ditches, the water levels of these ponds being controlled by the use of gates in outlet ditches (44). The connecting ditches allow top minnows and other fish access to all parts of the marsh, while the gates keep the water at a high level so that mosquito larvae are likely to wash into feeding ranges of the minnows. Another possibility of the use of gates in the outlets is that a marsh may be drained during the mosquito season and reflooded during the rest of the year. In California mosquito production was reduced by flooding the salt marsh at short intervals during the summer, a practice which resulted in flooding out the eggs and larvae of mosquitoes that would otherwise have hatched (44).

In fresh-water marshes mosquitoes can be controlled by digging a pond $1/10$ the size of the marsh in a central location and joining other parts of the marsh to this central pond with ditches. Top minnows (*Gambusia* spp.), a mosquito-eating fish, should be introduced into the new ponds. Such larvae-eating fish, plus other natural enemies of insect life, are thus allowed a suitable habitat in which to operate. The mosquitoes are controlled without destroying wildlife habitat, and wildlife is actually benefited because of higher water levels and a better interspersion of water and vegetation.

Various types of mosquito control have been tried out on the waters of the Tennessee Valley Authority and are reported by Wiebe and Hess (43). Under Tennessee Valley conditions it was found that many of the control measures for the malaria mosquito were beneficial to wildlife if handled with a little thought for wildlife interests. Reservoir sites are cleared before water is introduced, and drains are provided for marginal ponds before the water is impounded. In the fall the annual growth along the zone of water fluctuation is cleared by burning and mowing. This accomplishes mosquito reduction and also controls the water-tolerant woody plants, thus allowing production of annual plants favorable to wildlife. These beneficial species include rice-cutgrass (*Leersia oryzoides*), wild millet (*Echinochloa crusgalli*), smartweeds (*Persicaria* spp.), and others. Beneficial rather than useless species tend to develop after the water is drained off and thus are ready for wintering waterfowl when they arrive. Some water weeds, as alligator grass (*Achyranthes philoxeroides*), lotus (*Nelumbo* spp.), cat-tail flag (*Typha* spp.), water millet (*Zizaniopsis miliacea*), and water-chestnut (*Trapa natans*) are also controlled. If allowed to develop uncontrolled, these are of negative value to wildlife as well as a benefit to the malaria mosquito.

The Tennessee Valley Authority also uses a system of water-level management to control the malaria mosquito. These techniques include holding back water behind dikes and fluctuating the levels of water. According to Wiebe and Hess (43), such methods are either beneficial to or have no effect on fish production and are likely to be beneficial to waterfowl. Other measures beneficial to wildlife are the planting of wildlife foods during the summer on drained areas and the holding back of water on low areas that would otherwise be dry during duck migrations. The presence of top minnows (*Gambusia* spp.) and keeping streams free from pollution have helped control mosquitoes and maintain wildlife.

Larvicides. Many types of larvicides have been used to control mosquitoes including nonvolatile oils, paris green, pyrethrum, and DDT.

Oils not only destroy the mosquito larvae but also injure both wildlife and the plants that make up wildlife habitats. They should not be used in habitats where wildlife is present. Paris green is a poison and dangerous to all animal life, including humans. It is not dissipated readily, so remains a hazard over a long period of time.

Chemical control of mosquitoes is often the only practical method available. Where wildlife values are high, however, only chemicals that are not destructive to other animal life should be used. Pyrethrum is such a substance. It is cheaper than arsenicals or oil and is very effective in mosquito control. It has the added advantage that it can be used safely in situations such as domestic water supplies where other poisons are not safe (44).

DDT is the short name for dichloro-diphenyl-trichloroethane and is one of the most useful and effective insect-control materials in use today. It is frequently used for control of mosquitoes, black flies, and other harmful insects and may be applied as a spray, dust, or incorporated in blocks of calcium that are hung in streams. Usually dosages are small per unit of area, being generally less than 2 pounds per acre.

From results of research on the subject it is apparent that considerable damage is done to various forms of life, including nonharmful insects, other invertebrates, fishes, and the higher forms of life. On a salt marsh,

Goodrum *et al.* (18) reported an almost complete elimination of the fiddler crab but little effect on snails and mussels. Springer and Webster (38), testing DDT in salt marshes in New Jersey, noted no effect on birds, high loss of fishes with the heavier dosage (1.6 pounds per acre), a light kill especially for larger fishes with light dosages, severe reduction of insect life, heavy mortality to blue crabs and fiddler crabs, and varied effects on other animal life, but little or no effect on snails and mussels.

Drainage of Marshes and Swamps. A discussion of drainage as an agricultural development has no place in a book on wildlife management. In the past many drained marsh and swamp lands have provided excellent agricultural lands. Other drained lands have been a total loss, however, both to agriculture and to wildlife. Where marshes and swamps are not suitable for agricultural development, drainage should not be used.

Many conditions should be taken into account when drainage of marshes and swamps is considered. These include need for products of the land being drained, possible degree of success of the drainage, effect of drainage on surrounding water levels, quality and kind of soil in proposed drainage area, the economic aspect of drainage, and the values of the marsh or swamp before drainage, including values for wildlife (33).

It would appear that no attempt ought to be made to drain large areas of land which have high present values for water or wildlife (3). For several decades this is exactly what has been happening (12). Likewise, there ought to be some assurance before beginning a drainage project that the attempt will be an engineering success from the standpoint of its effectiveness in lowering the water table so that agricultural practices are possible (3). There should also be some guarantee that the land proposed for drainage is suitable for agricultural purposes and does not contain so much organic matter that it will dry out or burn out and blow away after the water table has been lowered. This is a job for the soil scientist. Drainage ought not to be attempted if the lowering of the water table will jeopardize the ground-water level to the extent that wells in the vicinity are destroyed or that the amount of ground water will be materially affected. Also, drainage of wet lands ought not to be attempted on the basis of a financial gamble or purely for the advantage of speculators, disregarding other values or other interests; and finally, marshes or swamps should not be drained where a high value exists in the form of wildlife in its present state. These values include capacity to produce fur from muskrats, minks, raccoons, and otters, value for either resident or migrant waterfowl, or values in protecting the habitats of other wildlife, including shorebirds and fish.

The danger of fire in drained marshes and swamps is one of the factors that makes the question of drainage a grave one. Even if great values accrue from drainage, these values are usually destroyed if fire occurs; thus, the profits may be changed to losses with the advent of a dry season. While there was some increase of growth of timber in some experimentally drained northern swamps (49), it is doubtful if this increase will pay for the cost of drainage and the additional risk of fires under drained (dried-out) conditions. As against any timber gains there are the wildlife losses that are sure to follow drainage in swamps, including losses of species of both plants and animals used for wildlife food and also the change of timber species, such as white cedar to red maple, due to a change of moisture conditions.

Lowering of Water Levels on Salt Marshes. Careful studies have been made by the U.S. Fish and Wildlife Service of the effects of lowering water levels on salt marshes. Such drainage usually results from cutting through the natural levee along the ocean side of marshes and allowing the water to drain out. Lowering of water levels exposes both animal and plant life, as well as the soil, to dessication. Such exposure increases the acidity of the marsh, sometimes to the extent of dissolving the limy shells of snails and mussels and also allowing plants like salt-marsh fleabane (*Pluches camphorata*), salt-marsh aster (*Aster subulatus*), salt-water elder (*Iva frutescens*), and groundsel tree (*Baccharis halimifolia*) to crowd out more valuable plants. Counts of animals in drained as against undrained salt marshes showed the reduction to be from 40 to 90 per cent after drainage (8).

The drainage of marshlands around the city of New Orelans was studied previous to 1945 by Penfound and Schneidau (34). Only 8 of the initial 70 drainage projects continued to be operated commercially. One abandoned project showed that plants valuable to wildlife had been crowded out and the land taken over by nearly worthless plants like goldenrod (*Solidago sempervirens* var. *mexicana*) and marsh cane (*Phragmites communis*). The original marsh was worth $5 per acre for muskrats. Two other abandoned drainage projects were found to be of no value for agriculture but very productive of fur, waterfowl, and fish.

Drainage of salt marshes has been discussed at length, but little has been said about the drainage of the multitude of ponds that dot the salt grass meadows. These ponds are likely to be less salty than the tidewater and support plants of high value to wildlife, particularly waterfowl. Such plants as widgeon-grass (*Ruppia maritima*), sago pondweed (*Potamogeton pectinatus*), and horned pondweed (*Zannichellia palustris*) are all found in these special niches. The open water and associated plants help to make desirable surroundings for protozoans, rotifers, worms, insects, mollusks, and fish, as well as the numerous lower forms of plants. In such surroundings, birds and mammals adapted to aquatic habitation find suitable conditions at few other places (39). Drainage of these ponds changes the entire situation; it usually produces less valuable plants and lower forms of animals and as a result drives the higher forms to seek new homes elsewhere (42).

Stabilization of Water Levels. Plants and animals are usually not too versatile in relation to a change from water to land habitats or the reverse. Certain animals are suited to both wet and dry conditions (amphibians), but usually the degree of versatility is pretty well fixed even with these. Some of the most successful techniques for managing wildlife have been the bringing back of water levels to drained lands and the stabilization of these levels after the water has been brought back. Such stabilization is concerned with both the retaining of water and the provision for passing it along when too much is available.

Many examples of the successful use of this technique are available, but only a few need be given. These include management of Seney National Wildlife Refuge in Michigan, Horicon Marsh in Wisconsin, Rice Lake and Mud Lake Refuges in Minnesota, Souris River and other wildlife refuges in the Dakotas, Bear River Marshes in Utah, Malheur and Klamath Lake Marshes in Oregon and California, and a host of others. Work of stabilization of water on the above locations has proved the value of first providing water and land in the right proportions and then holding the water at a nearly constant level. Occasional lowering of water levels is not so damaging as a long period of raised levels (37). Stabilization of water is carried out by a variety of means. Sometimes it requires only the stopping of pumping operations or the plugging of drainage ditches. Sometimes it requires dams and dikes to impound water so as to hold it back to a preestablished level. It may also require the release of impounded water to maintain a constant level against human use, evaporation, or lack of normal rainfall.

The values of these stabilizing processes are most noticeable in the increase in the number of animals that return to those wet areas. Waterfowl and shorebirds, such as gulls and terns, begin to take over as soon as water is evident. Invertebrates such as snails, crayfish, and insects, as well as fish, return. Raccoons, muskrats, and minks soon return to reestablished marshes.

Check Dams and Dikes for Water Stabilization. Thousands of sites are available in the eastern and northern parts of the United States where small earth or concrete structures will hold the moisture in a natural low depression. The author once stood at the site of such a structure in Minnesota where a dam built by two men in one day had reflooded more than 20 acres of swamp. It was less than 2 feet high, yet this simple device had rebuilt the soil water in the vicinity and created a mecca for water creatures in the surrounding swamp. Evidence was present of wood ducks and mallards, teal, muskrats, beavers, raccoons, minks, and a host of lesser creatures. Beavers, with their predisposition for building dams, have created desirable aquatic habitats in numerous other sites in the humid parts of North America.

Wet-land developments need not be great in either size or area to be important. An acre of wet land may keep the wells in the neighborhood at a high level and with a constant supply of water. It may furnish a place for a pair of nesting ducks or a family of muskrats. Even a wet cellar hole may produce cat-tails and a pair of red-winged blackbirds.

Low earthen dikes are being used on both tidal and inland marshes with excellent results. Such dikes are usually of simple construction and may be large or small, depending on the purpose for which they are constructed. Where the costs of dikes are extensive or the structures complicated, engineering as well as biological advice should be sought to insure satisfactory results. Dikes in flat tidal lands may be subject to seepage, wave action, or pressure, if not properly constructed. The backing up of water may do more harm than good if attempted on too large a scale or in a poor location. Each site has its own problems, both biologically and from an engineering standpoint, so each site should be treated on an individual basis. Dikes on tidal marshes must be built so as to keep out water during unusually high tides and storms.

Miscellaneous Marsh and Swamp Operations. Many changes have come about in the conditions of marshes and swamps, both inadvertently and deliberately, through the effects of ditching, fire, control of water levels, planting of vegetation, removal of plants, and grazing. This section will attempt to summarize these operations as they affect wildlife. It is understood that only general results can be given, as so many variables are involved.

Ditching. Cutting ditches through marshes has been tried in many cases and usually with beneficial results if the original water levels were not changed. Such ditches break up the monotony of solid stands of vegetation and not only create open water but also start new plant-succession series which are usually of benefit to wild animals. In marshes they also provide an easy means of transportation for boats and may act as a barrier against fire. They give the "edge effect" so valuable in making a habitat more productive by providing a variety of types. Ditching as used in the above conditions is not drainage. It is cutting or creating openings of various depths and widths which fill with water and in which vegetation of different kinds must begin *in water* rather than on *land.* How much of an efficiently producing marsh should be open water and how much vegetation cannot be categorically stated, but for fresh-water mid-Continent marshes a ratio of one-third open water to two-thirds vegetation would appear satisfactory, with the water and vegetation in irregular shapes, having disconnected islands and bays of water and vegetation. The ditching may be done in several ways, including drag lines, dynamite, and plows. High populations of muskrats or fire in dry peat beds may create openings that fill with water, but the use of fire to create open water is questionable. The use of dynamite for ditching has greatly increased in the past decade and has many points in its favor. The process in general is to place sticks of dynamite in rows or rings, depending on the kind of openings wanted, and to set them off

FIG. 2-2. A ditch constructed by blasting in a Massachusetts marsh to create more water surface and to produce a more diversified vegetation. (*Daniel Grice, Massachusetts Division of Fisheries and Game.*)

in strings in such a way as to throw out the soil or matted vegetation in the pattern desired. In general, the dynamite sticks are placed end to end in a hole punched in the soft marsh bed. The top of the last stick should be 1½ feet below the surface, and the dynamite holes from ½ to 2½ feet apart. Many conditions determine the effectiveness of the blasting method, and trial on the marsh to be managed should determine the amount and arrangement of the explosive. Costs vary, but Nightengale[5] gives 23 to 30 cents a lineal foot for blasting in a marsh near Boston. In this case the ditch was 2 to 3 feet deep and 8 to 12 feet wide. For

[5] Gordon Nightengale. 1950. Experimental waterfowl marsh management-blasting. *Pittman-Robertson Quart.* 10(2):167.

Iowa conditions, Provost (35) suggests the total cost for improving a 5- to 20-acre pond as $116 for dynamite, with an expected benefit for 10 years, or a cost of $11.60 a year.

Other methods of providing open water in marshes that have closed in are the marsh plow, slack-line dredge, and dipper or clam-shell dredge.

In a 15,000-acre fresh or slightly brackish marsh in Jefferson County, Texas, ditches were made by the use of a special marsh tractor and a marsh plow. The tractor operated from a stationary position by the use of a winch and 300 feet of cable. Eighty-five miles of ditches were constructed by this method, part of them double ditches with furrows turned to both sides. These double plow ditches were 20 to 40 inches deep and 4 feet wide. Single ditches were 15 to 24 inches deep and 30 to 40 inches wide. The levees were 18 inches high. The double ditches cost $35 a mile or less than a cent a foot (4, 24).

Various kinds of power equipment can be used for ditching, depending on the water conditions and the depth of solid footing in the marsh. Economy of operation and effectiveness of the ditch system are the determining factors.

Numerous benefits come from ditching in marshes. These include open water for use by waterfowl and escape sites for muskrats, minks, and otters. Water in canals furnishes routes of travel for both man and animals. Levees on the side of ditches furnish resting places for animals and nest foundations for some of the waterfowl, especially geese. Also, both the open water in the ditches and the newly turned earth set back the plant succession, so that different plants are produced in and along the ditches. These plants are usually desirable for wildlife food and supply house-building materials for muskrats.

Ditching of swamps is not desirable because of the variety that already exists in swamps. Usually ditching of swamps is for the purpose of draining and in general this is bad practice for both vegetation and wildlife.

Fire. Fire under control is a very useful tool in marsh management (23). The matter of control, however, is a most important item of the operation. Generally the solid matter in the marsh must be saturated during the burning operation so as not to destroy more than the superficial rough debris. Burning is only desirable at a time of year when game animals or nests of valuable species are not subject to damage. Also, burning should be done when the vegetation is in a dormant condition. Generally no site should be burned in its entirety, but rather small sections which are delimited by firebreaks, canals, or channels. The burning should be conducted under conditions where the fire will not get out of control. Lay and O'Neil (24) recommend severe burning on fresh to slightly brackish marshes in Texas to remove saw-grass and cane and to encourage cat-tails, smooth cord-grass, and three-cornered rushes. As geese are always attracted to the burns because of lush new vegetation, Lay and O'Neil (24) suggest fall burning of goose pastures and early spring burning of muskrat marshes. For muskrats, burning of alternate strips on alternate years will leave plenty of cover and house materials so that muskrats can move to the site of better cover if driven out of the burned area.

Burning of northern marshes and pothole borders is destructive if carried on during the duck-nesting season or at a time when it destroys cover that is used for nest protection. Hockbaum (31 *g.r.*) indicates that the first nesting at Delta, Manitoba, starts about April 15 and for some ducks may carry through August. However, he states that this may not be true farther north or farther west. Perhaps until better information is available it is safe to state that burning of marshes should not be carried out during late spring or summer and that burning should never be done when the roots of marsh plants are not partially covered with water.

As pointed out by Grange (26 *g.r.*), patch burning develops alternate cover and open conditions, reduces undesirable cover, and releases minerals to be used again. These burns are described by Lynch (26) as "cover burns" and "root burns." Cover burns are most successful under Gulf Coast conditions if conducted every second year at a time when there is 6 inches of water over the plant roots. A clean burn may result if the vegetation is dry and if burning is done during a steady breeze coming from a northerly or southeasterly direction. Spotty burns are obtained when the burn is made on dying winds or during damp weather. Lynch (26) lists the five benefits of cover burns as follows: better habitats for geese and ducks, removal of the "rough," acceleration of the roots, better fire protection by the removal of combustible materials with little damage, and better facilities for the movements of both animals and man on the marshes.

Root burns, on the other hand, kill off the climax vegetation and often burn deep pits into the peat of the marsh floor. This provides open water, which is preferred by both waterfowl and fur bearers.

Lynch (26) concludes that cover burns are not destructive to wildlife and that root burns are not particularly destructive to anything but rabbits. He points out that fire is a most useful tool on Gulf Coast marshes. Wiebe and Hess (43) indicate that fire is used on shore lines of Tennessee Valley reservoirs to control willow and other undesirable woody plants. This operation is carried on during the fall and winter when the water in the reservoirs has been drawn down and removal of plant debris is necessary for mosquito control. They also make mention of the control of alligator weed, lotus, cat-tails, and giant cutgrass along these shore margins but do not state that such control was accomplished by the use of fire (43).

Burning of marshes that have an accumulation of plant debris removes the overstory of dead material that blankets the roots, and under favorable conditions encourages the germination and growth of desirable marsh plants like smartweed, sedges, and cat-tails.

The burning of swamps is a doubtful practice and is not recommended. Until research has proved otherwise, it is probably better not to use fire in a swamp.

Control of Water Levels. Some of the disastrous results of drainage have already been discussed under mosquito control, so this subject will be covered only briefly at this point. Probably the most important item to consider here is to keep water levels as stable as possible. If these levels have dropped for some reason it is well to bring them back if possible and then keep them at the optimum level. If water has raised over a former normal level, it is well to drain the excess water away. Low and Bellrose (25) and Martin and Uhler (29) indicate that production of seed of aquatic plants is cut down by fluctuating water levels. Waterfowl nests are flooded out, and even aquatic animals are forced to leave places where floods are common. Ducks Unlimited is building dikes and floodgates along the south end of Lake Winnipeg to protect laying operations and duck nests, where northern winds raise the water of the lake over these low agricultural lands. Usually upland northern-timber species will die if the roots are covered with water for prolonged periods of time (47). Likewise, in the South, the normal swamp species will die if the swamps are drained. In general, it can be said that any management that holds water in swamps at preestablished levels will do the most good in relation to animal production (2).

Swamps have great value, both utilitarian and aesthetic. Usually these isolated woodlands are the last foothold of many of the rare plants and animals of a neighborhood. Even normal upland creatures often retreat to them with the increased pressure of civilization. Rare plants which have disappeared from the flora of a region may often be found in local swamps. Society would do well to consider these values in deciding what to do with the last remaining swamps of a neighborhood.

Planting of Desirable and Removal of Obnoxious Plants and Animals. Much can be done to encourage desirable plants and discourage undesirable plants in wet lands. Along the edges of reservoirs, where the water level is being manipulated for mosquito control or for other reasons, desirable plantings may be made during the summer season and harvested by waterfowl later in the season after the land is again flooded. Likewise, undesirable woody plants may be cut or burned during the low-water period. Davison (15) points out that much damage has been done by commercial aquatic nurseries that sell worthless or harmful plants for so-called "improvements" in fish and waterfowl habitats. He lists the useful species as smartweed, wild duck millet, chufa, potamogetons (the better species only), widgeon-grass, wild celery, wild rice, bulrushes, arrowhead lilies, and spike-rush (*Eleocharis* spp.). There are, no doubt, others that may be useful in suitable places. He lists lotus, white water lily, *Elodea* spp., and spatter-dock as species that interfere with useful duck-food plants, and duck's meat (*Lemna* spp.), coontail, and cat-tails which are found naturally in most locations. The majority

FIG. 2-3. Planting bulrushes along the dikes of a refuge in Utah. These plants control erosion and furnish food and cover for waterfowl. (*W. F. Kubichek, U.S. Fish and Wildlife Service.*)

of plants listed above may be planted in shallow ponds or in flooded areas. Some, like the smartweeds or chufas, will grow on sites that are alternately wet and dry. Such sites as the bottom of ponds where alternate drainage and flooding are possible are very economical to handle.

Details of marsh management are different for each different locality and almost for each marsh. Salt marshes, tidal marshes, alkaline marshes, northern marshes, and southern marshes all have their own peculiarities and should be handled on the basis of special knowledge gathered by application of scientific inquiry.

WILD RICE. The planting of wild rice has been so highly publicized that it seems desirable to comment on its culture. *In general, wild rice will usually be found naturally on sites suitable for its culture, and therefore it need not be planted.* It is a highly desirable food for waterfowl while it lasts during the fall of the year. The wild rice crop fails about 1 year in 4, so that waterfowl usually must depend on other more stable foods during years of rice failure. Good crops of rice produce from 50 to 400 pounds of grain per acre, a product that is eagerly sought by both man and animals. To succeed, the following conditions are necessary, according to Moyle (31): (1) clear water, 1 to 3 feet deep, with

FIG. 2-4. A muskrat house in an eastern marsh. (*Herbert L. Dozier, U.S. Fish and Wildlife Service.*)

alkalinity not more than 40 parts per million (ppm) and sulphur dioxide not greater than 10 ppm, (2) organic (black) soil 6 inches or more in depth, preferably with some calcareous material in it, such as snail shells, (3) some movement of water through the area, (4) fluctuation of water level not greater than 6 inches, (5) absence of carp.

Seed should be kept cool and wet (submerged) from harvest time until planting time, as well as protected from animals. Plant at the rate of 1 bushel per acre, or a large handful for each 6 by 6 feet. Plant as soon as the ice goes out in the spring.

PLANT AND ANIMAL CONTROL. Control of obnoxious animals and plants in marshes is a problem that determines to a marked extent the productiveness of such habitats. Some of the controls are simple and some more complex. Too few muskrats in a marsh may allow cat-tails to become too continuous, while too many cause destruction of valuable plant species. Krummes (22) and Lynch *et al.* (27) indicate that muskrats frequently damage plant life in new impoundments because of a scarcity of plants in an otherwise desirable location. These 'rats may also damage dikes and dams used to control water levels. Under conditions of superabundance muskrats ought to be trapped heavily. On the other hand, when marsh vegetation becomes well established and approaches the closed stage, muskrats in abundance keep part of the area open and so make a marsh highly suitable for waterfowl. Old muskrat houses are desirable bases for both goose and swan nests. Where waterfowl production is the objective of marsh management, financial returns from muskrats often help pay the management costs (5).

The presence of carp in any aquatic site of use for waterfowl or other fish is detrimental, and removal or control is a benefit to the habitat. Catching and sale of carp should be carried on where a market exists, but destruction is usually a benefit regardless of economic returns. The removal or suppression of undesirable plants in a marsh is just as important as in a garden or cornfield. Many of the most valuable plants for waterfowl are not able to compete with more aggressive aquatic species like cat-tails, giant cutgrass, coontail, and yellow lily. Two plants which have received special attention because of their objectionable characteristics are the water-hyacinth and water-chestnut.

Only a few of the management techniques available to the marsh manager can be given, but several general principles can be included which may help in this field. Annual plants are usually most susceptible to control in their earliest stages of growth. In general, this is in the spring, but it may be midwinter in the regions of milder climate. Thus, salt-marsh-fleabane (*Pluchea camphorata*), a land plant, can be drowned out by raising the water a few inches after the seeds have sprouted.

Another desirable season for control is after plants have spent their strength during the seed-producing season (30, 41). Usually this is in late July or August.

Other methods used to control plants in marshes include fires, mechanical devices, manipulation of water levels, and chemical herbicides.

Fire, where it can be used, is probably the cheapest method of plant control. Thus, when there are a few inches of water on a marsh, the dead debris can be burned off, and valuable plants given a chance to come through. Cat-tails and cord-grass can be handled to advantage in this way. However, seed production of saw-grass is stimulated by burning according to Uhler (41). Creation of marsh fires sufficiently hot to destroy roots can be accomplished by allowing the marsh to dry out to a depth of 6 inches. Giant cutgrass, reeds, saw-grass, cat-tails, mints, and river bulrushes may be controlled by this method. Peat (deep) burns on small areas may completely destroy river bulrushes, wool-grass, sedges, reeds, and mints. Uhler (41) points out such burning should always be done at a time when it will not injure nesting birds.

Mechanical devices for removing weeds include hand rakes, wire drags, underwater mowers, weed rakes, and mechanical weed crushers. Power-driven mowers are usually mounted on flat-bottomed boats and may cut as far as 4 feet below the surface. Giant cutgrass, cat-tails, spatter-dock, bulrushes, and water-chestnut can all be controlled in this way. One or more mowings can be made during a season. Care should be taken to control the plants before the seeds mature.

A plant crusher is described by Martin and Uhler (29) by means of which water-hyacinth (*Eichornia crassipes*) or any other coarse plant is run through corrugated rollers that crush both plants and seeds. This is an expensive piece of machinery and would be justified only where extensive beds of vegetation need to be removed. In New Jersey marshes a weed crusher was made up with wide cleated wheels so the sharp edge of angle irons crumpled the plants at intervals of several inches (29). Hazeltine and Ekdahl (20) used a special rake and dragline to remove vegetation close to shore in botulism control. Where water control is a part of the marsh-management system, variation in the water level can be used to control many marsh plants. The drying out of a wet marsh will eliminate most of the plants that require free water, whereas raising the water a few inches or up to 2 feet will eliminate the plants that require semidry conditions. A knowledge of the ecology of aquatic plants is necessary for any intelligent control, as conditions of climate, soil, and chemical content of water will vary the results for any operation.

A new interest in chemical controls has come about through the discovery of new herbicides. The use of chemicals to control plants is not new, however. The use of herbicides has the disadvantage of being expensive. Furthermore, some chemicals may be dangerous to animal life, but still they may be the only effective control method. The control of water blooms or frog scums which often form in late summer, and which are objectionable in bathing ponds and along beaches, may be accomplished by either spraying with copper sulphate (blue vitriol) or by suspending burlap bags of the crystals from the sides of a slowly moving boat. One to four pounds of crystals are needed for each million gallons or 133,700 cubic feet of water (29). The burlap-bag method seems to control underwater plants better than the surface spraying.

The control of water-chestnut in the Potomac River was accomplished by spraying with 1 pound of sodium arsenite and ½ pound of sodium chlorate dissolved in a gallon of water. This quantity would cover 150 square feet of plant beds and give a nearly complete kill when applied during a 12-day period in July. Spraying was done on hot, calm days at low tide. Care should be taken with the sodium chlorate, as it is inflammable. The use of 2,4-D is being attempted in New York and Massachusetts with some success. It has been found, however, that seeds may last over beyond the second year and that not all parts of the plants are killed with one spraying.

Sodium arsenate has been used in the control of water-hyacinth by army engineers, according to Martin and Uhler (29).

Ammonium theocyanate can be used to control needlerush (*Juncus roemerianus*), river bulrush (*Scirpus fluviatilis*), and beggar-ticks (*Bidens* spp.). One and one-half pounds of the crude chemical dissolved in water makes a gallon solution that will spray 150 square feet. This chemical is not poisonous and therefore does not leave the soil sterile as does sodium arsenate. The latter, however, will control needlerush but does little injury to three-square bulrush (*Scirpus americanus*) (29).

The use of 2,4-D[6] has been successful in the control of several emergent plants. Usually a wetting agent[7] is added to help spread out the active material. Bauman (6) suggests the use of the 2,4-D by volume as follows:

	Water
American lotus (*Nelumbo lutea*) 1 part 2,4-D	150–300
Water willow (*Justicia americana*) 1 part 2,4-D	130–250
Cat-tail (*Typha latifolia*) 1 part 2,4-D	130
Water-primrose (*Jussiaea repens* var. *glabrescens*) 1 part 2,4-D	100–500
Arrowhead (*Sagittaria latifolia*), no conclusion given	
Pondweeds (*Potamogeton nodosus* var. *diversifolius*) 1 part 2,4-D	130
Pickerelweed (*Pontederia cordata*), no conclusion given	
Duckweed (*Lemna minor*) (results not satisfactory) 1 part 2,4-D	75

Steenis (40) used both 2,4-D and ammate ammonium sulfamate to control lotus, giant cutgrass, buttonbush, trumpet vine, willow, green ash, and some of the water oaks. For 2,4-D the best results were obtained when foliage development was at its maximum and the environment wet. Temperature of 70°F. or higher seems optimum. For the ammate compound the most effective time for application is when the plants are fruiting. 2,4-D was used at 6 per cent strength and ammate ammonium sulfamate at a concentration of ¾ pound to a gallon of water. Control of submerged plants is possible but not practical by the use of 2,4-D because of the cost of this material (17).

[6] 14 per cent active ingredient of butyl ester of 2,4-dichloro-phenoxyacetic acid.

[7] Bauman (6) suggests 1 per cent Vatsol OS, 66 per cent paste to 10,000 parts of water as a wetting agent.

Agricultural Practices in Relation to Marsh Management. Grazing of cattle and the cutting of hay are operations that may be classed as agricultural practices. Grazing by wild geese may be difficult to control completely. The effect of grazing may be the same, however, whether done by wild or domesticated animals. Lay and O'Neil (24) suggest the fall burning of upland prairie to attract geese away from muskrat marshes, so that the geese do not destroy the food needed by muskrats. Moderate hunting also will keep the geese away from the muskrat marsh. Lay and O'Neil (24) also mention the use of electric fences to keep cattle away from muskrat marshes but do not indicate how effective this procedure may be. The damage to muskrats by cattle is great, including cost of broken traps, trap stakes, trampling of beds, and the use of muskrat houses for cattle beds.

Where waterfowl nest, the grazing of cattle and horses is destructive. Not only will the animals trample and destroy nests and young, but the entire effectiveness of cover may be eliminated. The practice of grazing all waste and wet areas seems justified to landowners on the basis that little other returns are available on this land so every opportunity must be used to get some possible return. However, this practice does limit the waterfowl crop and possibly may reduce other values. Local sportsmen's groups could well afford to furnish fences and encourage protection of choice waterfowl marshes to get increased yields of ducks on these lands.

Haying in marshes, if done early in the season, kills and maims many marsh animals, particularly birds. For the area of Delta, Manitoba, Hochbaum (31 *g.r.*) indicates the nesting season for waterfowl extends from April 15 to August 15, or even later. If haying can be delayed until after that date many nests of all kinds of marsh life will be saved (31 *g.r.*). Haying as an operation has a direct effect in destroying cover so necessary for marsh animals. Again, however, wildlife must give ground when opposed to the economic needs of landowners. On public lands, refuges, and land leased for wildlife production, careful consideration should be given to the damage done by this and other farm practices.

REFERENCES

1. Addy, C. E., and L. A. MacNamara. 1948. Waterfowl management on small areas, Wildlife Management Institute, Washington, D.C.
2. Agersborg, H. P. Kjerschow. 1935. The nature of swamps. When, if ever, should they be drowned or drained? *Amer. Wildlife.* **24**(6):88.
3. Anderson, Wallace L. 1947. Drainage—Dr. Jekyll or Mr. Hyde? *Outdoor Amer.* **12**(8):4–5.
4. ———. 1948. Level ditching to improve muskrat marshes. *Jour. Wildlife Mangt.* **12**(2):172–176.

5. Anonymous. 1949. Horicon marsh wildlife area: Its past, its present, its future, Wisconsin Conservation Department, Madison.
6. Bauman, Aden C. 1947. 2,4-D and some emergent aquatics. *Prog. Fish Culturist.* **9**(2):71–77.
7. Bellrose, Frank C., Jr. 1941. Duck food of Illinois river valley. *Ill. Nat. Hist. Survey Bul.* No. 21, Art. 8, pp. 237–280.
8. Bourn, Warren S., and Clarence Cottam. 1939. The effect of lowering water levels on marsh wildlife. *Trans. 4th North Amer. Wildlife Conf.* Pp. 343–350.
9. ———. 1950. Some biological effects of ditching tidewater marshes. *Fish and Wildlife Serv., Res. Rpt.* 19.
10. Bradbury, Harold M. 1938. Mosquito control operations on tide marshes in Massachusetts and their effect on shore birds and waterfowl. *Jour. Wildlife Mangt.* **2**(2):49–52.
11. Carpenter, J. Richard. 1938. An ecological glossary. University of Oklahoma Press, Norman.
12. Conservationist. 1939. Needed—sane program of ecology. *La. Conserv. Rev.* **9**(2):7, 58.
13. Cook, Arthur H., and Edward R. Maunton. 1950. Muskrat research that led to a marsh management program. *Proc. Northeastern Fish and Game Conf.*, Syracuse.
14. Cottam, Clarence, Warren S. Bourn, F. C. Bishopp, L. L. Williams, Jr., and William Vogt. 1938. What's wrong with mosquito control? *Trans. 3d North Amer. Wildlife Conf.* Pp. 81–107.
15. Davison, Verne E. 1942. Thirty million acres of undiscovered wildlife land in the United States. *Trans. 7th North Amer. Wildlife Conf.* Pp. 366–374.
16. Florio, Anthony J. 1950. Salt marshes, Delaware Game and Fish Commission.
17. Gerking, Shelby D. 1948. Destruction of submerged aquatic plants by 2,4-D. *Jour. Wildlife Mangt.* **12**(3):221–227.
18. Goodrum, Phil, W. P. Baldwin, and John W. Aldrich. 1949. Effects of DDT on animal life of Bulls Island, South Carolina. *Jour. Wildlife Mangt.* **13**(1):1–10.
19. Hall, William L., and H. U. Maxwell. 1910. Surface conditions and stream flow. *U.S. Dept. Agr. Foreign Serv. Cir.* 176.
20. Hazeltine, Benjamin M., and Vernon Ekdahl. 1945. Paul Bunyon rake for removal of marginal vegetation in botulism control. *Jour. Wildlife Mangt.* **9**(3):193–195.
21. Kenney, F. R., and W. L. McAtee. 1938. The problem: Drained areas and wildlife habitats. Soils and Men, *U.S. Dept. Agr. Yearbook.* Pp. 77–84.
22. Krummes, William T. 1940. The muskrat: A factor in waterfowl habitat management. *Trans. 5th North Amer. Wildlife Conf.* Pp. 395–398.
23. Lay, Daniel W. 1945. Muskrat investigations in Texas. *Jour. Wildlife Mangt.* **9**(1):56–76.
24. ——— and Ted O'Neil. 1942. Muskrats on the Texas coast. *Jour. Wildlife Mangt.* **6**(4):301–311.
25. Low, Jessop B., and Frank C. Bellrose, Jr. 1944. Seed and vegetative yield of waterfowl food plants in the Illinois river valley. *Jour. Wildlife Mangt.* **8**(1):7–22.

26. Lynch, John J. 1941. Place of burning in management of Gulf Coast wildlife refuges. *Jour. Wildlife Mangt.* **5**(4):454–457.
27. ———, Ted O'Neil, and Daniel W. Lay. 1947. Management significance of damage by geese and muskrats to gulf coast marshes. *Jour. Wildlife Mangt.* **11**(1):50–76.
28. MacNamara, L. G. 1949. Salt-marsh development at Tuckahoe, New Jersey. *Trans. 14th North Amer. Wildlife Conf.* Pp. 100–117.
29. Martin, A. C., and F. M. Uhler. 1939. Food of game ducks in the United States and Canada. *U.S. Dept. of Agr. Tech. Bul.* 634.
30. McAtee, W. L. 1939. Wildfowl food plants: Their value, propagation, and management, Collegiate Press, Inc., Ames, Iowa.
31. Moyle, John B. 1944. Wild rice in Minnesota. *Jour. Wildlife Mangt.* **8**(3):177–184.
32. Nichols, G. E. 1937. Introduction to plant ecology, A syllabus of lectures in plant ecology. Unpublished manuscript.
33. Page, John C., S. B. Locke, S. H. McCrory, and G. W. Grebe. 1938. What is or should be the status of wildlife as a factor in drainage and reclamation planning? *Trans. 3d North Amer. Wildlife Conf.* Pp. 109–125.
34. Penfound, William T., and John D. Schneidau. 1945. The relation of land reclamation to aquatic resources in southeastern Louisana. *Trans. 10th North Amer. Wildlife Conf.* Pp. 308–318.
35. Provost, Maurice W. 1948. Marsh-blasting as a wildlife management technique. *Jour. Wildlife Mangt.* **12**(4):350–387.
36. Schmidt, F. V. 1950. An evaluation of practical tidal marsh management on state and private marshes. *Proc. Northeastern Fish and Wildlife Conf.*, Syracuse.
37. Sharp, Ward M. 1951. Environmental requirements of a fresh water marsh and the ecology of some aquatic plants. Mimeo.
38. Springer, Paul F., and John R. Webster. 1949. Effects of DDT on salt-marsh wildlife. *U.S. Fish and Wildlife Serv., Spec. Sci. Rpt.-Wildlife* 10.
39. Stearns, L. A., Donald MacCreary, and F. C. Daigh. 1940. Effects of ditching for mosquito control on muskrat population of a Delaware tidewater marsh. *Del. Agr. Expt. Sta. Bul.* 225, *Tech. Bul.* 26.
40. Steenis, John H. 1950. Studies on the use of herbicides for improving waterfowl habitat in western Kentucky and Tennessee. *Jour. Wildlife Mangt.* **14**(2):162–169.
41. Uhler, Francis M. 1944. Control of undesirable plants in waterfowl habitats. *Trans. 9th North Amer. Wildlife Conf.* Pp. 295–303.
42. Vogt, William. (No date). Thirst on the land. *Nat. Assoc. Audubon Socs. Cir.* 32.
43. Wiebe, A. H., and A. D. Hess. 1944. Mutual interests of wildlife conservation and malaria control on impounded waters. *Jour. Wildlife Mangt.* **8**(4):275–283.
44. Williams, Louis L., Jr., Walter B. Jones, J. Lyell Clarke, Clarence Cottam, and Warren S. Bourn. 1939. Need mosquito control be incompatible with wildlife? *Trans. 4th North Amer. Wildlife Conf.* Pp. 114–136.
45. Wilson, Vanez T., and Rachel L. Carson. 1950. Bear River a natural wildlife refuge. *U.S. Fish and Wildlife Serv., Conserv. in Action* 8.
46. Wright, J. O. 1907. Swamp and overflow lands in the United States. *U.S. Off. Expt. Sta. Cir.* 76.

47. Yeager, Lee E. 1949. Effects of permanent flooding in a river-bottom timber area. *Ill. Nat. Hist. Survey Bul.* **25**(2).
48. Zon, Raphael. 1927. Forests and waters in the light of scientific investigation. *Final Rpt. Natl. Waterways Comn.*, 2d ed., appendix V.
49. ——— and James L. Averell. 1929. Drainage of swamps and forest growth. *Wis. Univ. Agr. Expt. Sta. Research Bul.* 89.

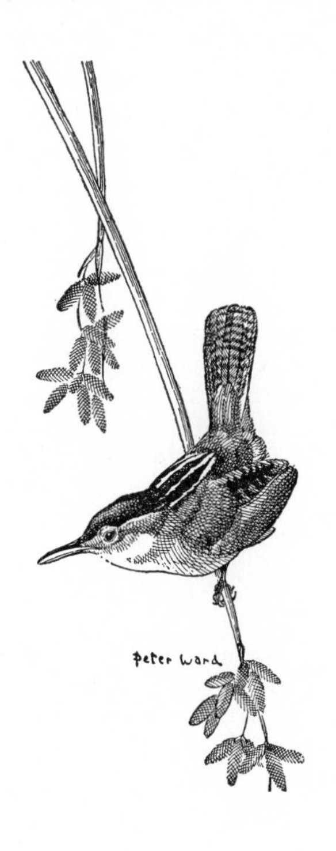

SECTION TWO

Fur Bearers

CHAPTER 3

Fur Bearers

INTRODUCTION

The fur bearers are unique among the wildlife of North America in that both the pelts and the carcasses of at least some of these animals are an economic resource of considerable importance. The owner of land on which fur is produced and the trapper who gathers this crop may both profit financially by the production and harvest of wild furs. This situation differs from that of wild game where direct sale is usually forbidden by legal restriction, even though the game bird or mammal was obtained during the legal hunting season. Such laws are designed to prevent market hunting and to make hunting a form of recreation—an avocation and not a vocation. In the case of wild fur, it is the money value of the crop which is the primary incentive for management. A secondary profit that should not be overlooked in this connection centers around the insect- and rodent-eating habits of many species, which are sufficient reasons in themselves for giving consideration to this class of wildlife (24). The economic and other beneficial aspects of fur-bearer production do not remove, however, the responsibility of guidance by public conservation agencies for managing these mammals.

Intelligent management of some fur-bearing species may be hampered because of the widespread belief that carnivorous fur bearers live primarily on game and therefore an increase in their numbers should be discouraged rather than encouraged. As a matter of fact, there is little definite evidence available to indicate that carnivorous fur bearers are directly responsible for any general reduction of game populations.

FUR BEARERS IN NORTH AMERICA

The value of fur and the esteem in which it is held have had much to do with the intensity of trapping and the numbers of each species trapped. Environmental changes due to cutting of forests and development of agricultural lands have helped to reduce some of the forest fur animals and have increased the open-land species. During the early

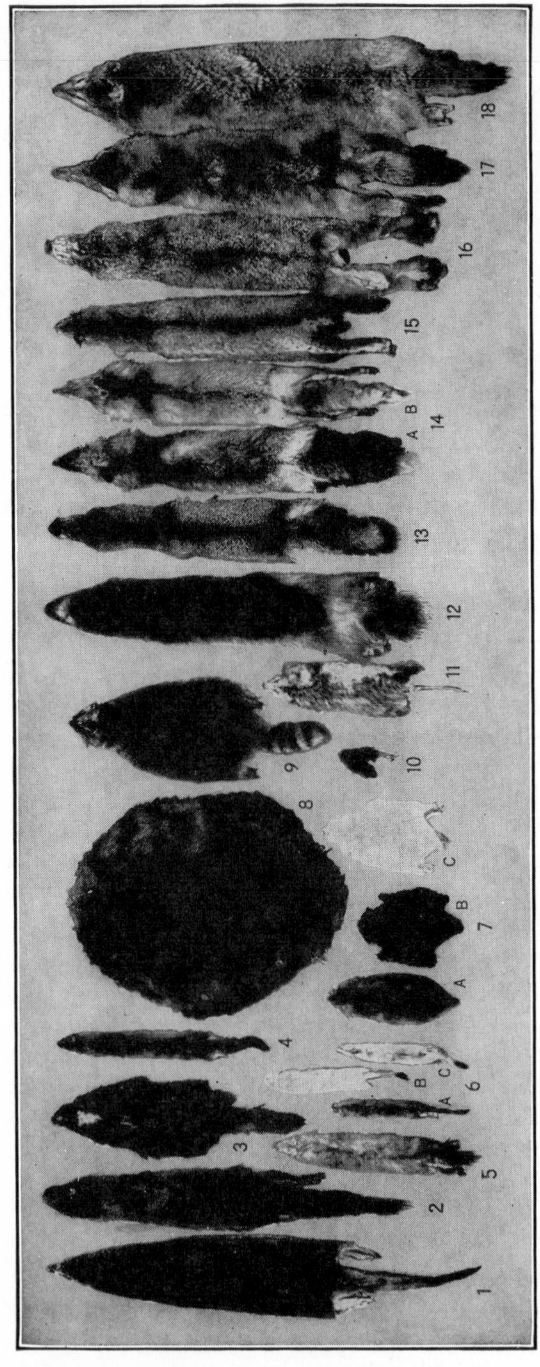

FIG. 3-1. Pelts of the more important fur bearers. (1) otter; (2) fisher; (3) skunk; (4) mink; (5) marten; (6) weasel, A. brown or summer pelage, *B*. white or winter pelage, and *C*. changing pelage; (7) muskrat, A. natural skin, *B*. Hudson seal, sheared and dyed black, and *C*. albino phase; (8) beaver; (9) raccoon; (10) mole; (11) opossum; (12) wolverine; (13) gray fox; (14) red fox; (15) bobcat; (16) lynx; (17) coyote; (18) wolf. (*N.Y. Conserv.*)

1920's long-haired furs, including skunks, raccoons, and foxes, were style favorites and as a result brought high prices. Currently these long-haired creatures are less in style-favor, and therefore unit prices are low. As opposed to the aforementioned animals, minks, muskrats, and seals have increased in both favor and value, with an accompanying increase in unit price. Other fur bearers, such as the sea otter, although not used in the fur trade, have gained slightly in numbers, owing to better law enforcement. The fisher has also gained in numbers in the past decade, especially in New York, New Hampshire, and Maine. Beavers seem to be gaining slightly. Muskrats are now being trapped more heavily than at any time in the history of the fur trade and as of 1952 have been on the decline for a number of years (12).

Three phases of the fur-bearer situation will be discussed in this chapter: (1) the capacity of the North American continent to produce fur as indicated by numbers of fur bearers formerly present, (2) value of the present fur crop, (3) the progress being made toward the management of fur-bearing species.

History. Fur bearers were the incentive for much of the early explorations in North America. A crop of fine fur was available when the white man invaded this continent and was one of the few readily available natural resources which could at that time be exchanged for gold and merchandise in the Old World. Trappers and traders penetrated all parts of the continent in search of the sea otter, beaver, marten, and other smaller fur-bearing animals. Local conflicts were common as explorers and traders strove for the control of choice fur-producing regions. Trappers and traders representing the fur companies of various European nations fought on the outposts of civilization for the control of territories and key trading routes all over North America. Some of the lands won and held during these early conflicts are now in the hands of the nations which contested for them 200 to 300 years ago.

Commerce in fur, which started as early as 1630 along the New England seaboard, was the forerunner of other commercial enterprises. In 1670, the Governor and Company of Adventurers of England Trading in Hudson's Bay, later incorporated into the Hudson's Bay Company, established forts on Hudson Bay and began a trade in fur which continues to the present time, giving this concern the unique honor of being the oldest business institution on the North American continent and also the oldest merchant trading company in the world (14). According to Grinnell *et al.* (23), fur trapping and trading began in California in 1785 when Spanish authorities issued regulations governing the collection of pelts in that state. It is said that between 1786 and 1790, 9,729 otter skins and some seal skins were sent to Manila from central California. This same reference tells of a thousand sea otter skins which were sold around that time for $10,000 in China. A Russian company under Kuskof is recorded as having established a settlement at Fort Ross, Sonoma County, California, in 1812 and from that time to 1841 obtained a total of 13,600 otter skins. Kuskof, while stationed in what is now Alaska, in 1811 sent a company of 22 "bidarkas" on a trapping mission with two parties of Aleuts down to the coast of California and obtained 1,200 otter skins during several months' trapping. In 1840 sea otter skins often brought a price as high as $60 apiece.[1] Grinnell *et al.* (23) also cite 19 trappers securing 1,000 beavers, or an average of over 50 beavers apiece, in the California territory in a single season. Another party organized by Ogden in 1825–1826 obtained 1,000 beavers for the first 5 months of the season and 4,300 for the entire trapping period. This party consisted of 43 men, and Ogden was disappointed because of the seemingly low average catch for his party.

Capacity of Land to Produce Fur. While the fur-bearing animals probably had reached a balance with their environment before man began the exploitation of either fur or the forests, there is evidence to show that the greatest capacity of the land to produce wild animals had not been reached. In this connection, O'Roke (32) states: "The great virgin forests of mature timber were not the place *par excellence* for the production of furs." He furthermore calls attention to the fact that, with the possible exception of the marten and the fisher, more areas of suitable conditions may be present where clear cutting, logging, and planting have opened the forest canopy and changed soil conditions. Openings encourage grass, and grass shelters mice and rabbits, which are basic foods for carnivores like the fox, lynx, wolf, coyote, mink, and weasel. Burns create openings in which aspen grows, and where such openings occur on stream and pond edges, aquatic vegetation soon appears. Such plants are utilized as food by the beaver. Ponds and pond borders created by beavers also will sooner or later develop muck in which aquatic plants flourish. Lay (28) believes that habitats for most fur bearers in the southern states, with the probable exception of marsh and streamside habitats for muskrat and beaver, are as good as or better than during primeval times.

When man learns to manage the plant and animal resources so as to produce satisfactory returns of timber, fur, game, and healthful recreation from lands submarginal for the production of domesticated species, he will have arrived at a milestone in human progress known as intelligent land management.

Value of the Fur Crop. Progress during the present century may be seen in the increased interest in the production of wild furs. This grow-

[1] Good beaver skins brought $60 in 1949 but only $12 to $15 in 1952. The presence of beaver in many parts of the United States is definitely the result of intelligent wildlife management.

ing interest is due not only to the higher prices received for furs following the First World War, but also to a better appreciation of our wild-animal resources. The economic importance of the fur animals was convincingly demonstrated within recent years when men, unable to find employment, derived some financial relief from their trap lines. Likewise, important fur-bearing animals like beaver are coming back as a result of better legal protection and the accidental provision of an ample supply of food, the latter in the form of aspen invading the logged and burned-over forest lands of northern and eastern United States.

The fur take seems to have reached its peak during the decade 1940–1950, if fur estimates given by the states are correct. From 1945 to the present there has been a steady decline in total numbers, with the muskrat leading both the greatest total value and greatest decline. In 1945–1946 Louisiana reported a take of 8,337,411 muskrat pelts, while 4 years later the take was only 2,195,324 (12). Ashbrook[2] suggests that the annual fur take in the United States is from 25 to 30 million skins a year. He estimates the raw fur crop is worth from 100 to 125 million dollars a year, with about 15 per cent of this, or $18,500,000, going to fur farmers.

The United States is now a world center of the fur trade, with New York and St. Louis leading the fur-processing business. Many raw furs are imported from foreign lands to be processed into garments of all kinds. The value of the processed materials for 1947 was estimated at $425,600,000.[2] Excise taxes for the same year were $97,481,000. This exceeds the tax for toilet articles and is about half that for jewelry.[3]

The fur crop of North America is taken under a variety of conditions and methods (25). Many Indians and Eskimos in northern Canada and Alaska derive their entire livelihood from hunting and trapping. Bonnycastle (14) believes that before many years all trapping in the northern provinces of Canada will be limited to these classes of people. In the United States considerable trapping is done by farm boys as a part-time activity and by professional trappers, some of whom are backed by well-established companies, many of which own large acreages of good fur-producing lands. Such companies are found in widely scattered localities, including Ontario in Canada, and New Jersey, Maryland, and Louisiana in the United States.

Hamilton (29 *g.r.*) and Miller and Powell (49 *g.r.*) are in disagreement as to whether farm boys or professional trappers take the larger share of the fur crop in the United States. A nationwide survey by Miller and Powell revealed that professional trappers from cities rather than farm boys take the largest proportion of wild furs. Hayne (26), in a

[2] Frank G. Ashbrook. 1948. Fur—An important wildlife crop. *Fish and Wildlife Serv., U.S. Dept. Int., Wildlife Leaflet* 314.
[3] U.S. census figures.

study of Williamston township (36 square miles) in southern Michigan, found that the average age of the trappers was 32 years and that the value of the take was $1,269.13 (season 1937–1938). The total value of the take of each trapper averaged slightly more than $40.

Finally, all fur animals are not secured via steel traps, snares, and dead falls. Thousands of raccoon and fox pelts are taken each year by hunters participating in the exciting and traditional 'coon and fox hunts.

The record of the inventory of the estate of a trapper in the vicinity of the Straits of Mackinaw, Michigan, for 1819 (4) shows that trapping in virgin territory, or at least on an area where the trapping pressure was not heavy, a single trapper during the period 1780–1819 secured 754 beavers, 1,061 raccoons, and 9,537 muskrats during an unknown period of trapping. At that time muskrat pelts brought 20 cents apiece, minks 25 cents, and beavers $3.20 (4). A hundred years later muskrats brought $1 to $3, minks $10 to $15 and beavers $19 to $25.

Progress toward Management. The management of fur bearers concerns itself with the production of fur animals in their natural habitats, as well as with furs produced under domestication. Excellent progress is being made in isolated cases in the production of wild furs by the control of the harvest in such a way that adequate breeding stock is always present and by the improvement of natural habitats. Probably the most widely known example of successful management of the breeding and harvest of a wild fur bearer is the handling of the Alaska fur seal herd by the U.S. Bureau of Fisheries since 1911. This resource, which originally numbered millions of seals, was reduced to pitifully low numbers by uncontrolled slaughter until it was placed under the control of the United States by international agreement. In 1911 there were only 123,000 seals left. By 1919 half a million seals were visiting the breeding grounds in the Aleutian Islands, and by 1947 under careful management the herd had increased to more than 1½ million seals, with a fur take of about 65,000 pelts (33).[4]

Many outstanding examples of environmental habitat improvement for muskrats can be found in the United States and the Canadian provinces, where control of water levels, burning, and predators have brought fur production to a higher level (2, 17). In fact, the management of muskrats can be cited as the outstanding example of the managing of a wild-animal species for profit.

The successful management of beaver has been demonstrated in numerous localities. In 1858, New Hampshire had one beaver colony, whereas 80 years later (1938) the census showed 7,500 beavers scattered through the state, with the breeding stock increasing rapidly. Likewise,

[4] Victor B. Scheffer and Karl W. Kenyon. 1952. The fur seal herd comes of age. *Natl. Geog. Mag.* **101**(4):491–512.

Michigan in 1920 was forced to close the trapping season on beavers to preserve the few remaining animals. Under management, the beaver in Michigan yielded a total crop of 52,509 pelts during the 14 years prior to 1943 with an approximate annual value of almost $86,000 (15, 16). For the past 10 years, Michigan has been conducting investigations in otter management, and the populations of this fur bearer had so increased by 1940 that trapping of otter was allowed in 25 counties. Under strict control 635 pelts were taken during 4 trapping seasons, and a good breeding stock still remains. Thus, wildlife management is not only bringing back some fur bearers but also is allowing a generous annual harvest with which to pay the costs of producing such crops.

Yield of Fur in Different Habitats. Fur values and fur yields for various types of habitat have been compiled by Allan (3) and published under the title "Furs from Farmlands" for use by technicians of the Soil Conservation Service. Portions of that bulletin are herewith included. The following summary of Allan's data (3) gives maximum annual fur values for muskrats, opossums, skunks, raccoons, and minks for different habitat types.

	Value per acre
Streams (stream banks)	$ 8.30
Drainage ditches	20.91
Marshes	2.70*
Lake shores	3.20
Ponds (water areas)	10.00
Strip-mine areas	5.00
Quarries	0.77

* $6.96 per acre on a managed marsh.

Fur Take by States. The annual fur take by states gives some idea of the extent and value of the harvest of wild animals from water and land areas not used for raising conventional agricultural crops. In America we are prone to disregard animal crops which are not visible or confined within fences and to think of wet and swampy land only as waste lands. Such is not the case, however, as will be shown by the figures for fur bearers given below.

The taking of pelts during 1949–1950 was as follows: Louisiana, 2,451,283; Michigan, 824,637; Minnesota, 628,293; Ohio, 615,079; Indiana, 546,788; Illinois, 524,262; Pennsylvania, 513,691.

Fur Take in North America. The number of fur animals pelted each year in the United States (including Alaska) and Canada runs into large numbers and high values if considered in the aggregate. An estimate of the number of pelts and their value for these two countries for the open season 1937–1938 and 1947–1948 has been made from reports of the U.S. Fish and Wildlife Service and of Canadian Department of Trade and Commerce. These data are shown in Table 3-1.

Table 3-1. Fur Statistics for the United States (Including Alaska) and Canada, 1937–1938 and 1947–1948 (5, 6, 9, 12)

Species of furbearing animal	Total fur take for the United States and Alaska		Total fur take for Canada	
	1937–1938*	1947–1948†	1937–1938	1947–1948
Badger	13,131	5,503	204	1,034
Beaver	34,749	76,151	54,148	135,629
Coyote	28,522	55,538	40,811	21,728
Fisher	128	3	3,505	2,823
Fox	248,197	353,241	412,600	289,384
Lynx and bobcat	5,937	13,747	11,631	7,847
Marten	17,962	19,193	23,851	15,090
Mink	485,200	659,879	139,740	654,506
Muskrat	9,547,596	11,969,568	1,748,239	3,569,157
Nutria	....	28,289	....	8
Opossum	3,692,118	1,208,948		
Otter	6,980	10,419	10,262	11,974
Raccoon	566,632	1,072,584	20,366	24,214
Seal	55,180	70,142		
Skunk	2,870,240	592,570	125,612	19,096
Weasel	399,956	129,894	680,752	528,029
Wolf	3,896	1,638	8,062	1,231
Wolverine	370	144	671	452
Total	17,976,794	16,267,451	3,280,454	5,282,212

* Does not include Alabama, Colorado, Kentucky, Nevada, North Carolina, North Dakota, and Rhode Island.

† Does not include Alabama, Kentucky, and Rhode Island.

Moss (31) reports a take of 183 muskrats from a 4-acre artificial pond over 8 seasons in Connecticut, or an annual yield of 23 pelts a year. Additional income accrued from frogs, ducks, and other aquatic products.

Laws and Practices Related to Trapping. A chapter on fur bearers would not be complete without a discussion of some of the difficulties of setting open seasons and administering the laws which control the fur take. One of the difficulties lies in the fact that some of the animals which produce fur are also edible and furthermore in many instances furnish fine sport as game animals. The raccoon is a good example of this type. Other fur bearers, such as the fox, may furnish sport for hunters and also be a menace to specialized agricultural activities, such as poultry farming. Thus, several conflicting groups are concerned with the management of some fur-bearing species.

Logically, much value is lost if fur bearers are taken when the fur is unprime or after the animals have injured themselves through fighting.

The time of open season is also of importance because of its relation to the animal left for breeding purposes. The Federal Lacy Act passed by Congress on May 25, 1900, provides, in general, that it is a Federal offense to bring into the United States or to ship from one state to another animals alive or dead which were killed or captured contrary to the law of the country, province, or state from which they came. State and provincial laws give open and closed seasons for each individual animal and specify what is legal or illegal as to the method of trapping. Some states and provinces divide their territory into districts with different regulations for each district. Where a state or province has information on the distribution and abundance of its fur animals, the subdivision into districts is a wise procedure.

In general, laws relating to fur bearers should aim at accomplishing the following results:

1. Fur should be taken only when prime. Usually this will be roughly between November 1 and January 31. The exception to this rule may be the muskrat, which often does not reach maturity until later in the season. Hamilton (24) suggests the following seasons for taking various fur-bearing species in New York state:

Mink	Nov. 10 to Jan. 15
Skunk	Nov. 1 to Jan. 1
Fox	Nov. 10 to Jan. 10
Raccoon	Nov. 15 to Jan. 1
Muskrat	Jan. 1–15 to Mar. 15
Beaver	Feb. 1 to Apr. 1

2. Open seasons for running raccoon dogs should be postponed until the young of the current year are mature. Open seasons for running 'coon dogs in August are too early; November 1 is much better.

3. Trappers should be licensed. However, where a landowner traps on his own land, no charge should be made for the license.

4. Each trap should be required to carry a tag on which appears the name and license number of the owner. The state license fee could well include a sufficient amount to pay for such trap tags.

5. Each trapper should be required to report the species and number of fur bearers he trapped within 30 days after the close of the current trapping season. He should also be required to indicate to whom he sold his fur catch.

6. Fur buyers should be licensed and be required to report at the end of each year, December 31, the kind and number of pelts purchased during the current year.

7. It should be illegal to buy or sell the flesh of fur bearers except

during the open fur season and for a reasonable time (not longer than 30 days) following the open season.

8. The law should prohibit the taking of fur bearers by unusual methods, such as by spears, poison or poison gases, snares, or by traps of unusual size. It should be illegal to set traps closer than 3 feet from a muskrat or beaver house. It should also be illegal to break open or use dynamite on a muskrat or beaver house (29).

The general practice of allocating one trapper to a given trapping territory and allowing him the sole trapping rights on this area is followed in Ontario, British Columbia, and possibly some of the other Canadian provinces (18, 20). The most recent trapping regulations in Ontario, which came into effect in 1947–1948, contain the following provisions:

1. Each trapper is issued a "resident trapper's license," which gives him the privilege to trap fur-bearing animals other than beaver on land owned by himself, or land owned by others with the owner's consent.

2. The trapper is issued a special beaver license if he wishes to trap beaver.

3. A special "trap-line license" is issued to those trapping on Crown (publicly owned) lands, the trap line being designated by watersheds, rivers, and canoe routes. The trap line is registered and numbered in the District Office.

4. No trapper may hold more than one "trap-line license," and each trapper must make an annual return to the District Office. In this return he indicates the amount of fur he has taken and to whom he sold it. A diagram of the trap line is drawn on the reverse side of the license.

5. The number of beavers a licensee can take is governed by the number of "live" (occupied) beaver houses on his trapping territory. Beaver may not be trapped until the licensee has at least five "live" beaver houses on his territory. After that he may take one beaver for each "live" house. The maximum number of beavers he may take is also stamped on the face of his license.

6. Trapping licenses must be obtained each year and may be canceled if the trapper does not look after his trap line.

7. Each beaver pelt taken by the licensed trapper must be sealed by an official of the Provincial Fish and Game Division with a metal seal through the eye or nose of the pelt before it can be sold. At the time the pelts are sealed, the number of pelts sealed is also stamped on the trap-line license.

8. The trapper may sell or will the trapping rights to anyone he chooses. This gives him the benefits of any work he does in building up his trapping territory.

This system of fur harvesting has many merits. It limits the harvest to the capacity of the land. It eliminates the competition of several trappers working the same territory and gives the trapper an incentive for looking after and improving his trapping territory. The trapper-territory system also works well in British Columbia, where it has been in use for many years (20).

Literature on Fur Bearers. Another indication of progress in our understanding of fur-bearing fauna is found in the reports of surveys and biological investigations which have appeared in various states during the past decade. California has developed an excellent two-volume treatise, "The Fur-bearing Mammals of California" (23). References on fur bearers can be found in the list at the end of the chapter (1, 10, 16, 19, 30).

An outstanding contribution of particular value to the fur research worker is the compilation of bibliographical material in "A Contribution toward a Bibliography on North American Fur Animals" by Yeager (67 *g.r.*). Numerous studies of the nature and values of fur in various parts of the United States have been made under Federal Aid funds; these have contributed materially to our knowledge of the habits and economic and ecological relationship of fur bearers. Such knowledge is fundamental for their sound administration.

Fur Farming. Fur farming has grown rapidly during the past 20 years in North America. Animals raised on fur farms include silver fox, black fox, mink, raccoon, skunk, marten, fisher, and muskrat. Minks are now the only animals which can be raised economically on ranches. Canadian statistics show that while the value of farm-raised fur in 1920–1921 was only about 4 per cent of the total value of all Canadian furs, by 1937–1938 it had risen to 43 per cent of the total (6). Hamilton (29 *g.r.*) states that roughly 20 per cent of the value of raw fur produced in the United States in 1938 was produced on fur farms. The total value of raw furs in the United States for that year was roughly 13 million dollars.

Fur farming is now well established as an industry but still suffers somewhat from the stigma of speculation that was an inevitable part of its early and rapid development. Much has been accomplished in the way of scientific feeding, selective breeding, control of disease, and reducing the cost of housing and care. Mink farming is particularly popular because of the small space needed for each individual animal and the ease with which these animals can be reared (38 *g.r.*). To date muskrats have not been raised successfully under close confinement, but they can be raised on good marshland where a satisfactory water level can be maintained.

While it is not the purpose of this book to give details of raising animals in captivity, a short section will be included on mink ranching.

Minks are better suited to back-yard operations than are foxes (39 *g.r.*). These little animals are housed singly in pens made of wire with an attached nest box, having a small platform for feeding and a trough for watering. The watering trough should be small enough so the mink can use the water only for drinking. Ingenious mink farmers have developed cages about a foot square and 6 feet long in which no wood is used except in the door frame and for the nest box. A nest box is about 16 inches each way, with a second smaller box inside of the larger one. Dry bedding should be supplied for the nest box. Minks are polygamous; one male will breed 6 to 10 females. Mating begins about the first week in March, and the gestation period is about 42 days. Litters vary in number from 3 to 10 young that stay with the mother until they are 8 weeks old. The young mink reach maturity by pelting time in the fall.

Nonbreeding mature mink eat from 4 to 5 ounces a day, while nursing females eat slightly more than this amount. Raw, fresh, or frozen meat or fish seem to be necessary in a successful mink diet. Kellogg (36 *g.r.*) states that the raw meat should be 50 per cent of the food ration in summer and fall and 70 per cent during the breeding and lactation periods. The meat portion of the diet can be two thirds muscle meat and one-third viscera. Whole fresh or canned fish can be substituted for one-third of the meat diet. A mixture of bread meal, oatmeal, alfalfa, leaf meal, wheat-germ meal, and vacuum-dried fish meal may be fed to the extent of 25 per cent of the food diet during the summer. Of the total food requirement, ground green bone-meal should form 5 per cent, fresh vegetables 5 per cent, and salt 0.5 per cent. The addition of fortified cod-liver oil to the extent of 0.3 of 1 per cent of the food diet is advisable. Fresh clean water should be available at all times, and fresh milk is desirable for lactating females and immature young. Female minks, suckling litters, should be fed twice daily, but nonbreeding animals need be fed only once each day.

REFERENCES

1. Aldous, C. M., and H. L. Mendall. 1941. The status of big game and fur animals in Maine, Maine Cooperative Wildlife Research Unit, Orono.
2. Allan, D. J. 1942. Marsh management for fur production. *Trans. 7th North Amer. Wildlife Conf.* Pp. 263–271.
3. Allan, Philip F. 1943. Fur from farmlands. *U.S. Dept. Agr. Soil Conserv. Ser.*
4. Anonymous. 1938. Fortune in furs. *Mich. Conserv.* 7(7):5.
5. ———. 1939. A survey of the annual fur catch of the United States. *U.S. Dept. Agr. Bur. Biol. Survey, Wildlife Res. and Mangt. Leaflet* BS-140.

6. ———. 1940. Fur production of Canada season 1937–1938. *Dom. Bur. Stat., Dept. Trade and Com., Census of Industry, Fisheries, Fur and Dairy Stas.*, Ottawa.
7. ———. 1944*a*. Annual fur catch of the United States. *U.S. Fish and Wildlife Serv., Wildlife Leaflet* 253.
8. ———. 1944*b*. Wisconsin trapping. *Wis. Conserv. Bul.* **9**(11):24–25.
9. ———. 1949. Fur production of Canada, season 1947–1948, *Dominion Bureau Statistics*, Department Trade and Commerce, *Agricultural Division*, Ottawa.
10. Arthur, Stanley C. 1931. The fur animals of Louisiana. *La. Dept. Conserv. Bul.* 18.
11. Ashbrook, Frank G. 1948. Fur farming for profit, Orange Judd Publishing Co., Inc., New York.
12. ———. 1951. Annual fur catch of the United States. *U.S. Fish and Wildlife Serv., Wildlife Leaflet* 315.
13. Baumgartner, Luther L. 1942. Fourteen years' wild-fur harvest. *Mich. Conserv.* **11**(11):4-5.
14. Bonnycastle, R. H. G. 1938. Canada's fur trade. *Trans. 3d North Amer. Wildlife Conf.* Pp. 531–537.
15. Bradt, Glenn W. 1941. Beaver management pays. *Mich. Conserv.* **10**(5): 4–5.
16. Brown, Louis G., and Lee E. Yeager. 1943. Survey of the Illinois fur resources. *Ill. Nat. Hist. Survey*, Bul. 22, Art. 6, pp. 435–504.
17. Cartwright, B. W. 1942. Regulated burning as a marsh management technique. *Trans. 7th North Amer. Wildlife Conf.* Pp. 257–263.
18. Crichton, V. 1948. Registered traplines. *Silva.* **4**(2):3–15.
19. Dearborn, Ned. 1932. Foods of some predatory fur-bearing animals in Michigan. *Univ. Mich. School Forestry and Conserv. Bul.* 1, Ann Arbor.
20. Eklund, Carl R. 1946. Fur resources management in British Columbia. *Jour. Wildlife Mangt.* **10**(1):29–33.
21. Gibbons, G. Donald. 1947. Economic importance of the fur industry. *Trans. 12th North Amer. Wildlife Conf.* Pp. 139–146.
22. Graham, Samuel A. 1942. The integration of fur and timber. *Trans. 10th North Amer. Wildlife Conf.* Pp. 92–94.
23. Grinnell, Joseph, Joseph Dixon, and Jean M. Lindsdale. 1937. Fur-bearing mammals of California, University of California Press, Berkeley.
24. Hamilton, W. J., Jr. 1935. The fur-bearers of New York in their relation to agriculture. *N.Y. Agr. Col. (Cornell)Ext. Bul.* 319, Ithaca.
25. ——— and David B. Cook. 1946. Primeness, condition and fur values. *Trans. 11th North Amer. Wildlife Conf.* Pp. 162–167.
26. Hayne, D. W. 1941. Michigan trappers. *Mich. Agr. Expt. Sta. Bul.* 307.
27. Kellogg, Charles E. 1950. Chinchilla raising. *U.S. Dept. Agr. Leaflet* 266.
28. Lay, Daniel W. 1943. Some aspects of administration of the fur resources. *Trans. 8th North Amer. Wildlife Conf.* Pp. 308–310.
29. Le Compte, E. Lee. 1930. Ideal furbearing animal laws. *Trans. 17th Amer. Game Conf.* Pp. 186–188.
30. Mohr, Carl O. 1943. Illinois furbearer, distribution and income. *Ill. Nat. Hist. Survey*, Bul. 22, Art. 7, pp. 505–537.
31. Moss, A. E. 1942. Income possibilities from a small artificial pond in eastern Connecticut. *Jour. Wildlife Mangt.* **6**(2):141–146.

32. O'Roke, Earl C. 1942. Furbearers—a neglected source of forest revenue. *Trans. 7th North Amer. Wildlife Conf.* Pp. 451–456.
33. Thompson, Seton H. 1950. Alaska fisheries and fur-seal industries: 1947. *U.S. Fish and Wildlife Serv., Statis. Digest* 20.

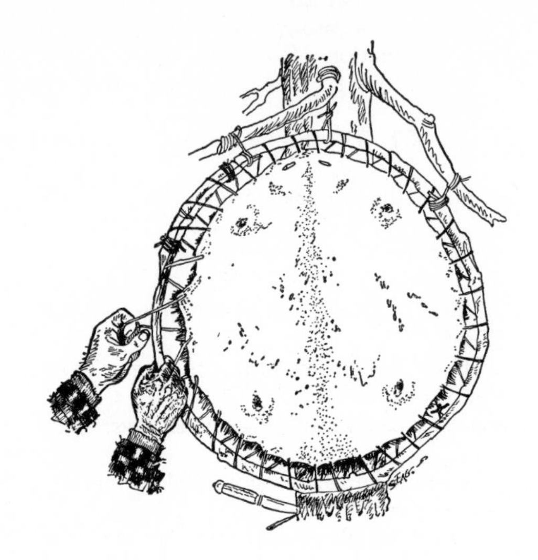

CHAPTER 4

Beavers

Castor canadensis[1]

FUR FACTS

To the early settlers, fur traders, and American Indians the beaver became a unit of value as well as an item of trade. Beaver skins were originally traded for merchandise, including firearms—the height of the pile of skins being equal to the length of the musket set with its stock on the ground. A wool blanket was worth six beaver skins. Later, however, the value of the beaver skin rose, since at present the best Hudson Bay blanket carries only four markers or "points," each "point" supposedly being equivalent to a beaver skin.

Modern fur practice uses only the soft underfur attached to the skin or leather, since the coarse guard hairs are plucked out and discarded. This underfur is fine and wavy, having a very attractive soft color and great density. After the skin is split up the belly, the pelt is stretched out flat, a practice at variance with the skins of most other fur bearers, which are cased or left in the form of a tube. The best quality of Canadian beaver has a bluish-brown color, while the Rocky Mountain beaver is light brown or straw-colored. Eastern Canada and northeastern United States furnish the highest-quality beaver pelts.

GEOGRAPHICAL DISTRIBUTION

The beaver is a rodent and one of the largest of this group of animals. It is an amphibious mammal excellently adapted by nature to fit the environment in which it lives. The fur of the beaver insulates it from the cold water, while its hind feet are adapted for swimming, and its teeth are well formed for both cutting and chewing woody materials.

[1] Scientific names in this book will be according to W. H. Burt and R. P. Grossenheider, 1952. A field guide to the mammals, Houghton Mifflin Company, Boston.

The beaver is known for its industrious habits, as is indicated by the saying "busy as a beaver." The beaver was most valuable to the Indian aborigines and pioneers in furnishing them with meat, clothing, and medicine. Many Indian tribes had great reverence for the beaver and buried the remains of a slain animal with a formal ceremony. Beaver pelts were among the first and most valuable of North American items of commerce. Since these early times beaver numbers have declined, but it is still a very valuable part of our fur-bearing fauna.

The original range of the beaver was all of wooded North America. Much of this cover range was destroyed by clearing of the land, but

FIG. 4-1. American beaver, a valuable fur bearer and hydraulic engineer. (*Photo Virginia Commission Inland Fisheries and Game.*)

lumbering and forest fires which followed logging have improved other millions of acres of beaver range by bringing back a new growth of aspen.

Beavers are now present in much of the wooded part of the North American continent north of the Ohio River. Some beaver colonies are found in the eastern part of the continent as well as in the wooded and mountainous regions west of the Mississippi River. Maine, New Hampshire, Vermont, New York, Pennsylvania, Michigan, Wisconsin, and Minnesota all have good populations of beaver. Canada, Alaska, and a number of other wooded and well-watered states and provinces of the Pacific Northwest also have substantial populations. Beavers were listed as present in 21 states and territories in the 1947–1948 summary of fur bearers of the United States and Alaska (2).

ANATOMY, LIFE HISTORY, AND ECOLOGY

The beaver is ideally suited to its environment and mode of living; its body is compact, and the feet and tail are well adapted to its needs. The eyes and ears are small, while the structure of the teeth is so arranged that cutting surfaces are kept sharp and replace themselves as the teeth wear off. The front feet are handlike and are used for handling mud, stones, and sticks, as well as for walking. The hind feet are webbed and are the chief implements of locomotion when the beaver is swimming. The tail is broad, flat, and hairless and is used for swimming and balancing. The sexes appear alike except when the female is suckling young, when four mammae are plainly visible.

Weights of beaver vary with the different species and subspecies as well as with the age and condition of the animals. At birth, a beaver weighs about a pound and at 6 weeks of age about 4 pounds. A yearling weighs 25 to 30 pounds, a 2-year-old 40 to 45 pounds, and a 3-year-old 45 pounds or more (16, 28 *g.r.*).

Beaver fur is one of the prized pelts of the fur trade, a pelt being worth from $8 to $30 or even more, depending on its size, color, primeness, and the condition of the fur market. Beavers of exceptionally large size and dark color are produced in the Lake Superior region of the United States and immediately adjacent areas of eastern Canada. The largest beaver pelts are classified as "blankets" and bring premium prices, provided the quality is good.

Breeding Characteristics. Beavers live together as a family group with a mature female, a male, the kits or young of the current season, and the yearlings of last year's litter composing the colony. Beavers are generally monogamous (14), but under unusual conditions may be polygamous (4). Beavers are capable of breeding at 2 years of age. This conclusion is based on inference rather than on specific data. Bradt (7) states: "Yearlings are permitted to remain in the colony, but two-year-old beavers leave or are driven from the colony shortly before the birth of the second annual litter." He implies that young which are approaching 2 years of age are driven out because of "possibly showing signs of sexual maturity." These conclusions are also borne out by Benson (6).

Mating takes place in shallow water near the beaver house (20). The mating season is midwinter, probably January or February in the northeast. Bradt (7) thinks the gestation period may be 4 rather than 3 months as is generally supposed.

The young are born in a dry nest usually of grass, shredded wood, or bark in the beaver house or lodge. The young are fully furred when born, and are nursed for approximately 6 weeks, but probably take solid food long before that time. At birth the sexes are about equal in number, but according to Benson (6) there are more males than females in the yearling group and decidedly more females than males among the two-year-olds and adults. No reason is given for this apparently contradictory situation. According to Bradt (7), the number in a litter may vary from 1 to 8, with slightly less than 4 being the average number. The colony method of life is a fixed habit with the beaver and serves a useful purpose in keeping the dam repaired and the supply of winter food adequate. The number of animals varies from 1 to 12, but 5 to 6 beavers per colony are found most frequently (4, 7, 8).

Movements. Ordinarily the movements of the members of a beaver colony are not extensive. The extent of travel is greatest when the dam is being built, inspected, and when food is being gathered in the fall. Beavers are known to go 650 feet away from a pond to cut trees (7) and much further to build a secondary dam or inspect a new source of food supply. The distance of travel may be much greater at the time when the population shifts, when beavers are looking for new locations for colonies, or when males are seeking new mates. Males seeking mates may travel as far as 15 to 20 miles during a single year. Atwood (3) records beavers released in Missouri as having moved 135 miles from the point of liberation during an 8-year interval.

Cover Requirements. Beavers need a wooded habitat for a source of food, building materials, and a supply of water. The type of cover may vary as to kinds of lesser vegetation, size of trees, and density of both. Both hardwoods and conifers are used for food and building materials, with the sizes chosen for cutting varying from a half-inch stem to a large-sized tree (22). The water part of the environment may be a stream, pond, or lake—all being acceptable for the storage of food and protection. It is the author's impression, however, that optimum conditions include a high percentage of aspen in the composition of the woody cover, and that dense stands of trees varying in size from 1 to 6 inches in diameter are more desirable than open stands of larger-sized trees. With regard to a comparison of streams versus ponds or lakes as being the more desirable habitat, it appears that in locations where lakes and ponds are numerous these situations may be more stable in supporting beaver than the stream habitats of the same locality. The latter frequently lose their usefulness, owing to the complete utilization and exhaustion of the food supply, while on a pond the colony may move to a different part of the pond until the vegetation is recovered in that section where the food supply became exhausted.

Food. The beaver is herbivorous, living on the bark, buds, roots, leaves, and possibly the flowering parts and fruits of many kinds of plants. The bark of aspen is a preferred winter food, but many other plants are also eaten. Orchard trees and domesticated plants are taken if other types of plants are not available. Food for the winter is cut in the fall—September to November—and transported to the vicinity of the beaver house, where it is stored at the bottom of the pond. As the winter advances, some is taken to the beaver lodge, and the bark is eaten. The naked stems are used to reinforce the house or dam or are left to float to the surface after the ice goes out.

In the fall, when the materials for storage are being cut, bark is eaten from the chips, and no doubt from some of the stems which are being transported for storage purposes. Seton (61 *g.r.*) claims that practically

FIG. 4-2. Beaver kit 4 months old trapped for transplanting. This is about the minimum age for transplanting. (*U.S. Soil Conservation Service.*)

any of the hardwoods are used for food by beavers, but that there is a decided preference for aspens and cottonwoods. Hosley (32 *g.r.*) states that willow is a definite second choice. He lists 35 species of woody plants used for both food and building materials; this list includes the following plant species: yellow birch, maple, alder, birch, dogwood, beech, ash, poplar, cherry, oak, willow, viburnum, hazel, rose, raspberry, Douglas fir, and buttonbush. Hosley further mentions that pine, hemlock, balsam fir, white cedar, spruce, and larch are often used for building materials but are seldom eaten.

Winter foods consist largely of water plants and the bark of materials stored in the fall on the bottom of the beaver pond.

Spring and summer foods include sedges, shrubs (bark), leaves, berries, rhizomes, and flags (12); spatter-dock, mushrooms, raspberries, grasses, wild roses, cow parsnips, and the roots of water lilies (27). Domesticated plants eaten include carrots, potatoes, rutabagas, turnips, apples, alfalfa, and clover.

The spring and summer food of beavers no doubt includes a host of plants which are available in and near the beaver pond. During these seasons, the lush plants are more desired, and there is no apparent shortage and little adverse pressure on the food supply. In common with many other herbivores, the first frosts of fall intensify their appetite for the woody foods, or in this case bark, buds, and twigs.

Population Density. Seton (61 *g.r.*) gives numerous estimates of beaver population densities during the time before the white man came to North America. Fifty or sixty to the square mile are given as averages for Algonquin Park in Canada (2,000 square miles) and the Adirondack Mountain region in New York before the white man came to America.

Present-day estimates are much less than this, however. Soper (24) estimates there are 15,000 beavers in half of the 17,300 square miles of Wood Buffalo Park, or slightly fewer than 2 to the square mile. The estimate of beavers for the Superior National Forest in 1940 was slightly more than 2 to the square mile.

Miscellaneous Habits. The beaver far surpasses the other members of the rodent order in its ability to use trees and manipulate water environments, but its knowledge is probably overestimated. Its persistence is prodigious, however. Beavers seem to have an instinctive desire to impound water, and every trickle is a challenge to build a dam. Water is useful to beavers in numerous ways, including protection from enemies, a place to store food, and a means of transportation. This animal takes every advantage of either a natural or artificial obstruction in a stream to help in building a dam.

Usually a beaver colony supplies itself with one or more dams with their accompanying ponds, one or more lodges with possible additional bank burrows, and a series of canals for transporting dam material and food to the ponds. Dams are made of mud, rocks, and stems and branches of trees. The site of the dam is usually a place where the stream is narrow or where some previous obstruction favors the starting place. The dam follows the highest terrain in the immediate vicinity rather than the shortest route across the valley. The woody material is placed with the cut ends or largest ends upstream. Stones and soil are used to reinforce the dam and hold the sticks in place. Mud is placed on the dam along the upstream side to make the structure watertight. The stems and other debris are arranged in one section of the dam so as to allow the animals to climb over the structure from either side without having to encounter the protruding ends of brush and trees.

Numerous secondary dams may be built both below and above the main dam. Those above the main dam may serve the purpose of impounding a supply of water in case the main dam is broken. It is not known what purposes may be served by secondary dams below the main dam.

Apparently beavers watch the water level very closely and investigate immediately in case the dam is broken. According to Bradt (7), the males first attempt to repair a broken dam, but all members of the colony take up the work if the males fail.

One or more lodges are usually slightly upstream from the dam in the deep part of the pond and are constructed of materials similar to those

FIG. 4-3. Beaver ponds in Black Hills, South Dakota. (*U.S. Forest Service.*)

used in the construction of the dam. An internal cavity is made in the lodge with an underwater entrance and a platform a few inches above the water level. This provides a well-insulated nest site and protection against the elements during the winter season. Bank burrows may serve as secondary escape cover and possible homes for solitary males.

Beavers build canals for convenience in getting to and from the vegetation surrounding the beaver pond and for transporting large stems of trees from the place where they are cut to the storage areas near the lodge. Canals vary in width from 18 to 36 inches and in depth from 1 to 3 feet. The length of a canal may range from a few feet to as much as half a mile.

Beavers are able to fell trees up to 3 feet in diameter, and possibly even larger. In felling a tree, the beaver sits upright, cutting the chips above and below the level of his mouth with his incisors, and then splitting out the chip which has been severed. Cuts are made on both sides of a tree until it falls. Many trees lodge in other trees and therefore cannot be utilized for food. After felling, a tree is cut into short lengths for convenience in moving it to the storage pond. This results in the leaving of piles of chips where the boles and branches were severed. So closely do these animals utilize the trees they fell that even the bark may be removed from the chips for food while the work is being done.

MANAGEMENT

Beavers may be either an asset or a liability, depending on the location, the numbers present, and the extent of their activities. Beaver colonies near orchards or farm lands may cut valuable orchard trees or destroy crops like corn or vegetables. Beavers may destroy shade trees near summer cottages, or their flowage areas may kill valuable forest growth. On the credit side of the ledger, beavers prefer aspen, which in many forests has little commercial value. Further, the flowage may prevent a fire hazard by flooding low grassy areas, and the impounded water may be useful in forest-fire control work. Finally, the fur crop from these animals may be of considerable annual value if properly harvested.

Census. Bradt (7, 8) believes that the use of the active beaver colony as the unit for enumeration is the most valid method yet devised for the census of beaver. In the past, counting both lodges and dens has been used. The final population estimate was obtained by multiplying the number of lodges and dens by the average number of animals found to be living in each type of structure. This method is in error in that the lodges may be present with no beaver using them, and also because beavers may be living in bank burrows without using a lodge. Erickson (11) used a system whereby he multiplied each active lodge by 7 and added 1 additional beaver for colonies using dens but not lodges. Bradt (7, 8) from an investigation of some 57 colonies, during which a total of 291 individual beavers were live-trapped and tagged, and Swank and Glover (26), using aerial methods of census, found beaver colonies in Michigan and West Virginia respectively to average slightly more than 5 animals per colony. However, all of these investigators emphasize two points: namely, that the average number of beavers should be determined locally, and that the presence of bank burrows introduces a source of error.

The use of aircraft greatly facilitates the counting of beaver colonies and can be done at a relatively low cost. Swank and Glover (26) covered 103 miles of streams in mountainous country at a cost of $21.50 and located 54 beaver colonies containing a calculated 286 beavers. They suggest the use of a high-wing monoplane powered with at least a 125-horsepower engine.

In using the active-colony count as a census method the following suggestions should be kept in mind:

1. Take the census during the fall when beavers are actively cutting and storing food for winter.
2. List active colonies only on the basis of fresh cuttings, dam work, houses, bank dens, and tracks.
3. Live-trap and tag enough individual animals from both large and small colonies to establish a valid average number of beavers for each type of colony.
4. Locate and classify all active colonies in the area to be censused, and apply to these the averages obtained by trapping and tagging.

Relation of Beaver to Trout. Beaver activities are sometimes detrimental to the maintenance of a suitable habitat for trout. Such impairment of trout water has occurred in parts of Wisconsin, Michigan, and Minnesota where lumbering and fires have removed the protective plant cover and allowed the sun to warm the water beyond the maximum temperature tolerated by trout. Where beaver dams have backed the water into ponds and slowed the current in these exposed areas, conditions have become incompatible for trout. Additional damage has resulted when ponds have backed up into former springs and where muck has covered gravel areas which were formerly used as trout spawning beds. On many potential trout streams, the beaver has been the final influence which changed the stream from trout water to a habitat suitable only for warm-water fishes. Beaver activities and beaver dams are not always a detriment to trout or trout waters, however. Where the gradient is rapid, as in many trout streams in rugged terrain, and where waters lack fertility and are too cold for rapid fish growth, the influence of a beaver pond with its deposition of silt, increased fertility, and higher water temperatures is beneficial (19). Thus Salyer (21) states "most of the stream improvement work to which such streams are susceptible consists mainly in duplicating the efforts of beaver-damming on a larger or smaller scale as the situation requires."

Beaver control or removal of beaver dams is a desirable procedure when it has been determined that damage to trout or a trout habitat is taking place. It should also be ascertained for each situation whether the beaver or the trout is the most valuable resource, and whether the removal of the beaver or their works will remedy the situation. Salyer (21) makes the following recommendations for the removal of beaver dams on trout waters in northern Michigan:

1. Keep one-third of the head-water tributaries of trout water clear of beaver activities at all times. Select the best springs and the best gravel beds together on the same stream.
2. Blow out every dam at least once every four years. This applies to streams where beaver ponds are essential for maintaining trout populations.
3. Give most attention to head-water streams and old dams thereon, and streams with little spruce-cedar reserves.
4. Keep all dams off of inlets and outlets of trout lakes and lakes in which trout retire in winter.
5. Consider one active beaver colony to a mile of trout water as saturation for beaver tolerance.
6. All dams which beaver no longer occupy should be blown out at once. . . .

It has been indicated previously that beaver-trout relations may be of decided advantage to the trout in locations where the water is cold or where the terrain is rugged, a condition that causes the water to move too rapidly for satisfactory trout habitat development. In Wyoming, and no doubt in other mountainous states, the beaver pond is a productive and valuable adjunct to the fishing waters of the state. Grasse and Putnam (13) state that in Wyoming both new and old beaver ponds offer excellent brook trout fishing. These investigators cite growth rates of eastern brook trout planted as 2- and 3-inch fingerlings, which when caught 13 months later were 11½ to 13½ inches long, a growth rate of from 7 to 10 inches in a little over a year. It should be borne in mind that in Wyoming most of the waters are normally too cold for optimum trout development or abundant insect production. Thus the beaver, by building dams and ponds and spreading out the water, contributes to better trout development and better fishing. As to the blocking off of spawning places, these investigators believe the spring spawners (rainbow and native western trout) can get over the dams because of high water during their spawning season, and that the fall spawners (brook trout) usually can get to the brooks for spawning even during the low-water period. In Alabama beaver ponds are reported to be excellent habitats for bass and other pan fish (18).

A few suggestions may aid the game manager in carrying through a dam-removal program. These are taken from the work of Salyer (21).

Survey the area on which dam removal is contemplated during the early winter after beaver activities have ceased. Remove dams in the spring during the runoff of the last snow water. Remove all dams completely. Use dynamite placed in iron pipes driven to the level of the old stream bed at intervals of 10 feet through the center of the dam. Use 3 to 6 sticks of dynamite in each pipe, depending on the size of the dam. Where dams are exceptionally broad, place the charge near the upstream side so as to take full advantage of the weight of the water. Use electrical detonators rather than fuses for setting the charges. If the charge is to be placed near the downstream face of the dam, allow water to flow over the charge as it is blown.

Water Conservation and Other Values. In the western states where rainfall is relatively low, and in places where streams are likely to dry up during the period of low rainfall, beavers furnish an excellent means of conserving water and at the same time causing the silt carried by the water to be deposited somewhere near its point of origin. At little or no cost, beavers find suitable sites for ponds and furnish the labor and skill to build the dams and keep them in repair. Rasmussen (19) says in a 625,000-acre watershed beavers built 1,143 ponds, which means the supply of water was kept in small impoundments and was available for man, livestock, or other animals. In this connection, water impoundments become useful to many forms of wildlife, including muskrats, minks, otters, ducks, and other water birds. Where aesthetic values are high, as in parks adjacent to large cities, the presence of a beaver colony and beaver flowage is considered an asset. In the East, the beaver is often spoken of as a bird-sanctuary builder because of these related values (23).

Preventing beavers from rebuilding a dam is a difficult task. Creosote, tar, or oil-of-tar sprayed on the exposed wood of an old dam site will tend to deter the rebuilding activity. Care should be used in the use of oil on trout water, as it may prove disastrous to fish life.

Reconnaissance and Manipulation of Beaver Habitats. The number of beavers a given stream or lake border will carry depends on the composition, age, and density of the stand. Among the hardwoods birch and aspen are the dominant food species of the beaver. Aspen will be used to illustrate how a calculation of the beaver-carrying capacity of an area can be made.

Kittredge and Gevorkiantz (17) give the number of aspen stems above 1 inch in diameter at breast height (dbh) as 980 in well-stocked stands and as 700 in poorly stocked stands. In making a reconnaissance of cover for beaver management, all calculation should be made on the basis of the average trees within 300 feet of the water, with special consideration to the degree of stocking and the age classes. Bradt (7) considers that an acre of aspen having trees that average 2 to 3 inches in diameter will support 1 beaver for 7 to 14 years. In studying beaver work in Minnesota, Aldous (1) found that the pounds of food per tree was greatest in the tree-diameter classes between 5 and 8 inches. There was a total of 3,020 pounds for 87 five-inch trees; 4,080 pounds for 69 six-inch trees; 3,943 pounds for 45 seven-inch trees; and 3,238 pounds for 39 eight-inch trees. While the amounts of food available to beavers were greatest for the large-diameter classes, Aldous also found that the wastage was likewise correspondingly greater with increase in the size of the tree, being 63 per cent in the 5-inch size class and up to 70 per cent in the 8-inch size class. Aldous (1) gives the weights of available bark of aspen for various-sized trees as follows:

Table 4-1. Relation of Weight of Available Aspen Bark and Twigs to Trees of Various Sizes (1)

Diameter breast high, in.	Bark and twigs, lb.	Waste, per cent
1	1.6	20
2	5.0	12
3	12.5	50
4	25.0	64
5	50.0	63
6	68.8	65
7	93.8	66
8	125.0	70
9	156.2	74
10	.....	54
11	.....	59

According to Aldous (1), a beaver consumes between 22 and 33 ounces of bark, or approximately 2 pounds, daily during the season when bark is used for food. This is approximately the equivalent of the food provided by 1 aspen tree 1 to 2 inches in diameter dbh (15 *g.r.*). Beer (5) gives the amount of wood species used for the winter season as 0.52 cord per beaver and estimates this is 65 per cent of all the food used. From these data he estimates that if woody species were used exclusively, 0.8 cord of hardwoods would be required per beaver to supply the required amount of bark for the winter season. Thus, with a known stand of aspen, the carrying capacity of a beaver habitat can be computed. Allowance should be made in the calculations for the loss through lodging of felled trees.

There are several operations which can be used to increase the carrying capacity of forest lands for beaver. These include knocking down all lodged trees along beaver flowages during the food-storage period of September to November, favoring such species as aspen, pin cherry, birch, and willow along beaver streams, and burning brush during early winter to induce the natural reproduction of aspen in areas where beavers have cut their winter food supply.

Management of beavers should be so adjusted as to balance the number of beavers with the food supply, in order that only the annual increment of aspen be used by the animals. The stand composition of food trees along beaver flowages should be kept well distributed as to age classes. The distribution of age classes should be as follows: $\frac{1}{5}$ trees up to 5 years old, $\frac{1}{5}$ trees 6 to 10 years old, $\frac{1}{5}$ trees 11 to 15 years old, $\frac{1}{5}$ trees 16 to 20 years old, $\frac{1}{5}$ trees 21 to 30 years old.

Stabilizing of Water Levels. Beavers frequently add height to an old dam to raise the water level and to increase the size of the flowage area. Such fluctuation of water levels may destroy additional timber, flood roads, or do other damage to property.

The New Hampshire Fish and Game Department has devised an ingenious method to accomplish this water stability and to counteract the industrious habits of the beavers. Sections of drain pipe of sufficient diameter are laid horizontally through the dam at the desired depth. The pipes are extended into the back water or flowage for 10 to 20 feet, and the open ends are plugged. Holes are then drilled through the pipes so the water enters the pipes through these small openings *on the underside* of the pipe. Preliminary studies determine how many pipes and what size openings are necessary to keep the water level at a predetermined depth (9).

Control of Beaver Population. Control of beaver population serves two purposes: (1) to keep the number of beavers within the carrying capacity of the range, (2) to remove animals alive from situations where their presence is incompatible with occupancy by man or perhaps to restock areas which have no beaver populations (25). Control of beaver populations is most satisfactorily accomplished by means of a legal open trapping season. This operation should be under careful supervision of game men, backed up by suitable laws which will allow (1) the opening and closing of the season by counties or other small land units and (2) legal authority to open or close the season for a particular year. The number of beavers that any trapper can take legally should be determined so as to allow a fair distribution of the crop. A limit of 5 to 10 pelts to each trapper is a fair allotment. On public lands in Ontario, one beaver pelt is allowed for each "active" house. An additional limitation should require all skins sold to be stamped and tagged. To prevent the cleaning out of any colony completely, all trapping should be kept to a distance of at least 50 feet from a beaver lodge.

Live Trapping. Restocking of suitable habitats with live-trapped beavers has proved successful in numerous states, including Missouri, Michigan, Pennsylvania, and New Hampshire. A number of states now maintain nuisance beaver crews, which are charged with removing beavers from locations where they are doing damage, to otherwise suitable territory. Live trapping can be done by the use of a special beaver trap (4, 10). Aluminum traps are desirable because of the smaller weight involved when traps and beavers have to be carried long distances. In trapping young beavers, traps should be set in shallow water and anchored securely to prevent the drowning of the trapped animal. Couch (10) recommends that trap sets should be visited every 5 hours to prevent chilling and injury to trapped animals. Trapped animals should be transferred to individual crates at least 2 feet wide and 3 feet long for shipping to new locations. The cost of a trap is about $15, and transfer costs from $7 to $15 per animal, depending on the distances involved. The U.S. Forest Service transferred 20 beavers successfully from northern Wisconsin to southern Illinois in the fall of 1935; the success of the undertaking is indicated by the report during 1941 of 100 beavers in the national forests of Illinois.

Harris and Aldous (15) have been successful in keeping beavers in predetermined locations in South Dakota by preparing temporary dams and making a crude lodge so the beavers would have some protection at the point of release. These, with suitable food available, seemed to hold most of the beavers where they were wanted. Another precaution was to release only animals from the same colony, so fighting was held to a minimum.

Beaver Administration in the Western United States. According to Wire and Hatch (28) of the Oregon Game Commission, in 1941 there were an estimated 324,000 beavers in 11 western states. During the 1940–1941 season 53,936 pelts were legally taken, which brought an average price of $20.33 apiece, or a total of $1,096,659.00. An additional 530 illegal pelts were confiscated. These investigators state there is room for a potential population of 564,000 beavers in the 11 states.

In general, because of the former scarcity of the beaver, the laws concerning this fur bearer are either archaic or nonexistent. This has made, therefore, the handling of beaver difficult. A résumé of the difficulties encountered may be summarized as follows:

1. Many states do not have laws for harvesting beaver pelts until complaints of damage by these animals are made.

2. Beaver-damage laws fail to give landowners a financial return for the raising of the beaver.

3. Illegal traffic in beaver pelts is a very lucrative transaction. As yet there are few devices to prevent illegal trafficking.

Wire and Hatch (28) propose the following basic legislation to make possible the handling of the beaver in an orderly and systematic manner:

1. Close the state to beaver trapping except as designated by the Department of Conservation.

2. Make it illegal to sell beaver pelts except through the Department of Conservation or as specified by them under a tag or stamp system.

3. Provide for cost of beaver administration by the state through a license system.

4. License all fur dealers and fur-processing establishments for all fur bearers protected by the law.

5. Give the Department of Conservation the authority to prescribe regulations for management and harvest of beaver with suitable penalties for violation.

6. Make it legally possible for the Department of Conservation to appoint a superintendent of fur resources and to carry on such activities as to give to the people of the state the greatest possible returns from the fur crop.

7. Make it possible for the Department of Conservation to enter into agreement with private individuals or corporations for the leasing and management of lands, hiring of trappers, and selling of furs.

REFERENCES

1. Aldous, Shaler E. 1938. Beaver food utilization studies. *Jour. Wildlife Mangt.* **2**(4):215–222.
2. Ashbrook, Frank G. 1951. Annual fur catch of the United States. *U.S. Fish and Wildlife Serv., Wildlife Leaflet* 315.
3. Atwood, Earl L. 1938. Some observations on adaptability of Michigan beavers released in Missouri. *Jour. Wildlife Mangt.* **2**(3):165–166.
4. Bailey, Vernon. 1927. Beaver habits and experiments in beaver culture. *U.S. Dept. Agr. Tech. Bul.* 21.
5. Beer, James. 1942. Notes on the winter food of beavers in the Palouse Prairies, Washington. *Jour. Mammal.* **23**(4):444–445.
6. Benson, Seth B. 1936. Notes on the sex ratio and breeding of the beaver in Michigan, University of Michigan, Museum of Zoology.
7. Bradt, Glen W. 1938. A study of beaver colonies in Michigan. *Jour. Mammal.* **19**(2):139–162.
8. ———. 1947. Michigan beaver management, Michigan Department of Conservation, Game Division.
9. Carpenter, Ralph A. 1950. Beaver control studies. *N.H. Fish and Game Bien. Rpt.*, 1948–1950, Concord.
10. Couch, Leo K. 1937. Trapping and transporting live beavers. *U.S. Dept. Agr. Farmers' Bul.* 1768.
11. Erickson, Arnold B. 1939. Beaver populations in Pine County, Minnesota. *Jour. Mammal.* **20**(2):195–201.
12. Grater, Russell K. 1936. An unusual beaver habitat. *Jour. Mammal.* **17**(1):66.
13. Grasse, James, and Euvern F. Putnam. 1950. Beaver management and ecology in Wyoming. *Wyo. Game and Fish Comn. Bul.* 6.
14. Green, H. U. 1936. The beaver of the Riding Mountain, Manitoba. *Canad.*

Field Nat. **50**(1):1–8; **50**(2):21–23; **50**(3):36–50; **50**(4):61–67; **50**(5): 85–92.

15. Harris, Dave, and Shaler E. Aldous. 1946. Beaver management in the northern Black Hills of South Dakota. *Jour. Wildlife Mangt.* **10**(4):348–353.
16. Johnson, Charles Eugene. 1927. The beaver in the Adirondacks. Its economics and natural history. *Roosevelt Wild Life Bul.* **4**(4):501–641.
17. Kittredge, Joseph, Jr., and S. R. Gervorkiantz. 1929. Forest possibilities of aspen land in the Lake States. *Minn. Agr. Expt. Sta. Tech. Bul.* 60.
18. Moore, George C., and Ernest C. Martin. 1949. Status of beaver in Alabama, Alabama Department of Conservation.
19. Rasmussen, D. I. 1940. Beaver-trout relationship in the Rocky Mountain Region. *Trans. 5th North Amer. Wildlife Conf.* Pp. 256–263.
20. Roth, Adolph R. 1938. Mating of beavers. *Jour. Mammal.* **19**(1):108.
21. Salyer, J. C. 1935. Preliminary report on beaver-trout investigation. *Amer. Wildlife* **24**(1):6, 13–15; **24**(3):39, 47–48; **24**(4):55, 62–64.
22. Shadle, Albert R., Alma M. Nauth, Edward C. Gese, and Thomas J. Austin. 1943. Comparison of tree cuttings of six beaver colonies in Allegany State Park, New York. *Jour. Mammal.* **24**(1):32–39.
23. Shaw, Samuel P. 1948. Beaver in Massachusetts. *Mass. Dept. Conserv. Bul.* 11.
24. Soper, J. Dewey. 1937. Notes on the beavers of Wood Buffalo Park, Alberta. *Jour. Mammal.* **18**(1):1–13.
25. Swank, Wendell G. 1949. Beaver ecology and management. *W. Va. Conserv. Comn., Div. Game Mangt. Bul.* 1.
26. ——— and Fred A. Glover. 1948. Beaver censusing by airplane. *Jour. Wildlife Mangt.* **12**(2):214.
27. Warren, Edward Royal. 1928. Cutting of oaks by beavers. *Jour. Mammal.* **9**(3):253–254.
28. Wire, Frank B., and A. B. Hatch. 1943. Administration of beaver in the western United States. *Jour. Wildlife Mangt.* **7**(1):81–92.

Shafer
Michigan Conservation

CHAPTER 5

The Cats

Bobcat *Lynx rufus*
Lynx *Lynx canadensis*
American Mountain Lion or Puma *Felis concolor*

FUR FACTS

As fur items, bobcats, lynxes, and pumas have little value. The skins of all three are used as muffs, for trimming coats, and for rugs and trophies. None of these furs take dye readily, and they are not distinctive in their natural state. Therefore, as a fur animal, the native cats of North America are of minor importance (7 *g.r.*).

BOBCAT AND LYNX

GEOGRAPHICAL DISTRIBUTION

The range of the bobcat or bay lynx exists wherever forest cover is present, extending from extreme southern Canada, including Nova Scotia, southward wherever the land is unsuited to agriculture (61 *g.r.*).

It is surprising that bobcats are still found in densely populated states like Massachusetts, and that they have been able to survive in localities that have been inhabited by man for several hundred years. In most of the New England states there is no closed season on bobcats; in some at least there is a bounty or reward for their capture. This bounty presumes to encourage the taking of a greater number of cats as a protection for traditional game like ruffed grouse and snowshoe rabbits. The wildcat hunter himself is anxious to maintain this concept, because it gives him the added joy of a money payment each time he gets a wildcat.

Wildcat hunting is a thrilling sport enjoyed by many hunters. Ordinarily, hunting is done during the winter time when the snow aids in tracking the bobcats. A trained bobcat dog is one that will not stray off on a deer track and often has a value of several hundred dollars if offered for sale. Some hunters keep a pack of dogs and would as soon think of selling one of their children as their best bobcat dog. In relation to the effectiveness of bounties, it is doubtful if there would be relatively fewer bobcats taken in the New England states if bounties were not paid.

The range of the Canadian lynx is generally north of the range of the bobcat, coinciding with most of the wooded land area of Canada, except for a narrow strip along western Alaska. The range of these two species may overlap slightly in New England, New York, the Lake states, and southern Canada. The range of the lynx also extends south into the United States along the northern part of the Rocky Mountains as far

FIG. 5-1. Bobcat, an important game animal as well as a fur bearer. (*Virginia Polytechnic Institute.*)

southward as Colorado. Along the west coast it is found in Washington, Oregon, and California in the Cascade and Coast ranges (61 *g.r.*).

The former range of the mountain lion included all of North America south of the Canadian border and small portions of southern Alberta and British Columbia (14 *g.r.*).

ANATOMY, LIFE HISTORY, AND ECOLOGY

The bobcat and lynx are both catlike in appearance with short tails and sharp, erect ears. The tufts on the ears of the bobcat are much smaller than those of the lynx. Likewise, the tail of the lynx has a black tip with solid gray on the remainder of the tail, while the bobcat's tail is spotted on the end and has alternate rings of dark and light hairs over the entire length. In general, the lynx is solid gray in color, while the bobcat is more mottled with black and rufus coloration. There is much variation in bobcats from different environments, the dark woods species being darker and the desert forms lighter. Rollings (11) indicates that in Minnesota bobcats may be considerably more gray in winter than in summer. In New England, on the other hand, the color of bobcats varies at all seasons. The bobcat is generally supposed to be a smaller and lighter animal than the lynx, but again this appears to vary with the locality of the two genera. The tail of the Canadian lynx is shorter than that of the bobcat, and the feet and legs are larger and give the appearance of greater strength. In part, this appearance is due to the abundant "feathering" of the feet and legs of the lynx. These long hairs make the lynx particularly well adapted to walking on the deep snows of the regions in which it lives. Palmer (8) gives the weights of Maine lynxes as 20–25 pounds, with a recorded maximum of 44 pounds. Bobcats in some parts of Maine attain unusually large size, but little authentic data can be found as to their exact weights. Marston (7) mentions one Maine cat weighing 40 pounds. Hamilton (5) gives the average weight of 74 Vermont bobcats as 15¼ pounds, with 9 of the 74 weighing more than 25 pounds and 7 of these weighing 30 pounds. The heaviest individual was a male weighing 36 pounds. Pollack (9) found the weight of New England male bobcats to be about 21 pounds and of the females 14–15 pounds. The largest bobcat weighed by this investigator was a male from New Hampshire weighing 35 pounds. Bobcats appear to be a little larger farther north in New England. Foote (4) gives the largest of 376 cats weighed in Vermont as 36 pounds for a male and 35 pounds for a female. Minnesota bobcats averaged 20 pounds and 7 ounces, with the heaviest weighing 34 pounds (11). Grinnell *et al.* (28 *g.r.*) give the weights of 4 subspecies of bobcats in California as varying from 12 to 20 pounds, with old males sometimes weighing as much as 27 pounds; in general the males weighed more than the females.

The bobcat and lynx are much alike in disposition; both are shy and seldom seen except when treed by dogs or caught in a trap. These cats are savage fighters when cornered or when in search of food.

Presumably, both the bobcat and the lynx are sexually mature at the beginning of their second season (9). Mating takes place in February or March, being later farther north in the range. The breeding season in New England is definitely March or later (9). The mating process is reported to be accompanied by a good deal of howling and spitting as with domestic cats. Little is known as to whether these animals are monogamous or polygamous. Seton (61 *g.r.*) seems to favor the former for the lynx. Opinions as to the length of the gestation period vary from 60 to 70 days for the bobcat to 90 days as a maximum for the lynx. Grinnell *et al.* (28 *g.r.*) says the breeding season of California bobcats is long, extending from February to September. The number in the litter may vary from 1 to 5, but is generally 3. Two is the average in the litter in New England (9). No evidence of the lynx being different in this respect has been noted. With both of these cats, 1 litter a season is the rule.

The young are cared for by the mother until they are able to forage for themselves. Numerous instances have been cited where a number of bobcats have been found hunting or traveling together, these no doubt being a family, the members of which have not yet separated. The family ties of the male appear to end when mating is completed. The degree to which the family stays together or spreads out may depend on the abundance of food in the home territory. In New England the female and young may be found together as late as January.

Movements. The extent of the movements of the lynx tribe varies with the season and the abundance or scarcity of food. Seton (61 *g.r.*) states that the lynx migrates during certain years and cites a case where this migration was at least 200 miles in extent. One would expect the daily movements of the lynx to be greater than the bobcat, because it lives in an environment that is less productive of animal food than is the habitat of the latter: that is, food is less abundant except when the cycle of abundance of the varying hare and grouse is at a high point. At such times it is logical to believe that both daily and seasonal activities are much reduced.

The extent of the movements of the bobcat is much better known. Grinnell *et al.* (28 *g.r.*) quote Cummings as saying the bobcat travels in a circuit and goes 4 or 5 miles in 1 night. Rollins (11) states bobcats travel as far as 5½ miles in a night and may cover an area of 10 to 15 square miles during the winter. Travel is done as much by day as by night, with the cats keeping to cover in the gulches rather than following the trails or exposed places on the ridges. Protected places like upturned trees or crevices in ledges are investigated and used whenever the bobcat is in the neighborhood.

Marston (7) cites explicit evidence as to the travel habits of some Maine bobcats. On March 5, 1941 one was trailed 5 miles from where the track was first found. On March 24 it was shot 6¾ miles from where the track was seen March 11. Within less than a month this individual had been located at 3 different points, the enclosed perimeter of which was 18 miles. Indications are this cat may have covered an area of 40 square miles.

Cover Requirements. The lynx is rarely found outside of the shaded zone of coniferous forests. It shuns light and rarely leaves the forest except in case of dire necessity. Contrasting with this, the bobcat may live in a variety of habitats but favors brier tangles, inaccessible ledges, and swampy places. Swamps are favored in winter, but the bobcat moves to higher ground during the summer (11). In the southern part of the United States, the canebreak is a favorite habitat. In its western range, the bobcat may be found at the extremes of desert and humid conditions, but with little preference as to high or low altitude. Cover of some kind is a requirement for bobcat tenancy, however. Rough country where a cat can occupy a rocky cavity high up on a ledge with a wall to its back is desirable and used when available.

Population Density. To date no one has ever counted the bobcats or lynxes within a given area; therefore, any estimate of numbers that can be cited is on the basis of signs or from trap records. Grinnell *et al.* (28 *g.r.*) quote Parkinson as having trapped 26 in the area of a township (36 square miles) in California. Presumably he did not trap all of the individuals, so it may be assumed there may have been 10 left, which would give 1 bobcat per square mile before trapping began.

In 1941, the U.S. Forest Service for Region 9 reported a population density of bobcats on three of its northern forests as follows (1):

Forest	State	Total bobcats	Calculated sq. miles per bobcat*
Chippewa	Minnesota	370	5.6
Chequamegon	Wisconsin	390	4.1
Ottawa	Michigan	700	3.9

* Calculations made on basis of gross area of each forest as reported by the U.S. Forest Service for 1941.

Food. The chief food of the lynx is the varying hare, according to Seton (61 *g.r.*). He states the lynx is the apex of a pyramid of rabbits (varying hares), a condition well illustrated by the graph in Fig. 5-1, which shows the rabbit fluctuations in relation to the annual take of lynxes in Canada. Cottontails, lemmings, spruce grouse, foxes, wild geese, deer, and moose are also part of the diet of the lynx. The food of the bobcat varies with the prey available in its range. In Michigan, Dearborn (20 *g.r.*) found 89.5 per cent of the material in scats of bobcats picked up during July, August, and September to be largely varying hare. Other items include white-tailed deer, muskrats, mice, birds, red squirrels, chipmunks, house cats, shrews, porcupines, skunks, snakes, and turtles' eggs. In Maine, Marston (7) found 34 white-tailed deer killed by bobcats in a limited range during 2 winters. Large male deer, as well as females and fawns, were attacked successfully. In some localities as high as 4 per cent of the wintering deer were killed. Marston stated bobcats hunted mostly at night and killed a deer by jumping on its back while it was resting and severing the jugular vein with its teeth (7). Rollins (11) indicated deer were killed in Minnesota by being strangled.

Hamilton and Hunter (6) examined the stomachs of 140 bobcats taken in the fall and winter of 1935–1938 in Vermont and found the percentages by bulk to be as follows: deer, 19.3 per cent; mice, 18.6 per cent; hares and rabbits, 16.4 per cent; miscellaneous birds and mammals, fishes, and insects, 45.7 per cent. These investigators include a note that some of the deer meat at least was taken as carrion. Based on the frequency with which individual food items were found in the stomachs, mice led the

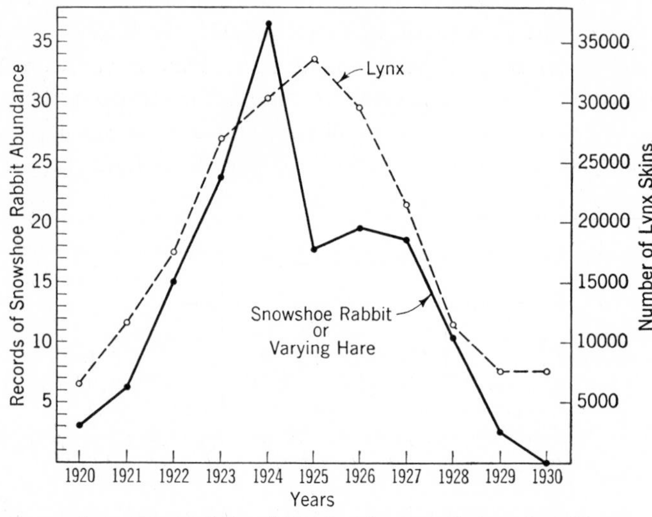

Fig. 5-2. Comparison of snowshoe rabbit abundance and the take of lynxes in Canada from 1920 to 1930. (*Dominion Bureau of Statistics, Ottawa, Ontario.*)

field, with deer next, and hares and rabbits third. Twelve of the 140 stomachs contained ruffed grouse, usually the feet. Pollack (9) found grouse remains in 1.4 per cent of 208 bobcat stomachs from New England, a section of typically good grouse range.

In California, of 257 bobcat stomachs examined, game was found in 78, with quail in 33, deer in 18, brush rabbits in 13, gray squirrels in 7, cottontail in 5, and grouse in 2 (28 *g.r.*). Some of the quail, cottontails, and brush rabbits may have been bait used by trappers. While quail is found occasionally in bobcat stomachs, these investigators believe that healthy quail are not vulnerable to bobcat attacks. This California study agrees with that of Marston's in Maine, namely, that bobcats may kill deer for food. A difference in the feeding habits within the two extremes of the range seems to be that in California bobcats hunt in the afternoon as well as in the morning and evening, while Marston (7) implies that they hunt mainly at night in Maine, although he does not say that they hunt only at night. New England bobcats kill more than they can eat (10).

MANAGEMENT

Many states now pay a bounty for bobcats as a measure to induce hunters and trappers to keep them in check. The question has been raised as to whether a bounty keeps the bobcat populations in check, and also whether a hunter or trapper kills more bobcats where a bounty is paid than otherwise. Bobcat hunting is a thrilling sport which can be indulged in throughout the year without restrictions of season or bag limit. Where greater reduction of these animals is indicated from a careful study of their food habits, perhaps a better method than the bounty system is to popularize the sport of hunting them by descriptions of hunting methods and accounts of successful hunting trips (12).

AMERICAN MOUNTAIN LION OR PUMA *Felis concolor*[1]

GEOGRAPHICAL DISTRIBUTION

The American mountain lion or the puma (*Felis concolor*) is one of the largest predatory animals of the Western Hemisphere. Exceeded in size only by the jaguar among the American wildcats, no other American predator approaches it in the number of names by which it is known. Such names as the mountain lion, puma, cougar, deer tiger, Mexican lion, panther, painter (corruption of panther), and catamount, or "cat of the mountain" are commonly applied to it in various parts of its range. Historically, the name puma is the oldest.

The puma's range extends from Patagonia in South America, near Cape Horn, through Middle and North America to the Peace River and Cassiar districts of northern British Columbia, including Vancouver Island.

In the United States the puma's present distribution includes the large wilderness areas west of the 100th meridian. The heaviest infestation is in the Rocky Mountain states and southward through the desert ranges of Arizona, Texas, and New Mexico. Farther westward the animal is much less numerous, except in the coastal ranges of California, Oregon, and Washington, where it is somewhat more plentiful. Throughout this range 30 subspecies of *Felis concolor* are now recognized.

At one time, the puma had a range in the United States from border to border and coast to coast, but today Florida is the only state east of the

[1] This section is contributed by Stanley P. Young.

Mississippi River still containing a few representatives of this once numerous race. However, occasionally within recent times other eastern states have reported the animal in localities where it has long been extinct. In most instances, it is believed, such animals may have been individuals liberated by small defunct circuses.

ANATOMY, LIFE HISTORY, AND ECOLOGY

Adult pumas vary from 80 to 227 pounds, the latter figure being the weight of one killed by the late President Theodore Roosevelt near Meeker, Rio Blanco County, Colorado. To date, that is the largest official weight recognized. This animal sometimes measures more than 8 feet in length. Covered with short reddish-brown hair, the animal's body is kept exceedingly clean and sleek through constant licking with the tongue. A long hairy tail terminates in a coarse blackish tassel of hair.

The puma's movements are the personification of gracefulness, and its strength and endurance are astounding. In making a kill the puma is always capable of producing a stunning impact of its entire weight, because of the strong muscular development of its shoulders. Its skull has a well-set heavy jaw with heavy teeth developed for slashing, ripping, and tearing. Its large paws, with long retractile claws, enable the puma literally to rip its victim to shreds. A puma usually attacks its large prey, such as deer often larger than itself, at the throat and breast.

To a remarkable extent the puma relies on its senses of smell and sight. Its smell is keener than that of its small cousin the bobcat, though less so than that of the wolf or coyote. The puma can see its prey for a long distance, but unquestionably it does much of its silent, cautious stalking by the sense of smell alone, taking advantage of every cover until within striking distance of its prey. Its sense of hearing also is acute.

Though a large animal, the puma is rarely seen in the wilds, and, like the ordinary house cat, its padded feet enable it to cushion its movements and facilitate the process of obtaining food.

After making a kill and taking a meal, the puma will sometimes, though not always, bury the remainder of the carcass under leaves or litter, apparently intending to return later. Whether it will actually return depends to some extent on weather conditions and on its ability to find prey elsewhere. Puma killing and feeding habits vary in other ways also. In one instance, a puma attacked a herd of ewes and killed 192 in one night. Frequently more than one puma may feed on a single carcass. Near one cow carcass, the writer once trapped six pumas of various sizes, evidently the parents and two litters of offspring.

The presence of a puma on a range may be indicated by its kill of deer or other game, even though domestic stock may not have been disturbed. If a kill is made in fall or winter, the meat may remain fresh for many weeks, thus affording food for many days if not disturbed, and if other prey is scarce.

Pumas find most of their prey near the rougher and more inaccessible canyons, and in such places they live and breed with the least disturbance. One of the most striking things about these animals is the distance they will go for food. Many have been known to travel 25 miles or more in a night, apparently without resting for any appreciable length of time. Because of their remarkable endurance, hunting them requires stamina and strength. Hunters on the fresh track of a puma have trailed the animal for 10 consecutive hours or longer before treeing it.

Being such a great wanderer, the animal generally has well-defined crossing points where it passes from one watershed to another in search of food. Many of these are in the low saddles of divides, and at such crossings it is not uncommon to find "scratch hills" heaped up by the mountain lion in covering its urine and scat. The writer has seen as many as 8 such hills in an area 4 feet square. They are sometimes 3 to 4 inches high and 4 to 6 inches in diameter. Frequently old or fresh feces may be noticed near them. These hills make ideal places for setting traps for capturing the puma. In its passage over its hunting routes or "travelways" the animal may cross and recross the route at regular intervals, or the travel may be circular. It may cover many miles, the permanency of the travelway depending on the food supply. When this becomes scarce, the puma will adopt a new travelway, often a long way from former routes. It has been known to cover its route as often as once in 15 to 18 days when in a country of good food supply.

When between 2 and 3 years old the female puma breeds, producing a litter of 1 to 6 kittens, which may be born at any time of the year. As with the female house cat, at times as many as 4 or 5 males will fight over the privilege of the first breeding.

The young are born in a den or lair, which may be located in a rocky cavern on a mountainside, under an uprooted tree, or in a dense thicket. In such spots the female seeks complete isolation from the male.

The gestation period is approximately 96 days. At birth, the young weigh between 8 and 16 ounces and are 8 to 12 inches in length. The eyes open a week to 10 days after birth. The normal suckling period is 4 to 5 weeks, after which they relish fresh meat, almost to the point of frenzy at the first bite. When 2 months old they will weigh approximately 10 pounds, and at 6 months 30 to 45 pounds.

The pelt of the young at birth is densely spotted, and the tail is ringed. All spots disappear after the animal attains the adult stage, when the reddish-brown color predominates. This adult coloration varies seasonally in different localities of the animal's range, being deeper or lighter in hue.

The hide is very tough, seldom marred by any mutilation. The adult skins are put to such uses as trophy rugs, arrow quivers, carriage robes, leather for boots or shoes, saddle cloths, and coverings for saddle cinch rings.

When fully matured, the young may remain in the company of the mother until at least 2 years old. Based on limited field and captivity records, the life span of this mammal seems to be between 10 and 18 years.

Cover Requirements. Although primarily preferring the rough, timbered, mountainous terrain for its main habitat, still the puma can maintain itself in swampy, canebreak, and brushy areas, often crossing open and flat country from one section to another.

Population Density. In the United States most of the pumas now occur within the national forests. The latest estimates of the U.S. Forest Service places the total mountain lion population near 7,000 in 7 forest regions; the greatest number—2,200—is estimated for Region 6, comprising the states of Oregon and Washington. The greatest Canadian puma population is in British Columbia, on both Vancouver Island and the mainland, where the animal appears to be more than holding its own. Here it is constantly hunted as sport, and in certain areas means for its control are taken from time to time by provincial game managers.

Food. The puma requires large quantities of food for proper sustenance. This need, coupled with its power to kill, leads to its preference for large prey. Game conservationists recognize it as the greatest natural enemy of deer where both are found on the same range. Stockmen learn to their sorrow that when game is scarce the puma attacks young domestic stock, particularly colts, lambs, kids, and even full-grown horses and cattle. In some western areas, it is practically impossible to raise young colts or sheep on open stock ranges in the rough, rocky, and broken country that forms the ideal habitat for the puma.

At times, moose, elk, mountain sheep, beavers, field mice, mountain beavers (sewellel), peccaries, porcupines, coyotes, martens, skunks, turkeys, fish, and snails form part of its food. It is not averse to cannibalism on occasion, and in rare instances has been known to attack and kill men.

Among domestic stock, pigs, calves, horses (particularly young colts whenever opportunity presents), burros, sheep, and goats are preferred. Often the puma will kill more than it needs to satisfy its food requirements at the moment. For this reason the animal in the United States has been grouped usually by stockmen and conservationists with such other predators as the wolf, coyote, bobcat, and the occasional stock-killing bear as a legitimate object of predator control.

Though the puma has a wide range of foods, there is no doubt that deer, when available, is preferred above all other items. Some biologists are of the opinion that as a normal requirement it kills one mule deer or equivalent a week, and that it may consume even more white-tailed deer. This being so, it may be said that the puma goes with the deer. Hence, its

fondness for venison makes it essential that this large cat be given full consideration in any management plans for areas where it occurs on deer range, and particularly so in tracts little grazed by livestock. Here pumas undoubtedly serve as a check on undue increases of deer, which increases in certain portions of the western United States during the past quarter of a century have resulted in overpopulations, far beyond the available food supply. Under such circumstances a moderate puma population may well be encouraged. If overabundance of pumas threatens the welfare of the deer herds, the balance can easily be restored by hunting them as sport or through the speed with which regular puma control may be applied (15).

MANAGEMENT

Where the control of pumas is essential, the principal means employed is the use of trained hounds. Kentucky foxhounds and a cross between the Walker hound and the bloodhound have been found most satisfactory for trailing pumas, though any good dog may tree one (2). The hunter must keep up with the pack, however, for a puma that fights at bay instead of treeing may kill all the dogs. When it chooses to fight, the puma uses teeth and claws, backed by powerful neck-and-shoulder muscles, in a telling way.

The use of poisons in puma control is not recommended. Hunting or trapping is more satisfactory. It is unsafe to expose poisons on ranges where hunting dogs are being used.

Under certain conditions pumas can easily be caught in traps of the sizes known as Nos. 14 and 4½. Although some persons oppose the use of such traps as inhumane, no better or more practical device is yet available. Partially decomposed fish, oil of catnip (of which it is just as fond as is the domestic cat), and urine saved from a captive puma are some of the main lures used in trapping (13).

REFERENCES

1. Anonymous. 1942. Annual wildlife report North Central Region calendar year 1941, U.S. Department of Agriculture Forest Service, Region 9, Milwaukee.
2. Catesby, Mark. 1754. The natural history of Carolina, Florida and the Bahama Islands. Two volumes (XXV). Reprinted for C. Marsh, 1754, and revised for B. White, 1771, London.
3. Church, George Earl. 1912. Aborigines of South America, Chapman & Hall, Ltd., London.

4. Foote, Leonard E. 1945. Sex ratio and weights of Vermont bobcats in autumn and winter. *Jour. Wildlife Mangt.* **9**(4)326–327.
5. Hamilton, W. J., Jr. 1946. Weights of eastern bobcats. *Jour. Mammal.* **21**(2):218.
6. ——— and Russell P. Hunter. 1939. Fall and winter food habits of Vermont bobcats. *Jour. Wildlife Mangt.* **3**(2):99–103.
7. Marston, Merwin. 1942. Winter relations of bobcat to white-tailed deer in Maine. *Jour. Wildlife Mangt.* **6**(4):328–337.
8. Palmer, Ralph S. 1937. Mammals of Maine. Unpublished B.S. thesis, University of Maine, Orono.
9. Pollack, E. Michael. 1949. The ecology of the bobcat (*Lynx rufus rufus* Schreber) in the New England States. Unpublished M.S. thesis, University of Massachusetts, Amherst.
10. ———. 1950. Breeding habits of the bobcat in the northeastern United States. *Jour. Mammal.* **31**(3):327–330.
11. Rollings, Clair T. 1945. Habits, foods, and parasites of the bobcat in Minnesota. *Jour. Wildlife Mangt.* **9**(2):131–145.
12. Warren, Ebb. 1942. 'Cat hunt. *Mich. Conserv.* **11**(3):4–5.
13. Young, Stanley P. 1945. Mountain lion trapping. *U.S. Fish and Wildlife Serv. Cir.* 6.
14. ———. 1946. Sketches of American wildlife, Monumental Press, Baltimore.
15. ——— and E. A. Goldman. 1946. The puma, mysterious American cat, Wildlife Management Institute, Washington, D.C.

CHAPTER 6

Coyotes

Canis latrans[1]

FUR FACTS

In the early part of the nineteenth century coyote skins were considered to have no value. No particular attention was given to them until the diminution of the beaver began about 1860, and then the take of coyote skins became one of the main objectives of the "wolf poisoner" on the Great Plains. In those times they brought between 75 cents and $1.50 per skin.

In the early days of the Hudson's Bay Company's fur trading, the pelts of coyotes were generally referred to as "cased wolves," because of the method in which the skin was removed from the animal. Instead of being skinned out "flat," as is the procedure for the large wolves, coyote pelts were removed much as one removes a tight-fitting glove from the hand. After removal, the skins were then turned fur side out and dried on suitable stretchers in a shady but well-ventilated spot. This is still the usual method. Then, as now, many skins proved to be what the Hudson's Bay fur personnel termed "stagy" skins, *i.e.*, unprime skins, or skins with dark-blue patches on the flesh side of the pelt. Twentieth-century fur terminology terms such a pelt as unprime.

Beginning with the present century, coyote skins became of considerable economic importance in the fur trade, at times bringing $5 to $25 per pelt, depending on the area where taken. Some are used in the making of full-sized garments, such as ladies' coats and jackets, scarves, or muffs, but they probably find their greatest use as coat collars and sleeves for various women's garments. Most coyote fur can be dyed black. In this color it is then made into garments as an imitation of black fox.

GEOGRAPHICAL DISTRIBUTION

In the course of their memorable expedition in 1805, Lewis and Clark gave the first good description of the coyote (*Canis latrans*). The name coyote is a Spanish modification of the Aztec word "coyotl." Other names

[1] This section is contributed by Stanley P. Young.

commonly applied to it are brush wolf, American jackal (because of its close resemblance to that South European and African mammal), prairie wolf, and steppen wolf.

No North American predator can compare with the coyote in its ability to hold its own in the face of the many hazards with which it must contend. The first great ordeal it faced as a species came more than 80 years ago, when, along with the wolf, it was subjected to the greatest poisoning assault probably ever instituted by man. But in spite of the thousands of coyotes killed by poison during this interval, the species survived, and by the close of the last century the animal appeared to be present in as great numbers as before.

The coyote seems to possess an anatomy that can withstand much in the way of shock and pain, as shown by its ability to overcome and completely recover from severe physical disability. Coyotes have been taken that had all four feet missing as the result of trapping injuries. The stubbed feet were found to be all healed, nor did the animal appear to be greatly handicapped in moving about. Often so-called "peglegs" are found, which have only one or two feet missing.

It has been observed that coyotes that are minus one to four feet, or that have broken elbows, the result of a rifle bullet, or are otherwise badly shot up, invariably turn out to be worse depredators of domestic stock than do unimpaired animals. This is probably because the physically handicapped coyote finds it easier to kill domestic stock than deer, rabbits, rodents, or other wild prey.

It may be that the coyote's recuperative powers account for its remarkable ability to extend its range, to hold its own in numbers, geographically speaking, and to obtain a livelihood on mountain, in the valley, or in a desert habitat in spite of every hand turned against it. Unknown in Alaska prior to the gold rush of 1898, it now ranges throughout the greater portion of that territory according to the latest estimates of wildlife populations. It was not known in the Central American Republics prior to the Spanish Conquest, but the introduction of sheep and goats following the Conquest caused the coyote to extend its range southward from Mexico, where it has always occurred. Therefore, at present we find the range of the coyote extending from near Point Barrow in arctic Alaska to tropical Costa Rica in Central America—a north-and-south distance of approximately 7,200 miles.

In the United States the coyote was originally an animal of the open plains. In comparatively recent years, however, it has followed livestock and game into forested areas of the mountains. In Mexico and Central America it is still an animal of the open plains, being absent in the tropical forested country on the eastern slopes of Veracruz southward and present on the treeless tablelands of Mexico and similar open areas of interior Chiapas and Guatemala.

Within the past 40 years the coyote has extended its range to the eastward in the northern United States and Canada. In the United States it now occurs throughout the greater part of all the states west of the Mississippi River, with the exception of Arkansas (other than the extreme northwest section), and all of Louisiana. East of the Mississippi it is found commonly in Wisconsin, Michigan, Illinois, Indiana, New York, and Pennsylvania.

Coyotes have been captured or reported in other eastern states, but many of these have come into those states as prospective pets in the automobiles of returning tourists, only to escape later from their owners.

Only the future will tell whether these plantings of the coyote, accidentally or otherwise, in the eastern United States, where it has never been known to occur naturally, will result in its finally establishing itself.

ANATOMY, LIFE HISTORY, AND ECOLOGY

Considered by many as a versatile wild dog of the western prairies, deserts, and mountains, the coyote possesses at least one never-to-be-forgotten characteristic. That is its howl or bark, actually several calls, which is particularly memorable when heard late at night or near daybreak. It is a high, quavering, staccato yip yap that often ends in a series of high, shrill-toned, ear-piercing howls. Favorite "yip-yapping" points are high promontories overlooking valleys, canyons, or dry washes. Sometimes the top of a field haystack is used.

Breeding Characteristics. Although of the same genus as the larger wolves, coyotes differ from them in breeding habits. Whereas wolves generally mate for life, coyotes do not, though some pairs may remain together for a number of years. Females may breed when 1 year old, and during the mating season much more yip yapping takes place than usual. Coyote young are born 60 to 63 days after mating. In the United States the birth of the young varies with latitude. Strangely enough, studies of embryos seem to bear out the fact that the season in the northern tier of states is somewhat earlier than farther south. In Montana, for example, breeding begins about February 1, being intensive until February 15, whereas in Texas the breeding is much later.

The size of its litter is another factor that has enabled the coyote to perpetuate itself in the face of direct conflict with man and has given it the reputation of being an animal of undaunted tenacity. Litters average 5 to 7 young, with specific instances on record of as many as 15, 17, and 19.

In bringing forth their young, coyotes use a den located in a canyon, washout, or coulee, on a bank or hillside, on a rock bluff, or even on level ground, as in a wheat field or sagebrush flat. Instead of digging a new den, coyotes will often enlarge abandoned rabbit or badger holes or use deserted porcupine dens in rocky mountains or canyon walls.

More than one den is usually chosen or made, sometimes as many as a dozen, so that if one den is disturbed the family can move to another. Infestation of fleas in occupied dens may also cause the family to move to a new den.

Parent coyotes have no set time for being at the den after the young are born. Most of their killing of prey for food is done early in the morning. Both parents will at times gorge on meat of prey killed some distance from a den, then return to the den, and around the entrance disgorge portions of the food for the young to eat. Pieces of meat and bones will also be carried to the den. Coyotes have been known to carry a leg of lamb as far as 8 miles to their young. The nursing period is very short, usually 1 month. After 3 weeks the young generally emerge from the den to play about the entrance; they abandon the den when 8 or 10 weeks old, and the entire family then roves about, remaining together until early in the fall. When weather permits, the mother coyote will occasionally take her pups to a sunning place a short distance from the den.

The life span of the coyote is between 10 and 18 years, about the same as that of the larger gray wolves.

Generally speaking, the average coyote weighs between 18 and 30 pounds, though some exceptionally rare, heavy specimens weighing between 42 and 74 pounds have been captured in the Far West.

The coyote makes a track similar to that of a dog, particularly the collie, but more elongated and not nearly so rounded. Its side-toe impression is longer than that of a dog of the same range in weight. The tracks of the female coyote are generally smaller and more pointed than those of the male.

Movements. There has always been much speculation as to the distance that individual coyotes will travel from their place of birth and as to the factors that influence their movements. Earmarking of both young and adult animals with special metal tags has brought to light some interesting information.

Some findings of interest concern 24 coyotes trapped and eartagged in New Mexico during 1932 and released in the locality where captured. Of 7 returns received, 4 coyotes were caught within 5 months in the immediate vicinity of the place where tagged; 2 were taken 13 months after tagging, one 10 miles away, the other 100 miles; and one was taken 8 months after release, 55 miles away as the crow flies.

In another experiment, completed in Arizona, 7 coyotes were marked and released during February on the southern-desert winter sheep ranges. The following September 5 of the animals were trapped a short distance from the rim of the Grand Canyon, more than 250 miles from the point of release. The movement of these coyotes was influenced by shifting sheep flocks, for the release was made on the sheep driveways beginning south of Phoenix, Arizona, and extending to the summer ranges of the Prescott and Coconino National Forests.

Cover Requirements. Though normally a prairie animal, the coyote can adapt itself to and perpetuate itself under almost any condition of cover. This trait of the animal has thus defied all efforts to control it permanently, regardless of the terrain. It has been said that this remarkable mammal "has cast his lot with civilization. His fortress is a barbed-wire fence; he can sleep under cover in a bed chamber walled by corn, wheat or grass; orchards and gardens are among his pantries."

Food. The coyote is almost as deserving of the reputation of being a scavenger as is the domestic goat. Carrion, lizards, toads, and snakes are frequently food for the species. Its main food habits, however, are much like those of the large wolves, except that its food is more varied. Among domestic stock and poultry, its favorites are sheep, chickens, turkeys, and young pigs. Among its wildlife prey, deer, young elk, mountain sheep, antelope, beavers, grouse, quail, pheasants, nesting wild ducks, meadow larks, other songbirds, fruit- and insect-eating birds, sage chickens, and birds' eggs are frequent items of its bill of fare. It also varies its diet with wild and domestic fruits; with the ever abundant rodents, such as the prairie dogs, pocket gophers, ground squirrels, rabbits, and all the field mice; and with such insects as grasshoppers and beetles.

Population Densities. Any definite conclusion as to population densities of coyotes has proved perplexing. Like other carnivores, the coyote increases and maintains its number in any area in direct proportion to the available food supply. The greatest concentration of coyotes found to date was from a high of 10 individuals to the square mile on 3,200 acres to 0.7 coyote per square mile on 240,000, in a portion of Maverick County, Texas. On these areas pack rats and mice existed in abundance together with quail, deer, and javelinas.

MANAGEMENT

At times, coyotes make serious inroads on the stocks of sheep and lambs, calves, pigs, and poultry, as well as on the wild-game mammals and the ground-nesting and insectivorous birds of the country. Wherever this predator occurs in large numbers, it is a source of worry and loss to stockmen, farmers, and sportsmen because of its destructiveness to wild and domestic animals. Moreover, it is a further menace because it is a carrier of rabies, or hydrophobia. This disease has probably long been prevalent among coyotes in the West, for those who first made contact with the Plains Indians soon learned that they were well aware of and administered a crude but unique treatment for it. Lewis and Clark experienced trouble with a rabid coyote in one of their camps established on the upper Missouri.

Since much of the country inhabited by the coyote is purely agricultural and contains vast grazing areas, and as a large percentage of the food of the animal consists of mutton, beef, pork, poultry, and wild game, when the animal becomes destructive, means for its control are essential. Trapping, various methods of poisoning and gassing, running with hounds, destruction of young in the den, and shooting, either from an automobile stripped as a racing car or from a hedge-hopping airplane, are the methods of coyote control prominently used on most of the ranges.

REFERENCES

1. Camp, Raymond R. 1948. The hunters' encyclopedia, Stackpole Co., Harrisburg, Pa.
2. Carhart, A. H., and Stanley P. Young. 1928. Senor Yip-Yap. *Sunset Mag.* **61**(6):28–30.
3. Dobie, J. Frank. 1949. The voice of the coyote, Little, Brown & Company, Boston.
4. ——— *et al.* 1938. Coyote wisdom, Texas Folk-lore Society, Austin.
5. Murie, Adolph. 1940. Ecology of the coyote in the Yellowstone. U.S. Department of the Interior, Park Service, Fauna of the National Parks of the United States, *Fauna* Ser. 4.
6. Nordyke, Lewis. 1944. Coyote cunning. *Nature Mag.* **37**(3):121–124.
7. Sperry, Charles C. 1939. Food habits of peg-leg coyotes. *Jour. Mammal.* **20**(2):190–194.
8. ———. 1941. Food habits of the coyote. *U.S. Fish and Wildlife Serv., Wildlife Res. Bul.* 4.
9. Young, Stanley P. 1926. The coyote and examples of its persistency. *Outdoor Life.* **57**(1):17.
10. ———. 1941. Hints on coyote and wolf trapping. *U.S. Fish and Wildlife Serv., Circ.* No. 2.
11. ———. 1943. What was the early Indian dog? *Amer. Forests.* **49**(12):571–573, 594, 603; **50**(1):26–28, 32, 45.
12. ———. 1946. Sketches of American wildlife, Monumental Press, Baltimore.

CHAPTER 7

Foxes

Red fox *Vulpes fulva*
Gray fox *Urocyon cinereoargenteus*
Arctic fox *Alopex lagopus*

FUR FACTS

During 1947, fur styles demanded short, rather than long, furs, causing a drop in the take of foxes, raccoons, and the other long-haired fur bearers. The long-haired furs, especially when used in scarves and jackets, are now once again coming into vogue, so that fox trapping will again be popular, and the fur trade will pay higher prices for these formerly desirable fur items. The trapping take of foxes in New York, at least, seems to fluctuate according to the price of a pelt (26).

Fox furs come mostly from some variation of the red fox group (*Vulpes fulva*). The natural color is a reddish-to-straw hue, but mutations may range from pure black to white, or some mixture of the two. Natural black foxes were at one time very valuable, but this color variation is now pretty well established by fox ranchers. The blue fox is a mixture of black and white hairs which may be a natural effect or may be produced artificially by inserting light-colored badger hairs in a dyed black pelt. Other colors, such as brown and black, may be achieved by dyeing. If pale shades of any color are desired, the pelt is bleached before dyeing. The platinum silver fox is a red fox mutation discovered by Hans Ervetsen in Norway, and is in great demand by fox ranchers for breeding (7 *g.r.*).

The white or Arctic fox (*Alopex lagopus*) is a native of North America. White fox fur is used for coats, jackets, scarves, and trimming for other fur or cloth coats. It may be used in its natural color or dyed several shades of gray, blue, or brown (7 *g.r.*). The blue fox is a color variation of the white or Arctic fox that is bluish or brownish in color.

Fox furs are used for coats, capes, scarves, and for decorating cloth coats. The tails of foxes are very distinctive, being thick and bushy, and are much used in scarf manufacture.

GEOGRAPHICAL DISTRIBUTION

The fox belongs to that group of animals which by different people are considered as game animals, fur bearers, and predators. The fox hunter thinks of the red fox as one of the finest of game animals, while many small-game hunters consider it as "vermin." In that part of the country where intensive agriculture and wild lands are interspersed,

Fig. 7-1. The gray fox is more of a woods animal than its red brother. The gray fox has little value as a fur producer and is not favored by the fox hunter. (*Photo Wisconsin Conservation Department.*)

the fox may be a menace to poultry, a condition which further involves its status. With all of these intricate crosscurrents of opinion concerning foxes and human relationships, the fox is likely to be a problem of major importance to the agencies responsible for its administration.

Foxes are quite cosmopolitan in their range requirements, being found in every part of the North American continent.

Arctic foxes, both white and blue, occur in the tundra and barren grounds north of the tree belt, while the reds and grays occupy the remainder of the continent, except the desert. Here a small animal called the kit fox (*Vulpes velox*) is found. There are some differences in the environmental requirements of the reds and grays, the former being found more in the open and the latter in denser forests. Red foxes are particularly adaptable as far as habitats are concerned, being found in as diverse situations as dense forests and salt marshes (19). Gray foxes are moving north and are still in a state of adjustment in the northern part of the United States and southern Canada (3, 14, 28).

ANATOMY, LIFE HISTORY, AND ECOLOGY

The fox is a member of the dog family (*Canidae*), and all species show many characteristics which we recognize as being doglike. They seem to like to follow roads and trails used by man and have a curiosity concerning the activities of man. Possibly this curiosity concerning man may help the fox to understand when danger is near as well as to discover abundant food supplies in close proximity to farm buildings. The red fox seems to be more doglike in character than the gray, kit, and Arctic foxes. These latter groups appear to be well adapted to special environments—the grays to a forested habitat, the kit foxes to less humid conditions, and the Arctic foxes to the tundra regions.

The weights of red foxes vary from 10 to 15 pounds, or even more. Seton (61 *g.r.*) mentions a male red fox from Dover, Maine, that weighed 16¾ pounds. This was an unusually heavy fox, however. Gray foxes in New York State average about the same as red foxes, weighing from 7 to 15 pounds (Sheldon, unpublished).[1] Arctic foxes appear to be about the size of reds, but kit foxes are much smaller (61 *g.r.*).

Breeding Characteristics. Female red foxes produce young when a year old, and presumably the males are capable of breeding at 1 year, although there seems to be little evidence on this point. There is some evidence that gray females may not breed until the second season (26). Mating activities begin in December for reds and January for grays. The height of the breeding season for red foxes in the northern states is January, and early March for the gray fox (26). Breeding activities are indicated by a noisy barking of the males and a good deal of traveling by both sexes. Fox tracks during early winter and through the breeding season are silent evidence of what occurs. After mating is completed, the vixen provides herself with one or several dens, usually underground, but possibly a dry crevice in a rocky outcrop.

During the denning period there is a high degree of intraspecific tolerance, according to the findings of Sheldon (27), with New York red foxes. Many dens with litters may be found in close proximity. A female may move a litter into a den already occupied so that pups of one litter may get mixed with those of another litter.

During the mating season the male is usually in the vicinity of a home den, but not in it (27). The male does manifest an interest in the family

[1] Weights furnished by William G. Sheldon, Leader, Cooperative Wildlife Research Unit, University of Massachusetts, Amherst.

but to what extent is not known. There is evidence that the female resumes hunting soon after the young are born.[2] Seton (61 *g.r.*) indicates that red and gray foxes are monogamous, but Sheldon (26) expresses doubt that mating is for more than one season.

The gestation period is 53 days for red foxes and 63 days for gray foxes (26). Red fox litters for both the East and West average between 5 and 6, with a range of from 1 to 9. Gray foxes have smaller litters, the average being about 3 to 4 and the range 1 to 7 (26, 28 *g.r.*). Both species have 1 litter per season, and the young stay in a family group until after the nursing period is over, which is about 16 weeks. The young and parents may stay together until early winter, but the young are presumably able to survive without the aid of the parents (26).

Movements. Knowledge of the extent of the movements of foxes is only fragmentary. Iowa foxes marked with tabs and released in a strange environment were retaken at various distances from the point of tabbing, some being found in the immediate vicinity and 1, at least, as far away as 160 miles. The average distance from the point of tabbing for 27 animals was 20 to 30 miles (9). No doubt the type of terrain, harassment by dogs, and other factors have much to do with the distances which foxes travel both daily and during the year (18, 22). Flat, unfenced country is more conducive to wide ranging than is land with fenced fields and much interspersion of tilled and wooded lands. Sheldon (27) gives some very pertinent facts regarding the movement of red foxes in New York State. These data were obtained by marking foxes with an expanding type of metal collar, so identity of the individual fox was certain. His conclusions are that for the first 16 weeks the fox family lives close to the den in which the young are born. When the young are about 16 weeks old, the family leaves the home den and lives more or less as a family within a mile or so of the home den until late September or October. The male pups disperse first and may move away up to 15 miles. Female pups also may disperse widely. The adult male roams widely in the fall months. Two marked males were caught 23 and 40 miles respectively from the points of banding.

The travel characteristics of the gray fox are not discussed in the literature. As the favorite environment of the gray fox seems to be swamps and woodland rather than open fields and orchards, its movements would be restricted to this type of cover. Where woodlands are extensive, however, the gray may roam as widely as the red. Two records of tabbed gray foxes in New York by Sheldon[3] showed one animal moved 11 and the other 55 miles.

[2] Unpublished data by William G. Sheldon, Leader, Cooperative Wildlife Research Unit, University of Massachusetts, Amherst.

[3] Unpublished data by William G. Sheldon, Leader, Cooperative Wildlife Research Unit, University of Massachusetts, Amherst.

Food. The food of foxes is of interest to both biologist and layman—to the former because of his interest in the interrelationships of animals and to the latter because of the possible damage foxes may do to domesticated birds and mammals.

The fox is omnivorous, eating both animal and vegetable matter. Small fruits and berries rank high in the summer and fall foods, and rabbits, hares, and mice are staple foods of both red and gray foxes during the winter. In general, birds and birds' eggs constitute only a small part of the diet of foxes. Incidental animal foods include woodchucks, porcupines, muskrats, game birds and songbirds, carrion, insects, and poultry. Grasses, corn, and tree seeds, including acorns, are quite consistently found as a part of the food diet. Grass appears to be eaten for other than nutritive purposes, as much of it comes through without being digested (23).

Red foxes have become relatively abundant in the New England states during the past half century. An analysis of 66 stomachs of red foxes taken over a period of years from Vermont, New Hampshire, and Massachusetts during the fall and winter (10) gives a typical cross section of the food of this animal in the East.

Seasonal foods of red foxes are of interest to trappers, hunters, and farmers. Such analyses are of particular importance where the results apply to a number of widely separated localities. The analyses of red fox stomach contents or scats for Pennsylvania, Maryland, Massachusetts, and New Hampshire are given in table on page 108.

English and Bennett (5) give data on the food habits of both red and gray foxes for Pennsylvania. One hundred and thirty-six red fox stomachs were obtained from various parts of the state; these were well distributed for different times of the year. These investigators believe some of the woodchucks and deer found in the stomachs may have been from carrion and also from bait used in trapping the foxes.

The food-habits–study material for Maryland was taken from the Blackwater Marshes in Dorchester County. This study was undertaken to discover whether the diet of red foxes includes the muskrat to any appreciable degree. Nearly 39 per cent of 95 red fox droppings collected during the season from March through August contained muskrat remains, indicating a relatively high degree of predation on this fur bearer (15).

Hamilton *et al.* (12) found more than 50 per cent of the fall food (by volume) of central Massachusetts foxes consisted of three items—namely, skunks, rabbits, and apples. The remainder was made up of miscellaneous items. Nearly 60 per cent of the winter food consisted of apples, fruit. rabbits, and mice.

The high percentage of bird remains occurring in the droppings were

Table 7-1. Comparison of Foods of Red Foxes as Indicated by Percentage of Volume or Percentage of Occurrence of Food Items in Stomach Contents or Droppings for Four Localities in the Eastern Part of the United States

Classes of foods	Pennsylvania, 136 stomach analyses, summer and fall, per cent volume (5)	Maryland, 95 droppings analyses, March through August, per cent frequency of occurrence (15)	Massachusetts		New Hampshire	
			57 stomach analyses, fall, per cent volume (17)	164 winter droppings analyses, per cent volume (17)	206 winter droppings analyses, per cent frequency of occurrence (4)	207 summer droppings analyses, per cent frequency of occurrence (4)
Mammals	79.0	98	68.9	62.8	95	82
Woodchucks	20.1	. .	6.1			
Meadow mice	4.6	49	3.0	7.5		
Muskrats	. . . . .	39	2.3			
Cottontails	19.5	12	17.9	46.8		
Miscellaneous	34.8	. .	39.6	8.5		
Birds	5.3	19	5.4	14.6	34	36
Insects	7.8	9	1.1	0.2	3	81
Vegetation	6.6	10	24.1	22.4	27	31
Miscellaneous items	1.3	. .	0.5	. . . . .	1	2
Total per cent	100.0		100.0	100.0		

largely unidentifiable. These included both songbirds and game birds. Some of the poultry remains were carrion. Although ruffed grouse were abundant, few remains of this game bird showed up in the fox droppings.

The red fox eats what is readily available, but mammals and fruit appear to be important throughout the range (23). Dearborn (20 *g.r.*) records as high as 91 per cent of the food of foxes in some locations in Michigan as being mammalian—mostly hares, rabbits, and mice. Errington (6, 7, 8), studying the food habits of Wisconsin and Iowa foxes, found small mammals constituted the staple year-round foods. Those most conspicuous in the list are cottontails, varying hares, and mice.

Nelson (20) in Virginia and Bennett and English (1) in Pennsylvania have worked out the food of gray foxes in these two localities; a summary of their findings is given in Table 7-2.

The analyses from Virginia are from stomachs collected through the winter, from December through March, and no doubt represent a good

Table 7-2. Comparison of Food of Gray Foxes as Indicated by the Percentage of Occurrence and Percentage of Volume of Food Items Found in Their Stomachs
[From Nelson (20) and Bennett and English (1)]

Classes of foods	Virginia, analyses 82 gray fox stomachs		Pennsylvania, analyses 29 gray fox stomachs, August through February	
	Per cent of occurrence	Per cent of volume	Per cent of occurrence	Per cent of volume
Rabbits	42.6	32.4	31.0	39.8
Opossums	....	.....	3.4	15.3
White-tailed deer	....	.....	17.2	11.2
Mice and rats	50.0	18.2		
Woodchucks	....	.....	6.9	5.7
Muskrats	....	.....	3.4	5.7
Fruits	62.2	22.0		
All other food items	....	27.4	....	22.3
Total		100.0		100.0

cross section of the food eaten by gray foxes in that locality. The items of greatest importance do not vary greatly from those of the red fox farther north (13, 21).

The results for Pennsylvania show new and important foods not listed for Virginia. Fur bearers and game mammals—including the opossum, the white-tailed deer, the woodchuck, and the muskrat—are taken as food in Pennsylvania but are not found in the food diet of the gray fox in Virginia. It is likewise surprising that the study of Pennsylvania fox stomachs did not show the inclusion of mice.

The main items of food of gray foxes in southern Wisconsin over a 2-year study period were cottontails and mice, according to Errington (6). He states the food of all foxes varies with the availability of the prey, and that, in general, small mammals constitute the staple foods during the greater part of the year. Errington (8) and Hamilton and Cook (11) point out that availability of food governs largely what the fox eats. During the late fall and winter, the fox diet is largely mammalian. In the fall and early spring, grass cover for meadow mice is matted down and the leaves which hide the cottontail are gone. During this period mice are quite plentiful and easily caught, so they become a large item in the fox diet. As snow again gives the mice cover, the cottontail becomes the most easily caught prey. In the spring after the snow is gone, meadow mice are eaten heavily, but so also are cottontails, since for both good protection cover is lacking, and therefore both are readily available. During the summer, fruits and insects are heavily consumed, again because of ready availability. Apples are consumed heavily in the fall and early winter for the same reason. Hamilton's findings support those of others already given—namely, that birds are never an item of heavy feeding by red foxes (16).

Items found around fox dens or even in fox stomachs may not be of value for food. Foxes may ingest gravel which goes through the digestive tract but serves no purpose in nutrition. Likewise, a trapped fox may regurgitate the food in its stomach and fill up with sticks or other nonfood material.

Population Densities. The home range of a fox will vary with the cover present, the use of the land, topography, and local disturbances. Estimates of fox population densities given by Seton (61 *g.r.*) are as follows:

General locality	Area for one fox, sq. miles
Manitoba	8
Great Britain	2
Pennsylvania, 1915–1922	2.25
Lesso Island (Denmark)	1

A report of the Division of Fisheries and Game for Massachusetts for foxes killed over a period of 5 years gives an average of 5,069 per year. If this figure can be taken as representing one-third of the total fox population, and if the distribution were to be uniform (which it is not), then the population density of foxes in Massachusetts on other than thickly settled land would be about 3 foxes for each square mile. In California, Grinnell *et al.* (28 *g.r.*) estimate the density of red foxes as averaging about 1 animal to the square mile. Gray foxes are much less abundant than reds, at least on the northern and eastern part of the range. MacGregor (17) maintains that red foxes outnumbered the grays at least 5 to 1 near Petersham, Massachusetts, during 1937–1938. Apparently on the western and possibly on the southern part of the fox range a different ratio of the 2 species may occur. Grinnell *et al.* (28 *g.r.*) estimate an average of 1 gray fox per square mile in the chaparral lands of California at the beginning of the trapping season.

In a study of foxes in New York State, Sheldon (27) points out that 1 gray and 3 red foxes per square mile seem a fair average. There may be many square miles without foxes, however, and some with 7 or 8 per square mile to give this average.

MANAGEMENT

Census. Scott and Selko (24) have employed a method of censusing red foxes and striped skunks in Iowa by an enumeration of dens on sample areas, each of which covered one section (640 acres). In this method, two sections were left unsampled between those that were examined. In censusing a section, fence rows were followed, utilizing high places for inspecting the surrounding terrain with powerful field glasses. Right of ways and railroad lines were likewise traversed and examined for dens. Dens were assigned to fox or skunk occupancy on the basis of external signs. Fox dens were usually well-marked by pathways, remains of prey, scats, odor, and other evidence left by their occupants. Only active dens in which young were being reared were used in the computations.

Total fox populations were estimated on the basis of the following factors: N—the number of fox families, as evidenced by the number of active dens; p—the average number of foxes per family; F—the conversion factor obtained by dividing the total number of sections by the number sampled; L—the percentage loss of fox production through excavation of dens.

The formula used in estimating the total fox population was:

$$P \text{ (total population)} = (NpF) - [(NpF)L]$$

Using the above data, Scott and Selko were able to make an estimate of the total fox populations in two Iowa counties. In addition, by further analyzing their data with reference to variations in the topography of the two counties as represented by differences in the areas of slope classes, they also were able to account for the variation in fox populations between the two counties, which both had equal total areas as well as similar acreages of land adequate for den sites.

Control. Little attention, except a sensible hunting take and limited trapping, is needed to maintain a good fox population. Digging out of dens and the destruction of young should be prohibited, except where these animals have become unusually numerous or particularly destructive to domestic livestock. Hunting and trapping should be allowed during the period just before extremely cold weather when the fur is prime and before the breeding season has begun. This would begin after November 1 and possibly last for 2 or 3 months.

Where foxes need severe control, as in an outbreak of rabies, all efforts must be used to protect people and livestock from this dread disease. New York's recent experience indicates that we have little knowledge as to how to control effectively fox populations.

Regarding the use of a bounty to control fox populations, the consensus of biologists and game administrators seems to be that it just does not work. The reasons lie deep in the biology of foxes and the psychology of people. For a further discussion on this point the reader is referred to the booklet "The Red Fox—Friend or Foe?" by the Michigan Conservation Department (2) and "The Fox in New York" by the New York Conservation Department (25).

REFERENCES

1. Bennett, Logan J., and P. F. English. 1942. Food habits of the gray fox in Pennsylvania. *Pa. Game News.* **12**(12):10, 22.
2. Douglas, Donald W., and G. W. Bradt. 1945. The red fox—friend or foe? Michigan Department of Conservation, Game Division, Lansing.
3. Downing, Stuart C. 1946. The history of the gray fox in Ontario. *Canad. Field Nat.* **60**(2):45–62.
4. Eadie, W. Robert. 1943. Food of the red fox in southern New Hampshire. *Jour. Wildlife Mangt.* **7**(1):74–77.
5. English, P. F., and Logan J. Bennett. 1942. Red fox food habits study in Pennsylvania. *Pa. Game News.* **12**(11):22–23.
6. Errington, Paul L. 1935. Food habits of mid-west foxes. *Jour. Mammal.* **16**(3):192–200.
7. ———. 1937*a*. Food habits of Iowa red foxes during a drought summer. *Ecology.* **18**(1):53–61.
8. ———. 1937*b*. Management of the red fox in Iowa. *Amer. Wildlife.* **26**(2):24, 30–31.
9. ——— and R. M. Berry. 1937. Tagging studies of red fox. *Jour. Mammal.* **18**(2):203–205.
10. Hamilton, W. J., Jr., 1935. Notes on food of red foxes in New York and New England. *Jour. Mammal.* **16**(1):16–21.
11. ——— and David B. Cook. 1944. The ecological relationships of red fox food in eastern New York. *Ecology.* **25**(1):91–104.
12. ———, N. W. Hosley, and A. E. MacGregor. 1937. Late summer and early fall foods of the red fox in central Massachusetts. *Jour. Mammal.* **18**(3):366–367.
13. Handley, C. O. 1934. Progress report of the study of the food habits of the red and gray fox in Virginia. *Ann. Rpt. Va. Comn. Game and Inland Fisheries.*
14. Harper, Francis. 1928. The northern spread of the cottontail and gray fox in New York and New England. *Jour. Mammal.* **9**(2):176.
15. Heit, William S. 1944. Food habits of red foxes of the Maryland marshes. *Jour. Mammal.* **25**(1): 55–58.
16. Kozicky, Edward L. 1943. Food habits of foxes in wild turkey territories. *Pa. Game News.* **14**(4):8–9, 28.
17. MacGregor, Arthur E. 1942. Late fall and winter food of foxes in Massachusetts. *Jour. Wildlife Mangt.* **6**(3):221–224.
18. Murie, Adolph. 1936. Following fox trails. *Univ. Mich., Misc. Pub.* 32.
19. Nelson, A. E., Clarence Cottam, and W. S. Bourn. 1945. Red fox breeding in salt marsh. *Jour. Mammal.* **26**(1):91–92.
20. Nelson, A. L. 1933. A preliminary report on the winter food of Virginia foxes. *Jour. Mammal.* **14**(1): 40–43.
21. ——— and C. O. Handley. 1938. Behavior of gray foxes in raiding quail nests. *Jour. Wildlife Mangt.* **2**(3):73–78.
22. Scott, Thos. G. 1943. Some food coactions of the northern plains red fox. *Ecol. Monog.* **13**(4):427–479.
23. ———. 1947. Comparative analysis of red fox feeding trends on two central Iowa areas. *Iowa State Col. Res. Bul.* 353.

24. ——— and Lyle F. Selko. 1939. A census of red foxes and striped skunks in Clay and Boone Counties, Iowa. *Jour. Wildlife Mangt.* **3**(2):92–98.
25. Seagears, Clayton B. 1945. The fox in New York, New York Conservation Department, Albany.
26. Sheldon, William G. 1949. Reproductive behavior of foxes in New York State. *Jour. Mammal.* **30**(3):236–246.
27. ———. 1950. Denning habits and home range of red foxes in New York State. *Jour. Wildlife Mangt.* **14**(1):33–42.
28. Shoemaker, W. J. 1938. Notes on mating and breeding habits of foxes in New York State. *Jour. Mammal.* **19**(3):375–376.
29. Williams, Samuel H. 1930. The distribution of foxes in Pennsylvania. *Jour. Mammal.* **11**(3):313–314.

CHAPTER 8

Minks and Weasels

Mink *Mustela vison*

Short-tailed or Bonaparte Weasel *Mustela erminea*

Long-tailed or New York Weasel *Mustela frenata*

FUR FACTS

No fur is more highly regarded by the fur trade than first-quality mink. No garment is held in such high regard by a well-dressed lady as a fine mink coat. Since short furs have come into leadership in the world of fashion, the well-selected northern mink is unquestionably the fur of the short-furred group held in the highest favor.

The fur of mink is used in a natural state with both the underfur and guard hairs contributing to the attractive appearance and durability of the pelt. The guard hairs of choice skins are even, dark brown, and held erect by a dense underfur which is also dark brown. It is the luster or reflecting quality of the guard hairs that gives the pelt its beauty. The best-quality skins come from the northern and eastern sections of North America, including Labrador, Quebec, northern New England, northern New York, and the northern Lake states. Mink furs are matched and cut so as to give a uniform dark brown color to a garment. The difficulty of getting pelts of matched quality and the labor involved in making a garment brings the cost of a coat high. Individual coats costing 3 to 10 thousand dollars are not unusual (7 *g.r.*).

The word ermine, which is the winter fur of the weasel, has for centuries been a badge of royalty. The costumes produced from these skins were used in the pageantry of the Middle Ages because of the fineness of the fur and the striking contrast of colors. They are still used at coronation ceremonies, 50,000 being used at the most recent coronation of an English king. The body of the pelt is pure white and the tip of the tail black. Use of this fur was for centuries prohibited for any but royalty. It is only during the past 100 years that the fur of the weasel has been used for ordinary wearing apparel and trimmings.

The fur of the weasel is either white with a black tip on the tail or brown with a white strip or white spot under the chin. Both guard hairs and underfur are short. Prime weasel fur has a smooth attractive appearance that gives a garment a dressy effect. As a result, weasel fur is used mostly for trimming dress coats. The pelt may be used naturally or bleached to remove the yellow stains and dyed a light color like beige or natural brown.

Because the guard hairs are often several times longer than the fur fibers and different pelts have variations of their own, it is difficult to dye weasel pelts exactly the same shade (7 *g.r.*).

FIG. 8-1. The mink is one of the more valuable fur animals. (*U.S. Forest Service.*)

MINKS

GEOGRAPHICAL DISTRIBUTION

The geographical distribution of the mink includes all the humid parts of North America. According to Burt's distribution map (14 *g.r.*), the range of the minks extends beyond the tree belt in Canada, and the animal is found in parts of the West where the rainfall is low, but where streams from mountain watersheds provide an aquatic habitat.

Minks are definitely aquatic, but not exclusively so. They are equipped to swim and forage in the water and are usually found along streams or around lakes and ponds, but they can, and frequently do, live on dry land. The author once kept a mink in a dry enclosure during a 3-month period when all water in the enclosure was frozen. However, snow was available part of the time. The animal did well and seemed to suffer no discomfort because of the lack of water.

ANATOMY, LIFE HISTORY, AND ECOLOGY

The mink is an amphibious creature, although less so than the muskrat. It lives near the water and has a body well adapted for swimming. The legs of the mink are short, but it is a very active, alert creature and well able to take care of itself (1). When pursued it usually attempts to escape into the water but will take refuge in a tree when forced to do so. Hunters often speak of the mink as being quick enough to dodge a bullet, but that is doubtful. The mink displays a high order of intelligence and courage and is said to enjoy slides in much the same manner as the otter (20).

The weight of a mink varies from 1 to 3 pounds, but exceptionally large specimens are heavier. Northern minks are generally larger than the southern minks, and the males are generally larger than the females. Schoonmaker (60 *g.r.*) gives the weight of a New York specimen as 2 pounds, and Seton (61 *g.r.*) refers to a Pacific male mink that weighed 4 pounds.

The size of the mink may vary according to different types of habitat in the same locality. Errington (6) gives a comparison of the sizes of freshly stretched skins of males from river and lake habitats; river males were 32.9 inches long, while lake-inhabiting males were 35.9 inches long. Females from river habitats were 26.9 inches long, and those from lakes 31.3 inches long.

Breeding Characteristics. Minks are able to breed during the winter following the spring they are born, or at an age of less than a year. In the northern range, activity of breeding is manifest by the males during February or March, at which time they travel extensively in search of receptive females. Marshall (21) found that female minks occupy one of several dens in a relatively small area, less than 20 acres, while the males travel from den to den investigating each by circling the opening of the den or going into it. Presumably mating takes place during these visits to the den of the female. Sex relations are polygamous. The sex ratio of minks killed in Missouri is given as about 2 males for each female (12 *g.r.*).

The gestation period varies from 40 to 60 days but is usually between 45 and 50 (29 *g.r.*). Burt (14 *g.r.*) gives the gestation period as 42 days. The young are born blind, naked, and helpless. In the northern part of the range parturition takes place between April 1 and June 1. Litters vary from 3 to 10 young, with an average of 4 to 6. The young stay in the den from 4 to 6 weeks and subsist on the mother's milk. The den is a protected place under the roots of a tree or in a rocky crevice with the nest made of grass and leaves, usually dry and warm. The mother hunts for food and cares for the young until they are able to follow her, at which time they are taught to forage for themselves. Cahalane (15 *g.r.*) states that the male joins the family of his last mate for the season and stays until the family disperses in early winter. Except during the period when the young are in this juvenile stage, mink are not gregarious but live a solitary life.

Movements and Cover Requirements. The mink is an animal which lives typically on the border between water and land. No doubt this habitat is favorable because of the abundance of food in such a location and the greater number of suitable dens along watercourses. The extent of the normal travel of minks appears to be related to food supply. Seton (61 *g.r.*) notes that the mink limits its travels to an area about 5 miles in circumference. This range is not used exclusively, since the ranges of several animals may overlap with patterns such as would exist if the perimeters of several theoretical circles of this diameter overlapped to a greater or lesser degree. There is likely to be more overlapping where food is most abundant.

There appears to be a difference in the extent of the travel of males and females, the former being the more extensive travelers, especially during the breeding season. Marshall (21) reports female minks living within a 20-acre area on Fleming Creek in southern Michigan during the winter, while the males occupied a wider, but undetermined, area. McCabe (22) indicates 1,100 acres are not large enough to encompass the activities of a male mink.

The area needed for minks appears to be more closely related to miles of watercourses or lake or pond edges than to total land area. Bennett and Nagel (12 *g.r.*) found this correlation to be very close in Missouri, except in the river-break region. In 1937 they estimated 3 lineal miles of permanent stream and 6 square miles of land for every mink in the breeding reserve in that state. These investigators conclude that an ideal mink habitat includes permanent water, good streamside vegetation, debris and other shelter along the stream, a good supply of fish, frogs, mussels, and other food, and a soil type in which minks can easily dig dens along the banks of streams.

Food. Food of the minks includes both aquatic and land animals. The choice of food, as with other carnivores, is probably closely related to abundance and availability of the forms eaten. The variety of food taken by minks helps to explain their ability to survive even where the land has been changed from wilderness to agricultural use. No doubt this conversion may have changed the type of food supply; possibly also it may have increased the quantity of mammals available, such as mice.

Minks are selective as to the quality of their food and like to catch it alive. This has been demonstrated to the writer in exposing both living and dead bait to wild minks.

Many observers have reported a mink on the banks of lakes and streams with a fish in its mouth. This can be explained by the fact that a mink is more readily visible in and around water habitats than in brush or grassy places where food like mice is hunted.

The following tables give the classes of food consumed according to volume and frequency for various parts of the mink range.

Table 8-1. Seasonal Food Preferences of Mink in Different Localities Based upon Analyses of Stomach and Visceral Contents

Classes of food	Michigan (20 *g.r.*)		New York (17, 18)		California (28 *g.r.*), volume per cent†	Pennsylvania (14), Nov., Dec., Jan., frequency per cent‡
	Summer, volume per cent	Winter, frequency per cent	Summer, volume per cent	Fall–winter frequency per cent*		
Mammals..	19.64	55.63	42.68	54.13	21.5	41.38
Crayfish....	68.22	7.91	......	16.47	......	14.06
Frogs......	5.75	8.55	3.35	2.36		
Fish.......	2.87	18.35	27.25	18.82	39.6	19.54
Birds......	0.89	5.70	9.05	......	27.0	3.12
Other......	2.63	3.86	17.67	8.22	11.9	21.90
Total....	100.00	100.00	100.00	100.00	100.00	100.00

* Based on examination of 70 digestive tracts.

† Based on examination of 129 stomachs.

‡ Based on examination of 105 digestive tracts.

Sealander (27) found in winter the muskrat was most utilized of all of the foods taken by mink, being found in 37 out of 102 stomachs studied. Muskrats made up 31 per cent of the volume of the stomach material. Cottontail rabbits were the next most important item, being 14 per cent of the volume of the food consumed. Meadow mice were third and deer mice fourth among the mammals used as food. In this study birds were found not to be so important as frogs, but the pheasant was found to make up nearly half of the total birds taken by the mink, being 7 per cent by volume of the total stomach contents.

In two mink investigations made in Michigan (20 *g.r.*, 27) and one in California (28 *g.r.*), the incidence of birds was of sufficient volume to indicate material damage to bird life. In southern Michigan, pheasant remains were present in considerable volume, and in the California study wild ducks were found in 4 per cent of the mink stomachs analyzed. Domestic poultry, like ducks, are sometimes killed by minks but do not appear as a staple article in the diet. Squirrels and chipmunks are also eaten if available (9). Since muskrat appears to be one of the chief items in the food habits of the mink, there is a very serious conflict between the needs of this animal and the interest of man. Where muskrats are being managed intensively for fur, the mink should be trapped systematically.

Population Densities. Few data have been published on mink population densities. A few trapping records are available which give a general clue as to the total population, but not an exact statement of conditions. Bennitt and Nagel (12 *g.r.*) estimated the breeding reserve of minks in Missouri to be about 12,000 animals and the annual trapping take as 24,000. This latter figure was considered to be slightly greater than the mink population would stand for a sustained yield, so perhaps a 50 rather than a 66 per cent annual take, or 18,000 animals annually, would be a safer proportion of the total population to trap. Errington (7) took 200 mink from 12 square miles in South Dakota. If he took half of the mink population there would have been a mink for approximately every 20 acres before trapping began. Seton (61 *g.r.*) estimated that there was a pair of mink to a square mile in Manitoba a few years following 1900 and quotes Guthrie as claiming there was a mink for each square mile in the 22 national forests of Oregon and Washington previous to 1929. According to the 1951 annual fur-catch report there appears to be a very gradual decrease in the take of mink pelts (6 *g.r.*). This probably reflects the effect of high prices for mink over a period of years and the heavy present demand.

MANAGEMENT

Census. Minks are likely to be found near streams or the edges of ponds or lakes, or along the seashore. The habitat preference can thus be used in conducting census operations. Where a sample of the total area is investigated, the findings on the sample should be applied to the entire area on the basis of the lineal extent of watercourses or pond, lake, or ocean edges rather than on the basis of total area in acres or square miles.

Based on the findings of Marshall (21) in southern Michigan, the census taker should follow these rules:

1. Conduct census work in late winter or early spring, when there are 1 to 4 inches of snow on the ground and when the temperature is not below 15°F.

2. Run the census lines across the contours, making the stream or lake shores the focal point, investigating at least an area ¼-mile wide on each side of the stream or this same distance back from the pond or lake shore.

3. Take samples each ¼ mile, and consider tracks crossed at each sampling point as belonging to a different individual, except where the evidence clearly indicates otherwise.

4. Conclusions as to whether females are living in localized areas, and also whether a male may simply be following along a stream for several miles, should be checked by following trails sufficiently far to determine these points. The final results should be adjusted on the basis of such points.

Management in Relation to Trapping. While minks are reasonably resistant to the effects of trapping or killing, in many localities the population is gradually decreasing. Errington (7) noted this condition after 1922 for Brookings County in South Dakota; he attributed the decline to the change from trapping with steel traps to a system of locating the animals with specially trained dogs and digging them out of their dens. The destructive effect probably included both a heavier take and the ruining of a necessary part of the habitat. The similar reduction of minks during the period of 1927–1937, noted by Bennitt and Nagel (12 *g.r.*) for Missouri, illustrates a similar trend.

Destruction of dens should be prohibited by law. This measure in itself may make the difference between taking more than is produced and a sustained yield. With ordinary protection, the mink will usually get along very well. The high prices of minks will of course have the effect of increasing the take and keeping the breeding stock at a minimum.

WEASELS

Short-tailed, or Bonaparte, Weasel
Long-tailed, or New York, Weasel

GEOGRAPHICAL DISTRIBUTION

The weasel is one of the smallest of the mustelids and one of the least important of the fur-bearing group. It is of interest to the biologist because of the mystery of the color change of the fur varying with the changes of the seasons. The black tip of the tail does not change color seasonally. Weasels have won a bad reputation for themselves because of their occasional raids on the farmer's hen house. Primarily weasels are mouse eaters and no doubt do more good than harm, except under unusual conditions.

Weasels are quite evenly distributed over most of North America, according to Anthony (4 *g.r.*, 23). The Bonaparte weasel appears to be a forest form occurring in the northeastern section of the United States and in the Lake states. The New York weasel occurs in the more open lands from southern Maine south to North Carolina and west to Illinois. Other species are found in practically all types of habitat. Because of their tolerance for both wet and dry situations, weasels of the various species occupy the entire North American continent.[1]

ANATOMY, LIFE HISTORY, AND ECOLOGY

The long-tailed, or New York, weasel is considerably larger than the short-tailed, or Bonaparte, weasel. In general, the female weasel is smaller than the male. One of the peculiarities of the eastern weasel is the light lemon-colored spot under the throat and belly. Yellow is an unusual color among the fur bearers, and this particular color may be due to a staining of the white fur with musk, a glandular secretion produced by the animal. The change of color which occurs in the coat of the weasel from brown to white in the late fall and from white to brown in early spring has been a subject of much controversy among trappers and laymen. It is probable that this phenomenon is a genetic property with each race of weasels and that it occurs in localities only where there is likely to be snow in the winter. Dearborn (20 *g.r.*) gives a map of Michigan showing that part of the state where 100 per cent of the weasels change to white in winter and also a part of the state where only 10 per cent grow a white coat during the winter period. On this point Hamilton (16) comments as follows: "To my knowledge *Mustela erminea* becomes white in winter throughout its range. *Mustela frenata* on the other hand, becomes white only where winters are cold. Where half the weasels are brown, these brown winter specimens are always males." The molt is the process by which the change of color is accomplished (11, 13).

It has been proven by Bissonnette and Bailey (3) that changes of pelage from brown to white in races of weasels which change to white in winter, and changes from brown to light brown in other races, occur because of a daily reduction of light. Reverse changes are induced by increased daily amounts of light. Bissonnette and Bailey (3) state that these changes are due to the growing of hair of different color, a phenomenon which may be controlled by the animal itself by exposing itself to more or less light, owing to its habits of day or night hunting or staying in or out of the den during the hours of daylight or darkness.

Breeding. Presumably weasels breed during the first year of life. The time of mating was formerly thought to be February and March, with a gestation period of 40 to 42 days. Hamilton (16) has pointed out that the gestation period may be 277 days, or possibly 9 months, as is true with the marten. The hypothesis is supported by the observations of War-

[1] William Henry Burt and Richard Philip Grossenheider. 1952. A field guide to the mammals, Houghton Mifflin Company, Boston.

ren,[2] who observed 2 male weasels with much enlarged testes during August in Gunnison County, Colorado, in 1931 and 1932. The fighting of weasels also described by Warren may have been a sign of breeding activities, as weasels are known to fight viciously during the breeding period. Hall (15) also contributes evidence to indicate that the 40- to 42-day gestation period may be incorrect. Warren[2] noted great variations in the sizes of young, but this is probably the result of dimorphism of the sexes.

The young are born from April through May in a warm nest of fur, feathers, or any soft materials available (2, 25). The nest is usually in a rock pile or under debris of some kind. At birth, the sexes are about equal, and the young are covered with a thin coat of white fur. One litter a year is born to each female, and the number in the litter varies from 4 to 10 young, with the average number being 6 or 7 (16). The young suckle from 3 to 6 weeks, but the family may continue together during the late summer and fall.

There are indications that weasel populations fluctuate both up and down in localized units of their ranges. The mechanism controlling such fluctuations has been suggested by Murray Werbiski, a trapper living near Delta, Manitoba (5). Werbiski, in trapping a square mile of marsh intensively, discovered that when weasel populations are low only 20 per cent of the animals are females, but when the numbers are increasing 40 per cent of the catch are females. This may shed some light on how a weasel population on its range may remain small, and how a balance with the food supply may be maintained. Although Elder (5) does not state so specifically, it is presumed that the sex ratio of all populations is low on females. This is an unusual condition, since many, if not most, of the mammals have about equal sex ratios. One can only speculate on the way this adjustment of sexes is brought about. A low food supply may bring about a resorption of embryos in which the females are less able to survive than the males. This would be a reversal of the presumed greater durability of the female mammal.

Movements. Weasels are extremely active creatures for their size and move about extensively when in search of food and possibly during the mating period. Criddle and Criddle (4) mention a weasel the tracks of which showed an extent of movement more than a half mile away from the home den in search of food. Hamilton (16) followed the track of a Bonaparte weasel 4 miles in soft snow and states that the larger New York weasel can travel half as far as a mink, which in turn may travel 8 to 10 miles in a single night. Quick (26) found the average cruising radius for weasels in southern Michigan was about 1/3 mile from the den,

[2] Edward R. Warren. 1924. Ground squirrels and weasels. *Jour. Mammal.* 5(4): 265–266.

and the average daily distance of travel was less than 2 miles. The home range in this locality was about 300 acres.

Cover Requirements. The cover requirements of the weasel are less specific than would be true of a diurnal animal. Good nest cover appears to be any well-concealed crevice that has an opening too small for a cat to enter and is dry. Stone walls appear to be ideal. An opening under an abandoned building is a favorite place for a weasel nest.

Fence rows are good both for nests and for foraging places. Deep grass and herbaceous material are much used for summer foraging, probably not because of their cover qualities but because they harbor mice and rabbits. According to Glover (10), however, both trapping and tracking studies showed that fairly dense ground vegetation is preferred.

Food. An extensive survey of the published food habits of the weasel indicates that it is a confirmed killer of rodents, including mice, rats, and rabbits. Dearborn's food analysis (20 *g.r.*) by percentage of class frequency shows the New York weasel eats 83 per cent mammals, including mice, cottontails, shrews, and moles. Birds and insects are also included in the diet, but to a lesser degree. Weasels appear to ignore birds as food where other kinds of food are plentiful. Small birds often nest within easy access of weasels but are ignored. Pheasant and domestic chicken eggs seem to hold no attraction for weasels, even when broken (19). Hamilton (16) gives the fall and winter food of weasels as nearly 97 per cent mammals. Only 5 of 354 stomachs examined by that investigator contained birds. Three of these he believed were taken as skunk bait. Insects are an important item of the weasel diet during the summer and fall (24). Hamilton (16) states that more food is eaten in summer than in winter and that these animals consume one-third to one-half of their body weight every 24 hours, or about 1 to 2 ounces. Quick (26) gives the food diet of southern Michigan weasels as 65 to 70 per cent white-footed mice, 23 to 33 per cent meadow mice, and 2 to 7 per cent small birds. In one township domestic fowl constituted slightly more than 1 per cent of the total diet. This corresponds to the findings of other investigators (29). Numerous accounts show that weasels are fearless and will attack animals much larger than themselves, but that sometimes these adversaries will come out first in the struggle for survival.

A comparison of the foods of weasels as indicated by analyses of stomach contents and droppings shows a striking similarity of the feeding habits of these animals.

Population Density. Weasels will kill and eat each other. Perhaps this is the reason weasels do not increase to greater densities than they do. There are never very many weasels in a locality, no matter how suitable the habitat appears and how abundant their principle food (mice) gets.

Weasels in a typical Iowa farmland are estimated as 5 for 160 acres, or a weasel for every 32 acres during late winter and early spring. On this area the best site was a weed patch of 5.5 acres, which was occupied by 2 weasels. Pocket gopher mounds and Franklin ground squirrel dens were present and used for weasel houses; mice and rabbits were also present (25).

Hamilton (16) estimates that there are about 300,000 weasels in New York State, and that about one-fourth of them are trapped each season. Seton (61 *g.r.*) estimates about 5 of these animals to the square mile, or a weasel for each 128 acres. This is probably a good average estimate of weasel population density. In Pennsylvania, Glover (12) showed weasel populations according to cover types as follows:

Marginal land..................	One weasel per 9.5 acres
Scrub oak—pitch pine..........	One weasel per 18.2 acres
Chestnut oak cover.............	One weasel per 22.9 acres
Agricultural land...............	One weasel per 40.22 acres

REFERENCES

1. Anonymous. 1938. Mink raising. *U.S. Dept. Agr. Bur. Biol. Survey, Leaflet* BS-82.
2. Bishop, Sherman C. 1932. Note on the nest and young of the small brown weasel. *Jour. Mammal.* **4**(1):26–27.
3. Bissonnette, Thomas Hume, and Earl Elmore Bailey. 1944. Experimental modification and control of molts and changes of coat-color in weasels by controlled lighting. *N.Y. Acad. Sci. Ann.* **45**(6):221–260.
4. Criddle, Norman, and Stuart Criddle. 1925. The weasels of southern Manitoba. *Canad. Field Nat.* **39**(6):142–148.
5. Elder, William H. 1951. Determination of weasel sex ratio by pelt examination. *Jour. Wildlife Mangt.* **15**(1):114–116.
6. Errington, Paul L. 1936. Sex ratio and size variation in South Dakota mink. *Jour. Mammal.* **17**(3):287.
7. ———. 1938. The decline of a mink population. *Jour. Mammal.* **19**(2): 250–251.
8. ———. 1943. An analysis of mink predation upon muskrats in north-central United States. *Iowa Agr. Expt. Sta. Res. Bul.* 320.
9. Follett, W. I. 1937. Prey of weasel and mink. *Jour. Mammal.* **18**(3):365.
10. Gerstell, Richard. 1937. Pennsylvania bounty system. *Pa. Bd. Game Commrs. Res. Bul.* 1.
11. Glover, Fred A. 1942*a*. Spring color change of the New York weasel. *Pa. Game News.* **13**(7):18, 23.
12. ———. 1942*b*. A population study of weasels in Pennsylvania. Unpublished M.S. thesis, Pennsylvania State College, State College.
13. Green, C. V. 1936. Observations on the New York weasel, with remarks on its winter dichromatism. *Jour. Mammal.* **17**(3):247–249.
14. Guilday, John E. 1949. Winter food of Pennsylvania mink. *Pa. Game News.* **20**(9):12, 32.
15. Hall, E. Raymond. 1938. Gestation period in long-tailed weasel. *Jour. Mammal.* **19**(2):249–250.

16. Hamilton, W. J., Jr. 1933. The weasels of New York. *Amer. Midland Nat.* **14**(4):289–344.
17. ———. 1936. Food habits of the mink in New York. *Jour. Mammal.* **17**(2):169.
18. ———. 1940. The summer food of minks and raccoons on the Montezuma Marsh, New York. *Jour. Wildlife Mangt.* **4**(1):80–84.
19. Ingles, Lloyd G. 1939. Observations on a nest of the long-tailed weasel. *Jour. Mammal.* **20**(2):253–254.
20. Marshall, William H. 1935. Mink displays sliding habits. *Jour. Mammal.* **16**(3):228–229.
21. ———. 1936. A study of the winter activities of the mink. *Jour. Mammal.* **17**(4):382–392.
22. McCabe, Robert A. 1949. Notes on live-trapping mink. *Jour. Mammal.* **30**(4):416–423.
23. Merriam, C. Hart. 1896. Synopsis of the weasels of North America. *U.S. Dept. Agr. Div. Ornith. Mammal., North Amer. Fauna,* 11.
24. Nichols, D. G., and J. T. Nichols. 1935. Notes on the New York weasel (*Mustela noveboracensis*). *Jour. Mammal.* **16**(4):297–299.
25. Polderboer, Emmett B., Lee W. Kuhn, and George O. Hendrickson. 1941. Winter and spring habits of weasels in central Iowa. *Jour. Wildlife Mangt.* **5**(1):115–119.
26. Quick, H. F. 1944. Habits and economics of the New York weasel in Michigan. *Jour. Wildlife Mangt.* **8**(1):71–78.
27. Sealander, John A. 1943. Winter food habits of mink in southern Michigan. *Jour. Wildlife Mangt.* **7**(4):411–417.
28. ———. 1944. A criticism of Marshall's method of censusing mink. *Jour. Mammal.* **25**(1):84–86.
29. Soper, J. Dewey. 1919. Notes on Canadian weasels. *Canad. Field Nat.* **33**(3):43–47.

CHAPTER 9

Muskrats

Ondatra zibethica

FUR FACTS

The muskrat is our most valuable fur bearer as judged by the total number of pelts taken in a year and the total value of the furs. Prime muskrat fur has excellent qualities of color, durability, and beauty. It can be used in its natural state and has many possibilities for processing. The skin or leather is strong and the fur wears well.

Because of their abundance and the extensive manufacturing facilities needed to handle them, muskrat peltries are used as barometers of the fur trade. Bachrach (7 *g.r.*) gives three types of muskrats used by the fur trade and three uses of muskrat skins. The brown muskrat is perhaps the best known. The black is a color phase of the common muskrat, while the southern or Louisiana muskrat is lighter-colored and has a thin skin.

The three uses are the processed pelt which is known as "Hudson seal," a sheared fur of muskrat that has been dyed black and made to look like Alaskan seal; dyed and striped pelts made to resemble mink, sable, or marten; and natural muskrat.

Muskrat furs are used principally for coats, although some are used for trimming. Three types of processing are used in coats: natural back, golden sides, and silver belly. The natural back is made from the darkest and thickest part of the skin, the back. The sides have less dense fur and are usually lighter in color to which the designation "golden" is applied. The under part or belly fur is still thinner and even lighter in color and of course is less expensive. Bachrach (7 *g.r.*) speaks of a new type of coat the "let-out" muskrat. This gives a long, narrow, uniform pattern that resembles the mink.

GEOGRAPHICAL DISTRIBUTION

Muskrats live in a variety of climates and under a wide range of vegetative conditions. Northern specimens are the largest, darkest, and the most valuable, however. In addition to the pelts, their flesh is excellent in quality as human food. The normal centers of demand are New Orleans and Baltimore. This fur bearer, along with skunk, is outstanding among wildlife because of its almost universal distribution, its tenacity under heavy trapping pressure, and because of the ready cash it returns to the army of trappers who reap a harvest of muskrat pelts each season.

It is most abundant on rich, moist soils, but will live almost anywhere where water is available. Its habits of movement in spreading to trapped-out territory and its tolerance to adverse conditions, including intense trapping pressure, make it unique among the fur bearers of North America.

ANATOMY, LIFE HISTORY, AND ECOLOGY

The muskrat is well adapted to life in an aquatic habitat. It has feet adapted to swimming, a coat of fur which keeps heat radiation at a minimum, and is omnivorous in its feeding habits, being thus able to utilize both animal and vegetable material as food. The tail is long and scaly being thicker laterally than vertically. The total length of an adult northern 'rat varies from 20–25 inches, the tail being 10 inches of this total (38). The usual weight of a muskrat varies from 1 to 2.5 pounds but sometimes reaches a weight of more than 4 pounds (14). Heit (28) gives the average weight of 275 'rats from western New York as 2 pounds and 11.4 ounces, with the largest weighing 4.5 pounds. Dozier (13) gives the average weights of male muskrats from Maryland as 2.3 pounds and females as 2.2 pounds. Also according to this investigator (14), male Montezuma Marsh, New York, 'rats weigh on the average 0.3 pound more than the females.

Muskrats are very prolific, but in the northern part of the range they do not breed during the current breeding season of their birth (14 *g.r.*). This high breeding capacity insures an abundance of animals where living conditions are suitable. There seems to be some question as to whether the muskrat is monogamous or polygamous. Arthur (3) believes the Louisiana species is polygamous. It is possible that monogamy, if it exists, is of the seasonal kind and that either male or female may accept a new mate if one or the other is lost during midseason. Errington (22, 23) points out that Iowa muskrats appear to be loosely monogamous during the breeding season and that at least some males participate in routine family life to the extent of arranging and covering semihelpless young in the absence of the female. Hewitt (29) regards the male muskrat in Ontario as promiscuous in its sex habits and quotes W. J. Hamilton as believing the same to be true for New York 'rats.

The breeding season for muskrats in Iowa extends from April through August (21). The breeding season for Wisconsin muskrats is from the first of April to the middle of June, with occasional animals being sexually active as early as the middle of February to as late as the middle of August (5). According to Arthur (3) and O'Neil (36), the breeding season farther south is more extended, and in the Louisiana marshes breeding occurs during the entire year except the hotter months of late summer (36). Smith (38) believes muskrats in the Maryland marshes breed every month of the year except during November and December.

The number of litters may vary from 2 to 4 under northern conditions, with 2 litters as the common occurrence and 4 as a maximum for the latitude of central Iowa (22). More litters, up to 5 or 6, may be born

FIG. 9-1. Muskrat. Note the ratlike eye and the scaly tail. (*Photo Henry S. Mosby, Virginia Polytechnic Institute, Cooperative Wildlife Research Unit.*)

on ranges farther south or where the seasons are less severe (36). The gestation period is from 29 to 30 days with a possibility that for some females it may be as short as 19 days, according to Errington (21). For Louisiana, O'Neil (36) gives the gestation periods as 26 to 28 days. The oestrous cycle in Wisconsin is 28 days (5). Apparently a female may breed again soon after the young are born since litters may arrive a month apart (22). The number of young in a litter varies from 1 to 9 with 2 to 5 being about the average; in Louisiana 3.6 to 3.8 is average litter size (36). Maryland female 'rats average between 4 and 5 per litter with 7 young being the greatest number found in any litter (38). Litters in Iowa are apparently relatively high since Errington (22) found them to vary from a low of 4 in April to a high of 8 the second half of August. Under situations where the food conditions are excellent, such as where drainage ditches cross agricultural lands, Errington found 3 females produced an average of 19 young apiece for the season. In Wisconsin an adult female may have as many as 22 young per season but on the average an adult female has 7 young per season (7).

The sex ratio of young muskrats is probably 50:50 at birth, but may become unbalanced under conditions where trapping creates a differential as to the sexes (7). A 6-year study of 31,867 muskrats trapped in the Montezuma Marshes in New York likewise showed the ratio of the 2 sexes to be equal. Since the Montezuma Marshes are noted for producing muskrats that are outstanding both in size and quality and the numbers examined are relatively large, it would indicate this sample may show a true condition (16). Studies by various workers of large numbers of trapped 'rats has shown the sex ratio to vary from nearly equal to 69 males to 31 females. Only 1 study showed fewer males than females (49 males to 51 females) and this could have been due to statistical difficulties (4, 7, 11, 14, 17, 27, 37).

The young are born in a dry nest in either a house or a bank den. They are tenderly cared for by the mother for a period of 2 to 3 weeks until they learn to eat and care for themselves. Growth is rapid, however, and before a month has passed the young begin to take on the appearance of adults.

Muskrats are busy animals. Cuttings of plants and droppings on boulders and logs indicate that they move around extensively. They are nocturnal in these activities, but not exclusively so, as one often sees them swimming during broad daylight.

Muskrats are frequently encountered along highways or in roadside ditches during the late winter and spring. The normal area of use of northern muskrats is about an acre. On this area the male seems to be more active than the female (6). The fact that trapped-out muskrat habitats usually support 'rats the following year indicates that populations shift and occupy habitable sites as they become vacant. Seton (61 *g.r.*) mentions fall migrations of muskrats in which the animals travel overland a considerable distance as far as a mile or two from water. Errington (22) and Takos (40) believe young muskrats typically spend the fall and winter close to the range of their birth. Errington (22) also contends that there is an extension of the range during fall and winter. There likewise appears to be a constant shifting of the population due to individual idiosyncrasies rather than to a general readjustment of the population. Errington further maintains that the majority of the winter migrants in the northern states do not succeed in establishing themselves and are lost by exposure, wounds, or are killed by motor traffic or natural enemies. This same author gives data on 17 tabbed muskrats showing a variation in movement from none at all to a distance of 3¼ miles. In late winter and early spring, muskrats may be evicted from winter habitats by floodwaters, thus forcing the population to seek new homes (22, 23). During this period the 'rats are found in all manner of out-of-the-way places and miles away from situations that are good wintering sites.

Spring dispersal results from seeking suitable breeding areas, the intolerance of breeding animals to other 'rats which wintered with them, the pairing off of the sexes, and the search for mates.

There appears to be a difference between the sexes as to movements, the males moving more freely during the summer season than the females, probably because of the restricting effect of the care of a family on the latter. Errington (22, 23) suggests that males predominate among the 'rats that wander during the summer period as indicated by selective trapping and the predominance of males found on highways. A true migration of 'rats is mentioned by Arthur (3) who cites a truck driver encountering a group of 20 'rats crossing a gravel road in Ascension Parish, Louisiana. During these mass migrations the 'rats appear to be especially irritable and ready to fight if an attempt is made to bar their progress.

The muskrat does not have the same reputation as the beaver for elaborate engineering works. This fur bearer does, however, have tendencies of a builder and a strong instinct for self-preservation. Both of these instincts are demonstrated by its house-building activities as the season advances. Two types of structure are built, feeding houses and dwelling houses, each with different dimensions and used for different purposes. Feeding rafts and food "push-ups" are also used by muskrats. According to Bellrose (8), feeding houses are 6 to 18 inches high. Dwelling houses are 4 to 6 feet in diameter and have walls 1 to 2 feet thick, while feeding houses are 2 feet or less in diameter and have walls only 3 to 8 inches thick. Feeding houses have no nest chamber and have only one "plunge hole," or access to the water (if ice is present). Dwelling houses, in contrast, usually have two "plunge holes" and a nest cavity.

Habitat Requirements. The muskrat is a typical border animal, living in or near the water but depending on vegetation for food, house or bedding material, and protection. Muskrats probably reach their greatest abundance in the Louisiana delta marshes, where water is 12 to 18 inches deep with cat-tails or other marsh vegetation interspersed with lanes or ponds of deeper open water. This marsh habitat may be no better than a suitable muskrat situation along a creek in fertile land with a constant water supply and plenty of both woody and herbaceous vegetation along the banks. However, in the marsh habitat favorable conditions are duplicated over the total area, whereas along the creek the favorable conditions apply only to the area immediately adjacent to the water. On the suitability of a stream habitat, Errington (20) comments as follows: "A small shallow creek running through a closely grazed pasture is about at the bottom of the scale of habitability in central Iowa . . . " He further states that larger streams flowing through ungrazed woodlands or fields with adequate supplies of corn or other food materials nearby furnish much more favorable conditions. He adds that for wintering environments a site with ample food and little water is preferable to one with much water but little food.

Protective cover is necessary for muskrat habitation. Protection may take the form of a den, a stream bank, a tunnel in a boggy marsh, or the

FIG. 9-2. Typical muskrat habitat and house. (*U.S. Soil Conservation Service.*)

cover of a lodge. In the Louisiana marshes, according to Arthur (3), the ideal marsh is one having one to several feet of peat or humus with a minimum of mineral soil. In this the 'rats can build tunnels which are ideal breeding and protective units.

With relation to water levels, Bellrose and Brown (9) found water with stable water levels carried nearly six times as many muskrat lodges as that with fluctuating water. Plant communities of cat-tails supported more muskrat houses per acre than other plant groups. The river bulrush is rated next as to plants favored by muskrats.

Little has been said of the swamp type of habitat. This is a wet situation advanced in the plant-succession stage where woody plants are prominent in the cover. It is probably not ideal for muskrats but furnishes in the aggregate many acres of good 'rat habitat over the muskrat range.

Irrigation ditches have afforded the muskrat the means to enter territory formerly not occupied by these animals. In the Imperial Valley, California, muskrats aided by extensive irrigation practices have moved into a formerly unsuitable locality (28 *g.r.*).

Food. The muskrat is omnivorous in its food habits, eating both animal and plant products, depending on their presence and accessibility. Errington (22) indicates that about the only herbaceous plant not eaten by the muskrat is the horsetail (*Equisetum* spp.).

Johnson (30) lists 26 species of plants as being important muskrat foods in New York, including broad- and narrow-leaved cat-tails, swamp loosestrife, duckweed, rice-cutgrass, arrowhead, woody nightshade, sweet flag, smartweeds, lizard's-tail, bur-reed, blue flag, cow parsnip, broad-leaved dock, bur marigold, water avens, yellow pond lily, dandelions, sedges, wolffia of two kinds, and the leaves of white ash, willow, red osier dogwood, buttonbush, and sweet gale. On the Maryland marshes, the three-square bulrush is considered the chief muskrat food (38). Errington (22) considers the younger animals as being more terrestrial in their habits than the adults, thus living more on plants which grow in a drier situation. In farming communities 'rats seek such food as apples and corn as well as natural vegetation (22). In fact, Errington (22) states that yellow corn is a most valuable food for wintering muskrats; he also believes that in this connection the cat-tail rootstock may not be far behind. This latter plant material produces yields which may exceed 5 tons per acre (dry weight) and has nutrient values equal to those of yellow corn except in fat content.

During the time when muskrats feed under the ice, bulbs and rootstocks of aquatic plants have an important place in the muskrat diet. In central Wisconsin, the tuber of bugleweeds is listed by Hamerstrom and Blake (26) as an all-season food.

In Illinois the highest-producing marshes are those in which the following plants predominate: (1) river bulrush, (2) cat-tails, (3) marsh smartweed, (4) hard-stemmed bulrush, (5) reed cane, (6) sedges, (7) American lotus, (8) wild rice, (9) duck-potato (reference 8).

Errington mentions grass as being an important winter food of muskrats, particularly of muskrats wintering in dry creeks and drainage ditches (22).

The flesh-eating propensities of muskrats are not well understood and therefore are given little attention in articles on the food of the muskrat. Cannibalism among muskrats is apparently a common occurrence (22). O'Neil (36) confined a group of seven 'rats in a pen which were reduced to one female over a period of several months. He indicates that cannibalism may be in part related to a lack of protein in the diet. These findings have a direct bearing on the many failures at muskrat farming in confined quarters over the past 50 years. Apparently availability determines whether flesh is freely eaten. Johnson (30) states that where fresh-water clams are plentiful, they are eaten by muskrats and are the first choice of all animal foods. Other animal foods are crayfish, insects, snails, fish, birds, and other muskrats, if and when available.

Muskrats eat about one-third of their own weight daily but will get along on less. Stearns and Goodwin (39) found the average content of muskrat stomachs to contain slightly more than 22 cubic centimeters of food materials. With relation to drought, adult 'rats can subsist on succulence in the absence of free water, but according to Errington (22) half-grown muskrats die of thirst under similar conditions.

Popuplation Density. An average of 7 muskrats per acre have been trapped on a 1,200-acre marsh in western Ontario (29). This would possibly imply a fall breeding population of 10 animals per acre or possibly more. Hewitt states that a good marsh should yield 6 to 8 'rats per acre per season annually. Maryland marshes yield an average of 3 to 4 'rats per acre annually and carry an implied population of 6 to 8 animals per acre (29). Habitats where only the border is suitable for muskrat habitation, such as drainage ditches and pond borders, are difficult to figure on a per acre basis. Therefore, some other unit of density must be given if population density is to be expressed. Territorialism is as characteristic of muskrats as it is of some birds and thus limits the numbers that may occupy a given length of shore line. Errington (22) gives the distribution along one Iowa lake shore as a muskrat for each 40 to 50 yards. On a drainage ditch in Iowa, 10 muskrats per mile were counted after a season with favorable moisture conditions and a closed trapping period. On large irrigation canals in the Imperial Valley, California, as many as 67 'rats were trapped in 1 day's trapping on a mile of canals. The average, however, was 20 (28 *g.r.*).

Some northern muskrat habitats are apparently very productive. An area of 4,500 acres in the Horican Marsh in Wisconsin produced an average of almost 6 trapped 'rats per acre in 1948, truly a remarkable yield. Several other marshes in Wisconsin produced as high as 16 pelts per acre (7). The average is likely to be much lower than this, however, with 3 to 4 per acre being about what can be expected for good locations.

MORTALITY

Because of their abundance and widespread distribution, prolific animals like the muskrat are certain to be the prey of numerous carnivores. The total numbers taken are, however, of less importance than the ratio this loss bears to the entire population.

Errington found that fighting among muskrats on heavily populated habitats caused considerable losses due both to actual killing and injuries which later resulted in death (19). Under crowded conditions the trouble appears to be at its worst when newcomers attempt to migrate into a habitat already populated. Scars and wounds on fall-trapped muskrats give evidence that severe fighting occurs among muskrats. Fighting is much more severe if food is scarce. Predatory animals no doubt take some 'rats, but there is little evidence available to show how extensive such losses are under any particular set of conditions. Minks, foxes, horned owls, and snapping turtles all will eat muskrat flesh when it is available, but muskrats are strong fighters, are nocturnal, and live underground so much of the time that they are not particularly vulnerable. Dearborn says (20 *g.r.*) that about 66 per cent of the stomachs of winter-trapped minks contain muskrats and states that the prejudice of trappers against minks in relation to muskrats is well founded. Errington confirms this condition for Iowa, especially if muskrat densities are high or habitat conditions unfavorable (19).

Johnson (30) gives some indication that snapping turtles are destructive to muskrats. No evidence is at hand to indicate how severe this destruction is, however.

In the Louisiana marshes, minks, raccoons, barn and barred owls, alligators, ants, marsh hawks, cottonmouth moccasins, bullfrogs, garfish, bowfins, snapping turtles, black bass, crabs, hogs, house cats, and dogs are all enemies of muskrats (36). Lay and O'Neil (34) indicate that alligators may be of assistance to muskrats through their activities of making water holes and keeping ditches open.

The great horned owl appears to be a predator of muskrat on occasions, but not a very important one when conditions are suitable for the 'rats. Thus, Errington *et al.* (24) found no remains of muskrats in 209 owl pellets collected next to a marsh where the density of 'rats was sufficient to trap almost 9 of these fur bearers per acre.

Overgrazing and soil erosion should be added to the influences affecting muskrats in the central states. Overgrazing destroys the bank vegetation, and the cattle close up the tunnels along the banks of streams and pot holes by stepping into them. Soil erosion tends to silt in the watercourses and reduce the richness of the bank vegetation. Over a wide area these agencies have, no doubt, reduced the muskrat crop to a considerable degree.

Fluctuating water levels have a marked effect on muskrat populations. High waters, such as floods, may flood out and drown young muskrats in nests and also cause mature animals to leave their shelters and take refuge on floating debris. Under such conditions the animals suffer losses due not only to exposure but also to predators.

Low water, resulting from drought conditions, does not seem to have the immediate destructive effect of high water, and the losses due to low water are not nearly so great. Dried-out marshes may cause muskrats to move around in search of food, and if this occurs during severe winter weather, there may well be some losses (9, 10, 19).

Under Michigan conditions, it was found that a pair of muskrats produce 14 young per year, but the harvestable number of young is 4 or 5 per pair. This indicates a loss of 70 per cent of the young between birth and harvest (4).

MANAGEMENT

Census. A census of muskrats is largely a matter of estimating the number on the basis of the number of houses and feeding mounds. Bellrose (8) states that "for the purposes of evaluating yearly population changes

FIG. 9-3. Muskrat marsh in Louisiana. This state is the leading producer of muskrats. Many Louisiana marshes such as this are intensively managed. (*Hermann Postlethwaite, U.S. Soil Conservation Service.*)

and the density in various types of vegetation, we believe the enumeration of houses provides a reliable index." Dozier (15) computed the 'rats on the basis of an average of 5 'rats per active house. It is presumed the above census would be taken after the house-building activities have been completed in the fall.

O'Neil (36) suggests a census by traversing ground strips and counting the houses or beds as far as can be seen on each side of the line traversed. A map is made from aerial photographs so the ground sampling is related to the area of a particular cover type. O'Neil walked a 50-mile line for 2 years and multiplied each house by 5. By computing the area covered (width times length) and figuring the number of muskrats per acre for each cover type, he was able to determine the total population.

Management of muskrat ranges resolves itself into two major and three or four minor activities. A major management activity centers

FIG. 9-4. A productive muskrat marsh in Maryland. (*H. L. Dozier, U.S. Fish and Wildlife Service.*)

around the flooding of drained or dried-out marshlands and keeping the water level constant. Hewitt (29) indicates water depths of 1 to 3 feet are about right.

Trapping. The second measure of major importance is to control the trapping season. Trapping too few animals may be as important as trapping too many. Lay (33) states that many southern trappers leave a minimum of 2 pairs of animals per acre and indicates this is a commendable procedure.

McCann (35) suggests that under Minnesota conditions not more than 50 per cent of the population should be trapped during any one year, but this is probably too conservative as other investigators agree 2 pairs per acre are sufficient seed stock for next year's crop (12, 23).

Minor activities include the planting of desirable food plants in marshes after the water level has been stabilized, the creation of refuges, supplemental winter feeding, and the control of grazing and burning.

Many fine muskrat habitats can be created by the erection of small inexpensive dams. Water will accumulate from natural rainfall if a barrier is made, or water may be pumped in. Many desirable plants like cat-tails and bulrushes will seed themselves in naturally and thus require no extra effort other than a suitable water supply to induce them to grow. To induce cat-tail to grow it is desirable to remove the other plant materials and also keep the muskrat population at a minimum (12). A seed stock of 'rats is usually present nearby anyway and needs only the encouragement of water and suitable food to bring them in.

Adults, or the oldest muskrats, taken from any marsh are likely to have a few spotted blue areas (unprime) on both the back and belly. Subadults, or those less than full-grown, will have a greater area of unprime skin both on the back and belly. Small skins, indicating small subadults or kits, are quite unprime. One of the indicators of immaturity is a lyre-shaped pattern of prime light-colored skin that crosses the back and extends along the flanks (2).

From the standpoint of primeness, the proper time to trap muskrats in the northern range is in the late winter before the spring breeding season gets into full swing. At this time the pelts are prime and the kits of the previous year have grown to full size, thus giving the trapper the advantage of less discrimination because of low-grade pelts. On the other hand, early trapped pelts even though smaller may bring a higher price. In this connection Gashwiler (25), after a careful study of all factors involved, suggests that a 21-day season in November would be better for trapping muskrats in Maine than the present late-spring season. Traps should be set near deep water in such a way that the 'rats will drown themselves as they dive into deep water after they are caught.

REFERENCES

1. Allan, D. J. 1942. Marsh management for fur production. *Trans. 7th North Amer. Wildlife Conf.* Pp. 263–271.
2. Applegate, Vernon C., and Henry E. Predmore, Jr. 1947. Age classes and patterns of primeness in a fall collection of muskrat pelts. *Jour. Wildlife Mangt.* **11**(4):324–330.
3. Arthur, Stanley C. 1931. The fur animals of Louisiana, Department of Conservation, New Orleans.
4. Baumgartner, Luther L., and Frank C. Bellrose. 1943. Determination of sex and age in muskrats. *Jour. Wildlife Mangt.* **7**(1):77–81.
5. Beer, James R. 1950. Reproductive cycle of the muskrat in Wisconsin. *Jour. Wildlife Mangt.* **14**(2):151–156.
6. ——— and Roland K. Meyer. 1951. Seasonal changes in the endocrine

organs and behavior pattern of the muskrat. *Jour. Wildlife Mangt.* **32**(2):173–191.

7. ——— and Wayne Truax. 1950. Sex and age ratios in Wisconsin muskrats. *Jour. Wildlife Mangt.* **14**(3):323–331.
8. Bellrose, Frank C. 1950. Relationship of muskrat populations to various marsh and aquatic plants. *Jour. Wildlife Mangt.* **14**(3):299–315.
9. ——— and Lewis G. Brown. 1941. The effect of fluctuating water levels on the muskrat population of an Illinois river valley. *Jour. Wildlife Mangt.* **5**(2):206–212.
10. ——— and Jessop B. Low. 1943. Influence of flood and low water levels on the survival of muskrats. *Jour. Mammal.* **24**(2):173–188.
11. Buss, Irven O. 1941. Sex ratios and weights of muskrats (*Ondatra zibethica zibethica*) for Wisconsin. *Jour. Mammal.* **22**(4):403–406.
12. Cook, Arthur H., and Edward R. Maunton. 1950. Muskrat research that led to a marsh management program. *Proc. Northeastern Fish and Wildlife Conf.*
13. Dozier, Herbert L. 1944. Color, sex ratios, and weights of Maryland muskrats, II. *Jour. Wildlife Mangt.* **8**(2):165–169.
14. ———. 1945. Sex ratio and weights of muskrats from Montezuma National Wildlife Refuge. *Jour. Wildlife Mangt.* **9**(3):232–237.
15. ———. 1948. Estimating muskrat populations by house counts. *Trans. 13th North Amer. Wildlife Conf.* Pp. 372–392.
16. ———. 1950. Muskrat trapping on the Montezuma National Wildlife Refuge, New York, 1943–1948. *Jour. Wildlife Mangt.* **14**(4):403–412.
17. ——— and Robert W. Allen. 1942. Color, sex ratio, and weights of Maryland muskrats. *Jour. Wildlife Mangt.* **6**(2):294–299.
18. ——— and Merton Radway. 1948. Pelting muskrats by air inflation. *Jour. Wildlife Mangt.* **12**(3):333–334.
19. Errington, Paul L. 1933. Reactions of muskrat populations to drought. *Ecology.* **20**(2):168–186.
20. ———. 1937*a*. Habitat requirements of stream-dwelling muskrats. *Trans. 2d North Amer. Wildlife Conf.* Pp. 411–416.
21. ———. 1937*b*. The breeding season of the muskrat in northwest Iowa. *Jour. Mammal.* **18**(3):333–337.
22. ———. 1940*a*. Versatility in feeding and population maintenance of the muskrat. *Jour. Wildlife Mangt.* **5**(1):68–89.
23. ———. 1940*b*. Natural restocking of muskrat-vacant habitats. *Jour. Wildlife Mangt.* **4**(2):173–185.
24. ———, Francis Hamerstrom, and F. N. Hamerstrom, Jr. 1940. The great horned owl and its prey in north-central United States. *Iowa Agr. Expt. Sta. Res. Bul.* 277.
25. Gashwiler, Jay S. 1948. Maine muskrat investigations, Department of Inland Fisheries and Game, Augusta.
26. Hamerstrom, F. N., Jr., and James Blake. 1939. A fur study technique. *Jour. Wildlife Mangt.* **3**(1):54–59.
27. Hatfield, Donald M. 1939. Notes on sex ratio of Minnesota muskrats. *Jour. Mammal.* **20**(2):258.
28. Heit, William S. 1949. Muskrat weights and sex ratio in the riverbend marshes of Wayne County, New York. *Jour. Mammal.* **30**(2):122–124.
29. Hewitt, Oliver Harold. 1941. A study of the ecology of an artificial fresh

water marsh with special reference to ducks and muskrats. Unpublished M.S. thesis, Cornell University, Ithaca, New York.

30. Johnson, Charles E. 1925. The muskrat in New York: its natural history and economics. *Roosevelt Wild Life Bul.* **3**(2):199–320.
31. Kellogg, Charles E. 1946. Variation in pattern of primeness of muskrat skins. *Jour. Wildlife Mangt.* **10**(1):38–42.
32. Lay, Daniel W. 1945*a*. Muskrat investigations in Texas. *Jour. Wildlife Mangt.* **9**(1):56–76.
33. ———. 1945*b*. The problem of undertrapping in muskrat management. *Trans. 10th North Amer. Wildlife Conf.* Pp. 75–78.
34. ——— and Ted O'Neil. 1942. Muskrats on the Texas coast. *Jour. Wildlife Mangt.* **6**(4):301–311.
35. McCann, Lester J. 1944. Notes on growth, sex and age ratios, and suggested management of Minnesota muskrats. *Jour. Mammal.* **25**(1): 59–63.
36. O'Neil, Ted. 1949. Muskrat in the Louisiana marshes, Louisiana Department of Wildlife and Fisheries, New Orleans.
37. Seamans, Roger. 1941. Muskrats in the Lake Champlain valley of Vermont. *Lake Champlain Fur Survey. Vt. Fish and Game Bul.* 3–4.
38. Smith, Frank H. 1938. Muskrat investigations in Dorchester County, Md., 1930–34. *U.S. Dept. Agr. Cir.* 474.
39. Stearns, L. A., and M. W. Goodwin. 1941. Notes on the winter feeding of the muskrat in Delaware. *Jour. Wildlife Mangt.* **5**(1):1–12.
40. Takos, Michael J. 1944. Summer movements of banded muskrats. *Jour. Wildlife Mangt.* **8**(4):307–310.

CHAPTER 10

Otters

River Otter *Lutra canadensis*
Sea Otter *Enhydra lutris*

RIVER OTTER

FUR FACTS

The river otter is large compared to other fur bearers and hence furnishes a pelt of considerable value. The fur is very dense and brownish or blackish-brown in color. The leather is thick and durable. The fur is used for collars and cuffs of overcoats and for ladies' sport coats and trimmings. The fur is either processed by plucking out the guard hairs or it is left natural. Eastern otter furs are considered as having the highest value because of their dark color and very silky texture. In the highest-quality pelts, the fur fibers are very dense and the guard hairs stand erect. The pelts from Labrador appear to produce otter furs of the highest quality (7 *g.r.*).

GEOGRAPHICAL DISTRIBUTION

The river otter has a geographical distribution which covers most of the North American continent (11). Populations of otter are never very dense, but in certain parts of the continent this fur bearer is found consistently and is probably increasing in numbers. Because of its fish-eating habits, the otter is considered a serious menace to game fish by fishermen. Whether this supposition on the part of the sportsmen is justified depends on whether you are interested in trout or warm-water fish. While river otters eat large quantities of game and pan fishes in warmer waters, their consumption of trout in the cold-water streams appears not to be excessive.

While there is only a small amount of available literature on the river otter, its characteristics and habits are fairly well known because of the intimate knowledge of Emil E. Liers, who has kept otters in captivity for the past 40 years (8, 14).

The river otter lives along streams and the edges of ponds and lakes. It is such a shy creature and so inconspicuous that even local residents

FIG. 10-1. The otter is an aquatic fur bearer of larger size than most other aquatic animals. It produces fur of high durability. (*New York Zoological Society.*)

in the otter's range seldom suspect its presence even in sections having dense human populations (7).

ANATOMY, LIFE HISTORY, AND ECOLOGY

The adult river otter varies in length from 40 to 48 inches; the body being about three-fourths of this length and the tail one-fourth. The tail is heavy at the base, very muscular, and tapered toward the tip. The fur has a brownish metallic appearance in its natural state, but when clipped it is a rich gray-brown color unlike any other fur. The adult otter weighs from 6 to 20 pounds and is streamlined from end to end. The legs are short but very muscular. Seton (61 *g.r.*) states that the otter has the advantage of both a waterproof fur and a heavy coat of fat to insulate it from the cold water in which it spends a great deal of time at all seasons of the year.

Breeding Characteristics. It is likely that members of the river otter family stay together the entire year, although lone individuals are often seen along streams and lakes. While positive evidence as to the fidelity of the father in relation to the family is not at hand, indications are that he stays near the family group and may be an important part of it.

Grinnell *et al.* (28 *g.r.*) report that on one occasion the male otter took over the care of a family of 4 young after the mother had been trapped. Several investigators have spoken of seeing 5 otters together in the summer and fall, and it is suspected these were a family of 2 parents and 3 offspring.

Mating begins in midwinter, during February or March, but may continue through the summer under favorable climatic conditions. Thus, Luscomb is quoted as seeing a female otter with quite small young as late as December in the delta region of California (28 *g.r.*)

The following notes are copied verbatim from Liers' (14) excellent notes on the river otter:

In Minnesota, otters breed in winter and early spring. Females in my care have been in heat in the period December to early April. The testicles of males begin descending in November. In general a male cannot be counted on as a successful breeder until it is five to seven years of age. For some reason younger males are usually unsuccessful. An otter is not sexually mature until two years old.

In the wild several males may follow a female in heat. While on a lecture tour in Florida, I often exercised my otters in canals and ponds. On two occasions I met hunters standing on otter crossings. One hunter had just killed a male otter that he said was following a female that he had shot two hours earlier. He stated that the female was in heat. He told me he had often shot two or three otters on such a stand. At another stand a trapper told me that he had killed as many as 15 to 20 otters a year at otter crossings. Most of them were boar otter.

Successful copulation can take place either in the water or on land. In wild otters it probably occurs exclusively in the water.

The gestation period of English otters is 61 days (61 *g.r.*). The American form has a gestation period varying from 9 months and 18 days to 12 months and 15 days (1, 14). The number of young varies from 1 to 4, and these are born in a nest made from dry grass or any other available vegetable materials. The home nest may be either above or below the ground and may be located in a hollow log, crevice, among rocks, or in a den dug in a stream bank if it is well concealed. The den may be near water or high up on a hillside away from the water (14). Only one brood of young is raised each year by a female.

The cubs are toothless, hairless, and helpless at birth, and the mother cares for them for a period of 5 or 6 weeks. They begin to play at 5 or 6 weeks and exercise outside of the nest at 10 to 12 weeks. The young are awkward in the water at first and have to be coaxed in by the mother. Liers says they are head-heavy in their first swimming attempts (14).

Movements and Cover Requirements. River otter live where water is plentiful and go from one feeding area to another in a circuit over and over again. By keeping to wooded streams and traveling overland at the headwaters from one stream to another, they are able to remain within a territory that is not too heavily worked for food. The otter may visit a given spot on a stream at intervals of 3 to 6 weeks, depending on the total perimeter of the circuit. This system of movement and feeding seems to resemble that of the timber wolf, in which a group feeds in one locality until the food becomes scarce or hard to catch and then moves on to new pastures. Bradt (7) maintains that families of otter may travel as far as 40 miles in a circuit which may take 2 to 4 weeks to cover. He gives 10 to 12 miles as the distance which these animals may travel overland. Liers states they cover from 50 to 60 miles of a stream course in a year (14).

Many trappers have noticed that river otters seem to disappear during the beginning of severe winter conditions. As suggested by Seton (61 *g.r.*), it is probable they may travel under the ice during this period or rest in subterranean dens during this time. It is known that the river otter does not hibernate.

One of the most familiar habits of the river otter is its use of the slide. This is a smooth muddy incline where the otter can slide on its stomach into a water hole. Often whole families of otters will indulge in this pastime over and over again (7). Otters love to slide and will use snow, ice, and grass for this pastime. According to Bradt (7), otters often play with such objects as sticks, stones, or old tin cans; they also indulge in sham fights or play a game resembling tag.

Ideal cover conditions for the river otter involve plenty of streams or pond borders with accompanying vegetation. Rocks, log jams, and debris of all kinds serve the purpose of escape and for keeping out of sight. Bank dens, hollow logs, and the bases of hollow trees supply the otters with ideal escape cover.

Food. Otters are feeders on aquatic animal life, but a controversy rages as to whether the food of these animals is predominantly of highly desirable fish species or of the less valuable varieties. The otter is a carnivorous animal and probably eats any kind of flesh it can find or catch. The aquatic forms eaten include fish, snakes, frogs, toads, crayfish, and even ducks.

Even in trout waters there are nearly as many bass and sunfish represented in the food diet of this fur bearer as trout, thereby indicating that otters take the slower-moving fishes even where trout are present. Forage fishes, fish remains, and amphibians constitute 65 per cent of the food diet of these animals, probably because such species are present in greater numbers and are more readily available than trout. Trautman analyzed 600 cubic centimeters of otter scats collected during April, 1936, at the inlet of Pickerel Lake, Dickinson County, Michigan. He found that 66 per cent of the remains were minnows and suckers, 28 per cent crayfish, and 6 per cent miscellaneous material.[1] Analysis of 568 otter scats by the Michigan Conservation Department showed 58 per cent to be fish remains, but none of these remains could be identified as being trout (13).

Lagler and Ostenson (13) in a study of 439 viscera of otter trapped during the spring season of 1940 and 1941 on both trout and nontrout waters found the following classes of food present:

Table 10-1. Early Spring Food of Otters in Michigan Based on the Contents of 173 Stomachs and 220 Intestines (13)

Classes of food	Stomachs, volume per cent	Intestines, volume per cent
Game and pan fishes	32.0	15.9
Forage fishes	17.6	22.7
Fish remains	3.0	13.8
Frogs and mudpuppies	16.1	7.5
Other vertebrates	25.8	0.9
Crayfish	4.7	35.0
Insects	0.8	4.2
Total	100.0	100.0

Population Densities. Seton (61 *g.r.*) reviews several localities as to otter population densities; in these he probably cites some of the best otter ranges. He mentions Ontario as being an excellent otter range where he estimates there is an otter for every 8 square miles. Bradt (6) suggests that 1 otter to 40 square miles is probably more nearly average. On 42,000 square miles of nearly primitive otter range in the national forests in Oregon and Washington, there is an estimated population of 1 otter to each 70 square miles or an area about 8.5 miles square on a side.

Some idea as to the number of river otters remaining in North America can be obtained from the report of fur take for the United States, Alaska, and Canada. Alaska harvested 2,596 otter pelts in 1947–1948, which was only 411 less than taken in 1937–1938 (2, 5).

In 44 of the states reporting fur harvested, approximately 8,800 otter pelts were reported for the season 1947–1948 (5).

This was 4,850 more otter pelts than were reported as being taken in the 1937–1938 trapping season. The total number of otter pelts reported in Canada for the 1947–1948 season was 11,974 or a total for North America for that trapping year of slightly less than 22,400 pelts. If there are 3 otters left for each 1 taken, the total North American population

[1] Milton B. Trautman. 1937. Otters feed on suckers. *Michigan Conserv.* **6**(9):6.

was about 89,600 before the trapping season in 1947 or about a seventh of the primitive otter population as estimated by Seton (61 *g.r.*).

MANAGEMENT

Experience in Michigan indicates that river otters respond favorably to a trapping season open for only a limited time during any year and possibly to an improvement in the habitat as a result of good fire protection. The open hunting and trapping season on otters should be confined to that period of the year when the otter fur is prime. A month during the spring following the breakup of the ice seems to be the period when most of the states allow trapping of the river otter, if there is any limit on the trapping of this fur bearer. For the past several years, Michigan has allowed a combined trapping take of 10 beaver and otter pelts, 2 of which may be otters.

SEA OTTER

FUR FACTS

Both historically and as a fur bearer the sea otter is one of the most interesting and spectacular of the fur animals. While the fur is now nonavailable, whenever a pelt of this fur bearer does appear on the open market it brings a fabulous price. Recently one pelt brought $1,400 at a London auction sale (7 *g.r.*, 12).

The early exploitation of the sea otter along the western North American coast is very closely linked with that of the fur seal. Many people who view with alarm the covetous attitude of Russia in relation to the resources of the United States at the present time are probably unaware that as early as 1700 Russia had an eye on the fur resources of this continent. Peter the Great and Catherine of Russia sent Vitus Bering to the western shores of North America to chart the coast and obtain sea otter skins. The wealth of furs obtained by Bering became famous, and immediately other countries sent expeditions to capture this most prized of furs of the then new land. Russia's later settlement of Alaska was no doubt made possible by these early expeditions (7 *g.r.*).

The fur of the sea otter is very deep and velvety, with a fine fiber and a very silky texture. In color it is bluish-blackish brown sprinkled with fine white hairs which give the fur a silvery appearance. The skins are uniformly well-covered with fur and are large; the skin, without the tail, measures 4 to 5 feet in length (7 *g.r.*).

Since 1911 by international treaty, the hunting and taking of the sea otter has been forbidden in North American waters, so only a few skins come on the fur market, and these are from foreign countries.

GEOGRAPHICAL DISTRIBUTION

The range of the sea otter embraces that part of the northern Pacific Ocean that is neither land nor entirely water but a combination of both. This animal lives along the rocky shores of both North America and Asia in a roughly horseshoe-shaped line extending from southern California northward along North America and the Alaskan islands and westward to Asia as far south as the Commander Islands, Kamchatka Peninsula, and the Kuril Islands.

FIG. 10-2. Sea otters on Amchitka Island, Alaska. Sea otters are found along the Pacific border. Once very abundant, they were hunted to near extinction. Today, under protection, they are on the increase. (*Robert D. Jones, Jr., U.S. Fish and Wildlife Service.*)

Originally this watery domain was probably quite complete as far as occupation by sea otters was concerned. After 300 years of fur hunting, however, only a few scattered colonies remained throughout the entire range. Since 1911, when legal protection was given, the animals in these few remaining colonies have slowly increased in numbers and are now once again appearing in portions of their range in which they had been exterminated by trapping. Given another hundred years or so of complete protection, the original range may possibly be well populated and quite continuous.

The total numbers of this fur bearer are low but are on the increase. According to the U.S. Fish and Wildlife Service there are now about

8,000 sea otters along the Aleutian Islands and the coast of California (1, 4). The line of suitable habitat extends for 5,000 miles. It should be possible to maintain 10 sea otter per mile of sea coast. If its habitat were filled to capacity, it would hold 50,000 or more of this animal. The increase in numbers of sea otters in the past 10 years has been promising. Let us hope that the strict protection against exploitation continues until they are again plentiful.

ANATOMY, LIFE HISTORY, AND ECOLOGY

The sea otter is a well-coordinated machine as to body covering, muscles, nerves, and intelligence. The forefeet are well furred and have padded toes and palm, while the hind feet are broad and webbed. The sea otter lives most of its life in the water, so its anatomy is constructed for this type of habitat. It is most agile in getting along in the sea among the beds of kelp and rocks of its surroundings. It can walk on land but seems not to be very agile nor very happy there.

No very clear accounts are given in the literature of the breeding habits of the sea otter. Probably mating varies with the latitude and may therefore be later in the Aleutian Islands than farther south. Fisher (9) observed a sea otter herd from April 14 to September 6 and states that there were attempts at mating for the entire period. Mating activity seemed to be stimulated by rough stormy weather. Cahalane (15 *g.r.*) gives the gestation period as 9 months. One young is born at a time so that the increase of a herd is slow even under the most favorable conditions. The young are unable to swim at birth and in fact must be cared for during several months before they are able to look out for themselves (10). Cahalane (15 *g.r.*) indicates that the young do not take solid food until 6 months old and that a sea otter pup continues to nurse until the animal is a year old.

The activities of the sea otter consist mostly of swimming and diving. This fur bearer is adjusted to a life in the ocean and seldom lives on land. In fact, the sea otter is so adjusted that it sleeps, eats, rests, plays, brings forth and raises its young, protects itself, and dies, all in the turbulent surroundings of a wind-blown sea.

The sea otter uses seaweeds or kelp for cover. In fact, the vast kelp beds of the Pacific Ocean are its typical habitat. This vegetation is used to anchor the otter in place as it lies on its back in the water. The animal wraps the stems around itself so it stays in one place as the waves roll and the winds blow. The kelp beds probably have a modifying effect on the wave action and act as a net to keep a herd together.

The area of the ocean within which sea otters live must be limited as to its depth, since the food of these animals must be obtained from the bottom and therefore must be within their diving distance. Also, when storms become too severe, rocky outcrops must be available to be used for protection from wind and waves.

Sea otters are gregarious. Herds of varying numbers are found together and seem to be well suited to living in close proximity to one another.

Food. The sea urchin (*Strongylocentrotus drobachiensis* or *S. franciscanus*) is the big item in the food of the sea otter in both its northern and southern habitat. Along the California coast the red abalone (*Haliotis rufescens*) is a favorite food. Other items include mollusks, chitons, crabs, snails, rock oysters, and seaweeds. Fish are eaten only sparingly and possibly only when found dead (10, 19).

The sea otter brings its food to the surface and uses its chest as a table. Here it dines with all the finesse of a gourmand. In case the food is encased in a protective shell, the sea otter either bites a hole in the shell or cracks it on a rock which has been brought from the bottom of the sea for that purpose. Sea urchins, mollusks, and crabs are probably plentiful along the shores of the ocean so food is seldom a problem.

GENERAL

Apparently the sea otter has few enemies except the killer whale and man that are able to destroy any considerable numbers. Under complete protection numbers of sea otters have increased all along the western shore lines of North America. At one time sea otters were taken in prodigious numbers throughout this long coast line, and San Francisco Bay was one of the choice spots for taking pelts during the early days.

Exploitation for fur has been the major cause of the reduction in numbers of the sea otters. Protection has now brought back this beautiful animal all along the western coast of North America.

There is little conflict between the sea otter and the commercial-fishing interests. Because of this fact it is hoped that the sea otter may continue to receive protection until such a time as a fur crop may be harvested without harm to the herd.

REFERENCES

1. Anonymous. 1936. Raising otters in captivity. *U.S. Dept. Agr. Bur. Biol. Survey, Leaflet* BS-75.
2. ———. 1939. A survey of the annual fur catch of the United States. *U.S. Dept. Agr. Bur. Biol. Survey, Wildlife Res. and Mangt. Leaflet* BS-140.
3. ———. 1944. Annual fur catch of the United States. *U.S. Fish and Wildlife Serv., Wildlife Leaflet* 253.

4. ———. 1950. The Alaska sea otter has been saved. *Outdoor Life.* **87**(12).
5. Ashbrook, Frank G. 1951. Annual fur catch of the United States. *U.S. Fish and Wildlife Serv., Wildlife Leaflet* 315.
6. Bradt, G. W. 1945. What about the otter? *Mich. Conserv.* **14**(2):4, 10.
7. ———. 1946. The otter—playboy of streams and lakes. *Mich. Conserv.* **15**(6):6.
8. East, Ben. 1938. He raises retrieving otters. *Outdoor Life.* (82):44–45, 55.
9. Fisher, Edna M. 1939. Habits of the southern sea otter. *Jour. Mammal.* **20**(1):21–36.
10. ———. 1940. Early life of a sea otter pup. *Jour. Mammal.* **21**(2):132–137.
11. Green, H. U. 1932. Observations on the occurrence of otter in the Riding Mountain National Park, Manitoba, in relation to beaver life. *Canad. Field Nat.* **46**(9):204–206.
12. Jones, Robert D., Jr. 1951. Present status of the sea otter in Alaska. *Trans. 16th North Amer. Wildlife Conf.* Pp. 376–383.
13. Lagler, Karl F., and Burton T. Ostenson. 1942. Early spring food of the otter in Michigan. *Jour. Wildlife Mangt.* **6**(3):244–254.
14. Liers, Emil E. 1951. Notes on the river otter (*Lutra canadensis*). *Jour. Mammal.* **32**(1):1–9.

CHAPTER 11

Raccoons

Procyon lotor

FUR FACTS

The fur of the raccoon is used for both coats and coat trimmings. In the 1920's coonskin coats were very popular with college students. Ladies' sport coats are still made from the thinner-furred peltries.

The fur of the raccoon is long with the darkest color, longest guard hairs, and thickest underfur on the back. The sides are lighter in color and the belly is usually both light in color and thin. Great variations in both color and density of the fur fibers exist in pelts from different parts of this country. The largest and silkiest pelts come from Minnesota. New York and New England also produce a fine silky type of raccoon pelt. Pelts with long silky guard hairs are used almost entirely for trimmings (7 *g.r.*). Raccoons from salt marshes are likely to be reddish.

GEOGRAPHICAL DISTRIBUTION

The coonskin cap with its banded tail hanging down behind was the favorite headgear of the pioneer. The raccoon was most used with the advent of the automobile, when robes and coats were needed for outdoor riding. During the 5 years just past, however, long furs including raccoon have been out of style, so that the demand has diminished to nearly zero. As a result of less trapping pressure, raccoons have increased. At the present time, because of a demand for sheared raccoon coats, the demand for pelts of this animal is increasing.

While the popularity of the raccoon as a trapper's item has diminished, the 'coon has not lost any of its attraction for the 'coon hunter. Raccoon hunting is a rugged sport because it must be done at night. The equipment consists of warm clothing, 'coon dogs, lanterns, and an abundance of fortitude. According to Bradt (3), Michigan, 'coon hunters took a total of 75,000 raccoons in 1945.

The range of the raccoon is given by Anthony (4 *g.r.*) as most of North America south of 50 degrees latitude. This does not include desert areas or land totally devoid of timber, not having at least some substitute for trees for nest dens and escape cover. Abundant water also appears to be necessary for raccoon habitation since much of the food of raccoon comes from a water habitat. For this reason this animal is seldom found far from moist places.

FIG. 11-1. Eastern raccoon, a highly sensitive and intelligent animal. As a fur bearer its value waxes and wanes with the fashions. The 'coon is also an excellent game animal. (*LeRoy Berge.*)

Raccoons have not only survived the change from virgin forests to open farm lands, but have in places been benefited by the addition of crops like corn to their former environment (18).

ANATOMY, LIFE HISTORY, AND ECOLOGY

The raccoon is largely nocturnal. Frequently, a family of 'coons will live in a neighborhood for years without their presence being suspected. Imprints of long, sensitive fingers in the muddy margins of streams or ponds give evidence of their presence, and a smooth, well-worn entrance in a good-sized cavity of a neighboring tree will give further proof of where they spend most of their daylight hours.

The raccoon has a round body, long banded tail, short legs, and a coat of gray-brown fur. The nose is pointed and the ears erect. The soles of the feet are naked and very sensitive. Much of the selection of food found in the mud or water is done through the medium of the feeling ability these animals have in the soles of their feet.

The 'coon is capable of taking on a layer of fat that helps to maintain it during the winter. Northern raccoons are heavier than the more southern species. They are heaviest in the fall previous to cold weather when food is most abundant. A 30-pound animal may be considered as an extremely large northern wild raccoon (17). Whitney gives 23 pounds as the average weight of Maine raccoons (17). In general, raccoons are probably much lighter in weight than the above figures suggest. Schoonmaker (60 *g.r.*) gives an average weight of 10 pounds for New York raccoons, which is probably a more representative weight for the central part of the raccoon's range. California 'coons average from 10 to 13 pounds (28 *g.r.*). In a study of Michigan raccoons, Stuewer, (13) found that the largest female handled weighed 18 pounds and 6 ounces, and the largest male, 21 pounds and 10 ounces. Both weights were taken in August when food was plentiful.

Raccoons are generally considered promiscuous in their sex relations. While raccoon populations are about equally divided as to sex, in 8 litters handled by Stuewer in Michigan (13) the females outnumbered the males 19 to 14, or a ratio of 42.4 per cent males to 57.6 per cent females. Stuewer (14) likewise found that the male and female generally live in separate dens. This investigator further noted that raccoons in the wild are promiscuous, the male traveling from den to den looking for receptive females. Mating takes place during January, February, or March, and probably also later in the spring. In Michigan, the mating period extends from the first week of February to the first week of March (13). Broods are produced once a year. Seton (61 *g.r.*) believes the females breed when they are a year old, and the males may also be capable of breeding at this age. However, later evidence indicates that males do not breed until they are 2 years old (12 *g.r.*, 13). The gestation period is 63 days (8, 13, 61 *g.r.*), and the litter varies from 3 to 7 in number, with an average of 4. The young may be born as early as March, but most of them are born in April and May or even later in the summer (4, 7, 12, 13, 17). Bissonnette *et al.* (2) were able to induce raccoons to breed in holding pens in December by exposing them to additional light from October 10 to December 17. These light-induced matings produced young 40 days earlier than is common for the wild.

Suckling of the young continues for 8 to 10 weeks (13), during which time the young follow the mother on her nightly foraging excursions. The young seem to depend on the mother to teach them the "ways of the world" and may go into dormancy in the family nest with the mother the first winter after birth. Whitney (17) believes that the litters which are born late in the summer are the result of later mating when the mid-winter mating has not occurred.

The evidence as to the denning together of several raccoons is not clear. Stuewer (14) states that mature animals usually den alone but does not indicate whether a mother 'coon and the young of the previous spring den together. He does state, however, that on one occasion 2 juvenile males were found together in one tree den. In Missouri as many as 9 'coons were taken from 1 tree. They were of assorted sizes and sexes. Of 102 taken from den trees, only 32 were found alone (16).

Types of dens may vary, but cavities in old trees are favorite den sites and are used in preference to others when available. Large old trees are the most likely to have suitable cavities, and the tree species is apparently not too important. The height of the den above the ground may vary from 10 to 60 feet, but the more highly elevated openings are preferred. All occupied dens in one Michigan study were within 900 feet of some source of water (14). Nest materials consist only of the decayed wood in the cavity and are not added to by the raccoon. Crevices in rocks, soil dens, and hollow logs may be used even though tree dens are available. The raccoon sleeps during the winter period but does not hibernate.

Movements. The movements of 'coons vary with conditions of the daytime refuge and the proximity of feeding grounds. Where the two are in close relationship, the animal's travels are short. Where hunters with dogs come upon the fresh trail of a 'coon, its travels may lead a tortuous route back to the seclusion of a tree den or a retreat among the rocks. This course of travel may vary from 1 to 2 miles, with some animals ranging as far as 15 miles in a single night (28 *g.r.*). Trappers contend that the raccoon may make a definite circuit, but will take several days or even a week to complete it. This may be a seasonal procedure when the family is grown and the animals are free to roam where food is plentiful. Certainly the extent of the nightly travels is more limited when the adult must return to a resident den each day to care for the young. Raccoons may hunt in pairs or families during the fall and singly at other times. Stuewer (14) describes two types of raccoon movements, namely, (1) nightly forages for food and tree dens, (2) those involving young 'coons leaving their home dens and looking for new territories. The maximum travel during this latter activity was found to be 27 miles, but the average was approximately 8 miles.

Cover Requirements. Raccoons are not found to any marked degree in the coniferous or in the hardwood forests, but probably prefer the latter (10). Deciduous trees of advanced age are of dual value to the 'coon; they furnish a home den and at the same time produce desirable food. Coons are also found in grassy marshes where trees are lacking. The alternative to hardwood trees for dens is crevices in the rocks of outcropping ridges. Giles (5, 6) mentions this as being true in Iowa, and it is most certainly true in the Connecticut Valley of Massachusetts. It is probably likewise true elsewhere.

Other requirements of an optimum raccoon habitat as listed by Stuewer (14) are sufficient tree dens, a permanent water supply, and food.

The water requirement is closely related to food. Water habitats may

FIG. 11-2. A raccoon searching for food on a marsh border. (*C. J. Henry and M. C. Hammond, U.S. Fish and Wildlife Service.*)

be marshes, ponds, lake borders, or streams. The streams may be sluggish creeks, or cold, swift-running brooks.

Food. The northern raccoon sleeps during the winter and thus escapes the season of most undesirable weather conditions and least abundant food supplies. In the south the animal continues to forage throughout the winter season (9). Like the bear, it preserves the abundant harvest of each fall under its skin in the form of fat. Another characteristic favorable to the 'coon is that it eats both plant and animal products. Of the plant foods, corn appears to be its favorite as soon as it is available in August as "roasting ears." This is true in widely scattered locations as Maine (10), New York (8), Iowa (5, 6), and California (5, 6, 8, 10, 28 *g.r.*). The origin of Iowa 'coon food is 72.73 per cent plant and 22.27 per cent animal for all seasons (5, 6). Dearborn (20 *g.r.*) found that crayfish ranked highest among the various food materials recognizable in the feces of southern Michigan raccoons. Of the food materials of plant origin, oats and corn were found to comprise slightly over 20 per cent, and cherries and berries over 12 per cent. When available, fruits, including berries, plums, and apples, are eaten extensively during the fall as well as beechnuts, buckwheat, and even melons (1, 5, 28 *g.r.*). Of the various animal foods, crayfish, frogs, snakes, and mollusks are staple summer foods. Mice, shrews, insects, and earthworms are also eaten when other foods are too difficult to obtain. Raccoons like birds and have been known to take chickens that were roosting in trees. Crippled ducks are cited as being one of the favorite 'coon fall foods in the vicinity of California duck clubs. Raccoons may also prey on nesting ducks when they can get them. Hamilton (8) lists fish and muskrat remains as found in the droppings of New York 'coons. Yeager and Rennels (19) report the fall food of raccoons in river bottomlands in southern Illinois as follows: vegetable matter, 72 per cent, animal matter, 28 per cent. More than half of the yearly diet of raccoons in eastern Texas consists of acorns and crayfish, with the remaining food items comprising a large number of plant and animal products.

Population Density. It is difficult to estimate a raccoon population on an area basis because of the fact that there are portions on a range which have little or nothing to do with its over-all welfare. Thus, a family of raccoons may have their den in a ledge or rock and travel a mile up and down a brook in the adjoining farm lands. Occasionally, the family may cut across to an adjoining marsh or hunt insects or mice in a neighboring orchard. In the fall, a nearby corn field may be raided for food. Seton (61 *g.r.*) mentions a pair of raccoons to the square mile, or 1 animal to 320 acres. He also refers to 3 'coons trapped and some left (possibly 2) on 100 acres, or a raccoon to 20 acres. Johnson (10) found a population density of 1 raccoon to 800 acres in Maine and quotes Williams as finding a 'coon to 100 acres in Ohio. Yeager and Rennels (19) report the taking on the average of almost 43 raccoons per square mile on 4 square miles of river bottomland in southern Illinois, or a trapping take of 1 raccoon for each 16 acres. One hundred and two raccoons were taken alive from trees in 102 acres of refuge in Missouri for restocking purposes. It was estimated this was 60 per cent of the raccoons on the area. This would indicate a denning population of more than 1 raccoon per acre (16).

Stuewer (14) studied raccoon populations intensively in two types of land in southern Michigan during 2 years with the following results: upland, 16 to 36 acres per raccoon before hunting and 31 acres per raccoon after hunting on marsh habitat; 16 to 46 acres per raccoon before hunting on flood plains and uplands (14).

MANAGEMENT

Census. It is relatively easy to determine the presence of raccoons in a locality by their tracks in the dust of a road or in the muddy margins of a pond or stream. This visual-examination method does not tell how many are present, but a careful observer can make a close estimate, if time is available to examine all the watercourses and borders of lakes, marshes, and ponds. Johnson (10) used a hound in hunting raccoons on roughly 10 square miles of 'coon territory in Maine and trailed 8 coons during the season. He was not sure whether some of these represented repeats. Because of the nocturnal nature of the raccoon and the almost inaccessible territory in which it is found, the use of a dog is probably one of the most reliable census methods now available.

The handling of a 'coon dog and the night hunting of this animal is an operation which requires experience and fortitude. Experienced 'coon hunters gather a wealth of experience as to the habits and actions of raccoons over a period of years. No amateur can hope to handle a dog or operate with much success. Thus, the observation method is likely to be more satisfactory for the neophyte. Stuewer (14) used the method of trapping, tagging, and retrapping, and calculating the population, a method already described.

Food and Cover Developments. Management procedures to improve the habitat for raccoons are limited to one or two specific procedures and a number of more general ones. Any process which creates or stabilizes a water supply in a 'coon territory or improves the general fertility of a region is likely to increase the food available for all the animals of the region. Thus, the creation of shallow marsh ponds will increase the food for raccoons. Johnson (10) attempted to improve the summer and fall food for raccoons in the vicinity of Weld, Maine, by planting corn and buckwheat in patches and by stocking ponds with frogs and a stream with crayfish. Of these improvement measures only the planting of corn gave evidence that it accomplished its purpose. Corn is so well-liked by raccoons and so universally used by these animals that the planting of this appears to be one of the few procedures which can be effectively applied. Corn should be planted in a location near a watercourse that is a natural feeding ground for 'coons and in such a manner as to produce good ears as early as the season will permit. Application of 300 to 500 pounds of balanced commercial fertilizer per acre and sufficient cultivation to control the weeds is recommended.

Cover-improvement measures include the maintenance of den trees and the development of a forest growth along watercourses. Den trees are usually decadent maple or oak trees, or possibly other hardwood species that are allowed to attain an age when cavities develop. The location of these overmature veteran trees may be in a stand of timber where they have been left after logging operations either because they were not worth removing or because of their value for wildlife. Frequently den trees may develop from trees left along fence rows, or watercourses, or on hillsides to prevent soil erosion. Old apple trees on abandoned farm lands may also serve as ideal raccoon dens. Where natural dens are lacking, artificial den boxes may be supplied. Boxes for this

FIG. 11-3. The woods border and corn patch provide a favored summer feeding site for raccoons.

purpose may be made of 1-inch thick lumber, and should be 14 inches square by 36 inches high, with a watertight roof and a hole 4 by 6 inches next to the roof. These den boxes may be placed 25 to 40 feet above the ground. Sawdust should be placed in the bottom of the boxes (15).

Miscellaneous Management Procedures. Several legal measures may be necessary to prevent the extermination of this fur bearer in localized areas. One of these regulations should be a law to prevent the destruction of den trees by raccoon hunters. Restocking of raccoons in uninhabited territory is feasible and is now being practiced by many progressive state conservation departments (3, 11). Ohio, Wisconsin, and Missouri have developed such restocking programs to a high degree and are releasing breeding stock of excellent quality in sections of these respective states suited to 'coon habitation. The process of raising raccoons for other than restocking unoccupied territory is too expensive to be practicable, however. The fact that both 'coon hunters and trappers are interested in the raccoon may mean an unusually heavy pressure on this animal. One month for an open raccoon season is sufficient.

The hunting and trapping season should open late enough in the year to allow the young of the current year to develop to maturity and yet close before the breeding season begins. Hamilton (8) recommends an open season for the northern states of between November 15 and December 31 and sufficiently short to allow a take of only the annual surplus.

REFERENCES

1. Baker, Rollin H., Coleman C. Newan, and Ford Wilke, 1945. Food habits of the raccoon in eastern Texas. *Jour. Wildlife Mangt.* **9**(1):45–48.
2. Bissonnette, Thomas Hume, and Albert C. Csech. 1937. Fertile matings of raccoons in December instead of February induced by increasing daily periods of light. *Proc. Royal Soc. London,* Ser. *B.* **122**(827):246–254.
3. Bradt, G. W. 1946. The raccoon–masked clown of the woodlots. *Mich. Conserv.* **15**(8):6.
4. George, John L., and Merle Stitt. 1951. March litters of raccoons (*Procyon lotor*). *Jour. Mammal.* **32**(2):218.
5. Giles, LeRoy W. 1939. Fall food habits of the raccoon in central Iowa. *Jour. Mammal.* **20**(1):68–70.
6. ———. 1940. Food habits of the raccoon in eastern Iowa. *Jour. Wildlife Mangt.* **4**(4):375–382.
7. Goldman, Edward A. 1950. Raccoons of North and Middle America. *U.S. Fish and Wildlife Serv., North Amer. Fauna,* 60.
8. Hamilton, W. J., Jr. 1936. The food and breeding habits of the raccoon. *Ohio Jour. Sci.* **36**(3):131–140.
9. Heinold, George. 1950. Burglar in the treetops. *The Saturday Evening Post.* **222**(41):34, 127–128.
10. Johnson, R. H. 1939. Life history and management of raccoons in Maine. Unpublished M.S. thesis, University Maine, Orono.
11. Preble, Norman A. 1941. Raccoon management in central Ohio. *Ohio State Univ. Coop. Wildlife Res. Sta. Release* 161.
12. Sanderson, Glen C. 1951. Breeding habits and a history of the Missouri raccoon population from 1941 to 1948. *Trans. 16th North Amer. Wildlife Conf.* Pp. 445–461.
13. Stuewer, Frederick W. 1943*a*. Reproduction of raccoon in Michigan. *Jour. Wildlife Mangt.* **7**(1):60–73.
14. ———. 1943*b*. Raccoons: their habits and management in Michigan. *Ecol. Monog.* **13**(2):203–257.
15. ———. 1948. Artificial dens for raccoons. *Jour. Wildlife Mangt.* **12**(3):296–301.
16. Twichell, Allen Reed, and Herbert H. Dill. 1949. One hundred raccoons from one hundred acres. *Jour. Mammal.* **30**(2):130–133.
17. Whitney, Leon F. 1931. The raccoon and its hunting. *Jour. Mammal.* **12**(1):29–38.

18. ———. 1933. The raccoon—some mental attributes. *Jour. Mammal.* **14**(2): 108–114.
19. Yeager, Lee E., and R. G. Rennels. 1943. Fur yield and autumn foods of the raccoon in Illinois river bottom lands. *Jour. Wildlife Mangt.* **7**(1): 45–60.

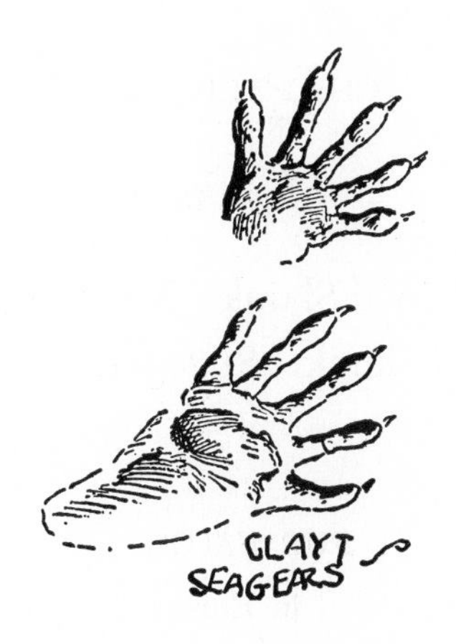

CHAPTER 12

Skunks

Striped Skunk *Mephitis*
Spotted Skunk *Spilogale putorius*

FUR FACTS

Skunk furs have long been used in Europe for coats, trimmings, and linings, and fur scarves. In America, buyers of furs formerly discriminated against the use of furs from skunks because of the belief that it gave off the characteristic odor of this animal. This misconception was gradually dispelled, and the fur came into general use for coats, jackets, and for trimmings, until the style of furs turned to the short fur recently. Since that time, the price of skunk pelts has been very low, in fact becoming so small that many trappers do not consider it worth while to skin a skunk (7 *g.r.*).

GEOGRAPHICAL DISTRIBUTION

Of all our wild animals none has adapted its mode of living to a changing environment so completely as the skunk. Its system of gas warfare is nearly perfect. Along with this excellent weapon, the skunk has both a nervous system and a diet which allows it to profit by its proximity to man. The sole exception to the rule of adaptability is its stupid habit of wandering on the highways at night where it is no match for a speeding automobile.

Three genera of skunks are found in North America: the large striped and hooded skunks, *Mephitis;* the spotted skunk, *Spilogale;* and the hog-nosed skunk, *Conepatus* (4 *g.r.*).

ANATOMY, LIFE HISTORY, AND ECOLOGY

The eastern skunk is about the size of a cat. Its head is small compared to the body, and its tail is long and bushy. The fur consists of long shiny hair, the under part of the body being black or dark brown with two white stripes of varying widths which meet at the top of the neck and extend along the sides of the animals. The scent glands are located on both sides of the anal opening and are connected to the anus by small canals. The claws are well developed, being used to dig burrows and for scraping away the grass and leaves in search of insects and mice.

The spotted skunk is smaller than the striped skunk and has a greater variety of black-and-white markings. The white stripes are narrower and

FIG. 12-1. Striped skunk looking for insects. The skunk is an inveterate insect feeder. During recent years its fur has been of low market value. (*Rex Gary Schmidt, U.S. Fish and Wildlife Service.*)

extend along the sides, hips, and over the head. The hog-nosed skunk is about the size of the striped skunk with markings of white along the entire back and with a bare hoglike muzzle and a less bushy tail.

The striped adult skunk varies in weight from 3 to 8 pounds, the average being about 5 pounds.

Breeding Characteristics. Evidence as to the age at which skunks breed seems to be lacking. Presumably females, and also possibly males, may mate during the winter following their birth or at less than 1 year of age. Eastern striped skunks go into dormancy as soon as it gets cold in the fall and do not emerge until the following February or later. Some of the males wander around intermittently all winter, but the majority appear to come out in February and early March in a search of females with which to breed. Mating often takes place in the den, under buildings, or in the open. It is believed that the females give off intermittent discharges of scent during the mating season, possibly to attract males to the den.

Allen (3) believes that the striped skunk is polygamous. In digging out 26 burrows containing skunks, he found some with both males and females. In 2 of these burrows, 1 male was found cohabiting with 10 females.

Both Seton (61 *g.r.*) and Allen (3) state that female skunks more than a year old come into the breeding condition in mid-February and that females born the previous spring, or less than a year of age, are ready for breeding in mid-March. Wight (13) believes, as indicated from controlled experiments and from the similarity in the size of litters of different females, that mating takes place during a very restricted period. Males may breed one or more females, depending on whether the females are available and compatible.

The gestation period varies from 62 to 72 days, the litters of eastern and northern skunks arriving during the first half of May, in late May, or in early June, respectively.

The number of young in a litter of striped skunks varies from 6 to 12, with the average near 5 or 6. Allen (3) gives the average of 17 litters as slightly less than 6 young. This is probably typical of this species.

The rearing of the young is apparently the responsibility of the mother, the male not only being indifferent to their care but actually antagonistic. The female is a watchful and devoted mother and will defend the young with her life if necessary. The young are not brought out of the home den until they are 4 or 5 weeks old, at which time they are able to follow the mother and to search for food for themselves. The period of maternal care apparently ceases during the fall when the young can seek their own food and care for themselves. Possibly some of the young spend the winter with the parents, but this may be more a matter of chance than a fixed habit.

Movements and Cover Requirements. Little is known about the extent of the travel habits of skunks. The skunk is nocturnal, preferring to travel in the twilight hours of morning or evening, the daybreak hours of the morning, or after dark. The numbers of dead skunks seen on highways indicate they are not fearful of open spaces and use these frequently. Male skunks seem to travel farther during the breeding season than at other times and probably travel more than do the females. Seton (61 *g.r.*) and Hamilton (8) give a half mile as the probable range of an individual skunk. Allen (2) found that a mile was the extreme limit of the known range of any individuals handled by him. California striped skunks are said to travel from ¾ to 1 mile from protective dens during their nightly foraging travels (28 *g.r.*).

Ideal cover for skunks must include a suitable place for retreat during the coldest part of the winter and for protection during the daytime at other seasons. Winter retreats may include cavities under buildings, hollow logs, crevices in rock piles, and dens in the ground (4). The last mentioned type may have been dug by woodchucks or by skunks. Summer cover consists of grass or other herbaceous and shrubby vegetation (4, 11, 12).

FIG. 12-2. Spotted skunk. The spotted skunk, several species of which are found in the South, Middle West, and Far West, is a smaller animal than the striped skunk. (*John E. Schwartz, U.S. Forest Service.*)

The ideal habitat as originally listed by Seton (61 *g.r.*) and restated by Allen (2) is as follows:

He loves variety—dry, rolling land, well watered, and alternated with sun and shade. In open fields, mixed with dense cover, he finds his ideal home. Croplands, grassy cover, spots of cover alternating with open fields, trees, and shrubs all well interspersed gives the skunk a habitat which fits its needs to a high degree.

Food. The skunk is omnivorous, living mostly on flesh or insects and vegetation. It should be borne in mind that skunks are rather slow in their movements, so probably are not normally able to catch an animal as large as a pheasant or mature cottontail except by chance. The predilection of the skunk to eat carrion may confuse the interpretation of skunk food habits, unless food data indicate the condition as well as the kind of flesh found in the stomachs of these creatures.

The food diet of skunks in New York, as well as in Iowa and Michigan, runs heavily to insects during the summer months (1, 5, 7, 9). Mammals, principally mice, rats, and shrews, constitute an important part of the diet during the late-fall and early-spring months. It will live exclusively on blackberries or blueberries in season.

From a study of California skunks, Grinnell *et al.* (28 *g.r.*) conclude that 10 per cent of the skunk's food is of a sort to render the animal harmful to man, 30 per cent is neutral, and 60 per cent beneficial.

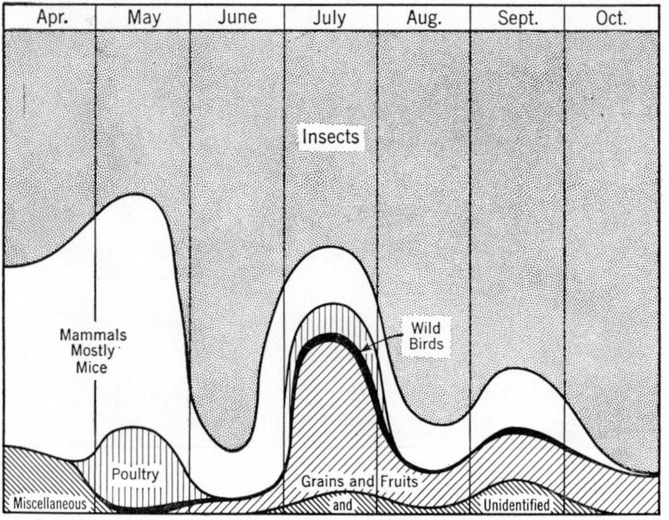

Fig. 12-3. Food taken by the striped skunk (*Mephitis mephitis nigra*) for the period April through October in the eastern United States (19).

The food of skunks in southern Michigan over a period of years is given by Wight (14), and the graph of classes of food by months gives a clear picture of the diet of skunks in that part of their range.

Population Densities and Miscellaneous Habits. Scott and Selko (24 *Foxes*)[1] found 4 skunks per square mile in Boone County, Iowa. The population high in this same locality was 1 skunk to about 6 acres. Allen (3) estimated a winter population of 1 skunk for approximately every 11 acres near Kalamazoo, Michigan. In comparing these 2 skunk population densities, it should be noted that Allen's population is a wintering population of breeding animals and the Iowa figures are breeders plus the

[1] References followed by chapter titles will be found at the end of the chapter referred to.

Table 12-1. A Comparison of the Classes of Food Eaten by Both Striped and Spotted Skunk

Classes of food	Iowa, per cent food materials (10) by volume*		Michigan, per cent class frequency (6), striped skunk
	Spotted skunk	Striped skunk	
Arthropods (insects, etc.)	30.78	64.06	57.34
Mammals	30.66	7.36	10.17
Birds, including eggs	25.14†	6.37	2.46
Vegetables	1.59	4.31	
All other	11.83	17.88	30.03

* Total percentages do not equal 100 in all cases. Data are given as originally published.

† Selko explains that the high percentage of bird remains shown in the table was accounted for by two individuals. Since these bird remains were probably eaten as carrion, they are of little importance as a true average indication of the food diet of the spotted skunk.

young. On the basis of the Iowa estimate, the Michigan summer population would be 1 skunk to about 3 acres.

The habit of winter dormancy by skunks is one of the not uncommon provisions made by nature to protect an animal when environmental conditions are adverse. In the northern part of the skunk range, dormancy begins from October to December, depending on the weather. The den is cleaned out and dry grass is carried in for the winter nest. Sometimes one animal may occupy a den alone, other times many occupy the same den curled up together. Females go into the dens earlier than the males and frequently males may wander out of the dens at any time during the winter. As already mentioned, Allen (3) took as many as 18 skunks from one den in southern Michigan.

Mortality. At birth, a litter of skunks may number as high as 10 or even 12 young. By fall, however, the usual number of young seen with the mother is only 3, or sometimes 4. Great horned owls and owls' nests invariably have a "skunky" odor indicating these large birds prey on their nocturnal neighbors. Foxes, dogs, cats, and automobiles all take a toll of both young and adults.

MANAGEMENT

Skunks are so well able to protect themselves and are so prolific that little worry need be directed in their direction. The loss of skunks on highways is considerable but difficult to prevent.

Many states have no closed season on skunks. This should be remedied to make the open season conform to the period when the fur is prime. Ordinarily this would be from November 1 to February 1 in the northern and eastern states. Digging out of dens should be prohibited, except as a control of skunks by landowners on their land.

Census. In censusing striped skunks in Iowa, Scott and Selko (24 *Foxes*) counted the active skunk dens by sample sections in two counties. The identity of a den was determined by nest material in the runways, tracks, scats, skunk hairs around the den, and the odor of skunk in the vicinity of a den. The number of dens was then converted into total skunks for a known area by multiplying the dens by a figure representing the family group, in this case 7 (5 young and 2 adults). The total census figure was then reduced to number of animals per section, which in this particular census amounted to slightly over 4 per section in 1 county and almost 2 per section in another county. This system requires data of the average number of skunk dens on the samples examined and the average number of surviving young at the time the census is taken.

Time of Trapping. The trapping season should take into consideration the time when the fur is prime and the protection of the females to insure a future fur crop. Since skunks are polygamous, a reduction of males is not detrimental. Likewise, since the females go into the dens before the males in the fall, an open season which is delayed until the majority of females are underground will ensure maximum populations.

REFERENCES

1. Allen, Durward L. 1937. The skunk: a boon or pest? *Mich. Conserv.* **7**(4):3, 9–10.
2. ———. 1938. Ecological studies on the vertebrate fauna of a 500-acre farm in Kalamazoo County, Michigan. *Ecol. Monog.* **8**(3):347–436.
3. ———. 1939. Winter habits of Michigan skunks. *Jour. Wildlife Mangt.* **3**(3):212–228.
4. ——— and Warren W. Shapton. 1942. An ecological study of winter dens, with special reference to the eastern skunk. *Ecology.* **23**(1):59–68.
5. Crabb, Wilfred D. 1941. Food habits of the prairie spotted skunk in southeastern Iowa. *Jour. Mammal.* **22**(4):349–364.
6. Dearborn, Ned. 1932. Foods of some fur-bearing animals in Michigan. *Univ. Mich. School Forestry and Conserv. Bul.* 1.
7. Hamilton, W. J., Jr. 1936. Seasonal foods of skunks in New York. *Jour. Mammal.* **17**(3):240–246.
8. ———. 1937. Winter activity of the skunk. *Ecology.* **18**(2):326–327.
9. Kelker, George Hills. 1937. Insect foods of skunks. *Jour. Mammal.* **18**(2): 164–170.
10. Selko, Lyle F. 1937. Food habits of Iowa skunks in the fall of 1936. *Jour. Wildlife Mangt.* **1**(3–4):70–76.
11. ———. 1938*a*. Notes on the den ecology of the striped skunk in Iowa. *Amer. Midland Nat.* **20**(2):455–463.

12. ———. 1938*b*. Hibernation of the striped skunk in Iowa. *Jour. Mammal.* **19**(3):320–324.
13. Wight, H. M. 1931. Reproduction in the eastern skunk (*Mephitis mephitis nigra*). *Jour. Mammal.* **12**(1):42–47.
14. ———. 1938. Food taken by the eastern skunk. *Pa. Game News.* **9**(3):12–13, 30.

CHAPTER 13

Fishers, Martens, and Wolverines

Fisher *Martes pennanti*
Marten *Martes americana*
Wolverine *Gulo luscus*

FISHER

FUR FACTS

The fur of an eastern fisher taken at the proper time, which is just before the coldest period of winter, is very dense and silky. The color of the fur is a dark brown, becoming darker toward the sides. The guard hairs have an excellent luster, especially on the females, and stand out straight away from the skin. In the East, the fisher is much darker in color than in the West, and in general the females are darker and softer than the males. Fisher furs are used mostly for scarves though a few are made into coats (7 *g.r.*).

GEOGRAPHICAL DISTRIBUTION

The fisher is one of the larger weasels living in the zone of spruce and hardwood trees in the northern parts of the United States and in the high mountain ranges of western United States and Canada. At the present time, this animal is so reduced in numbers as to be almost a novelty in the fur trade; it is rare east of the Mississippi River, although it is increasing in the Northeast. Burt (14 *g.r.*) gives the distribution as the "Northeastern States and Canada west through Saskatchewan and British Columbia and the mountainous states of the Northwest."

ANATOMY, LIFE HISTORY, AND ECOLOGY

The general appearance of the fisher is grizzly to dark brown or brownish black. It is darker on the back and around the caudal region than on the head. The male is more grizzled than the female.

Anthony (4 *g.r.*) describes the size of the fisher as follows: "Males longer than females. Males total length, 36–38 inches, weight 8–12 pounds or up to about 18 pounds as a maximum; weight of females, about 5 pounds." The weight of a male fisher from Essex County, New York, is given as 11 pounds. Grinnell *et al.* (28 *g.r.*) give the weight of the heaviest California male as 10 pounds and female as 5½ pounds.

Little has been added to the knowledge of the breeding habits of the fisher since Seton's description (61 *g.r.*). Pen-reared males and females will mate when 1 year old, but Douglas states no females conceive until 2 years old. Mating takes place during March and April. Males are polygamous and, according to Douglas (14), are very mild mannered at mating time.

FIG. 13-1. The fisher, an upland fur bearer, is an animal found in relatively inaccessible areas. Larger than a mink, it produces fur of high value. Although still rare, it is becoming more abundant. (*N.Y. Conserv.*, 1950.)

The gestation period is long, varying from 327 to 350 days with pen-raised fishers (14). Burt (14 *g.r.*) gives the gestation period as 351 to 358 days. In the spring of 1943, Douglas (14) raised 10 litters in captivity totaling 34 young. He does not give the maximum number to a litter, but it is probably about 5.

Under natural conditions, the nest may be in a hollow stump or tree cavity 30 to 50 feet from the ground, in a hollow log, stump, or even in a rock crevice on the ground. Young fishers follow their mother about and forage for themselves at an early age. One litter is born per year.

During its nocturnal travels the fisher covers a course or range repeatedly, coming back over the same route of travel at intervals of several days, much as do the wolf, wolverine, and otter. Seton gives the interval of appearance as 10 to 15 days and the extent of the circuit of travel as

40 to 100 miles (61 *g.r.*). According to de Vos (12, 13), the male fisher roams more widely than the female.

Cover Requirements. Information as to the relationship of the fisher and its habitat is sadly lacking, primarily because the fisher now exists only in those inaccessible places where investigations are difficult. In the literature the fisher is associated with the pine marten, but actually it is a stronger and more active creature than the latter. While formerly the fisher was found in unbroken tracts of forest lands with inaccessible and

Fig. 13-2. The fisher is a capable tree climber, but its preferred habitat is terrestrial. (*E. J. Zavitz, Ontario Department of Lands and Forests.*)

precipitous topography, in recent years it has invaded agricultural lands in New York State.

In California the fisher is found in the middle-forest belt from 3,500 to 7,500 foot altitudes. In Ontario, according to de Vos (12), both the fisher and marten live and hunt a good deal in the same territory.

Food. Douglas (14) states that the fisher in captivity is as shy of water as the common cat. It will take fish when available, but generally the fisher hunts on dry land in timbered country, following the low, swampy places of its habitat where snakes, frogs, and crayfish are available. Like the pine marten, the fisher eats mice, squirrels, rabbits, nestling birds, and in addition has acquired a technique for killing porcupines. Like the bear, the fisher feeds on the porcupine by going through the quill armor on the poorly protected section along the belly. The quills when eaten do not seem to penetrate the viscera of the fisher, but are passed along the digestive tract lengthwise so as to do little harm. This sturdy animal is also claimed to be more than an equal in a fight with a fox, raccoon, or even a lynx.

Population Densities. Much of the fisher range has been destroyed by logging. In California Grinnell *et al.* (28 *g.r.*) comment that even in the best fisher country one or two of these animals to a township (36 square miles) is about as dense a population as now exists there. Over the entire range, which is not more than one-fourth of the area of California in the rougher and more mountainous parts, one fisher to a hundred square miles is probably more nearly the average. For the 1939–1940 trapping season the total take of fisher for Canada was 2,886 pelts and the average price $48.92 per pelt. Ontario provides about half of this total, with Quebec in second place. It is estimated that the total fisher population in Canada is slightly better than 10,000 animals, or one fisher per 110 square miles of fisher range. It is also believed that the fisher follows a population cycle of about 10 years.

Fishers are on the increase in the northeastern part of the United States. Maine, New Hampshire, New York, and probably Vermont, all have sizable fisher populations. A lack of interest in the long-haired furs and good law enforcement are conditions that have helped to increase their numbers on suitable ranges where a few breeding animals remained (9).

MARTEN

FUR FACTS

The pine marten, or Hudson Bay sable, is the American marten as opposed to the old-world sable or marten. It is a weasel of the coniferous forests having the appearance of a large-sized squirrel. In the eastern marten, the guard hairs and fur fibers are nearly the same length. The color of good eastern pelts ranges from dark brown or bluish black to canary yellow. According to Bachrach (7 *g.r.*) these yellowish-colored pelts are used only after being dyed. The skins are carried mostly pelt out (fur in) and case-handled. Marten fur is used mostly for scarves and neckpieces. A few are used for trimming fur coats and wraps (7 *g.r.*).

GEOGRAPHICAL DISTRIBUTION

Martens live primarily in coniferous forests and are highly specialized in relation to their cover and food requirements. However, the marten in California is found near rock slides where its food, such as alpine chipmunks and rock rabbits, is abundant (28 *g.r.*).

Marten populations have been reduced to a very low point throughout its range owing to the change in the animal's home environment through logging and fires, and also to the apparent ease with which it can be trapped.

The states having populations of marten are Maine, New Hampshire, New York, Colorado, Montana, Idaho, California, Oregon, and Washington. The range includes the coniferous forest belt of both Canada and Alaska. In a review of the take of martens in North America, Yeager (24)

FIG. 13-3. The marten, a denizen of conifer forests in the North and West, produces some of the world's finest fur. Because of the ease with which it can be trapped, the marten is now comparatively rare. (*U.S. Fish and Wildlife Service.*)

indicates that of 10 Canadian provinces and 6 western states only British Columbia shows a sustained yield, and even this shows considerable fluctuation.

ANATOMY, LIFE HISTORY, AND ECOLOGY

The marten is frequently described as about the size of a cat with the climbing abilities of a squirrel. The body is muscular, the legs short, and the tail bushy (16). The weights of martens vary from 2 to 4 pounds (22).

The nest of the marten is usually high up in a tree cavity, well protected from interference from the ground and from inclement weather. Concerning the time of breeding and the length of the gestation period, Ashbrook and Hanson (4, 5, 6) have good evidence that mating takes place during the summer, from the middle of July to the third week in August, and that the gestation period is somewhere between 259 to 275 days. Brassard and Bernard (7) give the gestation period of pen-raised martens as 220–230 days. California martens breed but once a year and the number of young varies from 1 to 4 (28 *g.r.*). Grinnell *et al.* report several groups of female martens examined from October through January in which no embryos were found. This evidence, however, does not refute in any way the findings of Ashbrook and Hanson as to the time of breeding and the length of the gestation period. In Canada, the young are born in the spring—in March or April—and reach mature growth by the end of the first summer. The number of young varies from 1 to 3 (7).

Movements. Apparently under western conditions, the female marten stays close to the den during the period when the young need care, but at other times she may hunt with other martens over a wide territory. The Sierra Nevada martens travel 10 to 15 miles in 1 night and cover a circuit consisting of several times this distance. According to Hawbecker (17), martens have no inherent fear of man and will come in close contact with him if the occasion demands.

Cover and Food Requirements. The life needs of martens are found mostly in rough forested country. While these animals usually remain in forested habitats, they sometimes are seen in the open margins along lakes and on talus slopes and rock slides where conies, squirrels, and mice are living. The type of cover best suited to this creature seems to be mature or decadent conifers where decayed cavities and dense foliage are characteristic of the cover. Much of this animal's food is also found in the coniferous forests, so it naturally stays in that type of environment (20).

Red squirrels are an important food item in Montana, but it also eats mice, varying hares, birds and birds' eggs, snakes, frogs, insects, and any flesh available, including carrion, and also berries and honey (19, 61 *g.r.*). The staple foods of Sierra Nevada martens are mice, wood rats, chipmunks, squirrels, and a few birds. The pinch for food comes during the winter when mice are locked beneath the snow (28 *g.r.*).

A study of the food habits of the marten in the Rocky Mountains of British Columbia, as indicated by the remains found in droppings and in a limited number of stomachs, shows the food of this fur bearer to be predominantly rats and mice rather than of squirrel origin (11).

According to Cowan and MacKay (11), the marten takes a wide variety of food and is probably an opportunist as far as food habits are concerned. Carrion is avoided, and the red squirrel, which is supposed to be the main staple of marten food, is not assiduously hunted, nor is it of great importance as compared to mice, insects and berries. They also comment that if fluctuations of ruffed grouse and varying hare do not serve as marten population controls, which apparently they do not, then the answer to the marten cycle is more deep-seated than simply a question of food abundance and scarcity.

Population Densities. Martens have reached a low point in numbers on the entire North American continent. In the eastern part of the range, only a few still remain in isolated locations. On the western ranges there are apparently a few places where these animals are relatively abundant.

Marshall and Grinnell *et al.* (20, 28 *g.r.*,) indicate that one animal to a square mile is about as densely as martens ever populate a range. Other investigators are quoted as believing 1 marten to 3 square miles is a good estimate of the density of this fur bearer.

Western Canada and Alaska have the greatest residue of this animal at the present time. Alaska harvested a yearly average of 4,314 marten pelts over a period of 16 years (21 *g.r.*). Canada produced 265,680 pelts of marten during the year 1949–1950. This is about half the number harvested during the season 1947–1948, but this decrease may be the effect of a cyclic change in the marten population.

Enemies. Little is known of the ecology of the marten. Within the California range, the chief natural enemies of the marten are golden eagles and horned owls (28 *g.r.*).

MANAGEMENT

There is little that man can do to improve conditions for rare creatures like the marten, fisher, and wolverine except to prevent excessive trapping or killing. Where a remnant of a former population exists, as in the northern sections of Maine, New Hampshire, and New York, a closed season can prevent the legal trapping, but not always the illegal taking of these rare animals. The setting aside of special refuges or the creation of wilderness areas may be a further help in protecting these creatures. Giving a wilderness status to an area, as has been done in many national forests, will allow such forested areas to develop to the climax state and thus provide a suitable habitat for martens (2, 24).

WOLVERINE

FUR FACTS

The fur of the wolverine is coarse and there is little difference in the length of the guard hairs and underfur. The color is brownish black with areas of grizzly-colored fur. The pelts are case-handled with the fur out. The fur is in demand by the natives of the Far North to trim parkas, because the wolverine fur does not accumulate frost. The U.S. Army buys some of these furs for this same purpose.

GEOGRAPHICAL DISTRIBUTION

There are few mammals in the annals of natural history so vividly described with so few reliable available facts as the wolverine. Trappers regard it with awe, and Indians of the Arctic have woven fantastic superstitions about it. It has received a great variety of names, including glutton, skunk bear, Indian devil, and the French-Canadian term "carcajou."

Some of these names are without meaning, while others apparently are derived from the form and habits peculiar to the species (15). Its reputed notorious activities in the trapping regions of the North have made the wolverine "Peck's bad boy" of the animal world, and some trappers have sought to exterminate it to ensure the success of their business.

The wolverine is the sole representative of its genus. Under the careless impact of civilization's heavy heel its numbers have been reduced to a vanishing species in the United States not including Alaska. Here it is as numerous as ever.

FIG. 13-4. Wolverine, the Peck's bad boy of the fur animals. Although an excellent fur bearer in itself, this animal is poorly thought of by trappers because it robs their traps of bait and captured animals. (*LeRoy Berge.*)

Although the wolverine is of circumpolar distribution in both hemispheres, its numbers probably were never very plentiful. During the early settlement of America, wolverines ranged down the Alleghenies to central Pennsylvania and were occasionally seen in Massachusetts, Vermont, and New York, but these disappeared after the early 1800's from even the wild, unsettled parts of those states. On the West Coast, wolverines have been encountered as far south as Walker Pass below Mount Whitney, California. It is of interest to note that there is not a single authentic record of a wild wolverine ever having been seen within the borders of Michigan, often referred to as the Wolverine State.

Today, there are probably less than 100 wolverines existing in the United States outside of Alaska, and most of these are confined to the national forests and national parks of the West.

The number of wolverines trapped in California has averaged between 2 and 3 for a number of years. In 1942 the Hudson's Bay Company made the following statement:[1] "The number of wolverine pelts taken each year in Canada varies from six to seven hundred. The trend during the last 15 years has been downward from 1,500 to a low of 450, with the present collection of 650." In Alaska, the annual catch over a period of 16 years has averaged 420 pelts (21 *g.r.*).

ANATOMY, LIFE HISTORY, AND ECOLOGY

Somewhat larger than a badger, the general appearance of a wolverine is much like that of a bear cub, but the high-arched back and lowered head and tail give the animal the elongated form which characterizes the *Mustelidae*. Anthony (4 *g.r.*) describes the wolverine as measuring 37 to 41 inches in total length with the males slightly larger than females; weights of males are 30 to 35 pounds and females, 22 to 27 pounds. The robust body is supported by rather low, sturdy legs.

Little is known about the life history of the wolverine. However, it is thought that they mate during the month of March, the female bearing 2 to 3, sometimes 5, young that are born in June or early July in a nest of leaves under a ledge of rock or low-hanging tree branch. The task of raising the young is left to the mother and in the fall the young still may be seen following her. By the following spring they are full-grown and ready to shift for themselves (61 *g.r.*).

Cover Requirements. It is generally believed that wolverines need extensive and inaccessible wild-land areas, but they now are, no doubt, restricted to such areas because trappers have not been able to work these strongholds profitably.

With regards to the cover requirements of this animal, Joseph S. Dixon, formerly field naturalist of the U.S. Fish and Wildlife Service, comments as follows:[2]

> . . . in my field work in King's Canyon the summer of 1942 I found that the wolverine appears to be more inclined to inhabit the higher ridges and snowfields. . . . There are times when the wolverine comes well down into the timber. . . . But the wolverine and fisher are frequently found in the warmer south facing slopes and ridges. . . . This may, in a large measure, be due to the fact that food in the form of squirrels and other rodents are more numerous on the warmer south-facing slopes than on the cold northern slopes, especially in spring.

Food. The food of the wolverine is largely flesh, either fresh or tainted depending on which is available, although berries in season are not dis-

[1] Personal letter to Gordon T. Woods, Dec. 22, 1942.
[2] Personal letter to Gordon T. Woods, Mar. 24, 1943.

dained. Seton (61 *g.r.*) includes beavers, caribou, and moose among the prey of the wolverine.

An interesting account of how an abundance of available food may affect wolverine numbers is given by Cabot (8) as follows:

> In 1903 . . . mice were not noticeably plenty. . . . By 1904 mice were distinctly abundant. . . . The wolverine we shot was full of mice. . . . The next year, 1905, was the culminating year of the mice . . . birds, wolves, foxes, wolverines and what not, increased also. . . . In the spring of 1906 the mice disappeared with the snow. . . . Sixty wolverine skins came to Davis Inlet Post that year, where eight or ten would come ordinarily.

Many writers have applied the name glutton to the animal, and indeed there are numerous reports gravely recounting its gastronomic exploits, but actually there is little to show that wolverines are any more greedy than other carnivores (4 *g.r.*, 10).

MANAGEMENT

The length of time this species will survive depends upon the degree of protection afforded it. Already the wolverines within the United States proper have diminished to a few pairs, and most of them are confined to wilderness areas maintained by the U.S. Forest Service and National Park Service in the western half of the country. The lack of existing knowledge of wolverine habits, requirements, and ecology is a handicap to intelligent efforts at its restoration.

Every effort should be made to maintain suitable conditions in places such as the Sequoia National Park and King's Canyon National Park so as to allow rare native wildlife to perpetuate its kind (23).

REFERENCES

1. Anonymous. 1943. Convention between the United States and other American Republics. Nature protection and wildlife preservation in the Western Hemisphere. *Treaty Series* 981. Government Printing Office, Washington, D.C.
2. ———. 1945. Transplanting pine marten. *Mont. Wildlife Bul.* **2**(1):2.
3. Ashbrook, Frank G. 1951. Annual fur catch of the United States. *U.S. Fish and Wildlife Serv., Wildlife Leaflet* 315.
4. ——— and Karl B. Hanson. 1927*a*. Progress report of marten breeding experiments. *U.S. Dept. Agr. Bur. Biol. Surv., Leaflet* Bi-949.
5. ———. 1927*b*. Breeding martens in captivity. *Jour. Hered.* **18**(11):499–503.
6. ———. 1930. The normal breeding season and gestation period of martens. *U.S. Dept. Agr. Cir.* 107.
7. Brassard, J. A., and Richard Bernard. 1939. Observations on breeding and development of marten, *Martes a. americana* (Kerr). *Canad. Field Nat.* **53**(2):15–21.

8. Cabot, William B. 1920. Labrador. Small, Maynard and Company, Boston.
9. Cook, Arthur. 1950. The fisher. *N.Y. Conserv.* **4**(3):24.
10. Coues, Elliott. 1877. Fur-bearing animals: A monograph of North American *Mustelidae. U.S. Dept. Int. Misc. Pub.* 8.
11. Cowan, Ian McT., and R. H. MacKay. 1950. Food habits of the marten (*Martes americana*) in the Rocky Mountain region of Canada. *Canad. Field Nat.* **64**(3):100–104.
12. deVos, Antoon. 1951*a*. Recent findings in fisher and marten ecology and management. *Trans. 16th North Amer. Wildlife Conf.* Pp. 498–507.
13. ———. 1951*b*. Tracking the fisher and marten. *Sylva.* **7**(1):15–19.
14. Douglas, W. D. 1943. Fisher farming has arrived. *Amer. Fur Breeder.* **14**(2):18, 20.
15. Grinnell, George Bird. 1920. As to the wolverine. *Jour. Mammal.* **1**(4): 182–184.
16. Hall, E. Raymond. 1926. The abdominal skin gland of Martes. *Jour. Mammal.* **7**(3):227–229.
17. Hawbecker, Albert C. 1945. Activity of the Sierra pine marten. *Jour. Mammal.* **26**(4):435.
18. Macartney, J. 1947. The fisher. *Sylva.* **3**(6):11–12.
19. Marshall, William H. 1946. Winter food habits of the pine marten in Montana. *Jour. Mammal.* **27**(1):83–84.
20. ———. 1951. Pine marten as a forest product. *Jour. Forestry.* **49**(12):899–905.
21. Schorger, A. W. 1939. Wolverine in Michigan. *Jour. Mammal.* **20**(4):503.
22. Swanson, P. W. 1949. Live trapping of marten. *Sylva.* **5**(6):11–14.
23. Woods, Gordon. 1946. The wolverine. *Nature Mag.* **39**(8):426–428.
24. Yeager, Lee E. 1950. Implications of some harvest and habitat factors on pine marten management. *Trans. 15th North Amer. Wildlife Conf.* Pp. 319–334.

CHAPTER 14

Miscellaneous Fur Bearers

Alaska Fur Seal *Callorhinus alascanus*
Badger *Taxidea taxus*
Opossum *Didelphis virginiana*

FUR FACTS

The Alaska fur seal is of great importance, but except for a few pelts which are taken by the natives of Alaska, all Alaska fur seal pelts are handled entirely by the U.S. government. The badger and opossum are well-recognized members of the native fur bearers of our continent.

The term "Alaska seal" has long been a mark of quality among the wearers of fur. The fur is very fine, dense, and is processed into several colors and two shades of dark brown called "safari" and "matara." In processing, the guard hairs are plucked out and the underfur is sheared to an even depth. The entire pelt is dyed to give a very uniform color to the fur. The skins are large, so that a minimum of cutting and resewing is needed. Seal is used mainly for ladies' coats and to a limited extent for trimmings.

The over-all appearance of the badger is a gray or grizzly brown. This effect results from a combination of colors in the guard hairs and underfur. Badger furs are used for two purposes, namely, to trim ladies' cloth coats and in a fur process termed "pointing." The badger fur used for trimming is of a light gray or brownish-gray color and sets off the colors of cloth fabric well. "Pointing" is the process of inserting and gluing of badger fur fibers into other fur pelts. The fur fibers are dipped in a waterproof glue and inserted into the new position by hand, after blowing the fur aside. In pointing, the fibers are inserted in groups of one, two, or three, the single-fiber process being the most exacting and most expensive. The fur of the badger, which in itself is a low value fur, becomes an item of importance in the making of a high-priced fur (7 *g.r.*).

ALASKA FUR SEAL

GEOGRAPHICAL DISTRIBUTION

Alaska fur seals (*Callorhinus alascanus*) belong to a group of animals that inhabit the north Pacific Ocean and islands along the Bering Sea. Two other species of northern fur seals are found on Russia's Commander and Robben Islands along the Asiatic mainland.

FIG. 14-1. An Alaska fur seal bull and his harem. Breeding grounds are mainly restricted to the bleak rocky shores of St. George and St. Paul, two of the Pribilof Islands, in Bering Straits. (*V. B. Scheffer, U.S. Fish and Wildlife Service.*)

The entire history and mode of living of the Alaska fur seal is interesting and extraordinary. Our first knowledge of this fur bearer of the Pacific was its discovery by Georg Wilhelm Steller, a naturalist who accompanied Vitus Bering's second voyage of exploration to Alaska in 1741 (2). These animals appear mainly on five small islands collectively known as the Pribilof Island group in the Bering Sea off the coast of Alaska. They only frequent these islands during 2 months of the year for the purpose of breeding and bringing forth the young. The remainder of the year—10 months—is spent somewhere in the Pacific Ocean, but just where no one has as yet been able to determine. During their stay on St. Paul, St. George, Walrus, Otter, and Sea Lion Rock Islands, the seals confine themselves to the limited areas of the rocky shore and the bordering sea (13).

For a period of 100 years prior to the time that Alaska was transferred to the United States in 1867, the seals were slaughtered by fur hunters of various nations including the United States. By the turn of the nineteenth century, it was estimated that the numbers of the fur seal had been reduced from an initial population of around 6,000,000 animals to 132,000 animals. Since 1867, the United States through treaties with nations having an interest in fur sealing in the northern Pacific Ocean has taken vigorous measures to prevent this species of fur seal from becoming extinct. One of the most successful measures used in this connection was the enactment around 1893 of a set of rules which prohibited pelagic sealing, *i.e.*, killing the seals in the water. Success in the campaign for the preservation of the Alaska seal herd was assured, however, in 1911 when a treaty was signed between the United States, Great Britain, Russia, and Japan in which it was agreed to abolish sealing on the high seas for 15 years and which furthermore gave the United States sole custody of the fur seals of the Pribilof Islands. In return for relinquishment of their interest in pelagic sealing, Japan and Great Britain were each to receive in the future 15 per cent of any land-sealing harvest. The treaty of 1911 continued in effect until the summer of 1941, when Japan abrogated it just previous to the attack against Pearl Harbor. The present treaty protecting the Alaska fur seal is between Canada and the United States. The latter country still retains full guardianship over the seal herd and pays Canada 20 per cent of the annual fur seal harvest return (6, 13).

ANATOMY, LIFE HISTORY, AND ECOLOGY

Seals are round slick-appearing animals that are better adapted to living in the water than on the land, having four flipperlike appendages in place of feet. The body is covered with a thick fur and with a coat of fat under the skin to keep the seal warm. The fur has coarse guard hairs and thick underfur that appears black on the upper parts and gray or reddish-colored on the undersides. The mature male at about 6 years of age is approximately 6 feet long and on land stands 4 feet high. It weighs from 4 to 6 hundred pounds. The females are much smaller and lighter in weight.

Breeding Characteristics. Fur seals have a most complicated system of social behavior during the breeding season. This occurs as they assemble on the breeding islands in the Bering Sea. The breeding males, or bulls, arrive first and take positions along the shore during April and May. There seems to be some competition for the most favorable positions, and the strongest males get the best territories. As the females, or cows, arrive later in the season, each male defends his particular part of the beach and induces as many females as possible to become a part of his household. After a female has once joined a harem, she cannot change her mind and is treated pretty roughly by the head of the house if she attempts to stray across into the domain of another male. These harems number 20 to 30 females and occasionally up to a hundred or more. Cahalane (15 *g.r.*) states that a 6-year-old male has the smallest number of females in the harem, 3 or 4, and that the older males have the greatest number of females.

The female breeds at 2 years of age and is pregnant when she arrives at the beach of the breeding grounds. After several days, the pups, or young, are born, and she is presumably ready to breed again. During this period, she cares for her young, goes out into the ocean to feed, and goes through the breeding process that produces the next year's young. The gestation period is presumed to be from 11 to 12 months, at the end of which time the female gives birth to a single pup. The breeding period of seals is estimated at about 10 years (13).

The young are cared for after birth for a period of about 6 weeks. During that time the pup is taught to swim and catch its own food. By October or sooner, all the seals begin to leave the islands and put out to sea not to return again until the next summer.

The male seal is capable of breeding at 4 years of age (4), but ordinarily does not collect harems until he is 6 years old or more. The length of the breeding period for males is about 10 years. It is from the surplus of bachelor males that the seal skins are now harvested under supervision of the U.S. Fish and Wildlife Service.

Movements. The activities of seals are mainly of three kinds: migration, breeding and feeding. As the summer wanes, the females, pups, and young males leave the islands first, while the breeding males stay on and begin their migration last. During their migration, the seals are not commonly seen for several months, but some of them no doubt winter along the west coast of the North American continent.

During the time the seals are on the breeding grounds, the females move into the ocean to feed, sometimes swimming out for a distance of 100 miles off shore. Other movements of the females include swimming and exercising on the beach, mating, and care of the young. The breeding males stay in the vicinity of their harem and do not feed during the entire breeding season. They are very active, however, in ushering in the newly arriving females, maintaining the territory of their harem against any invading males, fighting, and mating.

Food. After birth the young feeds on its mother's milk for about 8 weeks. The food of the adult seals is largely fish (12). Percentages by weight show that herring (2 species) make up nearly 80 per cent of the stomach contents of 672 examined stomachs. Salmon were present in small quantities as were other creatures of the sea. Apparently other items are taken when available but in such small quantities as to be unimportant. Pollacks are commonly taken and are probably next in importance to herring as a source of food. Rockfish, squids, salmon, and pilchard are also taken in small quantities (12).

MORTALITY

Studies of the breeding grounds show that losses of young seals vary greatly from year to year and that the losses are greater where the breeding grounds contain pools of muddy water. Losses of young are likely to be high at the time that the weaned young leave their land habitat to take up life in the ocean. The killer whale also takes a toll of young seals, as is indicated by the fact that 18 young fur seals were found in one whale (13). Hookworms likewise kill a considerable number of seal pups during certain seasons (14). Tagging studies show that nearly half (48 per cent) of the young seals die during the first 2 years of their life (17).

The U.S. Fish and Wildlife Service has been very careful in the management of the seal herd to harvest only surplus animals that are not contributing to the increase of the herd. As the seal is a polygamous breeder, there will always be surplus males. These males are driven inland during the period July 15 to July 31 at a time when the pelt is prime and in the best condition. Here, after being sorted for age, they are killed at a place which is far enough away from the breeding grounds so as not to disturb the breeding animals. About three-quarters of the annual 3-year-old class is taken, the remaining quarter being left for future breeding stock.

The skins, after local processing to prevent their spoiling, are sent to the Fouke Fur Company of St. Louis, Missouri, where they receive final processing into fur and are sold at public auction to the highest bidders. The annual return may be as high as 3 million dollars per year. Other products derived from the fur seal are fats, and the skinned carcasses are processed and sold for soap, poultry feed, and other uses.

MANAGEMENT

A census of the seal herd is taken each year at the height of the breeding season. As the average number of females in a harem is known, it is only necessary to count the numbers of harems and idle bulls. This is usually done by two men on foot, one checking his figures against the other. In this way the Service is able to keep an accurate check on the increase each year and to regulate the kill accordingly. The yearly increase has varied from 5 to 10 per cent, but it is normally about 6 to 8 per cent per year. Since 1910 there have been 1,498,911 seal pelts taken, enough to make about 200,000 coats (4).

Treaties, sound regulations, wise management, and constant patrolling have kept the fur seal herd in good condition and on the increase. The numbers are now well beyond the danger of extermination. The handling of the seal herd is one of the bright spots in the annals of wildlife history.

BADGER

GEOGRAPHICAL DISTRIBUTION

The range distribution of the badger is usually given as the western part of North America. This includes the dry central and western part of the continent. It includes the land west of a line extending from the

FIG. 14-2. The badger lives mostly underground. Note the strong claws on the forefeet used for digging. Its fur is of minor value. (*E. P. Haddon, U.S. Fish and Wildlife Service.*)

west end of Lake Ontario to a point on the Gulf of Mexico where Mexico and Texas meet. Westerly it includes the prairie, plains regions, and the dry portions of the continent in both the United States and Canada, as well as Southern California and the northern sections of Mexico.

Apparently the badger can live in a habitat that has considerable rainfall, even up to as much as 30 inches annually, provided there are suitable soil conditions which favor dry earth dens, a soil that is fine and not stony, and suitable food (9, 14 *g.r.*). Badgers seem to have moved north and east during the past 50 years. No doubt this is related to the clearing of the land of forest growth with the resultant revegetation of such cleared areas by grass (8, 9).

ANATOMY, LIFE HISTORY, AND ECOLOGY

The badger has a strong muscular body with powerful legs and broad feet and claws. The head is broad and the jaws and teeth strong. It is mainly nocturnal, living underground, and seldom seen except when caught in a trap.

In size the badger is 28 to 30 inches long including the tail, which is conspicuous by its shortness. The nose is sharp and the ears upright.

Little is known about the breeding habits of the badger, but Cahalane (15 *g.r.*) gives the time of breeding as fall or early winter followed by a delayed development of the embryos. The young are born in May or June; there are from 1 to 7 young in the litter and only 1 litter a year.

The life of a badger is spent within the confines of a relatively few acres, certainly an area not more than a quarter of a section in size. When necessary, new hunting-and-den territory is sought, so that this drift movement may be for several miles in a season. The activity for which the badger is best known is its digging. It takes a good man with a shovel to keep up with a digging badger when the animal has a few minutes start. Few dogs are a match either in courage or strength for the badger and, because of the close-built anatomy of the latter, it is difficult for a dog to acquire a hold for the infighting.

The food of the badger is of animal origin. The thirteen-lined spermophile is one of the main items of food. Meadow mice are also common in the badger diet. Birds and birds' eggs, insects, turtle eggs, and any other meat that is available are all acceptable. Insects are a staple food for both young and adults (5, 7, 14 *g.r.*).

OPOSSUM

GEOGRAPHICAL DISTRIBUTION

The opossum is found in all the eastern part of the United States that has precipitation sufficient to grow trees. It has extended its range almost to the Canadian border in New England, and in the Lake states as far north as the western tip of Lake Superior. In the South, its range extends to the Gulf of Mexico and the eastern border of Arizona. It is also found in central California and northeastern Oregon (14 *g.r.*).

ANATOMY, LIFE HISTORY, AND ECOLOGY

The opossum has a reputation for playing dead or "playing 'possum" when captured and has an uncanny ability for getting out of a tight place. The first of these animals the author ever saw was destined for a

Thanksgiving dinner but escaped from the box it was confined in at Big Rapids, Michigan. Perhaps its progeny are still roaming the woods in that vicinity!

The opossum is about 24 to 30 inches from tip of the nose to tip of the tail. However, since both the nose and tail are long, its net body length is much shorter than this. In weight, mature males range from 5 to 10 pounds and the females, 3 to 5 pounds (16). Breeding begins in the north the first part of February. The young are born only 13 days after conception and the immature, fragile young must make their way

FIG. 14-3. The opossum, because of its great abundance, is one of the more important fur bearers. It has slowly extended its range and now occupies most of the eastern United States. (*L. G. Kesteloo, Virginia Commission Inland Fisheries and Game.*)

to the mother's pouch where they attach themselves to the mother's teats. Once there and attached to the source of nourishment, the youngsters are relatively safe. At birth the young are about the size of bluebottle flies. At 12 weeks they are about the size of mice. Though 12 to 18 young may be born in a litter, only 12 can find nourishment, so any surplus above this number is lost. Later others may be lost, so that the average number that emerges from the pouch is about 9 (11).

The tail of the opossum is long, scaly, and very handy. It is used by the animal to steady itself when climbing and may be used for carrying nest material and even food (15 *q.v.*).

The food of the opossum is anything it can catch, find, or steal. It is omnivorous and takes whatever is handy and plentiful. Carrion, grains, fruit, mice, birds, eggs, snakes, frogs, crayfish, or insects are all acceptable and seem to be sufficient to supply almost any number of the 'possum clan (15 *g.r.*).

The cover requirements of the opossum are again not very specific. It nests under brush piles, under barns, in hollow trees, and in strawstacks. Dens in the ground are acceptable, if they are dry and somebody else has dug them. The female is fussy about her nest and carries sticks, grass, and leaves into a den to make it warm and dry. Otherwise, it need not be any specific type of shelter.

Opossums are nocturnal and wander around under cover of darkness looking for food. The females probably do not go more than half a mile in their wanderings during the time the young are being carried.

The opossum is a most promising candidate for a tourist to put into a box and take back home. Whenever the crate is not carefully closed and locked, however, the animal is likely to escape. Thus the 'possum has been aided in the spread of its range by the gasoline engine and diesel locomotive. The end of its northward movement has not yet been reached (11).

MANAGEMENT

Hunters, biologists, and game administrators have been apprehensive as to the effects of the invasion of a new meat-eating mammal in territory occupied by such desirable wildlife species as the cottontail rabbit and the ring-necked pheasant. Would such an invasion have a detrimental effect by destroying young rabbits and pheasant eggs? Taube's conclusions are that the opossum will eat game birds and mammals if it can get them, but his study of the stomach contents of 133 autumn-caught and 8 spring-caught animals evidenced no detrimental effect on other game species (17). A more elaborate sample of spring-caught opossums covering the period April to July would, however, give better evidence as to the status of the food habits of this animal.

REFERENCES

1. Anonymous. 1943. Alaska fishery and fur-seal industries: 1941. *U.S. Fish and Wildlife Serv., Statis. Digest* 8.
2. ———. 1946. Fur seals. Encyclopedia Americana **24**:482–486, Americana Corp., New York.
3. ———. 1948. Alaska fishery and fur-seal industries: 1946. *U.S. Fish and Wildlife Serv., Statis. Digest* 17.
4. Ashbrook, Frank G. 1949. Nutria grow in the United States. *U.S. Fish and Wildlife Serv., Wildlife Leaflet* 319.
5. Atwood, Earl L. 1950. Life history studies of nutria, or coypu, in coastal Louisiana. *Jour. Wildlife Mangt.* **14**(3):249–265.
6. Day, Albert M. 1949. Old man of the Pribilofs. *U.S. Fish and Wildlife Serv., Wildlife Leaflet* 323.

7. Drake, Guy E., and Clifford C. Presnall. 1950. A badger preying upon game. *Jour. Mammal.* **31**(3):355–356.
8. Enders, Robert K. 1945. Research an important factor in fur seal management. *Trans. 10th North Amer. Wildlife Conf.* Pp. 92–94.
9. Errington, Paul L. 1937. Summer food habits of the badger in northwestern Iowa. *Jour. Mammal.* **18**(2):213–216.
10. Hanna, J. D. 1922. What becomes of fur seals? *Science.* **55**(May 12):505–507.
11. Lyon, M. W., Jr. 1932. The badger, *Taxidea taxus* (Schreber), in Indiana. *Amer. Midland Nat.* **13**(3):124–129.
12. Moseley, E. L. 1934. Increase of badgers of northwestern Ohio. *Jour. Mammal.* **15**(2):156–158.
13. Progulske, Donald. 1950. The Alaska fur seal *Callorhinus alascanus.* Unpublished manuscript. University of Massachusetts, Amherst.
14. Reynolds, Harold C. 1945. Some aspects of the life history and ecology of the opossum in central Missouri. *Jour. Mammal.* **26**(4):361–379.
15. Scheffer, Victor B. 1950. The food of the Alaska fur seal. *U.S. Fish and Wildlife Serv., Wildlife Leaflet* 329.
16. ——— and Frank G. Ashbrook. 1949. Conserving the Alaska fur seals. *Trans. 14th North Amer. Wildlife Conf.* Pp. 440–450.
17. Taube, Clarence M. 1947. Food habits of Michigan opossums. *Jour. Wildlife Mangt.* **11**(1):97–103.
18. Wiseman, George L., and George O. Hendrickson. 1950. Notes on the life history and ecology of the opossum in southeast Iowa. *Jour. Mammal.* **31**(3):331–337.
19. Worden, W. L. 1948. We put tags on seals. *The Saturday Evening Post.* **220**(March 20): 24–25.

SECTION THREE

Waterfowl

CHAPTER 15

Waterfowl Ecology[1]

INTRODUCTION

The waterfowl with which this section is concerned include a selected list of members of the family *Anatidae*—the ducks, geese, and swans. In this family of waterfowl there are three subfamilies: *anseranatinae, anserinae* and *anatinae.* Under subfamily *anseranatinae* is tribe *anseranatinini,* magpie goose; under subfamily *anserinae* are tribes *dendrocygnini,* whistling and tree ducks, and *anserini,* swans and geese; under subfamily *anatinae* are tribes *tadornini,* shelducks and shelgeese, *tadornini,* aberrant geese and ducks, *anatini,* dabbling ducks, *aythyini,* pochard or diving ducks, *cairinini,* perching ducks, *mergini,* sea ducks, *oxyurini,* stiff-tailed ducks, and *merganettini,* torrent ducks. The greatest emphasis will be given to the species that are the most desirable from the sportsman's point of view and that are found in sufficient numbers to carry the brunt of waterfowl gunning. Also included will be the wood duck and some of the less desirable of the diving ducks.

Extensive discussions of taxonomic features and morphology, while important, will be left to the many excellent books on waterfowl ornithology. The discussions which follow are included because they have a direct bearing on the management of waterfowl.

Drought, drainage, and overshooting reduced waterfowl populations to unusually low numbers during the years 1925–1936 (57 *g.r.*). During this period less than the average amount of moisture fell, which reduced the usefulness of the breeding grounds. Important breeding grounds in the United States and the Prairie Provinces of Canada were further impaired by agricultural drainage operations which have destroyed more than 100 million acres of waterfowl environment within the past 75 years (41 *g.r.*). To a lesser extent, overshooting helped directly to reduce the numbers of waterfowl. The development of better roads and the increased use of automobiles enabled hunters to follow the migratory

[1] Common and scientific names of the waterfowl will be according to Peter Scott. 1951. Key to the wildfowl of the world, Severn Wildfowl Trust, Slimbridge, Gloucestershire, England.

birds north into the breeding grounds and southward to their wintering grounds. By 1936, the number of waterfowl had reached an estimated low of 27 million, and many persons believed this resource was beyond saving.

Previous to 1936, some progress in waterfowl management had been made when the migratory-bird treaty was signed with Great Britain in 1916. This treaty finally clarified the then prevailing controversy as to the rights of the Federal government versus the states with regard to regulating the taking of migratory birds. However, even as late as 1930 the length of open seasons and bag limits were liberal. Baiting, sink-box shooting, and live decoys were used freely; illegal market shooting was practiced in some places due to the difficulty of apprehending violators. Some of the remedies applied by the U.S. Biological Survey (now the U.S. Fish and Wildlife Service) were restrictions of the methods by which waterfowl could be shot and a reduction in the length of season and of the number of ducks and geese which an individual hunter could take. The season was completely closed on some of the less abundant species. Based on the results of 25 years of research on waterfowl migrations, the Survey inaugurated an energetic program of waterfowl conservation, including the purchase and restoration of lands in the breeding-ground regions and flyways and the establishment and maintenance of wintering refuges. Since 1934 these activities have been vigorously continued.

Along with this program of development, both the Canadian government and Ducks Unlimited, a private corporation, have carried on a parallel program of water restoration and predator control in the central Canadian provinces. Under these combined programs, several thousand ponds and lakes have been created and many dry marshes reflooded (23 *g.r.*).

Without question the greatest aid to the waterfowl has been the general increase in moisture throughout North America since 1936 (4). This additional moisture probably has had more effect in increasing the waterfowl populations than all man's efforts combined.

According to Gabrielson (24 *g.r.*), waterfowl had increased to 119,-600,000 by 1943. In the fall of 1944 it was estimated that the number may have reached 125 million, a figure believed to be about equal to the number of waterfowl in North America in 1900.

On March 23, 1944, Fulton Lewis, Jr., a news commentator, spent 10 minutes of a 15-minute broadcast telling of the increase in migrating waterfowl. He said ducks, geese, and swans were everywhere from Kansas west to California. Ditches, rivers, open fields, rice fields, and even barnyards were crowded with waterfowl. Ducks were feeding on manure piles, in stockyards, and even from the stock troughs. These hordes of waterfowl were living off the land as they moved northward to their breeding grounds.

The promise of a return of the numbers of our waterfowl to a population level commensurate with precolonial conditions was at best only a mirage (36). While our waterfowl, it is true, have been saved from extinction by the miracle of increased rainfall and by man's numerous activities to conserve water and to restrict duck losses, our waterfowl are

FIG. 15-1. Concentration of pintails on wintering grounds in the Central Valley of California. Suitable wintering grounds for ducks and geese must provide shallow water, fertile soil, and abundant plant life. (*Peter J. Van Huizen, U.S. Fish and Wildlife Service.*)

still in a precarious position as this is written. Albert M. Day, director of the U.S. Fish and Wildlife Service (9), gives some of the reasons for this unhealthy condition. For instance, in 1948 there were 2 million waterfowl hunters in the United States and an estimated 17 million waterfowl were bagged. During that year it was believed that the waterfowl had just about held their own with possibly some slight increase in the breeding stocks of geese and certain types of ducks.

The changes in waterfowl environment are very discouraging, however. During a 20-year period the various state and Federal conservation agencies have restored or improved 4½ million acres of waterfowl habitat. During about 8 years of that same period the U.S. Department of

Agriculture in contrast drained more than 6 million acres! If these conditions continue the battle of waterfowl conservation will be lost no matter how much the hunter's take is restricted.

As contrasted with the above discouraging situation a better understanding of the waterfowl problem on the North American continent is appearing. The knowledge of waterfowl ecology gained through investigations of their life histories and particularly their use of flyways by the study of waterfowl banding records over a long period of years by the U.S. Fish and Wildlife Service is contributing to this clarification of the problem. Through the intelligent regulation of the annual waterfowl take and the vigorous campaign to prevent needless destruction of marshes and swamps it may be possible to manage this resource on a sustained-yield basis.

In 1933 funds were made available from Federal sources to the extent of 6 million dollars for a national system of breeding, flyway, and wintering refuges. The Federal Duck Stamp Act, passed in 1934, provided for the collection of a tax of $1 per year from each waterfowl hunter through the sale of a stamp which must be attached to each state small-game hunting license. According to the provisions of the Duck Stamp Act, 90 per cent of this tax must be used for the acquisition and maintenance of waterfowl sanctuaries, while not more than 10 per cent may be used for administrative purposes. In 1951 this Act was amended to raise the cost of the Duck Stamp from $1 to $2 as a means of giving more financial aid to the refuge program.

ANATOMY, LIFE HISTORY, AND ECOLOGY

A minimum of anatomy and life-history data will be given for the various waterfowl treated in this section. Weights of individual species and speeds of flight may have little value to the wildlife manager except as a possible means of judging the suitability of the environment or the effects of diseases. Information on age classes is likewise included because a knowledge of this factor is of importance as an indicator of the success or failure of breeding seasons. Finally, data on the sex ratios of the various species are appended, since each species appears to have a closely linked characteristic sex ratio which may possibly be related to the effects of hunting.

Food and grit are each of prime importance to waterfowl. Likewise, water is both a physiological and an environmental requirement. Mortality factors include predators, diseases, botulism, and lead poisoning. The degree and effect of hunting are also of the utmost importance.

Weights and Measurements. Weights and measurements are useful for the classification of bagged birds into juvenile and mature classes and possibily as clues to the time at which broods were hatched. Size, weight, and general condition of flesh may indicate the food conditions under which the birds lived. Kortright (41 *g.r.*) has summarized these items very completely, and a portion of his data is shown in Table 15-1.

Table 15-1. Average Weights of Waterfowl

Species	Male	Female	Species	Male	Female
	lb. oz.	lb. oz.		lb. oz.	lb. oz.
Mallard	2 11	2 6	Canvasback	3 0	2 13
Black duck	2 12	2 8	Common scaup	2 1	2 0
Blue-winged teal	0 14.6	0 13.6	Lesser scaup	1 14	1 12
American green-winged teal	0 12.8	0 12	American goldeneye	2 2.5	1 11.5
Cinnamon teal	0 12	0 12.5	Bufflehead	1 0	0 12
American pintail	2 2.5	1 13	North American ruddy duck	1 5.5	1 2
American widgeon (baldpate)	1 11	1 9	Canada goose	9 3	7 14
Common shoveler	1 7	1 4	Blue snow goose	5 5	4 14
Gadwall	2 0	1 13	Greater snow goose	7 7	6 2
Wood duck	1 8	1 2.5	Lesser snow goose	5 5	4 11
Redhead	2 8	2 4	American brant	3 3*	2 6
Ring-necked duck	1 11.5	1 8.5	White-fronted goose	5 5	4 13

* Based on 1 only.

Longevity. The life span of all game animals is important and interesting. A long-lived creature, if part of a breeding stock, is less costly from the viewpoint of production overhead than a short-lived animal. Among waterfowl, changes of color and plumage are directly affected by age. As a matter of fact, a knowledge of these plumage changes enables a person to determine to a high degree of accuracy the age of wild waterfowl. The longest known records of the longevity of birds are those for animals kept in captivity where food is always available, wild predators are absent, and hunting is prohibited. From such records Kortright (41 *g.r.*) believes the general lengths of life for the different groups of waterfowl are as follows: swans, 40 years; geese, 30 years; and ducks, 20 years. At present the banding of wild waterfowl indicates much shorter spans of life than those given by Kortright, although it is reliably reported that ducks may carry a band 10 years before being shot.

Sex Ratios and Age Classes. The unbalanced condition of waterfowl, as shown by a greater number of males than females, has interested the biologist, game manager, and game administrator because of its effect on waterfowl production. To date no satisfactory explanation has been given as to the cause of these phenomena. This disparity of males to females appears to be greater in the diving ducks than in the puddle or river ducks. Table 15-2 shows the condition as found by various research studies in this field.

The determination of a true sex ratio in wild animals is a difficult problem because of the unfavorable conditions under which the counts are taken. Differences in sex ratios may occur because the count is made after one sex has migrated and before the other arrives, because the enumeration is taken at a time when the males are banded together

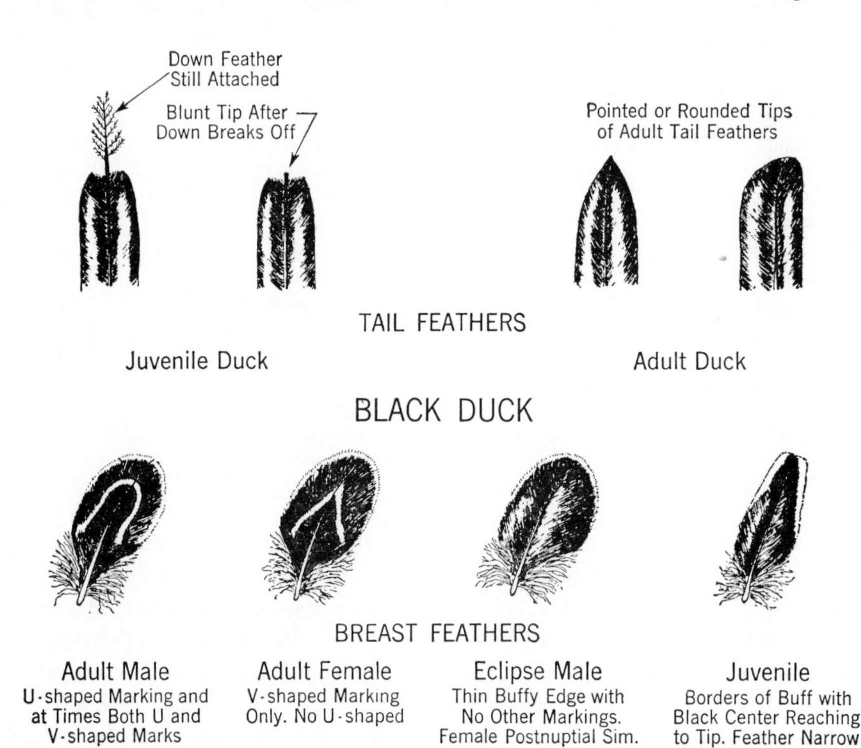

FIG. 15-2. Determination of sex and age in the black duck. (*Massachusetts Division of Fisheries and Game.*)

while the females are incubating and caring for the young, or because of a number of other reasons. Lincoln's count (26) taken from 50 banding stations well distributed over the North American continent would appear to give as representative a sample as can be obtained for any wild species. Until better data are available, it must be accepted that generally the ratio of males to females is unbalanced in favor of males.

Bennett's intensive study (1) of the blue-winged teal gives a sex ratio of 58 per cent males to 42 per cent females for 5,090 ducks observed during the fall flight, on the wintering grounds, and during the spring flight. The ratio of males to females of 36 ducklings was also 58:42. This

Table 15-2. Sex Ratios of Some North American Waterfowl

Waterfowl species	United States at 50 banding stations (30, 31), per cent		Saskatchewan at 20 quarter sections (14), per cent		Delta Marshes, Manitoba, Canada (21, 22) per cent	
	Male	Female	Male	Female	Male	Female
American goldeneye	..	..	52	48		
American green-winged teal	79	21	54	46		
American pintail	63	37	73	27	52	48
American widgeon (baldpate)	62	38				
Black duck	58	42				
Blue-winged teal	65	35	60	40		
Bufflehead	..	..	67	33		
Canvasback	64	36	60	40	66	34
Common shoveler	..	..	50	50		
Gadwall	..	..	60	40	65	35
Lesser scaup	65	35	61	39	67	33
Mallard	56	44	63	37	51	49
North American ruddy duck	..	..	77	23		
Redhead	..	..	55	45	57	43
Ring-necked duck	79	21	50	50		
Widgeon	..	..	58	42		
Wood duck	52	48				
Averages	60	40	61	39	67	33

comparison of the sexes of newly hatched ducklings corresponds to the foregoing ratio for adults, but it does not agree with Hochbaum's findings of a nearly equal ratio of sexes for juveniles (31 *g.r.*). As the numbers inspected by Bennett are low (only 36), perhaps this may be simply a statistical coincidence.

Hochbaum (31 *g.r.*) has presented the most lucid discussion concerning the unbalanced condition of the sexes and may have arrived at an answer to at least some of the underlying causes. Hochbaum indicates clearly that his hypotheses are preliminary and need further study. At the time they are hatched, the juveniles of all species of waterfowl are probably equal as to sexes. For 3,024 juveniles sexed at Delta, Manitoba, Hochbaum gives the figures of 1,502 males and 1,522 females or an almost perfect 50:50 ratio. He further states he has been led to the conclusion that the heavy loss of females does not take place until after they have made their departure from the breeding grounds.

In this connection, the following features of waterfowl ecology presented by Hochbaum (31 *g.r.*) and other investigators are significant. Females live a shorter life span because of greater hazards to which they are subjected. Females are particularly vulnerable to numerous dangers during the time they incubate the eggs. These include the depredations of both ground and air predators, fire, and perhaps haying operations. Furthermore, on the northern range more adult females are shot than males during the hunting season. This is because of the delayed development of flight feathers, incubation duties of the females, etc. (32). Also the delayed migration of the females may make them more subject to the effects of botulism than the males (15, 45 *g.r.*). Drought likewise may take a heavy loss of brood females. Cartwright (4) states that the loss of ducklings, and probably of their mothers, was tremendous during the dry years on the prairie provinces.

The above does not consider the differential mortality of the sexes on the southern migration, during hunting on the flyways, on the wintering

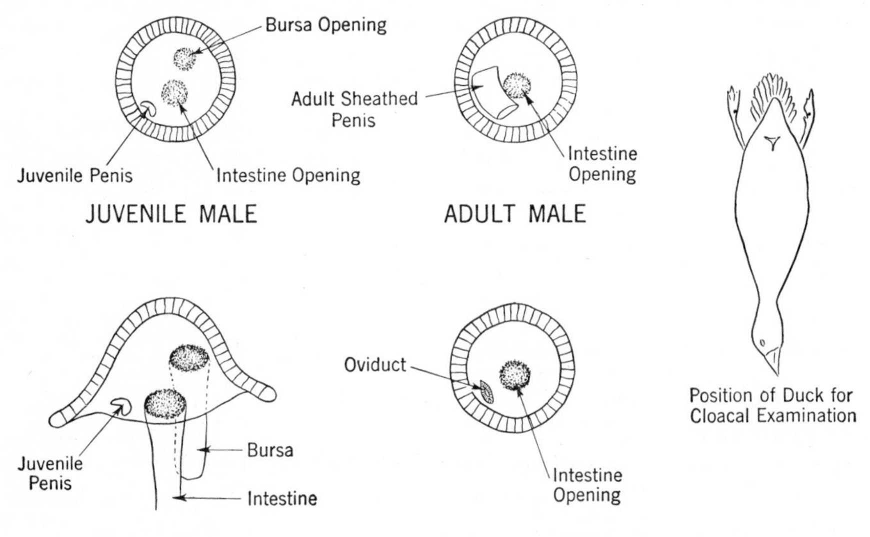

FIG. 15-3. Determination of sex and age in ducks by cloacal examination (41 *g.r.*).

grounds, or on the northern flight to the breeding grounds in the late winter or spring.

The importance of an unbalanced sex ratio is of more than academic interest in a monogamous species. Mathematically, there can be no greater number of broods than the number of mated pairs. This in turn depends on the number of females. Likewise, harassment by excess males may prevent the mated pairs from reproducing successfully. Lastly, the presence of a widely unbalanced sex ratio may indicate the decline of a species (45 *g.r.*). Thus, Hochbaum noted a count of 329 male ruddy ducks to 35 females during the height of the 1941 spring migration. He also noted that unmated males were more numerous than mated pairs.

Figure 15-3 shows the method of sex determination of ducks by cloacal examination. With ducks that are dead when examined, additional examination can be made of the gonads. With sexually mature birds, the plumage will indicate the sex during the breeding season.

The age of ducks is important particularly with respect to the number of young as compared with the number of adults following the breeding season. Research men and administrators use information on the ratio of young of the year to old birds in predicting the success of the next year's breeding season and in checking weak places in the environment. Figure 15-2 shows feather differences in both form and markings for the black duck as found along the New England Coast.

A summary of adult-young ratio data for various species of waterfowl, time of year, and localities is given in Table 15-3.

Table 15-3. Ratios of Adults to Young Waterfowl as Shown by the Inspection of Ducks Taken by Hunters or Trapping

Species	Location	Time of year	Adults	Juveniles	Ratio
Blue-winged teal (17).....	Delta, Man.	Fall, 1938	88	249	26:74
Lesser scaup (17).........	Delta, Man.	Fall, 1938	22	55	28:72
Mallard (20).............	Horicon, Wis.	1949–50	47	216	17:83

A ratio of adults to young is of little use until a standard or norm is established. It is believed that on good range during an average season, a relationship analogous to that indicated by the Delta figures is normal. A hypothetical case can be presented. Starting with 100 adult ducks, or 50 pairs with 4 young per pair brought through to the hunting season, the ratio would be 100 adults to 200 young or an adult-young ratio of 1:2. This will vary of course with the locality and with the season. After the norm has been established for a particular area, the success of a duck-breeding season can be ascertained by censusing a sample of ducks within that area for its components of juveniles and adults. Similarly, like data for different localities can be compared between one place and another.

To show the danger of accepting data without knowing the circumstances which surround their origin, one has only to look at the same treatment of duck figures from Delta, Manitoba, in 1941, in which all of the species listed show higher ratios of adults than young. Such figures may be a true expression of the adult-juvenile composition of the particular species, but it also may be the result of inadequate samples.

Food. If we are to enjoy an abundance of waterfowl in North America, food must be of sufficient quantity, of the right kind, and available throughout the year. Each of the various species of ducks and geese has

Table 15-4. Ratios of Adults to Young at the Time of the Open Hunting Season at Delta, Manitoba, 1941 (31 *g.r.*)

Species	Adults	Juveniles	Ratio adults to juveniles
American green-winged teal	26	14	65:35
American pintail	55	22	72:28
American widgeon (baldpate)	12	9	57:43
Blue-winged teal	83	59	58:42
Canvasback	292	259	53:47
Common shoveler	68	55	55:45
Gadwall	55	37	60:40
Lesser scaup	217	183	54:46
Mallard	407	297	58:42
Redhead	157	152	51:49

its own particular food predilection; thus, a variety of foods must be available. The quantity of food needed for a year's supply for 150–200 million ducks reaches astronomic figures, yet such food usually grows in places which interfere very little with the economic activities of man. Wet lands, marshes, swamps, river beds, salt marshes, beaches, and even the ocean floor are all places where waterfowl foods grow. Geese may be the exception, for these species are fond of domestic grains.

A study of nearly 8,000 stomachs taken from among 18 species of ducks from all parts of North America shows that plant materials constituted 73 per cent of the food of waterfowl, and animal matter the remaining 27 per cent (34), and furthermore that 19 genera of plants, the volumes of which were 1 per cent or more in these analyses, supplied vegetable food. Fifty-six additional genera made up the list of vegetable foods, which varied in volume from a trace to 0.94 of 1 per cent. The animal foods were divided among 5 phyla. Mollusks and insects constituted nearly 20 per cent of the total animal materials eaten. Crustaceans and fishes together comprised nearly 3 per cent and unidentified materials constituted the remaining 4 per cent.

Figure 15-4 shows the broad general regions from which the stomachs used in this analysis were collected.

Table 15-5 indicates the volumetric percentage of each of the genera, phyla, or classes of foods eaten by 11 species of surface-feeding ducks and 7 species of diving ducks.

Table 15-5 shows in the aggregate the principal kinds of food taken by waterfowl in the various regions of North America. It does not show the food diet of a single species at any particular place. The outstanding fact brought out by the data in the table is the relatively high amount of animal matter (47 per cent) consumed by waterfowl as compared to vegetable matter in the northern part of the duck range, namely, western Canada; this probably reflects the dietary needs of breeding and moulting birds. The lowest amount of animal food taken by waterfowl in any region is that for the Gulf Coast (7.36 per cent), which would seem to reflect the kind of food available during the winter season as

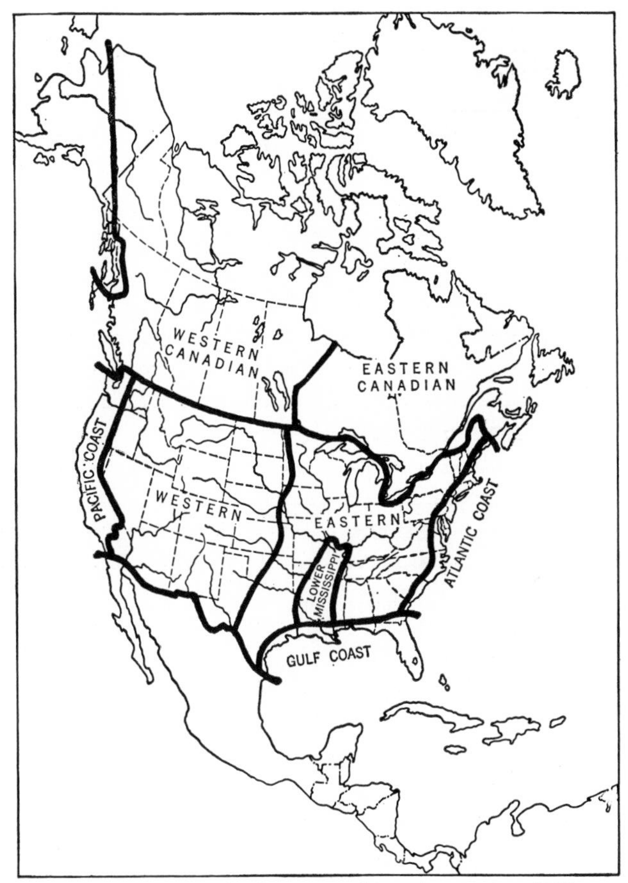

FIG. 15-4. Duck-food regions of North America (35).

well as to indicate the dietary needs of the birds on the wintering grounds.

For the continent as a whole, the pondweeds are the most important plants consumed. In the lower Mississippi and Gulf Coast region the items of most importance are chufa (*Cyperus* spp.) and widgeon-grass (*Ruppia* spp.). Bulrushes (*Scirpus* spp.) are important in all the regions, as are also wild celery (*Vallisneria* spp.) and wild rice (*Zizania* spp.).

Table 15-6 gives the percentages of plant and animal foods eaten by

Table 15-5. Volumetric Percentage of Plant and Animal Foods (1 Per Cent or Over) Eaten by Waterfowl in Eight Regions of North America (39)

Classes of foods	Geographic regions							
	Atlantic Coast	Eastern region	Lower Missis-sippi	Gulf Coast	Western region	Pacific Coast	Eastern Canada	Western Canada
Plant materials								
Pondweed, *Potamogeton*	11.73	13.29	6.06	3.99	16.29	12.14	12.47	12.73
Bulrush, *Scirpus*	4.62	4.90	2.52	5.39	11.19	4.78	11.02	10.58
Smartweed, *Polygonum*	4.96	6.69	5.54	5.94	3.89	1.79	.....	2.49
Widgeon-grass, *Ruppia*	6.37	.....	.....	8.47	6.26	2.19		
Muskgrass, *Chara*	.....	1.87	.....	.....	5.67	.....	6.12	9.29
Wild millet, *Echinochloa*	1.49	1.59	5.35	4.11	4.19			
Wild celery, *Vallisneria*	6.82	2.49	.....	1.06	.....	.....	5.53	
Naiad, *Najas*	2.48	4.32	2.68	1.71	.....	.....	1.80	
Wild rice, *Zizania*	2.61	5.10	.....	.....	.....	.....	9.58	
Chufa, *Cyperus*	.....	.....	12.25	.....	.....	4.38		
Water shield, *Brasenia*	.....	.....	.....	4.94				
Rice, *Oryza*	.....	.....	5.39	3.60	.....	1.52		
Spike-rush, *Eleocharis*	.....	.....	.....	2.07	1.08	2.91	4.02	
Duckweed, *Lemna, Spirodela, Wolffiella*	.....	2.97	7.04					
Corn, *Zea*	2.91	2.30						
Algae, *Ulva Spirogyra*	2.37	.....	.....	1.20				
Water lily, *Nymphaea* spp.	.....	.....	.....	4.50				
Coontail, *Ceratophyllum* spp.	.....	.....	8.35	.....	1.50	1.50		
Eelgrass, *Zostera* spp.	3.67	.....	.....	.....	.....	3.03		
Arrowhead, *Sagittaria* spp.	.....	1.00	.....	2.63	.....	.....	1.93	
Horned pondweed, *Zannichellia* spp.	.....	.....	.....	.....	2.95	3.12		
Sedge, *Carex* spp.	.....	1.21	.....	.....	1.62	.....	1.32	1.50
Saw-grass, *Cladium* spp.	.....	.....	.....	2.99				
Bur-reed, *Sparganium* spp.	.....	1.33	2.74	.....	.....	.....	2.01	
Sorghum, *Sorghum* spp.	.....	.....	.....	.....	3.62			
Barley, *Hordeum* spp.	.....	.....	.....	.....	1.48	1.17		
Little barley, *Hordeum* spp.	.....	.....	.....	.....	1.21			
Panicum spp.	.....	.....	.....	1.87				

Cutgrass, *Leersia* spp.	.....	2.02						
Water-hemp, *Acnida* spp.	2.51							
Beak-rush, *Rynchospora* spp.	.....	.....	.....	1.96				
Water-milfoil, *Myriophyllum* spp.	.....	.....	.....	.....	.....	.....	.....	2.28
Pigeon-grass, *Setaria* spp.	.....	1.62						
Buttonbush, *Cephalanthus* spp.	.....	.....	3.81					
Oak, *Quercus* spp.	.....	.....	3.46					
Glasswort, *Salicornia* spp.	.....	.....	.....	1.36				
Buckwheat, *Fagopyrum* spp.	.....	1.40						
Arrow-grass, *Triglochin* spp.	.....	.....	.....	.....	.....	2.57		
Spike-grass, *Distichlis* spp.	.....	.....	.....	.....	.....	2.24		
Pigweed, *Amaranthus* spp.	.....	.....	.....	.....	1.19			
Paspalum spp.	.....	.....	.....	1.02				
Manna-grass, *Glyceria* spp.	.....	.....	3.57					
Bald Cypress, *Taxodium* spp.	.....	.....	3.49					
Water-primrose, *Jussiaea* spp.	.....	.....	3.44					
Dock, *Rumex* spp.	.....	.....	.....	.....	.....	1.67		
Buttercup, *Ranunculus* sp.	.....	.....	1.33					
Water-elm, *Planera* sp.	.....	.....	1.77					
Frog's-bit, *Limnobium* sp.	.....	.....	1.41					
Water-hyssop, *Bacopa* spp.	.....	.....	1.36					
Sweet gum, *Liquidambar*	.....	.....	1.29					
Wild grape, *Vitis* spp.	.....	.....	1.10					
Total for materials forming less than 1%	9.81	8.90	6.56	6.62	8.46	9.46	3.61	4.68
Miscellaneous	7.40	11.36	2.13	9.73	8.75	14.25	6.14	9.64
Total plant materials	69.77	74.36	92.64	75.16	79.35	68.72	65.55	53.19
Animal materials								
Gastropoda	11.04	4.61	3.51	11.62	0.88	8.57	3.59	6.35
Plecopoda	6.35	1.21	0.09	1.35	.....	8.48	2.27	0.81
Crustacea	6.27	2.44	1.37	1.06	1.57	4.37	9.81	6.07
Insects	1.93	13.55	2.12	4.43	16.69	7.23	17.67	27.16
Pisces	0.98	0.25	0.06	2.86	0.12	.....	.....	1.58
Miscellaneous	3.66	3.58	0.21	3.52	1.39	2.63	1.11	4.84
Total animal materials	30.23	25.64	7.36	24.84	20.65	31.28	34.45	46.81

Table 15-6. Percentages of Plant and Animal Foods of North American Waterfowl and the Principal Groups of Food (31)

Waterfowl species	Percentage of matter consumed		Principal groups of food
	Vegetable	Animal	
Dabbling ducks:			
Mallard	91	9	Sedges, grasses, smartweeds, pondweeds, wild rice, duckweeds, coontail, wild celery, insects, mollusks
Black duck	76	24	Pondweeds, grasses, sedges, smartweeds, mollusks, crustaceans, insects, fish
Blue-winged teal	71	29	Sedges, pondweeds, grasses, smartweeds, mollusks, insects, crustaceans
American green-winged teal	91	9	Sedges, pondweeds, grasses, smartweeds, algae, insects, mollusks
Cinnamon teal	80	20	Sedges, pondweeds, grasses, smartweeds, insects, mollusks
American pintail	87	13	Pondweeds, sedges, grasses, smartweeds
American widgeon (baldpate)	93	7	Pondweeds, grasses, algae, sedges, wild celery
Common shoveler	66	34	Seeds of sedges, pondweeds, grasses, mollusks, insects
Gadwall	98	2	Pondweeds, sedges, algae, coontail, grasses, grains
Wood duck	90	10	Duckweeds, cypress cones and galls, sedges and tubers, grasses, pondweeds, nuts, insects, spiders
Diving ducks:			
Redhead	90	10	Pondweeds, muskgrass, sedges, grasses, wild celery, insects, mollusks
Ring-necked duck	81	19	Water lilies, pondweeds, sedge grasses, smartweeds, muskgrass, insects, mollusks
Canvasback	81	19	Pondweeds, wild celery, delta duck potato, grasses, sedges, water lily, mollusks, insects, crustaceans
Common scaup	47	53	Pondweeds, muskgrass, water-milfoils, sedges, wild rice, mollusks, insects, crustaceans

a selected group of North American waterfowl; the principal groups of foods are also listed.

Suitable habitat for waterfowl, including food, nesting sites, escape and loafing environments, and safe habitats for those birds while on their breeding grounds and during their flightless periods are determined by such natural phenomena as the weather, length of growing season, and

Table 15-6. Percentages of Plant and Animal Foods of North American Waterfowl and the Principal Groups of Food. (*Continued*)

Waterfowl species	Percentage of matter consumed		Principal groups of food
	Vegetable	Animal	
Lesser scaup	60	40	Pondweeds, grasses, sedges, wild celery, muskgrass, mollusks, crustaceans
American goldeneye	26	74	Insects, mollusks, fishes, pondweeds, wild celery, spatter-dock, bulrushes
Bufflehead	79	21	Insects, crustaceans, mollusks, fishes, pondweeds
North American ruddy duck	72	28	Pondweeds, bulrushes, sedges, muskgrass, wild celery, insects, mollusks (gravel)
Old squaw	12	88	Crustaceans, mollusks, insects, fishes, pondweeds (gravel)
Geese:			
Canada goose	High	Low	Waste grains, green plants, crustaceans, mollusks, grasses, insects
Blue snow goose	No data		Grasses and grass roots
Greater snow goose	No data		Three-square
Lesser snow goose	Mostly vegetable	Low	Grasses, bulbs, tubers
American brant	No data		Eelgrass
White-fronted goose	No data		Grains, nuts, berries, grasses, snails

economic pursuits of man. Drainage will reduce these habitats, while flooding or water stabilization may increase them. With shooting taking a fair harvest of birds, the numbers of waterfowl will come into balance with the other basic environmental factors if enough time is allowed. This has happened and will no doubt continue to happen and will be reflected in high or low populations of waterfowl from year to year.

Food production for waterfowl is to a great extent a natural phenomenon. Man may start food species where they are absent or may increase the amount of food adjacent to suitable duck habitats by planting, burning, or manipulating water levels. Nature and economic activities of man will determine to a maximum degree the yearly supply of food for the waterfowl, however.

There are conditions, though, when the emergency feeding of waterfowl may influence the survival and increase of a segment of the waterfowl population. Hagar (14) describes conditions which arise periodically along the New England Coast when losses of black ducks occur because they are cut off from their natural food supply by ice during unusually cold winters. Under these conditions, black ducks may become emaciated and finally succumb because of the loss of suitable food. He cites two cases where the losses in one group of 3,000 black ducks were held to less than 15 per cent by feeding corn, while another group of 3,700 black ducks sustained a loss of over 50 per cent because the emergency feeding was not so prompt. He suggests that poor nutrition may have two effects on these coastal ducks, namely, (1) of contributing to direct losses from starvation and related causes and (2) of preventing the waterfowl from maintaining a physical condition under which reproduction may proceed unimpaired (14).

The program of emergency feeding involves the supplying of food, in this case yellow corn, which is available on short notice, with an organization to distribute it. Also it involves careful and constant scouting of both the birds and weather conditions plus a conditioning of the ducks to preliminary artificial feeding so that they recognize the food material when it is presented to them.

Production and Mortality of Waterfowl. The natural productive powers of waterfowl are high, but of course vary with the different species. The American goldeneye may lay as many as 17 eggs, but the whistling swan lays a maximum of 7. The average number of eggs in a clutch is more important than the maximum as it reflects the general productive power of the species concerned. It is necessary for female waterfowl to be in excellent physical condition to produce a high average number of eggs. Certainly second clutches are dependent on high physical vitality.

Each season and each particular locality differs in its degree of productiveness. For this reason, if data with any degree of accuracy are to be used, samples must be taken by species, locality, and year (23). A knowledge of the extent of losses is of value to the wildlife manager in determining open seasons, bag limits, predator control, and habitat-restoration measures. The number of eggs in the clutches of the different species varies from 7 to 12, and on the average about 60 per cent of the mated females bring off broods. Losses of young vary, but an average of 4 to 5 young per nest will survive for the first 3 weeks. Table 15-7 gives the aggregate figures for average clutches, average number that hatches, and average number in a brood during the last week of July on 3 western duck ranges. These data are taken from studies in the Bear River

Marshes in Utah, in the Flathead Valley, Montana, and in the Canadian provinces of Manitoba, Saskatchewan, and Alberta. Kalmbach (24) gives the results of a compilation of 22 waterfowl nesting studies, including the histories of more than 7,600 nests. His conclusion is that nest successes are usually more than 60 per cent of the eggs laid. Murdy (33), by including the more recent work by Girard (12) and Low (28, 29, 30), found about the same results.

Table 15-7. Average Clutches, Average Hatches, and Average Number in Broods of Some North American Waterfowl during Last Week in July

Waterfowl species	Average clutch of eggs		Average number that hatches	Per cent that hatch		Average number of young per brood during last week in July (5)
	Montana (12)	Utah (39)	Montana (12)	Montana (12)	Utah (39)	
Dabbling ducks:						
Mallard	7.13	8.5	5.00	70.10	60.0	6.21
Black duck	....	....	....	....	....	7.79
American pintail	....	7.1	....	....	82.0	6.02
Common shoveler	8.60	8.2	6.00	69.69	80.0	6.00
American widgeon (baldpate)	9.55	....	7.15	74.88	....	5.78
Gadwall	....	9.0	....	....	85.0	6.39
Blue-winged teal	8.27	....	6.00	72.50	....	6.78
American green-winged teal	7.53	....	5.66	75.20	....	7.20
Cinnamon teal	6.20	8.0	4.70	75.80	84.0	
Diving ducks:						
Redhead	9.75 (28)	12.5	....	56.25 (28)	26.0	5.89
Ring-necked duck	....	10.0 (41 *g.r.*)	....	....	....	4.34
Canvasback	....	8.0 (41 *g.r.*)	....	....	....	5.69
Lesser scaup	....	10.0 (41 *g.r.*)	....	....	....	6.20
Common scaup	....	8.0 (41 *g.r.*)				
Bufflehead	....	11.0 (41 *g.r.*)	....	....	....	5.84
American goldeneye	....	10.0 (41 *g.r.*)	....	....	....	5.84
North American ruddy duck	....	8.3 8.1 (30)	....	73.00 (30)	52.0	5.03

Much ink and oral discussion have been expended in assigning the causes of waterfowl shortages. Kalmbach (22) lists the factors as losses from fluctuating water levels, and predatory birds and mammals, including the crow, raven, skunk, bullsnake, and coyote. For some western localities the coyote and the raven cause high nest losses. Losses by livestock and human beings are considerable in some places. None of the agents affecting nesting losses cause the same degree of loss in different localities. Kalmbach states that, in general, nest losses can be cut down 10 per cent where water levels can be regulated and destructive animals can be kept under control.

Damage by Waterfowl to Agricultural Crops. The history of the development of North America shows a constantly increasing use of land formerly utilized by wildlife. Usually such conflicts result in the elimination of the wildlife because of some change in the nature of the range. In the case of waterfowl, however, some of the changes brought about by man, such as irrigation of land for rice production, have improved range conditions by adding water and in addition have provided plant products that are acceptable for food. Such changes in environmental conditions have in some instances led to a conflict between man and wildlife similar to that which has arisen in California between the farmers of the state and the waterfowl that come back to California each fall to spend the winter. With their ancestral feeding grounds taken over for agricultural uses and the establishment of protected areas in the form of state and Federal refuges scattered through the state, it is inevitable that some conflict should result. Rice acreage in California increased from 1,400 acres in 1912 to 312,000 acres in 1949. Prior to their use for rice production, these lands were the wet marshlands formerly the home of waterfowl. By 1943 the loss of rice due to waterfowl depradations had reached a total of three-quarters of a million dollars. Other crops, such as alfalfa, barley, lettuce, and other grains and grasses were being damaged to a lesser degree. As a result the farmers were screaming for protection from waterfowl while the sportsmen were bending all efforts to increase the numbers. The problem is a difficult one to solve, as it always will be where a recreational resource is in conflict with an economic one.

Out of this inflammatory situation, the solution is slowly emerging. Feed-raising areas are being established where the waterfowl can be held during the critical period until rice can be harvested. In 1944 the U.S. Fish and Wildlife Service planted more than 2,000 acres of grains in addition to 1,500 acres of native aquatic plants. Grain was scattered in strategic locations to the extent of a quarter of a million pounds. These operations, together with herding of the ducks by gunfire and other means out of the agricultural crop lands and into the areas developed for waterfowl, have reduced the damage to reasonable figures. Further purchases of land for refuges and food plantings will help to bring the conflict of ducks and farmers under control (13).

In 1948 approximately 180,000 California hunters killed 356,000 geese and 3,077,000 ducks. These had a total value of $28,272,000, a capitalized value of more than 700 million dollars on a 4 per cent basis. Under conditions where waterfowl have such high actual values, it is logical to give very careful consideration to every means of solving the problem so that a compromise can be reached between wildlife and agriculture, rather than simply concluding that the traditional form of land use (agriculture) has complete dominance (13).

Losses from Water Fluctuations. Stable water levels are one of the most important conditions in the production and maintenance of waterfowl habitats. This is particularly true during the nesting season when eggs and broods of young are dependent on the proper amount of water. If, during this period, from May through August, the water disappears or is not available within walking distance of the young, the season's crop of young may be lost. If, on the other hand, tides, winds, or abundant rainfall cause the water level to flood the nests, then the waterfowl have to start their reproductive activities over again with the resulting later broods and greater seasonal hazards of a late hatch. This condition, of course, is not so disastrous as a lack of water because it does allow a chance for some of the young to come through.

Duck breeding grounds are scattered over vast areas of the North American continent. Many of these areas lie in a zone of both low rainfall and high evaporation. Operating in conjunction with each other, these two natural phenomena will probably determine the numbers of waterfowl and the success of each hunting season. While basically man has no control over rainfall or evaporation, there are two approaches to this problem which are within the power of man to control and which also may have an effect on his other crops. One is to trap all of the water possible at the time it falls. This may be done by the use of dams, but probably it is accomplished more effectively by the use of plant cover on lands where snow is the major source of the water supply. High grain stubble, windbreaks, vegetation around field edges and pond borders, etc., are all effective in this connection.

Where dams are used to trap surface runoff, a series of impoundments may allow the storage of more water that can be passed along as the season advances. Also, the building of ponds will help to maintain underground water at an optimum level and also to keep vegetation in a desirable condition for waterfowl cover.

The less obvious effects of the lowering of water levels on marshes along the ocean shore as well as inland are the changes in both plant and animal life in the zone where the water recedes, as well as the physical and chemical changes that take place there. Both plants and animals that are adjusted to a zone covered with shallow water are destroyed, and new sequences of life begin. During this time waterfowl must go elsewhere for their subsistence (2).

Losses from Diseases and Lead Poisoning. Waterfowl are subject to losses of various kinds from diseases, predators, poisoning, and difficulties arising from weather and during migration flights. Of all these botulism and lead poisoning probably are the two most universal and the most widespread (8, 10, 21).

Hunting Losses. The interest of a broad segment of American sportsmen is centered in waterfowl shooting. This sport holds a fascination for hunters in part because of the difficulty of shooting a flying bird and in part because of the surroundings of such shooting. The cold, foggy dampness of a sunrise on a marsh, the variety of sounds and activities, the thrill and beauty of the birds as they come over a blind or settle down to decoys—these are all part of the attraction of waterfowl shooting. Wildfowl are also attractive to the nonshooting public. A flock of migrating geese has great appeal. The habits of waterfowl of wintering in the tropics and rearing their young in the far north appeal to the imagination of anyone with an interest in nature.

The waterfowl hunter pays heavily for his sport. He must have a state or local game license as well as a Federal Duck Stamp that costs $2. His equipment, clothing, guns, ammunition, and travel all count up to a heavy expenditure. The visible return is the chance to shoot at a few ducks or geese. Just how high does this bill run in the aggregate? The number of Federal Duck Stamps sold in 1945 was 1,725,505, which by 1949 had increased to over 2 million (7, 9). In 1945, the Federal excise tax on arms and ammunition was more than 5¼ million dollars. That same year about 26 million birds were bagged, with perhaps an additional 50 million crippled and lost. In this connection, Hawkins and Bellrose (16) give figures taken during the 1938 hunting season on crippling losses along the Illinois River. Because of the greater tendency of diving as compared to dabbling ducks to hide, the crippling losses are greater in the former group. Also, crippling losses are higher on public hunting grounds as compared to hunting on areas controlled by private clubs. One record given by these investigators shows a loss by crippling of 319 diving ducks for 584 bagged, or a crippling loss of 35 per cent of the birds shot at. A group of hunters on public hunting grounds lost 755 cripples for 322 birds bagged, a loss of 70 per cent. In other words, for every bird taken, more than 2 were lost. In Illinois in 1938 it was estimated there were 52,000 ducks taken and 13,000 (20 per cent) lost by crippling. From a fluoroscopic examination of live trapped ducks, Whitlock and Miller (38) conclude that about 1 out of every 4 mallards or black ducks overwintering in Michigan, or passing northward through that state in the spring, carries a gunshot wound.

On the basis of Lincoln's estimate (26), 12 per cent of the ducks are killed each year. This estimate is based on data prior to 1930, so perhaps that value has gone up to 20 per cent in recent years. Since the killing loss is evenly distributed over all the species or over the hunting territory, it may be doing a great deal of damage to the continental waterfowl populations. As pointed out by Hochbaum (18, 19), hunting regulations should indicate the time and place of hunting as well as the bag limit. He points out that marsh hunting as early as September 20 takes an unusually large number of young and female ducks of the diving group that have not had time to mature and complete their molt and therefore are not worth shooting. Some of these ducks, such as the redhead and canvasback, have limited breeding grounds and are relatively low in numbers. He points out that shooting on the stubble instead of in the marsh lands would tend to take the ducks that are the most numerous and in the best condition as game.

Hochbaum also points out the danger of completely killing all birds on a given marsh. This is called "burning out" a marsh by the hunter. While river or puddle ducks readily take over a new habitat, this is not true of the diving ducks. Once the stock of diving ducks on a marsh is shot out, it may never again be repopulated by such species. This lack of pioneering quality in ducks like the redhead and canvasback may be the reason for their low numbers and poor showing in the face of much environmental development in their ranges.

Waterfowl Inventory. One of the most difficult and necessary tasks which confronts the wildlife manager is taking an inventory of waterfowl. Because of the ease with which these birds move about and their habit of ranging extensively, counts of birds on small local areas are of less importance than inventories on larger units. In general, waterfowl censuses are taken on relatively large breeding units. However, waterfowl counts are needed on small units of water areas, such as an isolated bay, an inland lake, or pothole, for a comparison of the numbers of breeding birds from year to year. However, such counts may fluctuate in numbers because of changes in available food and existing water conditions without any significant change in the population as a whole.

The opposite extreme, as to the extent of area for an adequate count, is the continental census. Several methods have been used in determining the numerical status of waterfowl in North America, namely, (1) estimating the relative numbers on the flyways, (2) calculating the population by knowing the number banded and proportions of banded birds among total number shot, (3) actual counts over extensive areas of the breeding grounds by crews on the ground and in airplanes. Local wintering populations have been determined by counting the number of waterfowl among rafting birds on aerial photographs.

The Lincoln index-census method is a calculation based on the number of banded and nonbanded waterfowl killed by hunters during the open shooting season. Lincoln (26) noted that the number of banded birds killed annually was approximately 12 per cent of the birds banded annually over a period of years. With this in mind, a sample census calculation can be made as follows:

Banded birds killed = 12%

Total number of birds killed in a given year = 5,000,000

P = total population of waterfowl

$$P = \text{kill} \times \frac{100}{12}$$

$$P = 5{,}000{,}000 \times 8.5 = 42{,}500{,}000$$

This census method obviously can be used only with the aid of a nationwide system of banding stations, such as is maintained by the U.S. Fish and Wildlife Service, and an accurate report of the total number of both banded and unbanded birds killed. As pointed out by Leopold (45 *g.r.*), this method will be in error to the degree that gunners fail to report the kill. Leopold also mentions the fact that while the crippling loss of both banded and unbanded ducks is omitted in the calculations of this census method, this factor probably cancels itself and does not alter the net results of the calculation. Furthermore, wildlife administrators are well aware of the tendency of some hunters to exaggerate their bag while others choose to underrate their hunting ability; but this should have little effect on the final census figures since sportsmen are quite consistent in these peculiar tendencies.

The U.S. Fish and Wildlife Service has developed a system of continental waterfowl surveys which covers samplings of waterfowl conditions each year beginning with the hunting season and including an inspection of the wintering grounds and along the flyways and on the breeding grounds. From the data assembled, the regulations for the next hunting season are established. Federal refuge personnel, flyway biologists, research workers, state and provincial officials, state and Federal game wardens, and volunteer workers all pool their knowledge of the current year's conditions in relation to waterfowl.

One of the most productive operations of these observers is the transect-sampling procedure. This is the process of inspecting a given route through the duck breeding grounds either on foot, by canoe, with a car, or by airplane. Along such routes standard observations are taken as to water conditions, number of waterfowl, predators, land use, and any incidental observations that affect the waterfowl. Directions are so specific and clear that the same route can be covered each year even though the personnel may change. These surveys are made as late as possible in the breeding season but early enough so that the information can be used to determine the current hunting regulations. The surveys along the transect are usually made in July.

Three standard types of data are collected by the U.S. Fish and Wildlife Service in making continental waterfowl surveys. These are the composition of the waterfowl for a given area, the average number of waterfowl per square mile, and the average number of three classes of young, namely, newly hatched or downy young, Class I; intermediate-aged young, Class II; flappers or young nearly ready to fly, Class III.

Samples of the three types of data are given below for illustration. These are from figures compiled by Murdy (34) for South Dakota for 1950.

Table 15-8. Data on Waterfowl Composition for South Dakota for the Year 1950
From Ground Transits in 49 Counties (34)

Species	No. of total pairs		Per cent composition	
	1949	1950	1949	1950
Blue-winged teal	2,227	2,413	45.2	43.2
American pintail	829	1,084	16.8	19.4
Mallard	853	975	17.3	17.5
Common shoveler	426	513	8.7	9.2
Gadwall	260	261	5.3	4.7
Redhead	161	151	3.3	2.7
North American ruddy duck	53	84	1.1	1.5
Lesser scaup	64	36	1.3	0.7
American widgeon (baldpate)	36	45	0.7	0.8
Canvasback	13	19	0.3	0.3
Total	4,922	5,581	100.0	100.0

The total density of ducks on a 309-square-mile sample in 1949 and 1950 was 25.4 and 31.0 per square mile respectively.

In 1950 the average brood sizes as indicated by the three classes of young were as follows:

Table 15-9. Average Brood Sizes for Three Age Classes of Waterfowl in South Dakota for 1950 (34)

Species	Class I		Class II		Class III		Total	
	No. of broods	Av. size of broods	No. of broods	Av. size of broods	No. of broods	Av. size of broods	No. of broods	Av. size of broods*
Blue-winged teal	107	8.11	80	7.15	62	7.42	249	7.67
Mallard	35	7.06	18	7.39	16	6.94	69	7.12
American pintail	22	5.00	15	3.73	46	5.30	83	4.95
Common shoveler	6	7.67	3	6.67	14	5.82	26	7.00
Gadwall	27	7.19	25	7.32	12	7.92	64	7.38
North American ruddy duck	8	5.50	8	6.63	1	5.00	17	5.00
Redhead	9	7.56	2	9.00	..	....	11	7.82
American widgeon (baldpate)	2	9.00	3	6.33	1	7.00	6	7.33
Canvasback	1	9.00	1	7.00	..	....	2	5.50

* While some of the average values in this column, notably that given for the canvasback duck, appear to be in error, they are given as published in the original source of these data.

Sometime previous to 1946, the status of waterfowl appeared to have reached a peak in population numbers, and a decline had already set in (36). The figures for 1945 and 1946 were considerably below the estimates for 1944 and gave the total number of waterfowl as being possibly below the 100 million mark. Increases in the number of gunners during the years 1940–1950 have placed a heavier burden on the waterfowl and further tended to reduce their numbers. Hunters have penetrated farther north, and no duck area is free from a heavy hunting pressure. As the greater demand for human food production increases, more and more wild land will be converted to agricultural use, with a subsequent decline in the natural waterfowl range. On the credit side of the ledger, however, there is the evidence that more facts are known about waterfowl than formerly and that the administrative agencies with the experience of former "duck depressions" are better organized to combat the bad effects of a waterfowl population slump. Both the United States and Canadian waterfowl management agencies are actively operating to improve the breeding grounds. The shooting public should be, at least, better able to understand and appreciate drastic shooting restrictions if such are now necessary to improve future waterfowl conditions.

Regional Waterfowl Habitats. To fully understand the intricate problems of waterfowl production, it would be necessary to know in detail the conditions of land and water the length and breadth of the continent. Such great variety of habitat exists in places for feeding, resting, and escape as to almost defy description.

There are, however, extensive regions that are used by several species of waterfowl for wintering and breeding. These regions include the Atlantic Coast from Nova Scotia to Florida, the coast of the Gulf of Mexico from Florida to Yucatan, the pothole country of the central Canadian provinces, Bear River Marshes, and the Central Valley of California. The Atlantic and Gulf Coasts are primarily wintering grounds. The pothole country is almost exclusively a breeding ground, and Bear River Marshes and the Central Valley of California are both.

Extremely careful research has been carried on for years by both state and Federal agencies on conditions found in these habitats. In the brief pages that follow, an attempt has been made to give the reader a picture of the localities mentioned.

WATERFOWL HABITAT OF THE ATLANTIC COAST[2]

The primary value of the Atlantic Coast as a waterfowl habitat is its winter use by birds whose summer ranges lie far to the north or northwest and generally in the interior of the continent. From November to March it provides accommodation for the entire continental stocks of greater snow geese and Atlantic brant, for the bulk of all the Canada

[2] This section is contributed by Joseph A. Hagar, Massachusetts Department of Conservation.

geese and black ducks produced east of Hudson's Bay, for major portions of the greater scaup, scoters, and canvasbacks which originate in northwestern and central Canada, for large contingents of dabbling and diving ducks from the prairie marshes of southern Canada, and for the wood duck and eiders of New England and eastern Canada.

Clearly, the wintering grounds of the Atlantic Coast are important, but no description of them can be both short and complete, for so great a diversity of using species implies a corresponding diversity of environmental conditions. In the interest of brevity, we must omit reference to the fresh-water habitats of the region, increasingly extensive toward the south, because they differ only in minor detail from those found in other parts of the continent. As the opposite extreme, we may disregard the deep-water ranges of the sea ducks because they offer so little opportunity for change by management. This leaves for consideration the tidal zone which lies between. This is the characteristic and interesting feature of Atlantic Coast habitat, for it results from the introduction of two new factors into the composition of the usual types of inland waterfowl range. So let us see what these factors are.

Generally speaking, the associations of the game ducks and geese are not with land alone, or with water alone, but with the edge where the two come together. In structural terms, a waterfowl marsh is a zone where land is building out into open water, and where open water, at times of flood, periodically reclaims some of its former hold on the land. Everything about a marsh—its surface contours, its fertility, its vegetation, its animal inhabitants—is influenced, and in the final analysis fixed, by the details of this interplay between land and water. Away from the coast the interplay is relatively simple; the water is usually fresh and reasserts its dominance over the land only at irregular intervals of weeks or months. On the coast the give-and-take is more complex because the twice-a-day cycles of the ocean tides are involved; there is, first, a constant flux between salt water and fresh, and second, a never-ceasing change of level, up and down. In a coastal marsh the vegetation, in particular, is determined by the most delicate balances between salinity and water levels, and in contrast to any fresh-water marsh, the changes are rhythmic. The whole tidal zone represents a transition, within the vertical range of a few feet, from the wetness and saltiness of its ocean edge to the nonsaltiness and relative dryness of its landward edge. This is its essence, which underlies every detail of its outward forms.

And now, what are these outward forms? Infinitely variable from place to place, they still fall into two broad categories. One, which is a step from the salinity and maximum tide action of the ocean toward the land, is the enclosed bay or sound. The other, a step from the elevation and dryness of the land toward the ocean, is the salt marsh. They merge by almost imperceptible degrees, both with each other and with their extremes on either side, but brief descriptions of their most typical features will supply what we look for here: a working picture of coastal waterfowl habitat for the wildlife manager.

The bays lie behind the outermost barrier beaches, through which, at intervals, they are connected with the ocean by inlets which may be wide and deep, because they afford egress to great rivers like the Delaware, or shallow and choked with sandbars as on the Jersey and Carolina coasts. The bays themselves are of the same two sorts—some deep

FIG. 15-5. Tidal marshes such as this one in South Carolina are favored wintering grounds for waterfowl. (*Edward H. Graham, U.S. Soil Conservation Service.*)

and tempestuous in their outer reaches but shoaling inshore, like the Chesapeake, others relatively shallow throughout their length and breadth, like Barnegat. Their surfaces are largely unbroken by islands or emergent meadows, but their underwater contours are characterized by extensive level flats. Tidal fluctuation runs ordinarily to 2 or 3 feet, with extremes of 5 or 6, and salinity varies widely, depending on the flow of ocean water through the inlets and the volume of fresh water coming in from the land side. The sequence of plant forms begins with eelgrass (*Zostera* and *Ulva*) in the saltiest outer reaches of the bays, and progresses through sago pondweed and the other brackish-water *Potamogetons* to wild celery (*Vallisneria*) and the fresh-water shoreline emergents of the inshore coves and the tributary rivers. The broad eelgrass zone is an important habitat of brant and Canada geese; the submerged beds of pondweeds and celery, the main gathering grounds of the bay ducks—redheads, canvasbacks, scaups—and of whistling swans.

The salt marsh forms a relatively narrow strip just behind the barrier beaches, and a very wide zone between the bays and the upland. It is laced in every direction with winding creeks, and at intervals is intersected by larger streams carrying fresh water from the land to the bays. Its surface is dotted with shallow pools and deeper pond holes, which may or may not connect with ditches and drains. In all the creeks and thoroughfares, from smallest to largest, the water level rises and falls with the tide in the open bay—at the ebb, a foot or two down the banks, at flood overflowing among the stems of the grasses on the marsh. Coupled with this fluctuation of level are changes in salinity, for at high tide the salt water is carried in toward the land, and at low tide the fresh water runs farther out into the bay. There are differences, also, in the level of the marsh itself, for it is not quite so flat as appears at casual glance. Its surface is slightly above the average height of flood tide, and slopes up very gently toward the upland. In addition, the banks of the creeks are built up, by siltation, a few inches higher than the meadows between, so that neither inundation or drainage of the top meadow is uniform. In sum, the whole marsh presents the most intricate interspersion of different degrees of wetness and salinity, and this is the key to its vegetation. Thatch grass (*Spartina alterniflora*) is not harmed by frequent periodic flooding and therefore forms a narrow band of tall thrifty growth along all edges of open water. It also tolerates, but less well, long standing in shallow salty water and so, in a lower, nonfruiting form, is the dominant plant of the poorly drained meadow top. Another cord-grass (*S. patens*) is tolerant of only occasional flooding; it occupies wide zones of the marsh just above the ordinary high-water mark. The bulrushes (*Scirpus*) are less tolerant of salt than the cord-grasses; the salt-marsh bulrush (*S. robustus*) appears in poorly drained spots toward the middle or inner part of the marsh, and then gradually gives way inshore to other members of its genus which prefer still fresher water. Across the whole width of the marsh this succession proceeds, until the vegetation at the edge of the upland is nearly the same as that of a fresh-water marsh. But although the grasses and bulrushes give the salt marsh its characteristic appearance, the important waterfowl foods are the submerged aquatics, widgeon-grass (*Ruppia*), and sago pondweed, and the pools and creeks where these two grow in greatest abundance are the gathering places of the chief marsh ducks—mallards, blacks, baldpates, teal of two kinds, and pintails.

Here, then, in these descriptions of its bays and salt marshes, is the briefest possible summary of the Atlantic Coast as a waterfowl habitat.

WATERFOWL HABITAT ALONG THE COAST OF THE GULF OF MEXICO[3]

Gulf Coast marshes are famed as wintering grounds for a high percentage of the continent's waterfowl population. Ducks and geese of many species winter here, and almost the total continental population of such species as the blue goose make this their winter home. A few species, such as the mottled duck and fulvous tree duck, find nesting habitat here most attractive. These marshes comprise some of the nation's most favored shooting grounds.

The Louisiana marshes, particularly, supply the major part of our muskrat and nutria crop. In Louisiana, some 10,000 trappers annually take from 3 to 9 million muskrats from the 4 million acres of coastal marshes. These extensive marshes may roughly be divided into three major classes: (1) the great delta of the Mississippi River, (2) the more extensive subdelta areas that in not too distant geological history were at one time the active delta zones, (3) the extensive prairie marshes which are best illustrated in the coastal region of west Louisiana and east Texas. Each of these major types can be further divided into several subdivisions that are quite distinct.

Back from this coastal strip, other types of choice waterfowl habitat occur. The wide flood plains, the grassy sloughs, and the extensive river bottoms, with their bounteous mast crops of acorns and nuts, afford an almost unlimited food supply for America's mallards, pintails, and other waterfowl that are not averse to a flooded timbered habitat. In this timbered zone of great fluctuation of water levels are many lakes such as Catahoula in central Louisiana which, because of its unique and periodic type of water fluctuation, provides a bumper crop of excellent duck foods in most years. The water level becomes low in late summer and fall, during which time the extensive mudflats produce a luscious crop of such choice foods as chufa, water millet, and other grasses and sedges, along with smartweeds, arrowweeds, and a host of other good duck foods. As the water slowly rises in the late fall and winter, the new crop becomes available to the birds. Thus, the fluctuating water level prevents a climax flora from developing, and yearly retains this "transition" type of association which provides the bumper crop of waterfowl foods.

The agricultural rice belt of the South, particularly Texas, Louisiana, and Arkansas, affords irresistible attraction to many waterfowl. Shallow coastal lagoons along the southern coast of Texas afford great attraction to many birds, especially wintering redhead ducks as they feed extensively on the submerged shoal grass (*Halodule wrightii*), widgeon-grass

[3] This section is contributed by Dr. Clarence Cottam, Assistant Director, U.S. Fish and Wildlife Service, Department of the Interior.

(*Ruppia maritima*), manatee grass (*Cymodocea manatorum*), and turtle grass (*Thalassia testudinum*).

The ecology of the Gulf Coast is complex and varied. The growing season is long, and winters generally are mild. Different sections of coastal Louisiana average from 290 to 350 days per year without killing frost. Precipitation, while variable, generally is adequate for heavy plant growth. It averages from 30 to 40 inches from Brownsville to Galveston, Texas, to over 50 inches northward to the Louisiana border. Eastward along the Gulf Coast to southern Florida the average for different sections is from 50 to 60 inches. Summer temperatures and humidities are high over most of the coast. This favors a luxuriant and rapid growth of vegetation, and competition between species is severe.

Delta soils are constantly being built up with a continuous deposition of soil, and generally are fertile. The Mississippi River is said to carry a load of 2 to 3 million tons of soil daily.[4] Natural levees are therefore constantly being built up, and new land is extending rapidly into the Gulf—up to 120 feet per year in some places. Subsidence near the mouth is surprisingly extreme, extending from 4 to 6 inches annually. Obviously these conditions greatly affect vegetative types and successions, which in turn affect waterfowl populations. The first invader on the new mud-flat soil extending into the Gulf is the three-square bulrush (*Scirpus americanus*), a species whose tubers and seeds are attractive to blue and snow geese, and also to a number of species of ducks. Back from the levees, the delta zone is composed of many shallow ponds and mud-flats, their value for waterfowl depending upon the plant species or association of species occurring at any particular time.

The prairie marshes of the coast are basically fresh-water marshes, and the distinctive plant associations occupy vertical ranges in relation to definite water levels in the marshes. The dominant plant associations include extensive solid stands of saw-grass (*Cladium jamaicense*) which in the deeper marshes are of limited use. At slightly higher elevations, and in firmer soil, southern bulrushes (*Scirpus californicus*), giant cut-grass (*Zizaniopsis miliacea*), and cat-tails (*Typha* spp.) dominate.

The most favored wildlife marsh may be described as the shallow marsh where Olney bulrushes (*Scirpus olneyi*), spike-rushes (*Eleocharis* sp.), and water-hyssops (*Bacopa* sp.) are among the more important and typical plants.

Marsh meadows are characterized by various species of cord-grass (*Spartina*) and reed cane (*Phragmites communis*) and are of most waterfowl value to geese following a burn and particularly during high-water periods.

[4] R. J. Russell, 1936. Physiography of the Lower Mississippi Delta. *Cons. Dept. Geol. Survey Bul.* 8, pp. 1–199.

A marsh complex also occurs in which the various associations above described are intimately associated with ponded areas to produce a complex environment used for grazing, agriculture, and wildlife.

THE POTHOLE COUNTRY OF CANADA[5]

The word "pothole," originally a well-defined geological term, has been introduced into waterfowl literature without any attempt at precise definition. Consequently, it is applied loosely to a wide range of situations, which have in common only that the water bodies referred to are small and temporary in nature.

The recession of the last glacier left most of western Canada covered by an uneven layer of glacial drift. Where the ice sheet paused in its northward retreat, masses of earth and stones were piled into low hills, producing the typical knob-and-kettle topography of pothole areas. Drainage has not developed in these hills. Spring runoff collects in the intervening pockets where it gradually disappears by evaporation and seepage during the summer months. In southern Saskatchewan there may be as many as 60 of these small water areas per square mile.

Potholes occurring in the aspen parklands of Manitoba and central Alberta are characteristically surrounded by a fringe of poplar or willow. On the southern plains of Saskatchewan the shore line is open and grassed. Reflecting the higher rainfall and lower evaporation of the aspen park land, and the water areas found therein tend to be less temporary in nature than those of the southern plains, 50 per cent of which may dry by August 1 in a normal year.

On the plains the rougher terrain is grazed while grain farming is practiced where the hills are less steep. Abundant water disperses grazing pressure, and this land use has little adverse effect on waterfowl production. Grain agriculture, on the other hand, almost completely destroys waterfowl habitat, for cultivation is extended to the water's edge, and the pothole itself is cultivated in dry years. In the aspen park lands, grain farming is carried on between the potholes, which are usually left with a border of willow or aspen.

Within the pothole areas of southern Saskatchewan two main types of water areas are found: the typical pothole (so known locally), which is small, basin-shaped and sometimes quite deep, and the slough areas which are larger with basins less well defined. Sloughs and potholes are further differentiated by their characteristic vegetation. Dominant plants of potholes are bur-reed, smartweed, and water parsnip, those of the sloughs, hard-stemmed bulrush, alkali bulrush, and sago pondweed. The bottoms of potholes are firm while the sloughs are soft and mucky. In a dry year the sloughs invariably outlast the potholes.

[5] This section is contributed by W. G. Leitch of Ducks Unlimited.

Prairie potholes are acceptable to waterfowl as territories, and as a result breeding populations are usually heavy in such areas. Sloughs and artificial impoundments are preferred for rearing, and once the broods are hatched there is a definite movement to them.

The breeding population of prairie potholes is composed almost entirely of surface-feeding species. The blue-winged teal is usually most common, closely followed by pintails, shovelers, and mallards. In the potholes of the aspen park lands of Manitoba, where the water areas might be more correctly classified as sloughs, canvasbacks and other diving species are abundant as breeders.

The prairie potholes produce a heavy crop of ducks in good years but are very vulnerable to drought. The most dangerous situation occurs when the spring runoff is sufficient to attract breeding ducks and subsequent drought dries up the water areas before the young ducks can fly. Potholes in the aspen park land are not so dependent on the precipitation of the current season, although they will disappear after a series of dry years.

WATERFOWL HABITAT IN BEAR RIVER MARSHES, UTAH[6]

Fame for the Bear River Marshes in Utah began when Fremont, Stansbury, Bonneville, and other early explorers recorded in their diaries and told tales of the myriads of wildfowl which could be seen where the Bear River entered the Great Salt Lake. Since that time, ornithologists working there have listed some 88 different kinds of waterfowl and wading birds and have estimated at least 2 million waterfowl during the peak migration period in the fall. Certainly, nowhere on the continent can so many different kinds of wildfowl and shore birds be seen in such large numbers so easily.

What makes these marshes so attractive to wildfowl? The answers lie in the histories of the Great Salt Lake and the river itself. Salt Lake is the remnant of old Lake Bonneville, a lake which at one time was over a thousand feet deep and covered most of Utah and Nevada, and fair segments of southern Idaho and southeastern Oregon. As Lake Bonneville receded, it left in its wake on the valley floor a series of extensive land benches and finally many miles of alkaline mud flats bordering the present shore line. Meanwhile, the Bear River, entering the Great Salt Lake on the northeast, cut its course back and forth across the benches as they became exposed, producing numerous channels, oxbows, islands, knolls, sloughs, and small lakes, and finally spreading its water over the mud flats to form larger lakes varying in depth from a thin film to about 3 feet.

[6] This section is contributed by Dr. Clarence Cottam, Assistant Director, U.S. Fish and Wildlife Service, Department of the Interior.

Soils of the benchlands became leached of their salts, but those of the lower areas were usually poorly aerated clays and extremely saline. The high salinity of the soil and the high water table in the lowland areas had a potent influence on the kind and distribution of the upland and marsh plants, while the salinity, turbidity, and muck deposition in the lake areas controlled the nature of the aquatic vegetation. Climatic conditions also had their influence. Annual precipitation is seldom more than 12 inches, and most of this takes place during the winter. Temperatures average about 52°F., while summer winds are strong and hot, adding to the evaporation rate which may amount to as much as .4 inch a day.

In all, some 137 kinds of plants of 37 families have been found in the marshes and on the adjacent banks and knolls. They fall into several well-defined communities. Starting with the open water of the lakes, sago pondweed predominates in the deeper areas and grows most densely at the mouths of contributing channels. The alkali-tolerant widgeon-grass and chara are prominent in the saline shallows. Invertebrates abound and are dominated by chironomids, water boatmen, and diving beetles. Fish life, however, consists almost entirely of carp and chub.

At a slightly higher elevation bordering the open water, the marsh or amphibious plant community is dominated by alkali bulrushes. Prominent, however, are cat-tails, hard-stemmed bulrushes, and Olney bulrushes, which occur in scattered stands and along bank edges. Snails, spiders, and the nymphs of damsel flies, dragonflies, mayflies, and lacewing flies are exceptionally abundant in this community. The alkaline marshes have no turtles and few snakes.

A large segment of the Bear River delta is taken over by the alkali mud flats. These are either barren of vegetation or covered in spots by the low-lying glasswort. The salt content in places runs as high as 31,000 ppm. Aside from the glasswort, salt bushes of several species and other alkali-tolerant chenepodes occur in sparse stands, and salt-grass tends to encroach on the slightly higher levels. Tiger and ground beetles and burrowing spiders frequent the community. The flats appear barren and useless to waterfowl, but appearances are deceiving, for when they are flooded in the fall of the year after the *Salicornia* has matured, they attract many thousands of ducks and geese.

Proceeding to the higher levels of the river banks and greasewood knolls, we find salt-grass, Mediterranean barley, foxtail barley, and rabbit-foot grass. Where the alkali has been leached, we find black and peach-leaved willows bordering the channels and weeds of many species taking over as succession progresses. All of these form a nesting zone for the puddle ducks. The greasewood association occurs on knolls and low-lying islands, and when not too dense it provides an excellent feeding ground for both snow geese and honkers.

This combination creates an environment which adequately meets the requirements of most species of waterfowl for nesting, brooding, rearing, molting, and migration. No one factor is more important than another. It is the set of conditions which is all-important.

THE CENTRAL VALLEY OF CALIFORNIA[7]

That portion of California known as the Central Valley is a basin comprised of the valleys of two rivers: the Sacramento on the north, and the San Joaquin on the south. These rivers join in the large "delta" area and have their common outlet to the Pacific Ocean through San Francisco Bay and the Golden Gate.

The Central Valley Basin contains about one-third of the area of California. The main valley floor is, essentially, a broad alluvial plain occupying about one-third of the entire Central Valley Basin area. It is this alluvial plain of the valley floor which provides most of the waterfowl habitat, both natural and artificial, in the Central Valley.

Agricultural development and exploitation of the valley's resources have reduced natural habitat almost to the nadir. In the Sacramento Valley, only portions of the Butte Sinks, Colusa Trough, and small overflow areas along the river courses still possess natural marsh vegetation similar to that which once occupied vast acreages of the valley. These remaining marshes support species of cat-tails, bulrushes, and sedges. In the San Joaquin Valley, the grasslands provide the only remaining natural habitat, and even this area is grazed by livestock.

Today, artificial waterfowl habitat is the more important in maintaining the vast numbers of waterfowl that winter in the Central Valley. Since the Sacramento Valley contains one-third of the irrigable land area and two-thirds of the water supply of the Central Valley, a gigantic water-development project, known as the Central Valley Project, has been evolved to correct this inequitable distribution of land and water. Constructed features of this project, as well as other flood-control, hydroelectric, irrigation, and domestic water developments, have altered the runoff of the basin streams; dams form foothill lakes where none were present before; canals and drainage ditches provide a pattern of water channels dissimilar to natural drainage systems; and man-made bypasses and leveed stream channels have replaced most of the natural flood channels and meanders of the valley streams.

Agricultural crops utilized by waterfowl include rice, barley, wheat,

[7] This section is contributed by Fred G. Evenden, Jr., and Clarence Cottam, U.S. Fish and Wildlife Service, Department of the Interior.

and alfalfa and clover pastures. Rice and irrigated pasture lands generally occur on those reclaimed lands that once supported natural marsh vegetation. This change to agricultural crops has been taken in stride by the waterfowl, but their feeding activities on agricultural lands have created serious crop-depredation problems. To offset this, the California Department of Fish and Game and the U.S. Fish and Wildlife Service have developed a broad management program for the refuges located in the Central Valley. This program emphasizes the production of agricultural crops for waterfowl food, in addition to the construction of ponds to provide refuge, loafing grounds, and natural foods for waterfowl. The state of California has one such waterfowl refuge, or managed area, in the Sacramento Valley, two in the delta, and one in the San Joaquin Valley. The U.S. Fish and Wildlife Service has three such waterfowl refuges in the Sacramento Valley and one in the San Joaquin Valley.

The Central Valley's primary function for waterfowl is as a wintering ground for several million geese, ducks, and other water birds. Canada geese, white-fronted geese, snow geese, mallards, baldpates, pintails, green-winged teal, shovelers, and coots are the most common wintering waterfowl. Large numbers of diving ducks winter on the deeper waters of the delta and San Francisco Bay.

About 35 per cent of California's waterfowl production is derived from the Central Valley, and most of this occurs on the irrigated rice lands of the Sacramento Valley. Mallards, gadwalls, pintails, cinnamon teal, and coots are the principal summering species.

REFERENCES

1. Bennett, Logan J. 1938. The blue-winged teal, its ecology and management, Collegiate Press, Inc., of Iowa State College, Ames, Iowa.
2. Bourn, Warren S., and Clarence Cottam. 1939. The effect of lowering water levels on marsh wildlife. *Trans. 4th North Amer. Wildlife Conf.* Pp. 343–350.
3. Bowman, Isaiah. 1935. Our expanding and contracting "desert." *Geog. Rev.* **25**(1):43–61.
4. Cartwright, B. W. 1941. Restoration of waterfowl habitat in western Canada. *Trans. 5th North Amer. Wildlife Conf.* Pp. 377–382.
5. ———. 1944. Waterfowl brood counts in Manitoba, Saskatchewan and Alberta, 1935, 1938–1942. *Jour. Wildlife Mangt.* **8**(1):79–80.
6. Coburn, Don R., David W. Metzlev, and Ray Treichler. 1951. A study of absorption and retention of lead in wild waterfowl in relation to clinical evidence of lead poisoning. *Jour. Wildlife Mangt.* **15**(2):186–192.
7. Cottam, Clarence. 1947. Waterfowl at the crossroads. *Trans. 12th North Amer. Wildlife Conf.* Pp. 67–85.
8. ———. 1949. Limiting factors of present waterfowl knowledge. *Trans. 14th North Amer. Wildlife Conf.* Pp. 42–57.

9. Day, Albert M. 1950. North American waterfowl. *Trans. 15th North Amer. Wildlife Conf.* Pp. 99–106.
10. Elder, William H. 1950. Measurement of hunting pressure in waterfowl by means of X-ray. *Trans. 15th North Amer. Wildlife Conf.* Pp. 490–504.
11. Furniss, O. C. 1935. The sex ratio in ducks. *Wilson Bul.* **47**(4):277–278.
12. Girard, George L. 1941. The mallard: Its management in Montana. *Jour. Wildlife Mangt.* **5**(3):233–259.
13. Gordon, Seth. 1950. California's fish and game program revised May 15, 1950, Report to wildlife conservation board, Senate of the State of California.
14. Hagar, Joseph A. 1950. Black duck mortality in the Parker River region, winter of 1949–50. Unpublished report, Massachusetts Conservation Department, Bureau Wildlife Research and Management, Boston.
15. Hammond, M. C. 1950. Some observations on sex ratio of ducks contracting botulism in North Dakota. *Jour. Wildlife Mangt.* **14**(2):209–214.
16. Hawkins, Arthur S., and Frank C. Bellrose. 1939. The duck flight and kill along the Illinois River during the fall of 1938. *Amer. Wildlife.* **28**(4): 178–186.
17. Hochbaum, H. Albert. 1939. Waterfowl studies at Delta, Manitoba, 1938. *Trans. 4th North Amer. Wildlife Conf.* Pp. 389–394.
18. ———. 1946. Recovery potentials in North American waterfowl. *Trans. 11th North Amer. Wildlife Conf.* Pp. 403–418.
19. ———. 1947. The effect of concentrated hunting pressure on waterfowl breeding stock. *Trans. 12th North Amer. Wildlife Conf.* Pp. 53–64.
20. Hopkins, R. C., F. A. Hartmeister, R. W. Michalek, L. R. Jahn, and W. M. Kitz. 1950. Waterfowl breeding ground survey in Wisconsin, 1950. Waterfowl populations and breeding conditions summer 1950—with notes on Woodcock and Wilson's Snipe. *U.S. Fish and Wildlife Serv., Spec. Sci. Rpt.: Wildlife* 8, pp. 194–202.
21. Jordan, James S., and Frank C. Bellrose. 1950. Shot alloys and lead poisoning in waterfowl. *Trans. 15th North Amer. Wildlife Conf.* Pp. 155–170.
22. Kalmbach, E. R. 1937. Crow-waterfowl relationship in the Prairie Provinces. *Trans. 2d North Amer. Wildlife Conf.* Pp. 380–392.
23. ———. 1938. A comparative study of nesting waterfowl on the Lower Souris Refuge: 1936–1937. *Trans. 3d North Amer. Wildlife Conf.* Pp. 610–613.
24. ———. 1939. Nesting success: its significance in waterfowl reproduction. *Trans. 4th North Amer. Wildlife Conf.* Pp. 591–604.
25. Lee, Forest B. 1950. Waterfowl breeding ground survey in Minnesota, 1950. Waterfowl populations and breeding conditions summer 1950—with notes on Woodcock and Wilson's Snipe. *U.S. Fish and Wildlife Serv., Spec. Sci. Rpt.: Wildlife* 8, pp. 176–182.
26. Lincoln, Frederick C. 1930. Calculating waterfowl abundance on the basis of banding returns. *U.S. Dept. Agr. Cir.* 118.
27. ———. 1932. A decade of bird banding in America. *Smithsn. Inst. Ann. Rpt.* Pp. 327–351.
28. Low, Jessup B. 1940. Production of the redhead (*Nyroca americana*) in Iowa. *Wilson Bul.* **52**(3):153–164.
29. ———. 1941*a*. The ecology and management of the redhead, *Nyroca americana* in Iowa. *Ecol. Monog.* **15**:35–69.

30. ———. 1941*b*. Nesting of the ruddy duck in Iowa. *Auk*. **58**(10):506–517.
31. Martin, A. C., and F. M. Uhler. 1939. Food of game ducks in the United States and Canada. *U.S. Dept. Agr. Tech. Bul.* 634
32. Mayr, Ernst. 1939. The sex ratio in wild birds. *Amer. Nat.* **73**(745):156–179.
33. Murdy, Horatio W. 1945. A quantitative analysis of waterfowl productivity. Unpublished manuscript, University of Massachusetts, Amherst.
34. Murdy, Ray. 1950. Waterfowl breeding ground survey in South Dakota, 1950. Waterfowl populations and breeding conditions summer 1950—with notes on Woodcock and Wilson's Snipe. *U.S. Fish and Wildlife Serv., Spec. Sci. Rpt.: Wildlife* 8, pp. 147–152.
35. Pirnie, Miles D. 1935. Michigan waterfowl management. Michigan Department of Conservation, Lansing.
36. Titus, Harold. 1946. Duck production falters. *Field and Stream.* **51**(5):22, 107–108.
37. Van Den Akker, John B., and Vanez T. Wilson. 1949. Twenty years of bird banding at Bear River migratory bird refuge, Utah. *Jour. Wildlife Mangt.* **13**(4):359–376.
38. Whitlock, S. C., and H. J. Miller. 1947. Gunshot wounds in ducks. *Jour. Wildlife Mangt.* **11**(3):279–281.
39. Williams, Cecil S., and William H. Marshall. 1938. Duck nesting studies, Bear River Migratory Bird Refuge, Utah, 1937. *Jour. Wildlife Mangt.* **2**(2):29–48.

CHAPTER 16

Management of Waterfowl[1]

INTRODUCTION

The Waterfowl Situation Today. Wildlife held its own on the North American continent until the white settlers began to appropriate its range. Although the aborigines lived principally on fish, game, and uncultivated native plants, they caused no permanent injury to these resources. This was because the simple agricultural operations of the Indians did not extensively deplete the soil, did not affect natural water levels, and neither changed nor destroyed the natural vegetation that provided food and cover for wild creatures. The white man, impelled by the necessity of increasing food supplies to support a growing population, began at once the exploitation of the soil, with results disastrous to wildlife and later to the human population as well.

By 1930 the situation of migratory waterfowl in the United States had become precarious. Drainage of millions of acres of marshland had deprived them of essential habitat. Improved roads and means of transportation facilitated access to the birds, and each fall they ran the deadly gamut of a constantly increasing army of hunters equipped with modern weapons and more powerful and dependable ammunition. In addition they were, as always, subjected to unpreventable losses from diseases, climatic disturbances, and predators. To maintain the waterfowl population, to say nothing of increasing it, demands a tremendous annual replacement.

[1] This chapter is contributed by Dr. Ira N. Gabrielson, Wildlife Management Institute, and was prepared while the author was in the U.S. Fish and Wildlife Service. It was intended as an outline of the management practices and techniques being followed on Federal waterfowl refuges. Since its publication has been long delayed, a revision seemed necessary. Members of the Branch of Game Management, Branch of Wildlife Research, and Branch of Wildlife Refuges have generously checked the manuscript and supplied additional material or suggested revisions based on experience acquired since the original draft was prepared. It is, therefore, essentially as originally planned, an outline of present U.S. Fish and Wildlife Service management techniques with some additions or suggestions from other sources.

Legislation. In 1900 only 9 states prohibited spring shooting of migratory waterfowl, and during the following decade only 5 more followed their example. It became more and more apparent that as the birds recognized no state lines in their movements, a central authority must be empowered to impose a law national in application.

Such a law was passed on March 4, 1913, when Congress enacted the Migratory Bird Law, conferring upon the U.S. Department of Agriculture the authority to adopt regulations fixing closed seasons. This was followed shortly by negotiation of a treaty with Great Britain for the protection of migratory birds in the United States and Canada, the treaty being ratified and proclaimed by the President on December 8, 1916. A similar treaty with Mexico came into effect on March 15, 1937.

The Migratory Bird Conservation Act of February 18, 1929, in furtherance of the purposes of the Migratory Bird Treaty with Great Britain, authorized the acquisition of areas of land and water for the establishment of a national system of inviolate sanctuaries for waterfowl and other migratory birds.

Numerous other laws designed to protect wildlife including waterfowl have been passed by state and Federal legislative bodies. These laws increasingly tend to authorize the establishment of hunting, trapping, and fishing seasons based upon surveys of available surpluses.

The basic concept of all these laws—the limitation of the legal kill by hunting—is a recognition of the value of the oldest management device. Laws, or regulations issued by authority of law, usually take the form of bag, possession, or season limits. Other limitations less widely used prohibit the use of methods that are wasteful or that becomes too effective as killing devices. Such regulations to the extent that they are observed or can be enforced are a necessary and valuable tool that can be used to insure the return of an adequate supply of breeding birds to the nesting grounds.

It is a widely accepted belief that the illegal take of waterfowl is equivalent to an appreciable percentage of the legal harvest, which means a direct loss of next season's breeding birds.

Law enforcement and the growth of better standards of law observance are the only known methods of reducing this drain on the resource. Both must be vigorously pursued while other efforts to provide more food and habitat at strategic places are under way.

Enforcement has never been adequate. It has been from the beginning a joint Federal-state program which has been good in many places but never sufficiently staffed to do a consistently good job in all waterfowl areas. The Federal staff has varied from 50 to 100 men in recent years, with the states, many of them with limited funds, supplying about 1,800 men, full- or part-time, in waterfowl work as deputy Federal agents.

Human nature being what it is, the need for stringent regulations, effectively enforced, will always be present in the waterfowl management program. These regulations must be based on more and more accurate appraisals of the breeding stocks, the season's production, and the amount of legal kill which can safely be taken.

Migration Studied through Banding. For many years the U.S. Fish and Wildlife Service and one of its predecessors, the U.S. Biological Survey, have been supervising the study of bird movements by the marking or banding of large numbers of individuals. Return of the bands or a report of the band numbers is requested whenever the birds are retaken. On migratory waterfowl, reports are ultimately received for approximately 1 out of every 6 birds; for songbirds the proportion is much lower. Over 5½ million birds have been banded, and from the returns a mass of data has been compiled that indicates clearly certain fundamentals in the behavior of many species, including migratory waterfowl. It is on these banding records and on information accumulated by biological studies over a period of more than 50 years on the breeding, wintering, and feeding grounds of the birds, that migratory-waterfowl management policies are based.

Migratory-waterfowl Flyways. The existence of four principal migratory-waterfowl flyways has been indicated by the bird-banding studies. In the northern breeding areas, these flyways overlap to a considerable extent, but there are distinct migration lines within their boundaries. The Pacific flyway lying west of the Rocky Mountains is clearly defined and overlaps others only in the breeding grounds in northern British Columbia, Alberta, and farther north in Canada and in Alaska.

The Central or Rocky Mountain flyway is relatively narrow and is normally used by the smallest number of birds. The Mississippi flyway, sweeping from northern Alaska eastward to Baffin Island and converging southward, narrows into a funnel in the lower Mississippi Valley through which the birds pass and spread along the Gulf Coast. The Atlantic flyway, drawing from a wider northern territory, Northwest Territory to Greenland, also narrows southward and is restricted to a strip of country east of the Appalachian Mountains. The bulk of the birds drawn from the vast northern breeding grounds spend the winter from Long Island to Texas. Some go on to the West Indies, Mexico, and even further southward.

Flyway banding studies have revealed that adult waterfowl are rather consistent in their behavior. Individuals return year after year to the same breeding ground, so long as that breeding ground remains in a satisfactory condition. The same bird also may for years use the same wintering ground and traverse about the same path in migration. There is a record of one banded mallard hen that nested 9 consecutive years

Fig. 16-1. Pacific waterfowl flyway.

near the same spot in western Nebraska. The young birds show a tendency to scatter, and it is these, rather than adults whose habits are rather fixed, that occupy new breeding grounds and populate restored areas.

An interesting development has come from investigations in the Great Bear River Marshes, Utah, where bird banding has been carried on for a number of years. The returns indicate that redheads from these

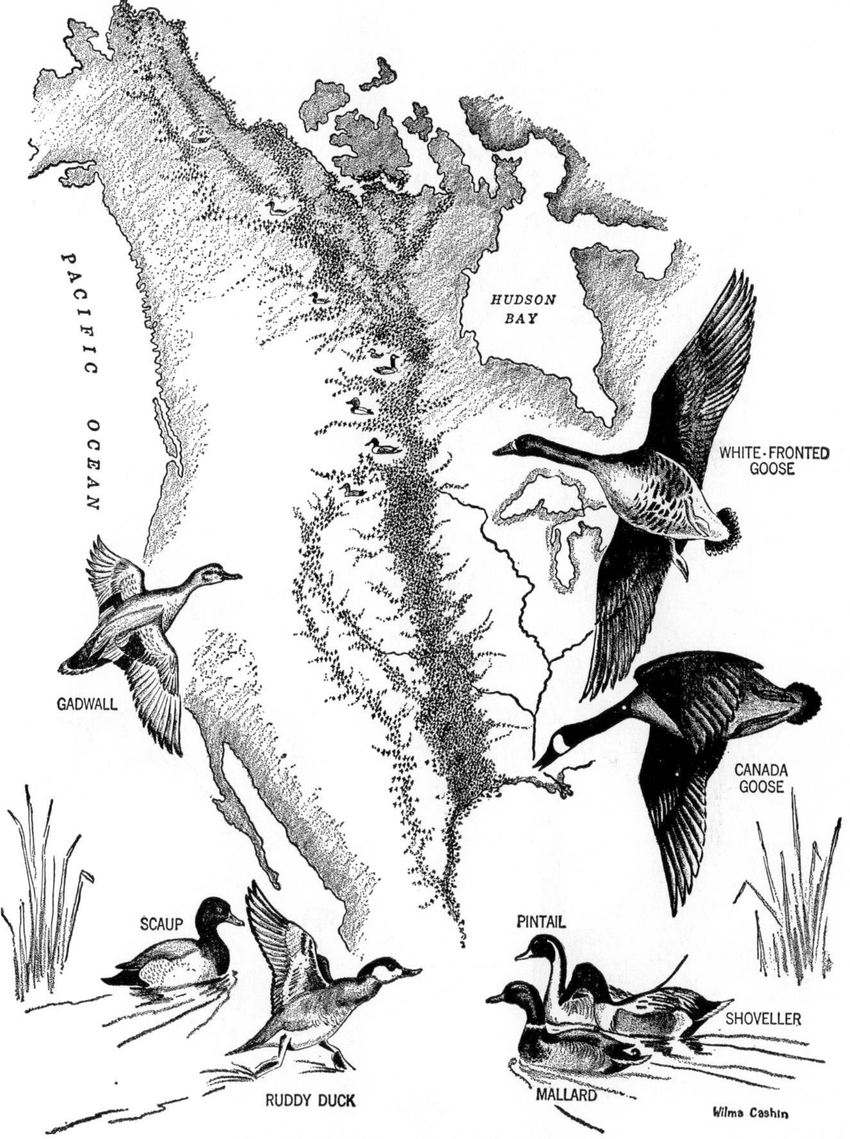

Fig. 16-2. Central waterfowl flyway.

marshes travel by two distinct flyways and winter in two widely separated areas. Some go westward to the Pacific and winter along the coasts of southern California, in Baja, lower California, and other parts of Mexico. A second group migrates southeastward across the mountains, down the Rio Grande and other rivers of Texas, and winters on the Gulf Coast from the vicinity of Corpus Christi, south into Mexico.

Fig. 16-3. Mississippi waterfowl flyway.

Another small contingent, most likely only a few scattered birds of the year, moves north and becomes mixed with birds traveling east through the Great Lakes region.

Waterfowl Inventories. The estimated number of waterfowl in the early days varied with the enthusiasm and imagination of the estimator,

FIG. 16.4. Atlantic waterfowl flyway.

but there is general agreement that by 1935, owing to the combined efforts of drainage, drouth, and shooting, the waterfowl population had become critically low. At that time drastic hunting restrictions were adopted, and a gigantic habitat-restoration and improvement program by both state and Federal agencies was aided with both money and manpower by the emergency-work programs. Similar programs were soon developed in Canada.

By 1942, through the combined benefits of improved climatic conditions, restrictive legislation, and the habitat restoration program, the waterfowl population increased appreciably. The population reached a peak in 1944, and since that time it has had a downward trend in spite of more restrictive regulations and the continuing efforts to increase habitat.

A number of reasons are advanced for this condition. Among those given considerable weight by waterfowl students are the increase in the number of hunters, the reduction in breeding areas by agricultural or other developments as compared with the restoration and development of breeding areas by all agencies, and the decrease of suitable wintering and feeding habitat south of the breeding grounds that causes a concentration of the birds in remaining habitat.

The methods of taking inventories are developing so rapidly that any detailed discussion would be quickly out of date. The development of a large body of trained wildlife men since 1935 and their employment in state and Federal agencies and by comparable agencies in Canada has made it possible to use better and more accurate methods.

Much reliance is still placed on a winter inventory after all hunting seasons are closed. This comes also when the continental waterfowl population is concentrated in a relatively small area. In recent years methods have been improved and coverage extended to include not only the wintering grounds in the United States but many of the major ones in the West Indies, Mexico, and Central America. This census is used as a measure of the increase or decrease of the breeding stock.

Combined with this is a greatly enlarged coverage of the breeding grounds by groups of trained men that provides a much more reliable index of breeding success and of the crop produced than was possible for the original flyway biologists to secure. These groups use a transect system, both by aerial observation and by ground coverage, as a scientific sampling system. The same transects are used as a basis for comparison from year to year. In addition these crews remain in the field reporting on all factors that may appreciably influence the annual waterfowl production.

Canadian provincial and dominion officers, U.S. Fish and Wildlife Service biologists, and individuals from private organizations participate in Canada, and in the United States nearly all state conservation agencies now have personnel assigned to winter or breeding-ground inventories, or both, as well as to securing data on the kill in their states. Efforts are made to secure comparable data in all these studies, the result being basic data that is becoming increasingly useful each year.

WILDLIFE-REFUGE MANAGEMENT PRACTICES AND TECHNIQUES

Origin of Wildlife Refuges. At the turn of the century, several wildlife species were so reduced in numbers that their survival was a matter of doubt. The bird reservation and sanctuary plan, generally credited to William Dutcher and Abbott H. Thayer, originated at that time. From small beginnings, it has vastly expanded, and large areas where shooting is prohibited have been established.

In 1903, President Theodore Roosevelt, by executive proclamation, established the first national wildlife sanctuary, Pelican Island Bird Refuge in Florida. Within the next 30 years the number of Federal and state wildlife refuges within the United States has increased to an estimated 1,300 in number, while Canada reported 233 Dominion and provincial refuges. These estimates do not include the many sanctuaries in park systems nor those maintained by private organizations or by individuals.

Selection of Refuges and Management Areas for Migratory Waterfowl. To provide for waterfowl it is important to select habitat restoration areas, either refuge or management areas, with reference to the waterfowl flyways. When the birds to be managed move the length of the continent in a single season, it is necessary to provide nesting sites within the breeding ranges, feeding and resting areas at not more than 250- to 300-mile intervals along their migration routes, and sufficient territory within the wintering range to provide for their needs during the season in which they are crowded into the smallest area.

Water Development and Restoration. Decision to impound water should be based upon a previous determination of the biological suitability of the area for waterfowl management. The development plan and operating procedure should afford maximum utility to waterfowl and other species of wildlife. Water and marsh areas under 3 to 5 feet in depth usually are the main food-producing zones. It is important to consider fully all possible variations in the water supply during the growing season as well as the character and distribution of precipitation, which have a direct bearing on flooding and maintaining wildlife pools at the most desirable depth. In the northern latitudes, pools should include areas of 7 feet or more in depth to protect fishes and other aquatic life through the winter.

In planning the development of a wildlife pool it should be remembered that generally production of food and cover is proportionate to the length of the shore line. The broad alluvial flats of a meandering stream afford much better opportunities for developing waterfowl habitat than does a narrow stream valley. Most waterfowl development projects may be classified as one of the following procedures:

1. Damming a stream.
2. Restoring a drained pond or marsh by closing the outlets or by the bringing in of additional water.
3. Impounding surface runoff by diking natural depressions.
4. Developing fresh or brackish water pools in tidal areas by means of dikes and tide gates.
5. Establishing controlled water levels in shallower parts of large storage and flood-control reservoirs.

FIG. 16-5. Horseshoe Lake in southern Illinois, an artificially impounded body of water, is a key stopping point for waterfowl in the Mississippi flyway. (*Leland J. Prater, U.S. Forest Service.*)

In addition, wildlife pools can often be developed by impounding artesian water, excavating sumps, or making low dikes to concentrate water which would otherwise spread over extensive flats and be lost through excessive evaporation. At times considerable improvement may be effected in unbroken marsh areas by excavating or blasting potholes with dynamite or by a system of channels to insure the circulation of water that is beneficial to the production of food.

After an adequate water supply for the proposed impoundment has been assured, a topographic survey should be made of the area to be flooded. This will permit a rather accurate determination of the normal flowage line and of the areas that will require attention in the planting program. As a general rule, a freeboard of from 3 to 5 feet above the ordinary water line should be provided, depending somewhat upon the use made of the adjacent land. The need of nesting cover and agricultural land for producing supplementary food should be carefully considered. In addition it may be found advisable to include some upland habitat, thereby permitting management for other wildlife forms on the same unit.

FIG. 16-6. Alternate land and water in the Bear River Marshes of Utah. Dikes and canals were constructed to control water levels. This is excellent breeding grounds for ducks and geese. (*Rex Gary Schmidt, U.S. Fish and Widlife Service.*)

The type of structures to be used for impoundment and water control is dependent not only on the type of foundation present but may require modification to conform with irrigation and drainage requirements of other lands, or applicable local, state, and Federal laws. In districts subject to malaria, provision for safeguarding public health may be found necessary.

Habitat Improvement Prior to Impoundment. It is desirable that organic debris such as tree stumps and any growing vegetation be removed prior to flooding. The slow disintegration of such material if unremoved will cause the water to remain stained and at a low productive level for several seasons. In at least part of the areas to be flooded, the soil should be broken by disking or plowing to expedite the development of food and cover plants.

If it is planned to manage part of the water for sport fishing, it may be necessary to provide fish shelters or spawning beds. Under ordinary circumstances, however, the development of marsh and aquatic vegetation will provide adequate cover for sport fishes.

Preliminary to planting, a study should be made of the area so that the sowing of species already present in satisfactory quantity may be avoided. Identification of the existing vegetation is desirable, not only to avoid unnecessary propagation of established kinds, but also to take advantage of the clues it may furnish to the selection of additional varieties for planting. Plants which otherwise would be most desirable may have climatic, soil, or water requirements quite different from those that will prevail in the habitat to be developed.

Submerged and emergent aquatic plants furnish by far the greatest proportion of the food of wild ducks. In addition, however, large quantities of waterfowl food can be produced on margins subject to flooding, which, if water is available at the proper season, will make additional food available when most needed. The quantity of food that can be produced through a combination of disking, plowing, planting, and managing the water level on such areas is often greater than can be produced on an equal acreage of permanent aquatic habitat.

Selection of planting materials should be based upon a knowledge of feeding habits of species of waterfowl for which the area will be managed. If the management area lies within the breeding range of diving ducks, such as the canvasback, redhead, or ruddy, which build their nests in emergent vegetation, the development of suitable nesting cover should be a part of the planting program.

Habitat Improvement after Impoundment. If revegetation is left to nature, the natural development of marsh and aquatic plants often results in quick domination of species that are of low value to wildlife or that are otherwise undesirable. To avoid this, it is necessary to propagate plants that give the most promise of success in and adjacent to each unit and which at the same time will be most attractive to the common waterfowl species that need the food. Inability to procure propagating material quickly and cheaply is often responsible for the postponement of vegetative improvement, but meanwhile, noxious species encroach upon territory well suited to good food-and-cover plants. Hence, it is important that the most desirable species be established immediately.

Smartweed, wild millet, and bulrushes should be planted only on the periphery of impoundments or in the zone of water-level fluctuations where conditions during the growing season will be favorable for maturing a seed crop and where subsequent flooding will make these seeds available. It is usually undesirable to plant several species of food plants on the same area. Instead, the sites best adapted for each species should be selected and these plots planted with the idea of establishing colonies from which the plant can spread to occupy those portions of the impoundment best suited to its development. This is particularly important when it is impossible to obtain sufficient seed to permit complete planting of the flowage. It is important that "nursery plots" be planted, in view of quarantine laws which are making more difficult the inter-

Fig. 16-7. Wild rice beds such as this one in northern Wisconsin can be produced by artificial seeding. (*R. Dale Sanders, U.S. Forest Service.*)

state shipments of wild millet, smartweed, and other species classed as weeds. Such patches can serve as a future source of seed supply, in addition to furnishing material for vegetative plantings.

Many planting efforts have been made useless by planting at a time when waterfowl were present in numbers sufficient to eat the seed or tubers. To avoid such losses, it is best to plant after waterfowl have left southern areas or that the planted area be dragged or raked to cover the seeds before flooding.

While the bulrushes and some other food plants commonly found growing in shallow water areas may be flooded to a depth of 3 or more feet, their seeds and those of the smartweeds and wild millet germinate best if planted in moist soil that will not be covered with water for some time after good growth has been attained. Few good stands of these species will be obtained if seed is planted where it will be flooded permanently even to a depth of only 1 or more inches.

It is often desirable to supplement seed planting by using rootstocks, tubers, cuttings, or whole plants, thus expediting the development of the desired vegetation, particularly of species that have seeds which germinate slowly or irregularly. Some of the important marsh plants, such as wild rice and wild millet, are annuals and must be propagated by seed. Submerged aquatics generally produce an annual crop of seeds, but they also produce tubers or winter buds in addition and may, therefore, be established either by seeding, transplanting of whole plants, or by the planting of winter buds or tubers.

Planting the rootstocks of perennial species can be carried out during the growing as well as during the resting season. Best results are obtained ordinarily by making these plantings in early spring before growth is very far advanced or in the fall after it has ceased. Rootstocks should be handled as carefully as nursery stock. Care should be taken to keep them covered with wet burlap or moss during the time they are out of the soil as drying is usually fatal. During the season at which the plants are dormant, there is less likelihood of damage, although even at that time unnecessary exposure to drying should be avoided.

Tubers can be planted safely at any time from fall through early spring. Again, it is important that the material be kept moist and not allowed to become heated in the interval between collecting and planting. If it is necessary to hold tubers or winter buds for more than a short time, they should be stored in cool circulating water. The transplanting of entire plants should be carried on only in the early part of the growing season, as those moved later frequently fail to produce seeds or winter buds before the end of the growing period. In transplanting aquatic plants to new areas, it is best to secure materials from pure stands in order to avoid the introduction of undesirable species.

The smartweeds common on the margins of aquatic or semiaquatic habitats can be propagated readily by cuttings. Sections of the stem having at least two nodes readily establish themselves when planted with one node below the surface in moist or wet soil. Opportunities for establishing smartweed in this manner should not be overlooked, particularly where it is desirable to establish competitive vegetation following the control of noxious species.

Whenever possible, it is best to plant an impoundment before flooding, as it is possible at that time to cover sites not readily accessible later. This practice permits broadcast sowing and disking or dragging to cover the seed. At times it may be possible to use a grain drill, thereby avoiding the heavy cost of hand seeding.

Supplies of seed can usually be obtained from dealers, but often the desired material can be harvested locally at a reasonable cost. Seeds of smartweed, wild millet, bulrushes, and pondweeds can be harvested and stored dry for a considerable period without reducing the germination potential; hence such seeds can frequently be collected well in advance of the time they will be needed.

Smartweed and bulrush seeds are subject to weevil attacks while in dry storage; and to guard against losses from this source, they should be frequently inspected. If weevil activity is noted, the seed should be fumigated with carbon disulphide, in accordance with instructions in *U.S. Department of Agriculture Bulletin* 1483.

Harvesting of Seed. The collection and storage of seeds at low cost requires that the plants be present in relatively large, pure stands. Seeds of wild millet (*Echinochloa crusgalli*), alkali bulrush (*Scirpus paludosus*), Pennsylvania smartweed (*Polygonum pensylvanicum*), as well as the hard- and soft-stemmed bulrushes (*Scirpus acutus* and *S. validus*), may be harvested under favorable conditions with a small combine or other grain-harvesting machinery. Operations should begin as soon as the seeds are mature, because all these heads shatter badly if the plants are allowed to become too ripe.

Sago pondweed (*Potamogeton pectinatus*) seeds may be gathered during the latter part of September by pinching off the ripe seed heads or raking out the plants. The seed-bearing tops should be spread out and thoroughly dried, after which they can be flailed and the seeds screened out or the whole put through a separator to remove the plant stems and other debris. Sago-producing lakes with clean shore lines offer an unusually easy opportunity of obtaining seeds, for the plants with attached seeds are often washed ashore in windrows after early fall storms.

Habitat Management. A major objective of marsh plant management is the production of the maximum food supply at the period of the greatest waterfowl concentrations on that area. As a rule no single waterfowl management area embodies all desirable features, but the plan of management followed should aim at securing the maximum value from each area.

Diving ducks, as a group, are primarily dependent upon aquatic plants and animals, though at times they utilize some of the foods produced by marginal plants in zones of water-level fluctuation. The puddle ducks, on the other hand, live principally upon foods produced in shallow waters or temporarily flooded areas. It can thus be readily determined whether a waterfowl impoundment will provide for both classes of ducks. The value of a flowage to the diving species is generally in proportion to the water area ranging from 3 to 10 feet in depth and to the abundance of food produced therein, and to shoal-water ducks in proportion to the area less than 3 feet in depth and the food-producing area in fluctuation zones. Geese are primarily grazers, although their diet is often supplemented extensively with shallow-water vegetation.

Wild millet and smartweeds are consistently heavy seed producers on the margins of a flowage, but, where the water level is stabilized, the growth will be limited to a relatively narrow zone. Their range may be readily extended on flats where the degree of flooding can be regulated by lowering the water level in spring leaving wide areas of exposed moist flats. Reflooding in fall and maintaining the water at a shallow depth through the spring migration will make the food produced available, especially to the shoal-water ducks.

Such flats, if not occasionally drained dry and plowed or disked, may be taken over by plants having little or no food or cover value. Plowing or disking the soil has the additional advantage of creating an excellent seedbed for wild millet and smartweeds and of encouraging a good growth of these species. The frequency of cultivation must be determined by local conditions, but usually once in 3 years should be sufficient.

Under heavy use, natural food resources may be exhausted long before the birds normally move on to other feeding grounds. In such heavy concentration areas, supplementary food in the form of agricultural crops can sometimes be provided. Mallards, pintails, and baldpates accept such grains as corn, barley, oats, buckwheat, milo, and millet. The first three plant species are generally most valuable during the fall migration, and their availability is increased by pulling a drag or driving a tractor or wagon over the rows. If the plantings are intended primarily to provide food for spring migrants, this process should be omitted if the grains break down during the winter. These methods have been used successfully not only to provide additional food, but also to reduce crop damages on agricultural lands by holding the birds on waterfowl refuge or management areas during critical crop periods.

Both during migration and in winter, geese feed largely upon grass and other herbage. Planting grains so that they will produce a short succulent growth during the period geese are expected to be present is desirable if a large number of birds are to be accommodated for any length of time. Geese browse on young plants of the cereal grains and also on alfalfa, clovers, soybeans, and other grains and grasses.

Winter Feeding. Feeding grain except as outlined above is usually undesirable except in emergencies when other food becomes unavailable. Any apparent necessity for artificial feeding of waterfowl is suggestive of poor management. The birds will always take such easily obtained food and thus give the impression that continued feeding is necessary. However, as soon as it is apparent that the emergency, such as heavy snow or freeze that covers or locks up available food, is over, the waterfowl should be left to forage for themselves and allowed to resume their normal habits.

Supplying Grit. Well-placed piles of grit along the shore line may supply the needs of both waterfowl and upland game birds, but for waterfowl alone graveling the sloping ends of islands or other resting places is also a useful method. In the absence of gravel, coarse sand will serve, although apparently it is not so acceptable. Grit deposits in extensive marsh areas may be covered and thus are useless. In such cases, the

FIG. 16-8. Winter feeding of trumpeter swans and goldeneyes at Red Rock Lakes, Montana. (*Winston E. Banks, U.S. Fish and Wildlife Service.*)

removing of patches of vegetation and soil to expose the gravel is useful.

Overflow Lands. Bottomland hardwoods bordering many of the rivers in south central and southeastern states are subject to varying degrees of flooding during the waterfowl migrating and wintering seasons. An abundance of mast is thus made available to the birds. The management of such areas for waterfowl should be planned to maintain a good distribution of mast-producing trees of which water oak, Nuttall's oak, willow oak, and pin oak are the most valuable. A reasonably close canopy should be maintained in overflow woodlands being managed for waterfowl in order to prevent a rank growth of sapling trees, shrubs, and vines which are of little value to the birds and may prevent them from obtaining the mast.

If bottomland hardwood stands are cut selectively so as not to open the canopy more than 30 per cent at any one time, the feeding area will be largely usable by waterfowl. Black ducks, mallards, and pintails derive the most benefit from this type of management. In some areas there may be opportunity to handle water development in such a manner as to flood bottomland hardwoods in migration seasons or at the time of heavy winter concentration of birds.

Planned Burning. The value of carefully planned and executed burning in the management of waterfowl marshes along the Gulf Coast has been amply demonstrated. The use of fire in managing other coastal, as well as inland, marshes has not yet been fully investigated. Experience in marsh burning in certain fresh-water areas indicates the possibility of temporarily changing the ecological succession where the fire burns with sufficient intensity to destroy rootstocks. Following prolonged drouths the same effect can be obtained by burning coastal marshes wherever inundation is largely controlled by runoff or by wind tides.

Three types of burns are utilized in marsh management: (1) cover or light burns designed to remove old plant debris, thus providing grazing for geese, making food available for other waterfowl, and encouraging the growth of desirable plants; (2) root burns accomplished by a hot fire designed to alter the composition of marsh vegetation (in many instances it will be necessary to follow such burns with planting to establish desirable species and to prevent the growth of undesirable plants); (3) peat burns designed to develop holes in the marsh floor, thus breaking up extensive stands of vegetation and diversifying waterfowl habitat through the creation of potholes.

The difference between root burns and peat burns is merely in degree of intensity. Peat burns cannot be accomplished with any degree of regularity since their success depends upon a heavy accumulation of plant remains and upon a very dry condition in the marsh. Generally speaking, the use of fire is most important in the South, particularly on the coastal marshes, due to the longer growing season and consequent greater accumulation of vegetative debris. On the Gulf Coast in some areas burning followed by moderate cattle grazing is useful in preventing the new growth from quickly becoming too tall and coarse to be of value to geese.

The burning programs for any marsh area should be based on the type of foods produced, on the changes in marsh vegetation that may follow burning, and on the periods during which the burned areas are of greatest utility to waterfowl. It is not always possible to burn some marsh types annually as sufficient growth may not be present to insure a satisfactory fire. In some areas there are dense stands of three-square sedge (*Scirpus americanus*) which are of little use to waterfowl in that condition. However, by burning the beds and impounding surface run-off or tidewater on them, the seeds as well as the rhizomes of the plants are made available to waterfowl.

The rhizomes are relished by Canada and greater snow geese, and the seeds are eaten by most shoal-water ducks.

Nesting Cover. Nesting requirements are quite similar for all shoal-water ducks. Stands of the tall grasses mixed with a small percentage of weeds are generally preferred as cover if the growth is not too dense. Such nesting cover may easily become so dense as to have little value, and unless grazed lightly or mowed occasionally it may become unattractive. The majority of nests are usually located within 300 feet of the water's edge, and their greatest concentration will be found within the first 100 feet of cover. This applies generally to shoal-water ducks but not to black ducks. This latter species may nest a quarter to a half mile or more from water and does not tolerate the nesting density acceptable to other species of the group. Some mallards and pintails also nest at considerable distances from water, but the majority conform to the general pattern of their close relatives.

The diving ducks, with the exception of the goldeneye, nest in stands of bulrush or cat-tail, and such cover should be preserved or provided on management areas within the breeding range of these birds.

Canada geese show a preference for broken marsh areas where their nests can be built on muskrat houses or on natural accumulations of coarse vegetation above the general level of the marsh surface. Therefore, a fair population of muskrats is of value in marsh areas which may be utilized by nesting geese.

Nesting Boxes. Nesting sites for tree nesting ducks are in many places scarce or entirely lacking. In their proper ranges, breeding populations of the wood duck and goldeneye can be increased by developing potential nesting cavities in timbered areas or by building nest boxes. The size of the entrance hole and the inside diameters of the box are more important than the material used. The boxes may be made from hollow logs, slabs, or old or new lumber. Construction from lumber is economical, and the resulting boxes are lighter in weight and thus easier to transport and install.

Where stands of mature or overmature timber exist close to suitable water areas, hole-nesting ducks can be aided by improving potential nest sites. Equipped with climbing irons, safety belt, ladder, hand axe, and chisel, a worker can easily increase the number of usable cavities by enlarging openings and removing rotten wood so as to give a depth of about 18 inches below the entrance. Trees with hollow trunks can be made usable by chopping an entrance hole and plugging the cavity about 18 inches below the opening. In some instances, the removal of an obstructing branch or cutting away of callous growth that decreased the size of a possible entrance hole is the only necessary change needed.

To attract tree-nesting ducks, the nest box or cavity should have about 4 inches of sawdust or rotten wood in the bottom. Boxes should have an inside diameter of at least 10 inches, although it has been found that natural cavities of somewhat smaller dimensions are occasionally used. An entrance hole 4 inches in diameter is large enough for wood ducks, and 5 inches is sufficient for the goldeneye. A few ¼-inch holes should be bored in the bottom to provide drainage. It is recommended that the nesting boxes be placed 12 to 15 feet above the ground and on trees 12 inches or more in diameter.

Wood ducks have shown a preference for nesting boxes located a quarter to a half mile from the water, although those placed nearer are usually readily accepted. Raccoons are more likely to usurp nesting boxes close to the water, and predation is greater there than at a distance.

In open marshes with no available natural nesting sites close by, nesting boxes placed on posts well out in the marsh have been readily accepted and used by wood ducks in New England.

MAMMALS IN RELATION TO WATERFOWL MANAGEMENT

Fur-bearing Species. Good waterfowl habitat is generally good muskrat habitat. Consequently, muskrats frequently invade new flowages before the habitat can accommodate them properly. The complete absence or scarcity of vegetative cover forces them to make their dens in the banks, or more often in the newly constructed dikes, and to feed extensively on new aquatic plantings. Neglecting to keep muskrats under rigid control at this time may seriously delay the development of desirable marsh and aquatic vegetation.

After a marsh is well vegetated, muskrats aid by maintaining openings in extensive stands of marsh plants, thus making them more accessible to waterfowl. However, an overpopulation of these animals can do serious damage and so change the ecology that the marsh will be of little value to other wildlife for several seasons. This is especially true of coastal marshes containing good stands of the three-square sedges. A marsh managed primarily for waterfowl can be maintained in better balance by a carefully controlled muskrat trapping program. The revenue derived from proper management of these fur resources may equal, or even exceed, the cost of marsh development and management.

Minks are known to do considerable damage to the eggs and young of waterfowl. Nevertheless, it is advisable on refuge or management areas to hold the mink population in check by trapping, rather than to attempt extermination. Minks perform a limited service as scavengers, but their greatest importance is in their fur-producing value. It is a good general principle that no native form of wildlife should be entirely excluded from refuge areas. However, close control of certain species may sometimes be necessary in important nesting areas.

Raccoons may become even more objectionable on a waterfowl refuge than minks, if permitted to become too numerous. They are known to destroy large numbers of eggs, particularly in nesting boxes and they also prey on the muskrats.

Special precautions are frequently necessary to safeguard waterfowl in banding traps from raccoons. Live trapping, using box traps, has been found successful in catching the animals, which, if desired, can be released in some other part of the area.

While raccoons have proved especially objectionable in coastal breeding areas, skunks appear to be responsible for the destruction of large numbers of waterfowl nests in the Upper Mississippi Valley and northern Great Plains region. These animals, along with raccoons, are also of considerable value for their fur, and satisfactory control can usually be accomplished by trapping during the open season.

On western areas it is necessary to keep coyote populations down to prevent destruction of eggs and young birds. These animals have proved particularly troublesome in the efforts to protect nesting Canada geese, sand-hill cranes, and trumpeter swans.

Other Forms in Relation to Waterfowl Management. *Snakes and Turtles.* In the sand-hill regions of western Nebraska more waterfowl nests are destroyed by bull snakes than by any other species. After several seasons of experimentation, traps with long guide fences were developed, that successfully reduced the snake population.

Snapping turtles have proved troublesome in some breeding areas, especially in the Missouri River Valley. In such cases their numbers can be reduced both by the trapping of adult turtles and the destruction of nests. An interesting management problem results from the fact that skunks, while of aid by preying on turtle eggs, are equally proficient in finding and robbing duck nests.

Birds. Crows and ravens, when especially numerous, occasionally cause serious losses of duck eggs or newly hatched young. The instances of serious losses from crow activities have been largely on waterfowl nesting areas in the Great Plains, but those caused by ravens have been on a few Great Basin breeding units. Reduction of the numbers of these birds by shooting or trapping is sometimes necessary.

Predation by other birds is usually of little importance, although various hawks, particularly the marsh hawks, are sometimes accused of systematic predation on young ducks.

Duck hawks unquestionably catch some adult ducks, among a variety of other birds on which they feed, but the duck hawk population is so small that the effect of their activities on continental waterfowl populations is negligible.

OTHER FACTORS IN RELATION TO WATERFOWL MANAGEMENT

Botulism. The occasional large losses of waterfowl from botulism present an unsolved management problem, although progress has been made in devising some helpful practices. In 1910, extensive mortality among birds in the Bear River Marshes, Utah, attracted nationwide attention, and during the years immediately following, the death rate, though reduced, still indicated heavy inroads on western waterfowl. Botulism is poisoning by a toxin produced by the common bacterium, *Clostridium botulinum,* Type C, an organism best known in the United States as a cause of limber-neck in poultry.

The accumulation of organic debris in shallow, especially alkaline water, subject to water-level fluctuation, furnishes a favorable breeding place for the botulism bacteria. Removal of this material tends to prevent outbreaks of the sickness, and wherever water is available, flooding to eliminate shallow pools is also a good preventive measure.

The vegetation in new impoundments may constitute a serious botulism hazard where other factors are favorable for the development of an outbreak. It is, therefore, essential to remove excessive growths of grass and weeds, as well as haystacks and other organic debris, prior to flooding. The most practical and economical method of removal is by burning during the late fall or early winter.

Lead Poisoning. Numbers of waterfowl are victims of lead poisoning, caused by absorption of lead from shot picked up from pool or marsh bottoms. Only a few pellets, sometimes even one, may constitute a fatal dose. The afflicted birds frequently are in good flesh, death being caused by general paralysis of all organs. Much research work has been done and some is still under way in an effort to find a solution to this problem.

The most satisfactory measure now known for reducing this loss appears to be the use of frightening devices to keep birds away from areas known to contain considerable quantities of shot.

GAUGING RESULTS OF WATERFOWL MANAGEMENT

The enumeration of waterfowl populations and the determination of their trends may be accomplished by several different but interrelated methods. These normally include bird counts or inventories, bird banding, nesting studies, and brood counts.

Bird inventories on managed areas should be taken once or twice a month throughout the year and more frequently during periods of migration. To have comparative value, they should be made over approximately the same area and by the same number of qualified personnel. To avoid duplication, definite units should be assigned to each person. With limited populations, actual counts are frequently possible. With larger populations, accurate estimates may be made by determining the percentages of representation based on typical samples that are carefully checked.

The banding of waterfowl has proved one of the best means of determining the movement of populations through a management area. The departure of banded birds and the arrival of new migrants may be gauged rather accurately by the decrease in "repeats" and the increase in nonbanded birds.

Field surveys should be conducted annually during the peak of the waterfowl nesting season to check on the condition and use of nesting cover and the extent of predation. These surveys should embrace typical nesting covers over a fixed percentage of the total available breeding habitat. As the majority of waterfowl nests are located within 300 feet of the water, cover lying beyond that limit need not be intensely surveyed. This type of study should supply information on the extent of use, the need for change in management techniques such as burning, grazing, or mowing if cover is too dense, and the effects of predation.

Brood counts, rather than nesting studies, are ordinarily used as a basis of estimating the waterfowl productivity of an area. These can be made over a considerable area with a limited personnel and during a relatively short period of time. They are a more reliable index to productivity than are nesting studies as they reflect the number of birds actually taking to the water, whereas nest counts include, and must allow for, eggs that may be lost through predation and many other factors.

FUTURE PROGRAMS

While the prospects for migratory waterfowl have been somewhat improved, there is still much to be done. Many additional thousands of acres of habitat must be brought under management, and hunting regulations must continue to be based on the annual increment. The U.S. Fish and Wildlife Service estimates that at least 4,500,000 additional acres of favorably located land and water areas should be acquired and developed for waterfowl use. In addition, every effort must be made to preserve existing waterfowl habitat.

Careful watch must be kept on projects involving irrigation, drainage, flood control, mosquqito control, etc., to safeguard important habitat.

Review of the plans for such projects will frequently permit modifications to provide for controlled water levels and food and cover plantings that will safeguard waterfowl habitat. Often alterations involving little or no increased cost will add greatly to the efficiency of the projects themselves and materially increase their value for wildlife.

REFERENCES

1. Anonymous. 1937. Wildlife and the land: A story of regeneration. Senate Report (*pursuant to Senate Resolution* 246, 71*st Cong.*), 75*th Cong.*, 3*d Sess.*, Washington, D.C.
2. Bennett, Logan J. 1938. The blue-winged teal: Its ecology and management, Collegiate Press, Inc., Iowa State Colllege, Ames, Iowa.
3. Fassett, Norman C. 1940. A manual of aquatic plants, McGraw-Hill Book Company, Inc., New York.
4. Imler, Ralph H. 1945. Bullsnakes and their control on a Nebraska wildlife refuge. *Jour. Wildlife Mangt.* 9(4):265–273.
5. Kalmbach, E. R. 1937. Crow-waterfowl relationships based on preliminary studies on Canadian breeding grounds. *U.S. Dept. Agr. Cir.* 433.
6. Lynch, John J. 1941. The place of burning in management of the Gulf Coast wildlife refuges. *Jour. Wildlife Mangt.* 5(4):454–457.
7. Martin, A. C., and F. M. Uhler. 1939. Food of game ducks in the United States and Canada. *U.S. Dept. Agr. Tech. Bul.* 634.
8. McAtee, W. L. 1939. Wildfowl food plants; their value, propagation, and management, Collegiate Press, Inc., Iowa State College, Ames, Iowa.
9. Pirnie, Miles D. 1935. Michigan waterfowl management, Department of Conservation, Game Division, Lansing.

CHAPTER 17

River or Puddle Ducks

Subfamily *Anatinae*
Tribe *anatini*

Only the outdoor man knows the thrill of seeing V formations of waterfowl winging their way northward high in air. Where did the birds come from? Where are they going? What guides them? Will the season be successful? What will the fall flights bring?

Each hunting season and each waterfowl habitat holds a delight for the group of men interested in waterfowl, and this group is large. To it belong the rich and poor, the young and old. As a group, wildfowlers have no equal for enthusiasm, sportsmanship, and aggressiveness.

The sections which follow contain short life-history sketches of selected members of the family *Anatidae,* more commonly called the waterfowl. These discussions make no pretense at being either complete as to species or details of life history. Nor are they intended to be original. Completeness and originality will be left to the monographs on waterfowl. This is primarily intended as an aid to the student, administrator, or layman who needs general information about the common waterfowl and who lacks other and more detailed sources of information. Every reader of this book is urged to read the host of books that have been published in the last decade on life histories and ecology of waterfowl.

Three groups of waterfowl will be included, namely, the river or puddle ducks, the sea or diving ducks, and the geese and swans. For convenience the ruddy duck will be discussed with the diving ducks.

The dabbling ducks (Subfamily *Anatinae*) are inhabitants of inland shallow waters and feed generally on vegetable matter. Some of the dabblers, however, such as the black duck on the East Coast of North America, may use brackish water and may feed to a high degree during the winter season on animal rather than vegetable foods. In flying, the river ducks spring straight up from the water, while the diving ducks run along the top of the water when they are attempting to get into the air.

The river ducks are larger and more brightly colored than are their deep-water cousins. As food for man they are generally considered more palatable.

Kortright (41 *g.r.*) states there are 100 forms of surface-feeding ducks in the world, of which 16 are found in North America. Ten of the sixteen will be discussed in this book. These include the mallard, black duck, blue-winged, green-winged, and cinnamon teals, pintail, baldpate, shoveler, gadwall, and wood duck.

MALLARD *Anas platyrhynchos platyrhynchos*[1]

Description. Of all the waterfowl, the mallard, or greenhead, is the most typical and best-loved of the American ducks. This honor of being the favorite where so many individual species are represented is due to

FIG. 17-1. Male and female mallards.

many characters that are worthy of high esteem. In the first place, the mallard is widely distributed, being present in the entire North American continent except northern New England, northern New York, and eastern Canada. Moreover, it takes to new habitats readily and is not too fussy about the place where it lives. It eats a variety of foods and is not too afraid of man, although as it develops a knowledge of the sting of shot it becomes wary and hard to approach. Furthermore, the mallard is a large, handsome duck, the male having a green head and a diversity of body colors that gives it great beauty. Its smooth lines and the saucy turned-up feathers at the base of the tail seem to appeal to waterfowl hunters. Lastly, it has good size so that not too many are

[1] For details of feather topography of waterfowl see Kortright (41 *g.r.*).

needed to feed a family. It is not surprising therefore that this duck is well known and highly respected among waterfowl hunters.

The mallard is readily distinguished from other ducks by its typical long head and well-proportioned body. On the water the conspicuous parts of the male are its green head and curled tail feathers. The chest is chestnut in color, and in flight the belly and wing linings are silvery. There is a partial white ring on the neck of the male and the edges of the tail feathers are white. The speculum on the wings is colored bluish purple with white bordering bars, and the bill is light green or orange.

On the water the female is a drab-appearing duck, having a mottled chestnut-colored body with a lighter colored bill and legs. In flight the wing linings and tail feathers appear white or silvery in color, and the speculum has two white bars.

Average weight of adults: male–2 pounds, 11 ounces; female–2 pounds, 6 ounces (41 *g.r.*).

Distribution. Some forms of the mallard are found in all parts of the entire northern hemisphere. Many of the domesticated ducks originated from mallards (54 *g.r.*).

In North America, the mallard breeds straight across the continent from New York to Central Alaska and as far south as a line from Chesapeake Bay, Maryland, to San Francisco, California. This species of duck is typically a prairie species during the nesting period, but is also found in nonforested areas as far east as Massachusetts. It winters along the southern half of the continent extending northward along the East Coast to Long Island and the entire West Coast up to and including the Aleutian Islands (62 *g.r.*). Inland, the mallard winters wherever open water and food are available, often taking advantage of the waste grain left in the corn and rice fields of California and the southern states. During mild winters it may remain in parts of Canada, where open water and food are available (2, 11). Banding studies show that few mallards banded in the north go farther south than the Gulf Coast in Texas, Alabama, and Mississippi (3 *g.r.*).

Movements. Mallards are a hardy duck and as winter wanes start for the breeding grounds. The sex instincts are already operating and the birds seem eager to get at the job of nesting and rearing their broods. Annually each spring, mallards are among the first species of ducks to appear in the Canadian prairies, arriving there about the middle of March. The peak of the spring migration reaches Central Canada from April 1 to 10, but varying with the weather and the season (62 *g.r.*).

The migration south begins in August, but September and October are the main migration months. The movement south takes the form of a broad belt depending on weather and food supply. Ontario mallards may move to the Atlantic Coast or to the Mississippi Valley. Mid-Continent birds in general funnel down the Mississippi flyway, but a few pass westward to the Pacific flyway. The goal is open water and abundant food. If the winter is mild, the trip south is halted just beyond the line of ice on the ponds. Some birds winter as far north as southern Alaska. Phillips (54 *g.r.*) states that the greatest wintering areas are in

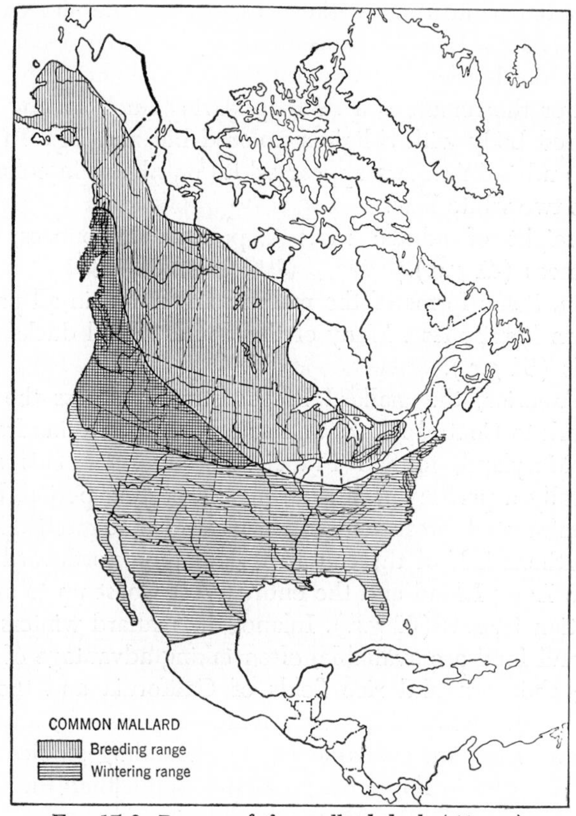

FIG. 17-2. Ranges of the mallard duck (41 *g.r.*).

the states of Alabama, Kentucky, Tennessee, Arkansas, Louisiana, and Texas.

The daily movements of mallards vary with the season and the degree to which they are disturbed. The mallards on the Atlantic Coast spend their daylight hours at sea and come in to feed at night (54 *g.r.*). The ducks that stay in the marshes move about early in the afternoon, but the birds from out at sea come in to feed only after dark. The flight back to sea takes place before daylight in the morning.

The period of courtship and summer molt each have a marked effect on movements. After the summer molt, the males may make migratory flights northward before being joined by the females and late young for the trip south.

Courtship and Breeding. Courtship apparently begins on the wintering grounds or during the migration to the summering territory. It is indulged in by several males seeking the favor of a female. The courting activity consists of nodding and swimming displays on the water as well as fancy flying and pursuit in the air. Finally, a male is chosen and from then on the pair defends a breeding territory.

FIG. 17-3. The mallard duck is the best known of all the waterfowl. It has withstood heavy hunting pressure and the habitat changes brought about by settlement. (*Russell Daigle, U.S. Forest Service.*)

Nests may be formed on the ground or on some convenient platform away from the ground. They have been found as high as 50 feet above the ground in old hawk or crow nests. The nests usually are near water, but may be as far as 2 miles distant (62 *g.r.*). On the Bear River Marshes, Utah, mallard nests were found in seven different cover types, but the hard-stemmed bulrush was the favorite cover site (64 *g.r.*). Girard (3) maintains that the food supply largely determines the location of mallard nests and that these birds will adjust their nesting activities accordingly.

The nest is made of grass, reeds, rushes, or any material available and is lined with down. The clutch of eggs varies from 5 to 14 with the average about 10 (54 *g.r.*). Girard (3) gives the average clutch of eggs for mallards in Montana as 7. The eggs are light green to white in color. The incubation period averages from 22 to 24 days but may vary from 21 to 28 days (31 *g.r.*). On the Bear River Marshes, Utah, 60 per cent of 1,582 eggs hatched (64 *g.r.*).

Habitat. Close inspection of the accompanying range map will indicate the habitat of the mallard to be diversified. Wintering grounds will obviously vary from southern Alaska to northern Florida. This duck likes shallow fresh water but will tolerate brackish waters, and apparently seems to be able to get along at almost any latitude if water and food are present. It reaches greatest wintering densities in the areas along the lower Mississippi River, where a variety of water, open lands, wooded streams, and shallow river borders are present. Acorns are one of the mallard's favorite foods so that a wooded site is not unwelcome. Contrast this vegetative cover with that of the open farm lands and potholes of the wheat country and one can appreciate the adaptability of the mallard. However, it is not found commonly in coniferous forest country, so this is one type of habitat the mallard does not like.

At Delta, Manitoba, the mallard nested in 11 of the 13 types listed by Hochbaum (31 *g.r.*). The edges of phragmites on dry ground were the only type commonly used, and the emergent cover types were used only rarely. All dry-land vegetation was used except pasture, and no doubt this was passed up because of a lack of sufficient concealment.

At Bear River Marshes, Utah, the mallard nested in all cover types except two, but more than half of the nests were in the hard-stemmed bulrush types. Nests were close to the channel and usually not more than 3 inches above the soil or mud (64 *g.r.*).

BLACK DUCK *Anas fulvigula rubripes*

Description. The black duck is to the duck hunters of the New England Coast what the mallard is to the Mississippi River Basin and Western Plains hunters. It is a fast-flying duck which furnishes sporty shooting, while its large size and fine-flavored meat make it well worth the efforts of any hunter. This duck will stand heavy gunning and still produce goodly numbers of new ducks each season. If anything, it is more wary and shy than the mallard and shows fewer tendencies to become domesticated.

Formerly it was considered that there were two subspecies of black ducks, the common species (*Anas rubripes tristes*) and a red-legged black duck (*Anas rubripes rubripes*). In recent years, however, it has been pretty well accepted that the black ducks with unusually bright-colored legs are mature male ducks and not a different subspecies (15).

The black duck has a nearly uniform pattern of brown and black colors. The head of the male is especially large and bold, while the general color of the body and wings is brown. The lining of the wings of birds in flight is silvery. The color of the speculum is purple bordered with black rather than white. During the breeding season the legs of the males are bright red, and those of the females a paler red. The bill of the male during the late fall and winter is yellow, changing to green during the eclipse molt. The bill of the female is olive yellow, yellow, or green, with many mottled dark markings midway between the base and the tip. During the eclipse, this changes to a greenish cast but retains

FIG. 17-4. Male and female black ducks.

the mottled effect (15). The buff markings on the breast feathers of the male are U-shaped, and those on the females are V-shaped.

Average weight of adults: male—2 pounds, 12 ounces; female—2 pounds, 8 ounces (41 *g.r.*).

Distribution. The black duck is the favorite game duck of the eastern hunter, particularly along the North Atlantic Coast. Formerly it helped to support duck-hunting clubs on Cape Cod and along the East Coast.

The domain of the black duck is the North American continent east of the Mississippi River. Along the coast the breeding range extends southward as far as Virginia, but inland the southern limit is farther south, extending roughly westward along the northern Pennsylvania line. Black ducks are found as far west as Delta, Manitoba, but do not breed there, according to Hochbaum (31 *g.r.*). The northern line of the breeding range touches James Bay and extends northeastward covering all of the maritime provinces including Newfoundland.

The wintering range includes that part of the United States lying east of a line extending southwestward from the coast of southern Maine through the lower Lake states region to St. Louis, Missouri, and thence southward to the Gulf of Mexico at the junction of Texas and Mexico. The most northerly point of wintering depends on the severity of the weather, but extends always as far as Nova Scotia and sometimes to Newfoundland. While the wintering range on the accompany-

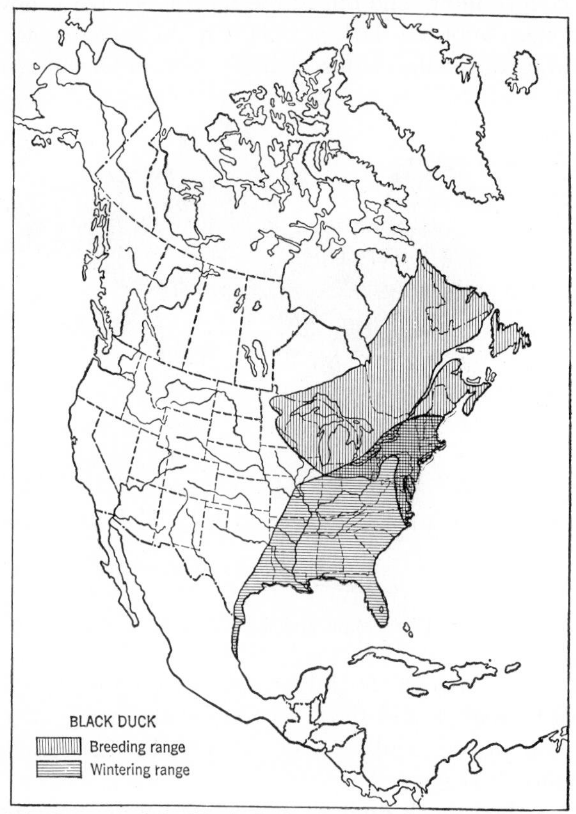

FIG. 17-5. Ranges of the black duck. (*U.S. Fish and Wildlife Service.*)

ing map includes inland points, the black duck tends to be found largely along the coast or along the Great Lakes where open water is available for escape and where marshy shores, open waterways, or tidal flats are available for feeding.

Hagar (6) indicates that a segment of black ducks wintering on Cape Cod, Massachusetts, is a unit that does not move south of the New England Coast. Thus New England is a terminal point for a large group of eastern black ducks. The breeding habits of the black duck differ from those of some of the more gregarious species and are reflected in the distribution of this duck. During the nesting season the birds spread out in very thin numbers, each pair seaking suitable nesting sites and feeding grounds along the borders of ponds and small streams. On the other hand, during the winter the birds collect in large flocks along the coast where resting and feeding grounds are available and where they remain in compact groups until the beginning of the next breeding season.

Movements. Movement toward the breeding grounds occurs in flocks which are neither large nor very conspicuous. Flight is swift and usually high in a V formation. When they arrive at the breeding grounds, and just previous to the time the eggs are to be laid, the pairs separate from the flock, each pair investigating small bodies of water and adjacent land suitable for nesting sites.

After the males get their flight feathers they collect in small packs and are joined later by the females and young of the year.

Along the New England Coast the black ducks that have bred nearby form in flocks that feed on the meadows along the coast. Later the birds from farther inland and from the Maritime Provinces arrive to join the local ducks already assembled.

Phillips (54 *g.r.*) indicates that black ducks are diurnal and not very shy of man until after they are shot at; then their habits change and they move to open water during the day for protection and come to the shore at night. The flights in are made high, with many turns and swings to observe possible danger. Also, while inland, the birds live largely on a vegetable diet. This is changed to a high percentage of animal matter when they begin feeding on the tidal flats along the shore and in the estuaries of streams flowing into the ocean.

Black ducks are among the most shy of the waterfowl. On the inland ponds it is very hard to get within gunning distance after the first morning of the open season, and on the coast they are shy and wild even during the winter after the hunting season has closed.

Courtship and Breeding. The courtship of black ducks occurs during a long season beginning as early as October (18). These early activities are mostly displays on the water and are probably the operations concerned with the selection of mates. After mates have been selected, the paired birds tend to stay together during the winter and fly to the nesting grounds together in the spring. Courting activities are intensified during the spring up to the time incubation begins. These activities have been ably described by Trautman (18) and others, so that they need not be repeated here.

The nesting season extends from late April to mid-June depending on the latitude and the lateness of the season. In Massachusetts egg laying begins in April. The nest is usually on the ground near water; it is built of leaves and stems of nearby vegetation and is lined with down. All investigators state that the nest of the black duck is hard to find, probably because of the great variety of situations for nesting. Phillips (54 *g.r.*) mentions nests found in stumps, in leaning trees, and in hawks' nests as well as on the ground.

The clutch consists of 6 to 12 eggs that are pale green or buff-colored. The eggs are identical in color with those of the mallard and are incubated by the female (54 *g.r.*). The incubation period is 26 to 28 days (41 *g.r.*).

Habitat. Black ducks usually spend the winter period in open water either along the seacoast or on inland fresh water from Maine to the Mexican border (14). It is a typical bird of the salt water and uses the open sea as a means of escape. Feed and water are obtained on the salt meadows and along the tidal flats and streams that border the ocean. Farther south, it feeds on rice beds and in fresh or brackish swamps.

Pairs of black ducks are found in the breeding range as long as there is open water. If there is plenty of food and open water inland it is believed that many of these ducks do not move to the seacoast. This duck is very adaptable, however, and will move to wherever a situation is available. Where large numbers are present, the sea with its bordering marshes and exposed tidal flats is the only place where enough food is available. As previously indicated, sometimes along the shores of New England extremely cold weather closes in the meadows and bays with snow and ice, and many black ducks starve to death for lack of available food (4, 5, 6, 7, 8). It is not surprising that a bird like the black duck which crowds the northern edge of its wintering range should get caught when the extremes of weather get beyond the tolerance of even this hardy species.

BLUE-WINGED TEAL *Anas discors*

Description. The blue-winged teal is a duck of the central American prairies. Perhaps it may be said that this is the most typical as well as the most beautiful waterfowl of the potholes. It is also one of the species that was most likely to suffer when the march of civilization changed the face of the land from natural vegetation to a terrain dominated by domesticated plants and animals. Drainage likewise took away much of the water so necessary to both the waterfowl and its food plants. The blue-winged teal is the product of small shallow ponds and lakes. When drained, this land produces domesticated grains including wheat, corn, barley, and oats and is the center of the livestock industry.

The blue-winged teal has long been famous for the excellent quality of its flesh. Many old menus speak of the fine flavor of teal served with

Burgundy. In America, the teal has a reputation for fast flying so is valued by waterfowl hunters for its sporting qualities.

The blue-winged teal is small compared to the black duck and mallard. It has very trim lines and beautiful colors. The male has a dark gray or purple head with a half-moon marking of white on the cheek extending from above the eye. The foreneck and under parts are dotted with black spots on a dark-brown background, and it has a shoulder patch of blue bordered at the rear with white. The female is drab- or brown-colored and smaller than the male, with no conspicuous color markings except as seen in flight, when the blue and white of the wings are visible. The throat and chest of the female are lighter-colored than

FIG. 17-6. Male and female blue-winged teals.

the neck and back, and light buff-colored streaks extend across the side of the head and over the eye. The female blue-winged is difficult to distinguish from the female green-winged or cinnamon teal. The American green-winged female is decidedly smaller, but the blue-winged and cinnamon teal females are indistinguishable. Females of the various species are more readily identified when accompanied by males.

Average weight of adults: male—14.6 ounces; female—13.6 ounces (41 *g.r.*).

Distribution. The breeding range of the blue-winged teal extends from New York to eastern Washington and Oregon, with the southern line of nesting extending southward in the central part of the United States. The northern boundary of the breeding range runs across British Columbia to the latitude of Juneau, Alaska. From here the range swings southeastward to the vicinity of Lake Nipigon, Ontario, and then eastward along the basin of the Great Lakes and the St. Lawrence River to the eastern shore of Nova Scotia. Bennett (1) estimates that as of 1935, 80 per cent of the blue-winged teal were produced in Canada. It is also breeding in an isolated range adjacent to Chesapeake Bay. In the provinces of Alberta, Saskatchewan, Manitoba, and British Columbia,

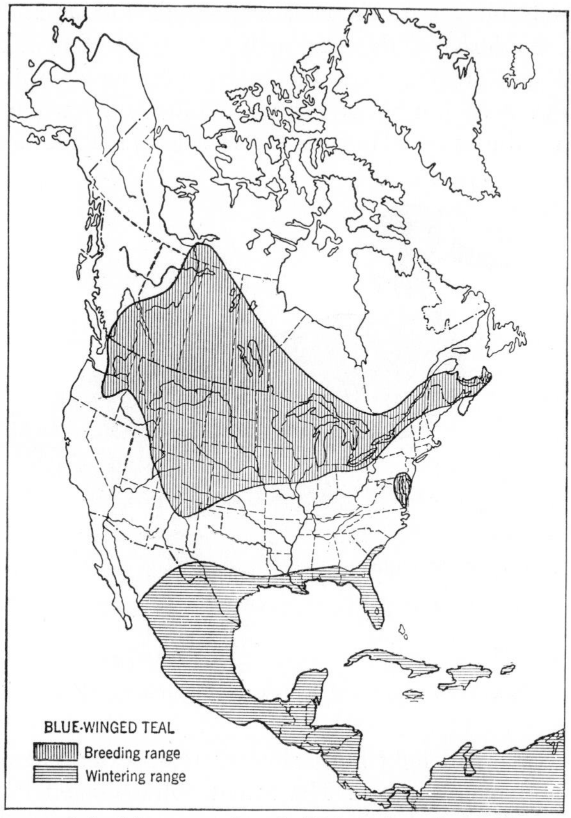

FIG. 17-7. Ranges of the blue-winged teal. [*U.S. Fish and Wildlife Service and L. J. Bennett* (*1*).]

agriculture and drainage have greatly damaged the breeding grounds of this bird.

The wintering grounds include the southern portion of the mainland of North America, all of Central America and the islands to the east, and the northern part of South America to a latitude approximately 5 degrees south of the equator. Ninety-five per cent of the blue-winged teal winter south of the United States. This bird does not stand cold weather readily and therefore goes to sunny climes during the period when cold stormy weather prevails in the north.

Courtship and Breeding. The selection of males and courtship begins on the wintering grounds as early as December (1). It consists of nodding of males and display of plumage both on the water and in the air. Before the selection of mates is made, several males may be going through their displays in the presence of a female.

Apparently the courtship activities and migratory instincts are concurrent phenomena, so that as the birds start north the process of selecting a mate is intensified. Both Hochbaum (31 *g.r.*) and Bennett (1) give the height of the nesting season as the latter part of May to the end of June, with a secondary season extending from the last week of June to the first week of August. The nest is built by the female in any one of a variety of locations, including pastures, hayfields, among the bog plants, or on muskrat houses. The nest is made of soft blades of grass intermixed with down feathers from the female. The nest may be adjacent to or as far as a mile from water. There are from 6 to 14 buff-colored eggs in a teal clutch, with an average of slightly more than 9. Incubation takes from 21 to 23 days, and the eggs all hatch about the same time.

Movements. Little is known of the activities of the blue-winged teal on its wintering territory. Outside of sporadic winter shooting in Central and South America, the sojourn in the southland is probably a pleasant interlude of loafing and feeding. The spring migration is leisurely, the birds keeping south of the ice line and within a belt of water-filled ditches and field puddles. The flocks are small, usually less than 30, and usually there is plenty of food left for them by harvesting operations.

Courting, nesting, and feeding are summer activities that are local in nature and are usually confined to scattered potholes or nearby lake borders. Rearing of young is also a routine matter carried on at the edges of water holes or along the borders of streams (1).

As soon as the male gets his flight feathers he is off to the south, not waiting for the females and broods. At Delta, Manitoba, females and young gather in bands and usually leave for the south intermittently from late August to the last of September (31 *g.r.*).

The shooting season no doubt has some effect on the movements of blue-winged teal. It is one of the first waterfowl to migrate and gives some shooting to the early-season crop of hunters. Jump and pass shooting both fit the habits of this duck, since it flies relatively low, seeking food and rest on the small bodies of water.

By September flocks of blue-winged teal are moving down all the flyways with the heaviest movement in the Mississippi and Central flyways. By October 25 most of these ducks are south of the Missouri River and well on their way to their winter home.

Habitat. The nesting vegetation used by the blue-winged teal varies according to what is present and the whims of the female bird. Hochbaum (31 *g.r.*) cites this duck as nesting in grass-sedge-sow thistle meadows, hay meadows, and lightly grazed pastures. A note added states that white-top (*Fluminea festucacea*) is the preferred nesting-cover plant for all the waterfowl using meadows. Bennett (1) lists five cover types in which this bird nests, including the true prairie with its potholes, sloughs, marshes, and lakes; mixed prairie or short grass plains; boreal forest with bog, woody vegetation, and grasslands intermixed; deciduous type of forest area including the wood lots and farms from Iowa to Maryland; and the lake forest area.

CINNAMON TEAL *Anas cyanoptera cyanoptera*

Description. The cinnamon teal belongs to a genus that is found in many parts of the world. This particular species is limited to North and South America and in the former continent is found mostly west of the Rocky Mountains. The North American cinnamon teal does not mingle even during the winter with the South American form, each bird staying in its own continent. Phillips (54 *g.r.*) quotes Coues (1874) as believing that the North American cinnamon teal originally came from South America comparatively recently and may still be widening its range.

The cinnamon and blue-winged teal are closely related with some modification of plumage, size, and bill structure. The male is a handsome duck with head, neck, chest, and flanks a bright cinnamon color when in breeding plumage. The back is dark brown, and the sides are brown or cinnamon-colored with lighter markings. The wings are much like those of the blue-winged teal with the undersides gray to white in color. The adult female in its breeding plumage is slightly darker than the blue-winged teal.

Average weight of adults: male—12 ounces; female—12.5 ounces (41 *g.r.*).

Distribution. The breeding range of the cinnamon teal extends from the Rocky Mountains west to the Pacific Coast. A few of these birds get east of the Rockies in the Prairie Provinces of Canada but these appear to be scattered individuals that have followed other species of ducks. According to Shortt and Cartwright (62 *g.r.*), the entire range from southern interior British Columbia to southwestern Mexico is used for breeding, but only a limited area in western Mexico and a small area in the southwestern United States are used for wintering.

Movements. The migrations and daily movements of the cinnamon teal are much like the blue-winged. The entire distance which this bird migrates is short compared to the movements of the latter and is accomplished in short flights with the birds banded together in small flocks. Migration in the fall starts in September and October. There is probably a good deal of loitering on the way, if weather is favorable and food conditions are suitable.

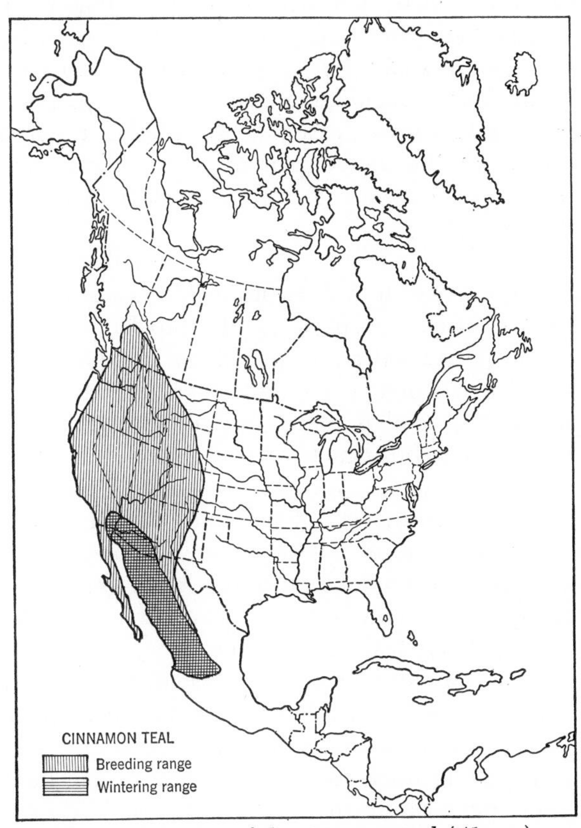

FIG. 17-8. Ranges of the cinnamon teal (41 *g.r.*).

The northward migration begins in March and continues in April. Shortt and Cartwright (62 *g.r.*) state that some individuals migrate only a short distance, but probably those birds which winter the farthest south also fly the farthest north to breed. Limited banding returns show very sporadic results. Birds banded in California were later retaken in that same state. A bird banded in Saskatchewan was also taken in California. Birds banded in Oregon and at the Bear River Marshes in Utah were taken largely in southern Mexico. One was taken in Venezuela, South America (10).

Courtship and Breeding. The cinnamon teal displays great exuberances in its courtship and breeding activities. There are many fights among the males, and the courting displays include much nodding, splashing, and rushing around. The nest may be over water or on dry land. It may be elaborately made or simply formed in a slight depression on the ground with scarcely any concealing screen (62 *g.r.*). It is always lined with down.

The clutch consists of 6 to 14 eggs with an average of 10 to 12. The eggs are white or pale pink buff in color. Incubation is by the female only and takes from 25 to 26 days. The male, at least in some cases, is in attendance both during incubation and after the young are hatched. There is some question in such cases as to whether the male in attendance is the male of the mated pair or some other unattached male (54 *g.r.*). Of more than 2,600 eggs studied at Bear River Marshes, Utah, 84 per cent hatched (64 *g.r.*).

Habitat. The cinnamon teal is not very particular as to its habitat. Any wet situation seems to satisfy its needs. These include drainage ditches, irrigation canals, seepage ponds, brooks running out of the higher lands, and permanent rivers and lakes. Tule beds border many of these ponds, and it is among these and other vegetation that the cinnamon teal thrives. The food is found in shallow water so the border of any water area is sure to be attractive.

The nest is also found in a variety of vegetative types. Williams and Marshall (64 *g.r.*) in studying 524 nests at Bear River Marshes, Utah, found 50 per cent of them in salt-grass cover, a low type of vegetation, and 23 per cent in hard-stemmed bulrush, a taller-growing type.

There are numerous conditions that have a tendency to change the habitat of the cinnamon teal. The section in which it lives is a region of low and varying rainfall. During dry seasons, the potholes dry up. As opposed to this unfavorable condition, irrigation may create new duck habitat. Little is known concerning the extent of hunting pressure on this species. It is a trusting duck so probably suffers from hunting. On the other hand, hunting pressure in its range, except in California, is light due to thin human populations. The fact that some cinnamon teals stay in the California valleys while others move early to Mexico makes it an uncertain species to predict.

AMERICAN GREEN-WINGED TEAL *Nettion crecca carolinense*

Description. The green-winged teal is the smallest of the North American waterfowl. Its size, however, is in no way an indication of its hardiness or its ability to protect itself. The breeding range of this bird extends across practically all the western half of the continent, and it winters as far north as Vancouver Island, British Columbia. It is a strong and erratic flier, having been given credit for speeds over 100 miles per hour.

The true speed, however, is probably not more than 50 miles per hour. The green-winged teal is a bird which generally prefers fresh water, although when necessity arises it rafts in salt water for protection.

The male in breeding plumage has a dark chestnut-colored head with a darker band over the eyes. The eye patch is bordered by a cream-colored line. In flight, the green speculum on the wing may show, but more frequently it is not visible. On the water a light-colored crescent-shaped marking may show in front of the folded wings, and also a light spot occurs along the underside of the tail coverts.

FIG. 17-9. Male and female green-winged teals. (*Lynn Bogne Hunt.*)

The female is a drab-appearing duck, unusually small with few distinguishing marks, except its diminutive size and possibly the green speculum which may be seen when the bird is flying. The wingbeats are rapid.

Average weight of adults: male—12.8 ounces; female—12 ounces.

Distribution. The breeding range of the green-winged teal is more extensive than that of the blue-winged or cinnamon teals. Apparently this species is not so fussy about either climate or vegetation, since it is found nesting in New Brunswick, Newfoundland, Labrador, and west around the southern end of James Bay, and bordering on the west side of Hudson Bay. West and north the breeding range includes all but the northern part of Alaska and eastward it extends to Victoria Island, Northwest Territories, Canada.

The wintering range includes the South Atlantic and Gulf Coast states, practically the entire western half of the United States, and the northern half of Mexico to Vera Cruz. It also winters in the West Indies and some of the Central American countries. The green-winged teal will use both fresh and salt water, but seems to prefer the former to the latter. It likewise prefers open lands to forests as indicated by the range map.

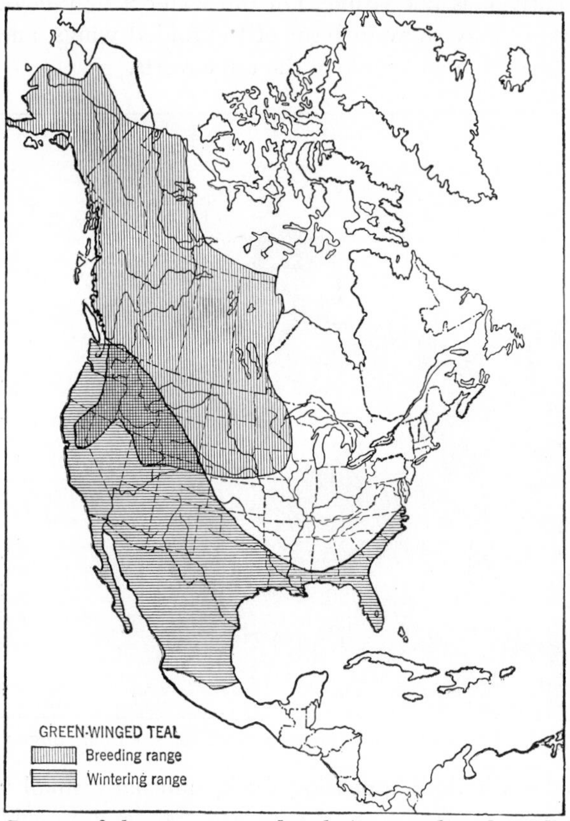

FIG. 17-10. Ranges of the green-winged teal. (*U.S. Fish and Wildlife Service.*)

Movements. Green-winged teal seem to be more hardy and less susceptible to cold weather than the blue-winged species and therefore do not move south so early to the wintering grounds. Hochbaum (31 *g.r.*) indicates that the males are seen at Delta, Manitoba, during the flightless period and then move south and the bulk of the females and young move in from the north about the first week in October and stay until the freeze-up. Shortt and Cartwright (62 *g.r.*) give the third week in October as the time of general migration southward in southern Canada.

The green-winged teal tends to be nocturnal in its movements, resting on mud banks or on logs during the day and feeding and moving about mostly during twilight and semidarkness. This duck may form in rafts where pressure of gunning requires it, but generally it is found in small flocks or in pairs.

The northward migration begins early with the birds arriving at the Canadian line by the middle of April. They are more concentrated in Saskatchewan and Alberta than elsewhere as they move to the breeding grounds (62 *g.r.*).

Courtship and Breeding. The green-winged teal apparently begin courtship early in the winter, and mates are selected by the middle of February (31 *g.r.*). Courtship behavior consists of displays of plumage on the water by several males before a female, rapid flight of both sexes, and the usual antics of the mated pair. The nest is near the water, but on a dry spot, and is made from bits of leaves and parts of plants found nearby. Down is also used. Usually the nest is well hidden. The eggs are a dull white, cream, or olive buff in color, and the clutch varies from 7 to 12 eggs. Incubation takes from 20 to 23 days (54 *g.r.*).

The male leaves the female after the clutch is laid and proceeds to molt at once. No attention is paid to the family by the male once the eggs are laid.

Habitat. This duck finds suitable habitat wherever water is available. It is not a shy bird and feeds persistently wherever shallow water plants are present. It is a typical puddle duck and is often seen in shallow water with its head underwater and its tail pointing skyward. When it comes out of the north its flesh has a fine flavor. As it reaches the wintering grounds it may be found on open ponds or in the wooded swamps of the southland. Where necessary, it may move out to sea to escape gunning pressure. Along the borders of both the Atlantic and Pacific Oceans, the green-winged teal lives in both fresh and brackish waters as necessity demands (54 *g.r.*).

AMERICAN PINTAIL *Anas acuta tzitzihoa*

Description. Pintails along with mallards and black ducks are among the most abundant and most popular of American waterfowl. According to Shortt and Cartwright (62 *g.r.*), their numbers were estimated as 20 million in 1945.

The pintail is popular with gunners because of its wariness, trim body lines, large size, and abundance. The long neck, long tail, and long slender head all combine to give it a somewhat snaky appearance. However, its flesh is excellent and it is sufficiently large to repay the gunner for the expense of going after it. Because of the extent of its breeding range the pintail is likely to be present during the entire open season of waterfowl hunting on many parts of the range.

The male in breeding plumage has a black-colored head and a long slender tail. The belly is light in color with the front and sides of the neck nearly white. There is a lighter shaft of color extending along each side of the neck into the darker background. In flight, the speculum shows a white bar along the trailing edge.

The female is dull-colored but is large and has the same long graceful head and neck as described for the male. In flight the female also shows the white bar on the rear edge of the speculum. The bill and feet are gray in color.

FIG. 17-11. Two male and one female pintail.

Average weight of adults: male—2 pounds, 2½ ounces; female—1 pound, 13 ounces (41 *g.r.*).

Distribution. The pintail is the most widely distributed of all the American ducks. It breeds across the continent from New Brunswick and Labrador to California and from Minnesota across Alaska. Breeding is generally thin in the eastern part of the continent. It avoids the rougher parts of British Columbia.

It winters in a widespread pattern near or on the coast from Maine southward to the Panama Canal and as far north as Vancouver Island and British Columbia on the Pacific Coast. Inland wintering territory includes all of Mexico and the coastal portions of the states bordering on the Gulf of Mexico and the Pacific Ocean.

On the basis of world distribution, the pintail is found commonly throughout the northern hemisphere. Phillips (54 *g.r.*) indicates that on a world-wide basis this duck is more common than the mallard. Among the United States possessions it is found on all the Alaskan islands and crosses the Pacific Ocean to the Hawaiian Islands as well.

Movements. The pintail is a gregarious bird, appearing mostly in family groups up to large aggregations of several thousand. On the

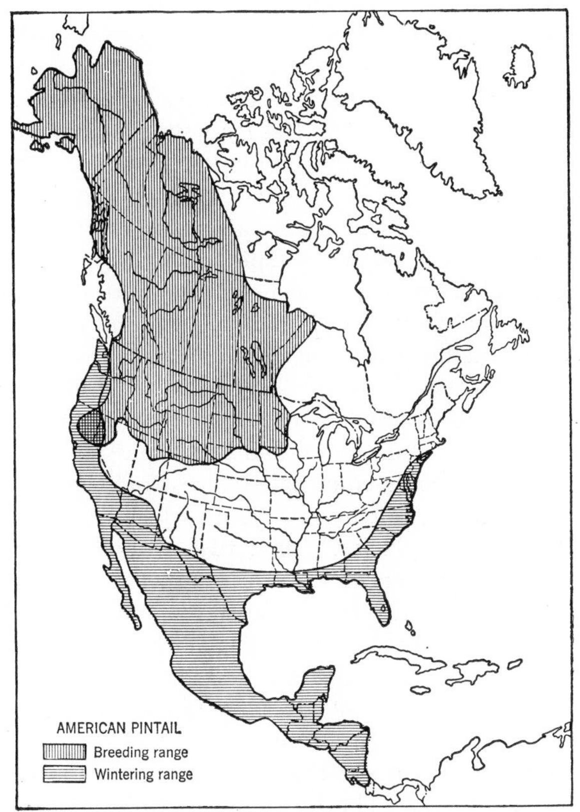

FIG. 17-12. Ranges of the American pintail (41 *g.r.*).

flights northward in the spring, the pintail follows open water, and generally fair weather, from the wintering to the breeding grounds. Migration starts in southern Canada during the last week in March and is heavy all through April (62 *g.r.*). Farther west, the flights continue to the middle of May.

The journey south, following the breeding season, is of long duration, because of the extent of the breeding range and the instinct of some of the birds to migrate early. The earliest movement takes place in July, but the bulk of the birds move through southern Canada in October with some staying later until driven out by frost and the freezing of the ponds.

A study of banded birds shows the wide distribution of the pintail as it moves south in the fall. A summary of birds banded in Manitoba shows that 14 per cent were taken in the Mississippi flyway, 28 per cent in the Central flyway, and 58 per cent in California. Birds banded in northern Canada were taken as far east as Louisiana and as far south as Vera Cruz, Mexico (12).

The flight of the pintail is rapid and it flies high, especially after being disturbed by gunners. It begins feeding early in the morning, and like the black duck and mallard, may go out to sea or to some open expanse of water during the day. Phillips (54 *g.r.*) states that some pintails become entirely nocturnal on their wintering grounds.

Courtship and Breeding. Pintails pair early, probably mostly before going north in the spring. The mating antics are extensive, consisting of elaborate displays in the water and spirited flights of male and female. Sometimes these flights are at great heights and are followed by abrupt dives or descents that may end by plunging into the water.

The nests are usually placed on dry land and often as far as a mile from the nearest water. However, according to Hochbaum (31 *g.r.*), they may be built over water. The nest is well made of grass, weeds, and down. Sometimes it is well hidden and sometimes not. The clutch consists of 5 to 12 pale olive-green or pale buff-colored eggs. The incubation period is 21 to 22 days, but may vary to as long as 25 days (31 *g.r.*). Shortt and Cartwright (62 *g.r.*) state that an average of 6 young is hatched. Eighty-two per cent of the eggs studied at Bear River Marshes, Utah, hatched (64 *g.r.*). The nesting season is similar to that of the mallard, beginning in mid-April and running until the third week in July. The last nests at Delta, Manitoba, are started the last week in June, and the pintail is one of the earliest waterfowl to complete nesting activities in the above location (31 *g.r.*).

Habitat. The pintail is a shy duck, but strong on the wing and well able to look out for itself. The bird appears to be at home in a great variety of places, as shown on the distribution map and by the widespread nature of its migration flights as indicated by the results of banding.

It is a very adaptable duck and gets along well in fresh water, brackish marshes, or on salt water. It is not afraid of cold weather and does well under rugged weather conditions.

At the Bear River Marshes, Utah, Williams and Marshall (64 *g.r.*) found some of the pintail nests in salt-grass, a low type of vegetation, and others in hard-stemmed bulrush, a taller cover. On the basis of area, however, willows and weeds were the favorite nesting site. At Delta,

Manitoba, pintail nests were found in nearly every type of cover but more commonly in the dry-land cover types and only occasionally in the plants growing in water.

The winter range varies from large fresh-water lakes to small potholes, coastal rivers, and salt-water marshes and swamps bordered by the sea. The pintail prefers fresh to salt water, however.

AMERICAN WIDGEON BALDPATE *Anas americana*

Description. The baldpate, or American widgeon, is the New World counterpart of the European widgeon, which is a popular game bird in the old world and sometimes visits our eastern shores in winter. The

FIG. 17-13. Male and female American widgeon (baldpate).

baldpate is a clean-cut, active bird that seems to have acquired many of the habits of diving ducks and is often associated with them. One of the common names of the baldpate is "poacher," because it waits for canvasbacks or redheads to bring wild celery from the bottom of ponds and then steals it from these larger and slower-moving ducks. Baldpates are active, restless birds; they are always alert and fly together in a close formation, wheeling about like pigeons. They do not seem to care for marshes but like open water where they can see danger before it approaches too near.

The baldpate is a small duck with a small head and short bill. The male in breeding plumage has a light-colored, almost white head with a dark green patch extending back from the eye. In flight, the under parts of the wings are white, and there is a white patch along the forward part of the fore wing. The speculum is green, while the breast and under parts are snow-white. The males can be identified by the three or four whistling notes uttered as they fly. On the water, a white-colored patch shows between the folded wing and tail.

The female is not so conspicuously marked as the male. The head is gray in color, and the under parts are white. The color of the forward wing patch is gray instead of white as in the male. The feet of both sexes are gray, and the birds ride high on the water (62 *g.r.*).

Average weight of adults: male—1 pound, 11 ounces; female—1 pound, 9 ounces (41 *g.r.*).

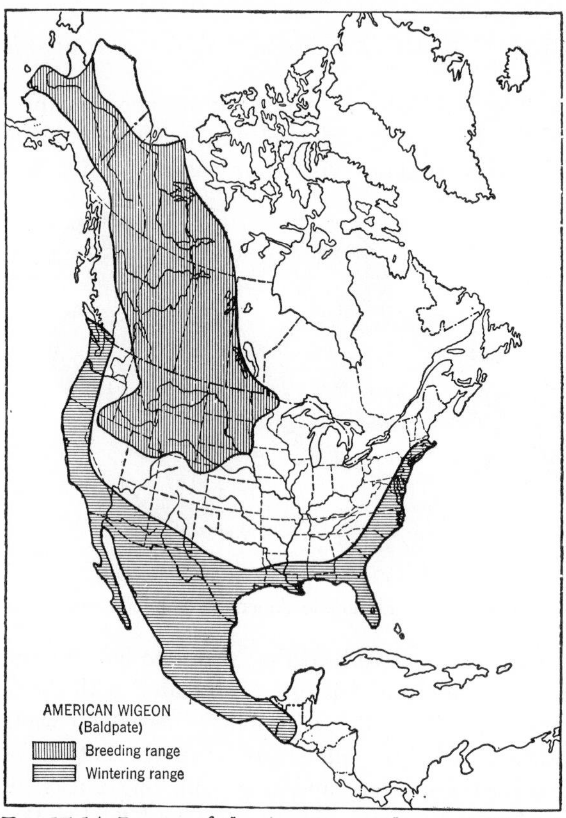

FIG. 17-14. Ranges of the American widgeon (baldpate).

Distribution. The baldpate is a western bird except during the wintering period, when it sometimes winters as far north as the southern New England Coast. It breeds in the central western part of the continent from Nebraska, Colorado, and Utah northward; westward the breeding range extends to Seward Peninsula in Alaska. In Canada, the breeding grounds extend from Hudson Bay to northern British Columbia, but it appears to prefer the inland waters to the coastal ones for nesting. Hochbaum (31 *g.r.*) refers to only one clutch of baldpates at Delta, Manitoba, so that apparently the breeding grounds are farther north and west.

The species winters in a wide territory on both coasts of the North American continent from Chesapeake Bay, Maryland, on the Atlantic Coast to Vancouver Island, British Columbia, on the Pacific Coast. The coastal portions of all of the states bordering the two oceans, as well as all of Mexico, are included in the winter range. It also winters in the islands of the Caribbean (62 *g.r.*).

Movements. Baldpates start northward in March and April but are not in so much of a hurry as are some of the other early nesters. Weather conditions of the nesting grounds to the north seem to hold up the migrations so that the birds loiter along the way waiting for the better conditions which are sure to come along later. At Delta the baldpates come along with the mallards and pintails after the first good thaw in mid-April (31 *g.r.*). Because of the long distances which these ducks travel, the time of migration depends on the location. They move northward as weather permits and arrive on the nesting grounds so as to begin the nesting season with suitable weather. Far north in Alaska this may not occur until the middle of June or later.

The migration southward does not show this leisurely tempo. The long distances ahead seem to be an urgent reminder to the birds to get on their way. As a result they start out of the breeding grounds to the north in concentrated flights, going down the Mississippi and Central flyways and crossing over the mountains to California and the Pacific flyways in great streams. In Manitoba, Hochbaum (31 *g.r.*) says only a few are found at Delta after the middle of August and very few are taken in the fall hunting bag. The heaviest southward migrations are in western Canada and the western United States.

The baldpates are much like some of the diving ducks in their daily habits. They are nervous and sensitive to danger. As a result they associate with rafting bodies of ducks on wide expanses of water. Like the mallards, they feed during the twilight hours and at night and leave the feeding grounds before daylight for the safety of open waters. On the East Coast the baldpate uses the brackish lagoons for feeding, but on the Pacific where it is more common, the birds use the tidal flats.

Recoveries of baldpates banded chiefly in the provinces of Saskatchewan and Alberta show the birds widely scattered through the states of the Central flyway and the western states with large numbers taken in central and northern California.

Courtship and Breeding. The courtship activities of this species are slow in developing and do not reach their greatest height until the nesting grounds are reached. The antics on the water consist of splashing, nodding, and numerous other maneuvers. The nuptial flights are erratic and spectacular, as would be expected of a duck with such superb flight equipment. These mating flights are indulged in by several males in pursuit of a single female, so perhaps the actual selection of mates may not be made until the approach of the nesting season.

The baldpate nests from mid-May on the southern border of the range to July farther north. The nest is on dry ground, often in brush or at the foot of a tree. The nest is made of grass or weeds, lined with gray down, and is well concealed.

The eggs are deep cream to nearly white, and the clutch varies from 8 to 12. Incubation takes from 22 to 24 days (54 *g.r.*). It is carried on by the female. The average brood is slightly less than 6 (62 *g.r.*).

Habitat. The baldpate seems to require a habitat that is somewhere between that of a puddle duck and a sea duck. It prefers the leafy type of plant for food and is not particularly fond of the marshy habitats, preferring open water that is shallow enough so that it can obtain its food. It prefers fresh to brackish or salt water, but probably because of necessity has adapted itself to the less desirable situations. Like the black duck, it feeds on tidal flats as well as in shallow lagoons and wooded swamp borders. In the south central states and Mexico, it uses any water available and adapts its mode of living to the habitats that are available.

GADWALL *Anas strepera strepera*

Description. Hunters have a habit of calling almost every species of duck that has an over-all pattern of color "gray ducks" or "mallards." Of all the ducks so far described, the gadwall seems to fit this description better than most of the others as it has so few characters of color or form that separate it from other monocolored waterfowl.

The gadwall, like the baldpate, is a duck of the western part of the United States. It is large with clean-cut outlines and a nicely shaped body and head. The coloring of the plumage of both male and female is somber with rich blends of browns and grays.

On the water the male appears like a mallard, but the tail region is velvety black, and there is a patch of lighter color ventral to the folded wings. During the breeding season the bill of the male is a deep black. The female shows less contrast of color than the male, and the sides of the bill are orange. Both male and female have a white speculum that shows clearly when the birds are flying. This is the only American waterfowl with a white speculum.

Distribution. The gadwall is circumpolar in distribution but is found only in the northern hemisphere. It is common in Europe, Asia, and northern Africa. The breeding range in North America is much smaller than that of the mallard, extending from Nebraska to the western shore of Hudson Bay and west from these points to the Pacific shores of Oregon and Washington. Apparently the gadwall does not like the type of country in the northern half of the Canadian provinces for its breeding range is limited to the southern sections of Canada and the northwestern portions of the United States.

The wintering range consists of the states bordering the coasts of both oceans and the Gulf of Mexico. It is also found in northern Mexico as far south as Mexico City. It winters inland as far as Kentucky and Tennessee in the eastern part of the United States and Texas, Arizona, and New Mexico, as well as California and western Oregon, in the West.

The breeding range is shrinking as compared to former times, but nests are still found as far east as Long Island, Delaware, and Maryland.

Fig. 17-15. Male and female gadwalls.

Movements. The gadwalls are like the shovelers and the blue-winged teal in not caring for cold, stormy weather. All these species regulate their activities so as to avoid inclement weather. The gadwall moves north in March and April so as to arrive in southern Canada by the middle of April or early May. The peak of the migration is May 5 according to Shortt and Cartwright (62 *g.r.*). In the fall gadwalls leave early, departing from the Canadian provinces during the first half of October. Generally the direction of the fall movement is south, but later it branches both east and west. Band recoveries of birds marked in the Canadian provinces show very few recovered east of the Mississippi River, so apparently the fall migration is more south and west than east (10). Of the daily habits, little has been written. Phillips (54 *g.r.*) says they are much like the mallard with which they are often associated. They feed by tipping in shallow water and feed largely by night if harassed by gun pressure. Gadwalls are strictly fresh-water birds and are not found in salt-water marshes if any other habitat is available. They do not seek the open spaces but frequent fresh-water watercourses and ponds.

At Delta, Manitoba, Hochbaum (31 *g.r.*) says that during the hunting season the gadwalls are very wary and feed in open water, where very few are taken by jump shooting.

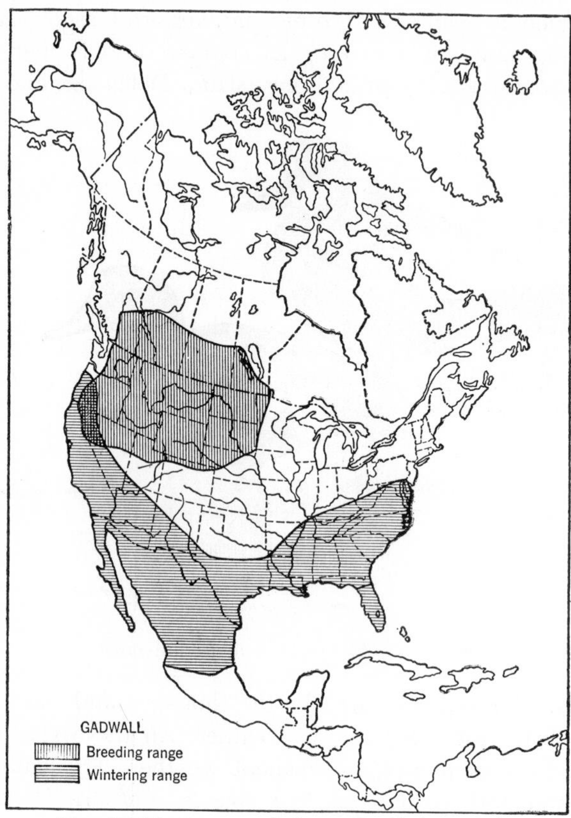

FIG. 17-16. Ranges of the gadwall (41 *g.r.*).

Courtship and Breeding. Gadwalls are slow to arrive at the nesting grounds so are late in getting started laying and incubating eggs. This time lapse is as much as 3 weeks behind the mallard (54 *g.r*). They begin nesting in southern Manitoba the first week in May, and the height of their nesting activities takes place the last 2 weeks of May. Second nests may be as late as the last of July. As a result of this late nesting, the young may be still flightless by the last of September. In the courtship period many males, as many as 12 to 14, may pursue a single female. On the water the courtship antics consist of display of plumage, head bobbing, and maneuvering by the males to show their plumage to the best advantage.

The nest is on dry land and protected locations are favored. It is a deep cavity lined with grass and down and is well concealed. The eggs are creamy white and vary from 7 to 15 in number, with 10 to 12 being the most common. Incubation takes 21 to 25 days, with an average of 24 days, according to Hochbaum (31 *g.r.*), but is usually given in the literature as 28 days (54 *g.r.*). At Bear River Marshes, Utah, 85 per cent of the 2,600 eggs studied hatched (64 *g.r.*).

Habitat. Little can be said about the habitat of the gadwall. It lives in the same general location as the mallard and appears to resemble the shoveler in its habits. No two ducks are exactly alike, so it is suspected that the gadwall has a choice of surroundings that is characteristic of this species. Hochbaum (31 *g.r.*) found the nests of both gadwalls and mallards in the phragmites edges which were on dry ground; these were the only two species nesting in this situation at Delta. It also nested in the grass-sedge meadow and hay meadow and casually in thickets or in brush piles. At Bear River Marshes, the choice of nest cover was willow and weeds, although it nested in all cover types except those standing in water (64 *g.r.*).

Food-habits studies of the gadwall show that it is a vegetarian and is very fond of seeds. It does not respond to decoys as readily as some of the other ducks and uses the shallow edges of the marsh rather than the open fields.

COMMON SHOVELER *Anas clypeata*

Description. The shoveler, or spoonbill, gets its name from its exceedingly large broad bill. The bill is shovellike and has a row of comblike teeth along each side with which to strain insects and seeds from the mud and ooze in which it feeds. The shoveler is only slightly larger than a teal, but its head and bill are out of proportion to the rest of its body, making it appear larger than the latter. The male in breeding plumage has a handsomely colored head of purple and green, the neck and chest white, the undersurface of the wings gray and white, and the belly chestnut brown. The fore part of the inner wing is chalky blue. The speculum is green, bordered by white lines fore and aft. On the water the head and tail appear dark with the tail bordered with white.

The female is a drab brown color except for the wings, the inner wing being marked like the male. The tips of the tail feathers are also light tan. Sitting on the water, the female is like a mallard, except that she tilts forward, appearing to be overbalanced by her enormous head and bill.

The feet of both sexes are red orange during the breeding period.

Distribution. The shoveler is a world-wide duck, being found in all the continents of the world except South America and Australia. Some may wander to the islands of the Caribbean and northern South America during the winter. Phillips (54 *g.r.*) gives these areas as possible wintering grounds.

The breeding grounds in North America are a broad cone-shaped area with its base extending from New York State on the east through the

FIG. 17-17. Male and female shovelers.

central part of the United States to California and gradually narrowing to the north and west like a gnome's hat, with the narrow peak ending in the valley of the Yukon River in Alaska. Breeding birds are scattered through the Lake states. The shoveler is mostly a breeding bird of the mid-Continent west of the Mississippi River, however.

The species winters in the states that border both oceans from Virginia south on the Atlantic Coast and British Columbia south on the Pacific Coast. Mexico is occupied as far south as the Gulf of Campeche. In the United States and Mexico, the shoveler is a bird of the inland water rather than a resident of the ocean border.

Movements. The migrating shovelers reach Canada during the middle of April or about as soon as the ice melts in the spring. May is the time when most of the birds pass north to the breeding grounds. They appear to be sensitive to cold weather and go north late and return south early to avoid the severe storms of late spring and early fall.

The males are the first to move south, some leaving the breeding grounds as soon as they get their flight feathers after the breeding

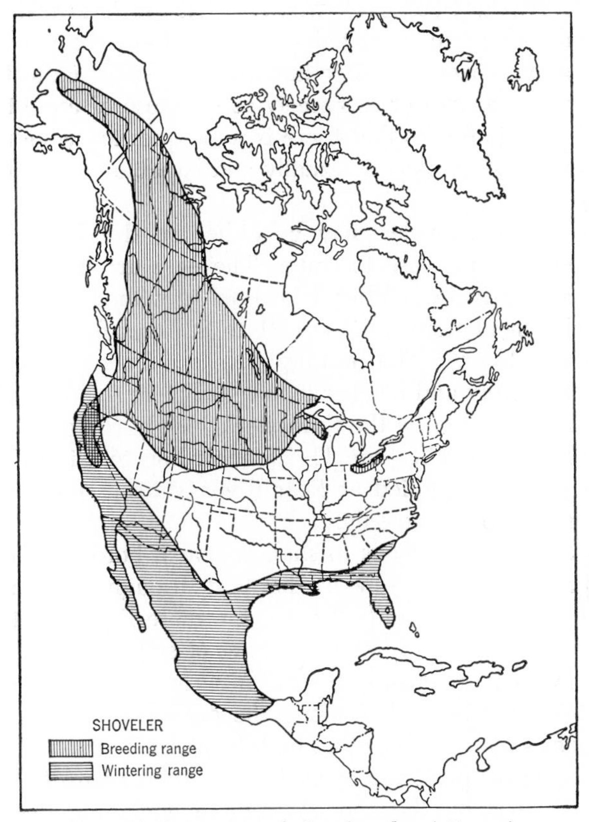

FIG. 17-18. Ranges of the shoveler (41 *g.r.*).

season. The bulk of the fall flight is during September and October. Some stay through the winter as far north as Vancouver Island. In migrating from Canada, shovelers branch out east and west, but mostly the movement is south and west rather than east. Birds banded in Saskatchewan and Alberta were retaken in about equal numbers in the Mississippi, Central and Pacific flyways, indicating the general nature of the spread as the birds moved into the United States from the north.

The daily movements are quite similar to those of the teal. It occupies secluded streams and ponds where shallow water makes feeding safe and productive. According to Phillips (54 *g.r.*), it is more nocturnal in its feeding than any of the other puddle ducks.

Courtship and Breeding. The courtship antics of the shoveler resemble those of the teal. Up to 18 males have been seen courting a single female. The antics in the water include nodding, swimming, and plumage displays. Kortright says that the female shoveler is polyandrous and normally has two or more male consorts, but this is disputed by Shortt and Cartwright (62 *g.r.*), who say that the extra males in attendance are hangers-on to a mated pair. The former says the multiple husbands get on peacefully together, but the latter indicates that the sexually mature males fight as fiercely as do those of any other species. Phillips (54 *g.r.*) indicates that there is some question whether the year-old males are fully developed sexually and capable of breeding the first season.

The nest of the shoveler may be either on dry land distant from water or a moist spot close to water. The eggs are pale olive, buff, or pale green, and vary in number from 8 to 14 with the average about 8 or 9 (3). The incubation period is 21 to 22 days for mechanically incubated eggs (31 *g.r.*). The nesting season at Delta, Manitoba, begins the first week in May and reaches its height before the end of the month. All nesting is completed by the third week in July (31 *g.r.*). In Montana nesting reaches its height June 11–20, according to Girard (3). Eighty per cent of the eggs studied at Bear River Marshes hatched (64 *g.r.*). Incubation is by the female only.

Habitat. The shoveler feeds in shallow marsh borders in either fresh- or salt-water situations. It screens the mud through its mandibles, sorting out any solid matter and allowing the more liquid parts to escape. It will feed in any water whether running or stagnant where there may be enough bottom organisms to furnish a meal. It is found inland or close to the shore rather than along the ocean and is not so afraid of human beings as many of the other puddle ducks.

The nesting cover preferred at Delta, Manitoba, seems to be about the same type as used by the teal and pintail, including the grass-sedge meadow, hay meadows, and pastures which have been lightly used. (31 *g.r.*). The preferred nest sites at Bear River Marshes were in weeds and hard-stemmed bulrushes, although salt-grass was also used freely. In Montana short-grass types are favored for nesting over other types (3).

WOOD DUCK *Aix sponsa*

Tribe *cairinini*

Description. The wood duck has many qualities which appeal to outdoor enthusiasts. The male in breeding plumage is considered the most beautiful of the American waterfowl. Wood ducks require some kind of protective cavity for nesting, so are found in the wooded parts of the country. During the breeding season the birds are quite unafraid and often are seen in towns and villages peering into any opening that might provide a suitable opening for a nest. They will use artificially made nest boxes, so can be induced to nest and rear their young almost anywhere where water is available. Sportsmen and bird lovers erect many nest boxes for their use.

The trusting nature of the wood duck has not always worked to its advantage however. Hunters were able to take them freely, and the woods in which they lived were cut and the ponds drained. Thus by the beginning of the twentieth century, wood ducks became so scarce that they were given complete protection in 1918 in both Canada and

FIG. 17-19. Male and female wood ducks in flight.

the United States. Since about 1945 most of the states have allowed one wood duck in the legal take of the hunter, a provision which allows a wood duck shot by mistake to be utilized.

The male wood duck in breeding plumage has a delicate bill, a crest of alternate green-and-white bars, a white throat with two bars that extend upward along the side of the face and neck. The belly is white and two white crescent-shaped markings extend upward in front of the wing. The sides are chestnut, and the back is bronze green. The tail is long, and the speculum is blue green.

The female is more evenly colored, but the delicate bill, crested head, and light patches over the eyes are conspicuous. The breast and belly are white, and the sides are marked with light-chestnut streaks. Both male and females fly with the bill pointed down. Wood ducks make a squealing sound when they fly rather than the usual coarse quack.

Distribution. Wood ducks are found in the eastern humid parts of North America as far north as the St. Lawrence River and Lake Winnipeg on the west and south to the Gulf of Mexico. Another habitable spot is found along the Pacific Coast from Washington and southern British Columbia to central California.

Breeding occurs on all the wintering grounds, but they do not winter north of Virginia nor in the states that do not border on the Atlantic

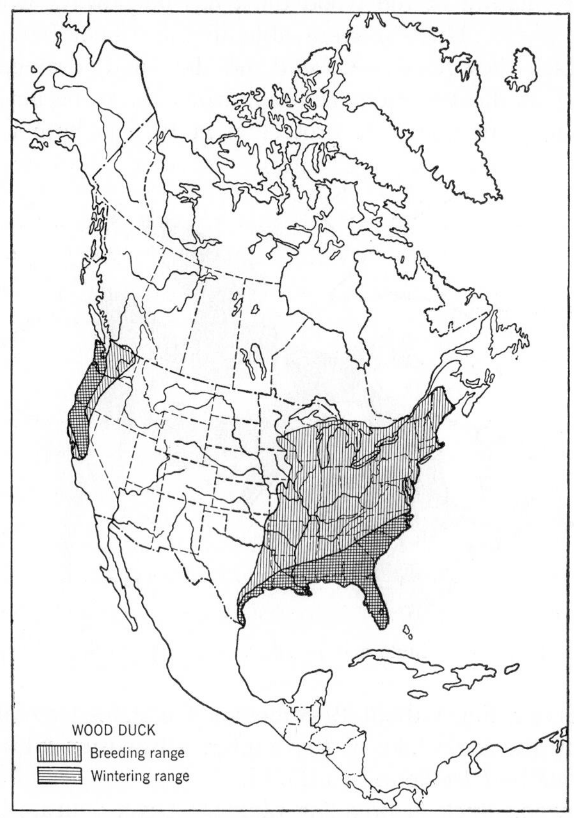

FIG. 17-20. Ranges of the wood duck. (*U.S. Fish and Wildlife Service.*)

Ocean or on the Gulf of Mexico. On the Pacific Coast they winter from central California to Vancouver Island (62 *g.r.*).

Movements. Wood ducks breed in many of their wintering grounds so migratory movements are not conspicuous. In the eastern part of the United States where the migration north is the most extensive, they begin moving north in midwinter and reach the Canadian border in March or early April depending on the weather. Where their nests are made in hollow trees near houses or in buildings, people have come to look for them when they return to the nesting grounds. In the fall they begin to move southward in late September and October. In central Massachusetts they are the most numerous waterfowl on the ponds during October but by November they have moved southward.

Daily activities of the wood duck are typical of the dabblers. They feed along the shallow streams and edges of ponds, tipping down to explore the bottom for food. By September the males with new plumage and females with broods nearly grown assemble together to enjoy the ideal weather of early fall. During the hunting season they are much disturbed by hunters and seek the seclusion of backwoods ponds and streams as well as refuges. As the weather gets cold and the ponds begin to freeze, they move south just ahead of the ice.

Courtship and Breeding. The courtship antics of the wood duck are not too different from those of the other river waterfowl. The borders of wooded ponds, backwaters of woodland streams, and oxbows of large rivers are all used if there are forests nearby. Logs are favorite spots on which to rest, or a leaning tree may be used for a safe perch when the birds are not in the water.

The accounts of mating are not very clear but seem to follow the pattern of a display and maneuvering of males and females before a mate is finally chosen. Just previous to the nesting season the mated pair begin looking for suitable nest quarters in hollow trees, chimneys, buildings, etc. Both male and female take part in this search, but it is not known whether the male actually has any part in the choosing of the nest site or is just keeping the female company.

The nest of wood ducks is made in cavities in trees made by pileated woodpeckers or gray squirrels, or just cavities where decay has removed the heartwood. Such sites may be near the water or at a considerable distance from it. Frequently nests of wood ducks will be in a farmyard or old orchard. The entrance hole can be unbelievably small and still be large enough for the female to enter. She flies directly into the opening and by some unknown mechanism stops with little injury to herself. The nest cavity may be shallow or exposed, or may be far down in the bole of the tree. Usually there is decayed wood on which a nest of down is made at the time incubation begins. Where boxes are used, several ducks may lay in one nest. Possibly this may be true with tree cavities as well. The eggs are creamy white or pure white and vary in number from 9 to 14 with 11 as the average (55 *g.r.*). Where unusually large clutches are found, the eggs probably belong to 2 females. The incubation period is from 28 to 31 days and is performed by the female alone. After the eggs are hatched, the female coaxes the young from the nest by calling to them and leading them to the nearest water. The young birds are able to swim as soon as they are dry and look like yellow bumblebees on the water.

Habitat. The breeding habitat of the wood duck includes both the mixed forest of the northeast part of the United States, the hardwoods of the Lake states, and the semitropical swamp forests of the south and central part of Mexico. There seems to be great variation in the nesting grounds, but trees or some nest site above water is needed, as well as a water situation where resting and feeding sites are available. The wood duck is not a shy bird, so fence posts or nest boxes erected by man may make an otherwise unsuitable situation habitable.

In the wintering grounds the wood duck likes the slow-moving streams and ponds in the cypress woods but will use the marshes and shallow water away from the wooded grounds. Open meadows and isolated backwaters seem to fit the needs of this species, if the water is shallow and food is present.

The practice of providing nest boxes has become quite common in the north. These boxes are made of rough lumber with a cross-section cavity of 10 inches and a height of 24 inches. The hole diameter should be 4 inches and within 6 inches of the top of the box. The cavity should contain sawdust for a nest and the top or roof should be waterproof. The boxes should be set on poles or posts in the water to prevent their use by squirrels and other land animals that are also seeking nest sites. Bees' nests and other debris should be cleaned out of the nest well in advance of the duck-nesting season. If the boxes are fastened to trees, they should be 10 to 15 feet from the ground.

REFERENCES

1. Bennett, Logan J. 1938. The blue-winged teal, Collegiate Press, Inc., Iowa State College, Ames, Iowa.
2. Farley, Frank L. 1924. Large numbers of mallards remain in Buffalo Lake, Alberta, throughout winter. *Canad. Field Nat.* 38(6):119.
3. Girard, George L. 1941. The mallard: Its management in western Montana. *Jour. Wildlife Mangt.* 5(3):233–259.
4. Hagar, Joseph A. 1946*a*. Black duck bandings at the Austin Ornithological Research Station on Cape Cod, Massachusetts. *Bird-Banding.* 17(3): 97–124.
5. ———. 1946*b*. Black duck bandings at the Austin Ornithological Research Station. Part III. Southward recoveries of Cape Cod black ducks. *Bird-Banding.* 17(4):145–160.
6. ———. 1947. Black duck bandings at the Austin Ornithological Research Station. Part IV. Recoveries of summer-banded black ducks. *Bird-Banding.* 18(1):17–26.
7. ———. 1950*a*. Black duck mortality in the Parker River region, winter of 1949–50. Unpublished manuscript, Massachusetts Division Fisheries and Game, Bureau Wildlife Research and Management.
8. ———. 1950*b*. Black duck feeding program, winter 1949–50. Unpublished manuscript, Massachusetts Division Fisheries and Game, Bureau Wildlife Research and Management.

9. Jensen, G. Hortin. 1949. Migration of the gadwall. Migration of some North American waterfowl. *U.S. Fish and Wildlife Serv., Spec. Sci. Rept.: Wildlife* 1.
10. ——— and Allen G. Smith. 1949. Migration of the cinnamon teal. Migration of some American waterfowl. *U.S. Dept. Int. Fish and Wildlife Serv., Spec. Sci. Rpt.: Wildlife* 1.
11. Lawrence, A. G. 1929. Mallards tardy in migrating. *Canad. Field Nat.* **43**(2):42.
12. Low, Seth H. 1949. The migration of the pintail. Migration of some North American waterfowl. *U.S. Fish and Wildlife Serv., Spec. Sci. Rpt.: Wildlife* 1.
13. Mendall, Howard L. 1949. Food habits in relation to black duck management in Maine. *Jour. Wildlife Mangt.* **13**(1):64–101.
14. Pirnie, Miles D. 1932. Fall migration of black ducks from northern Michigan. *Mich. Acad. Sci., Arts, and Letters.* **15**:485–490.
15. Shortt, Terence M. 1943. Correlation of bill and foot coloring with age and season in the black duck. *Wilson Bul.* **55**(1):2–7.
16. Smith, Allen G. 1949. Migration of the baldpate. Migration of some North American waterfowl. *U.S. Fish and Wildlife Serv., Spec. Sci. Rpt.: Wildlife* 1.
17. Stout, Jerome H. 1949. Southward migration of the shoveller. Migration of some North American waterfowl. *U.S. Fish and Wildlife Serv., Spec. Sci. Rpt.: Wildlife* 1.
18. Trautman, Milton B. 1947. Courtship behavior of the black duck. *Wilson Bul.* **59**(1):26–35.
19. Wright, Bruce S. 1947. Can we restore the black duck? *Field and Stream (New York)*. **52**(1):42–43, 128–132.

CHAPTER 18

Bay or Diving Ducks

Subfamily *Anatinae*
Tribe *aythyini*

The diving ducks are different in many respects from the river or puddle ducks. Generally they are more wary and shy and feed in deep rather than in shallow water; they are more likely to feed on marine forms, especially during the winter, and are gregarious and tend to group together in rafts during the nonbreeding season.

In getting off from the water, the bay ducks paddle along the surface before getting into the air in contrast to the initial vertical flight of the river ducks.

The diving ducks are most interesting because of their intricate social behavior, strength, skill in flying, and fortitude in braving the wind and sea during migration flights and on their wintering grounds. There are few sights as inspiring as the flight of the canvasback, the rafting habits of the bluebills, and the low, swift flight of the bufflehead. In no case, are the markings of the diving ducks as striking as the puddlers.

The bay ducks appear to have suffered more than the puddle ducks through the use of their breeding grounds by man. Perhaps this is because the bay ducks are less adaptable to changes in their habitat.

REDHEAD *Aythya americana*

Description. The redhead duck is comparatively large, being next in size to the canvasback with which it frequently associates. It is wary but not too wary to become a target for any persistent hunter. Hochbaum (8) considers the young of the redhead very vulnerable to shooting; in fact, he states some hunters pass up these ducks because of the ease with which they can be shot and the need for conserving future breeders. Its pattern of migration makes it available to hunters in the Lake states as well as those of the western prairies.

The redhead has received attention in recent years because of the downward trend of the population at a time when other ducks are on the increase. This failure to respond to increased rainfall may be due to the fact that nesting birds require emergent vegetation and to the restricted area of the breeding range.

The male redhead in breeding plumage has a red head, a black chest, gray back, and a dark tail. The breast and belly are white; the bill and feet are blue gray.

The female is drab with a light-colored throat and light speculum. The most prominent distinguishing mark of both male and female is the short neck and bill and massive appearing head. These ducks often

Fig. 18-1. Male and female redheads.

associate with canvasbacks but are slightly smaller than the "cans" and have shorter necks and heads.

Distribution. The breeding range is small in area compared to the canvasback and mallard. Also its range is largely in the parts of the United States and Canada which are heavily utilized by man (2). The over-all range is likewise deceiving because only a very small part of the range is suitable for nesting purposes (3). Lincoln (11) pointed out that while the range included the states of Iowa, the Dakotas, the Bear River Marshes in Utah, Oregon, and portions of the four western provinces of Canada, in reality less than a fourth of the area so designated was producing birds in any quantity. To be effective these units must have stable water levels and have had water sufficiently long to produce emergent aquatic vegetation.

The wintering ranges include coastal areas along the Atlantic Coast, the coast of the Gulf of Mexico, as well as northern Mexico and California on the Pacific Coast. Along with coots and scaup, the redheads congregate in large rafts along the coasts. They go out to deep water if disturbed by shooting but come in to protected bays for feeding and protection from storms.

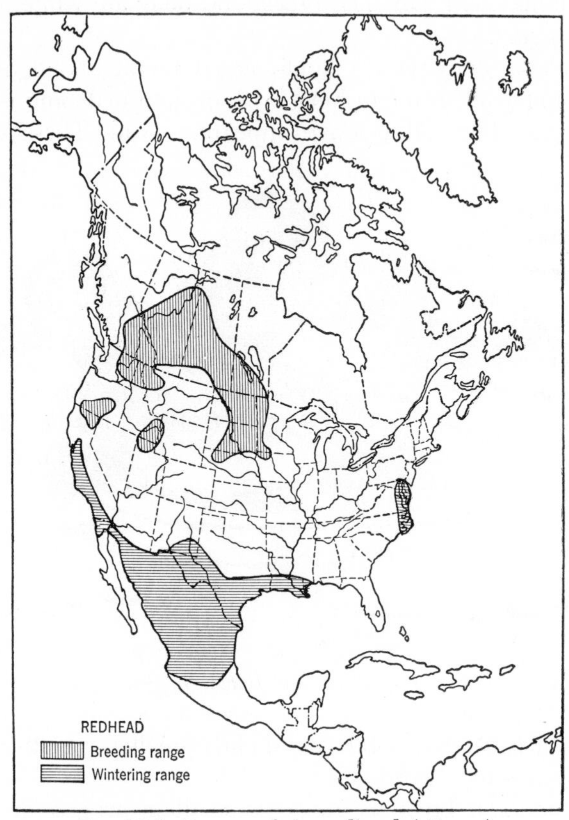

FIG. 18-2. Ranges of the redhead (41 *g.r.*).

Movements. The migratory movements of the redhead are the most complex of any of the American waterfowl. Some birds from the Canadian breeding grounds move east through eastern Canada to the Atlantic Coast, while others move west to the Pacific. Many birds that breed in Central Canada move down the Mississippi and Central states flyways. Birds at Bear River Marshes move not only west to California but south, southeast, and northeast across the Great Lakes. Few if any move on east from the Great Lakes to the Atlantic flyway, however (17).

Redheads are hardy and stay on in the breeding grounds until late in the season. They depart from Canada in mid-October with little regard for the weather (62 *g.r.*). Hochbaum (31 *g.r.*) calls attention to the large number of young redheads at Delta, Manitoba, in the fall and says that some young birds are still unable to fly at the time of the freeze-up.

The northward flight of redheads is early, ending in Canada during the first half of April (62 *g.r.*). Northbound birds reach central Iowa about March 20, and migrations continue for a month (13).

Redheads, like other diving ducks, travel by night during migrations and fly in and out of the feeding grounds in the evening and during the early morning. They feed during the night and raft out of danger on large sheets of open water if such are available. Inland where extensive bodies of water are not available they come into the bays and marshes during the day to feed (13). Band returns from Canada and the Bear River Marshes in Utah indicate the hunting pressure on this species is the heaviest of any of the waterfowl banded (62 *g.r.*).

Courtship and Breeding. The diving ducks mature more slowly than the river ducks, so there are probably fewer courting activities during the early winter than with the puddle ducks. Also the sex ratio is heavy on the side of males, so the competition of males for a mate may change the normal activity somewhat. Hochbaum (31 *g.r.*) points out that with both redhead and canvasback the female goes through the neck-stretching process during the courtship antics. Nuptial flights are common with all bay ducks, and according to Hochbaum (31 *g.r.*), copulation always takes place on the water. The redhead nesting season in southern Canada begins the first week in May and lasts until late in August. Nests are started over a period of a month, and the renesting season is late, occurring during the last week in August (31 *g.r.*). Most of the investigaticns show that redheads nest over water, the nest being a complicated structure of debris woven into emergent vegetation. Redheads do nest on dry land, however (62 *g.r.*).

The females sometimes use the nests of other females for laying their eggs, thus accounting for large clutches of eggs. Redhead females also lay eggs in the nests of other species, including the mallard, pintail, blue-winged teal, gadwall, lesser scaup, white-winged scoter, ruddy duck, and even the Canada goose. Down is used to line the nest, but the nests are not well concealed. The eggs are olive buff and vary from 10 to 15 in number. Low gives the average number of eggs in 115 complete redhead clutches as slightly less than 10 (13). The incubation period varies from 22 to 24 days (62 *g.r.*).

Of more than 2,600 eggs studied at Bear River Marshes, Utah, only 26 per cent hatched. Seventy-four per cent were lost from various causes, the one cause of greatest mortality being flooding (64 *g.r.*).

Habitat. The winter habitats of the redheads are weed-filled ponds or agricultural lands adjacent to large bodies of open water (7). Here the birds feed, rest, and escape disturbance. In the north they appear to prefer large inland lakes like Seneca and Canandaigua Lakes in New York State, and in the east Chesapeake Bay, Back Bay, and Currituck Sound. In the south they use lagoons of the Gulf Coast. In the north during the breeding season the birds prefer the open water of lakes for resting at night and the bays and large marshes for use during the daytime.

For nest sites in Iowa emergent marsh vegetation is preferred. Mostly the nests are suspended on upright vegetation like bulrushes some distance from the marsh edge and usually over water. The average area per nest was about 10 acres but sometimes there were 2 nests on an acre (13).

At Delta, Manitoba, redhead nests were found in 8 cover types but were most commonly found in bulrush islands, bulrushes in shallow water, cat-tails, and dense stands of phragmites (31 *q.r.*).

CANVASBACK *Aythya valisineria*

Description. The canvasback duck belongs to a group of game birds that may be spoken of as royalty. It has power, dignity, and great beauty

Fig. 18-3. Male and female canvasbacks.

and is mysterious, all qualities that capture the imagination and inspire admiration.

The bold wedge-shaped head of the canvasback is its most conspicuous feature. The head, neck, and chest of the male in breeding plumage are dark, as is also the rear portion. The chest is dark brown and the head and throat a reddish chestnut. Resting on the water the wings and back have a light-gray appearance. The feet and speculum are blue gray.

The female is somber-appearing with lighter colors on the wings and back. The under parts are paler than the back, head, and tail.

Distribution. The canvasback breeds in the same general location as the redhead, but the range extends farther north to the vicinity of the

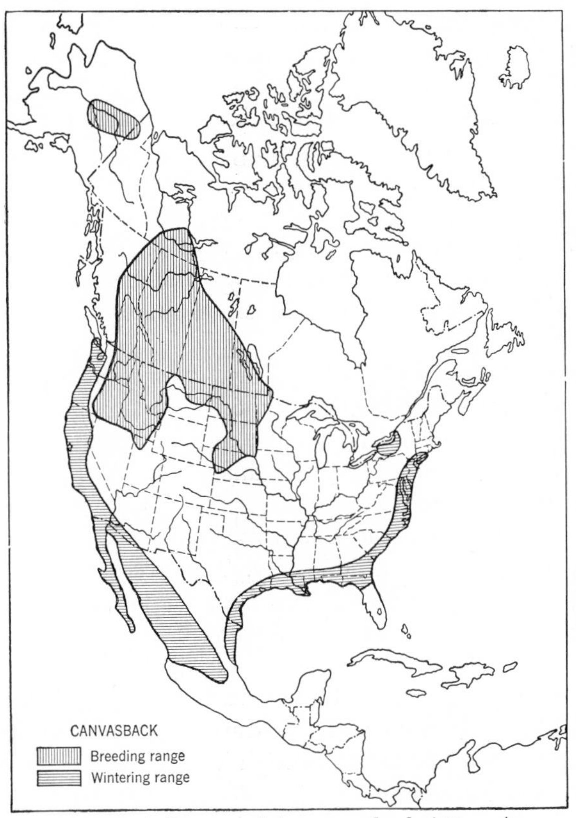

FIG. 18-4. Ranges of the canvasback (41 *g.r.*).

Arctic Circle in Canada, with an isolated breeding range in Alaska in the valley of the Yukon River. Birds breed as far east in Canada as central Manitoba and as far west as British Columbia. In the United States the breeding range includes the Dakotas, Nebraska, and the northwestern states, including Oregon, Washington, Wyoming, Idaho, and Montana.

The wintering range includes the Finger Lakes in New York State and the Atlantic coast from Long Island to the latitude of Mexico City. The wintering area along the coasts does not extend inland beyond the bays and river estuaries along the East Coast, but the species tends to be more of an inland species on the western side of the continent.

Movements. The first arrival dates of the canvasback at Delta, Manitoba, are April 12 to 23 (31 *g.r.*). The birds come in after the first thaw in small bands, usually on a south wind. They may remain at Delta or may move on to the breeding grounds farther north. This northward movement begins in the evening, as like most of the diving ducks, the canvasback migrates at night. By the end of the first week in May, the movement toward the north is complete and the birds are starting to nest.

The migration south in the fall is late compared with that of the puddle ducks. The drakes do not finish growing their new flight feathers until September and as a result linger on in the north until late in September and October. Some move north after the breeding season before going south (4). Hochbaum (31 *g.r.*) says the birds move with the calendar rather than the weather and go through southern Manitoba from October 10 to 24. This is well before the lakes of that region freeze over.

Daily routine includes feeding, resting, defense of territory, and the activities of keeping feathers clean, exposure to sunshine, breeding, egg laying, incubation, care of the young, and preparation for migration. The flightless period is no doubt very difficult because the usual method of escape by flight is denied during this time.

The canvasback gets its scientific name *valisineria* from its love of the roots and winter buds of wild celery. This plant grows in relatively deep water and has to be brought up from the bottom. The canvasback excels at obtaining wild celery and lives well in any open water where it grows.

In the autumn and winter the canvasbacks feed during the early morning and late afternoon and rest during the middle of the day. If disturbed, they move out to sea in high V-shaped flocks, resting on the ocean unless storms drive them in.

Courtship and Breeding. The courtship of canvasbacks begins on the northward migrations, but the selection of mates is not completed until just previous to nesting. Hochbaum (31 *g.r.*) indicates mates may not be selected even as late as the first of April, but Dr. Allen found courtship of this species going on at Cayuga Lake in New York during February and March.

Several males court a female by various maneuvers including a headthrow, neck stretching, and numerous courting calls. In the nuptial flight the drake attempts to catch the upper tail feathers of the female in his bill. Copulation takes place on the water.

Nesting of canvasbacks begins in early May in southern Canada and lasts until the last week in July. Nests are usually built in emergent vegetation over water and of the materials at hand, including leaves of cat-tails or other plants. The nest is built not far from open water and sometimes at its very edge. The eggs are large and pale green with a smooth shell. The average clutch varies from 6 to 13 eggs, with 10 as an average. The incubation period is 23 to 29 days, with an average time of 24 days. Incubation is by the female only.

Habitat. The breeding grounds of the canvasback consists of the shallow marshy borders of lakes, stretches of open water, and the vegetation that is necessary to supply ducks with feed, nest sites, and places to rest, loaf, and escape from enemies, especially during the flightless period. The conditions of water and land which prevail in the prairie and intermountain regions of North America supply these needs and therefore support high populations of canvasbacks.

When water disappears because of low rainfall, drainage, or some other reason, canvasbacks and other waterfowl also disappear. Not only is it necessary to have water in the form of ponds and lakes, but for some of the ducks the aquatic habitat must have enough time to develop emergent vegetation. This means enough fertile soil and the right depth of water to produce cat-tails, bulrushes, or phragmites. At Delta, Manitoba, the canvasback nests commonly in only two cover types, on bulrush islands and among bulrushes in shallow bays and sloughs. It is a casual nester in cat-tails and a rare nester in phragmites in shallow water as well as in grass-sedge-sow thistle meadows (31 *g.r.*).

There is another factor which affects nesting canvasbacks. When nests are flooded out, the eggs are lost and the birds may not renest. High water may also destroy suitable vegetation, so again canvasbacks may be required to go elsewhere to nest.

The condition of the habitat on the migration routes usually is adequate. The canvasback is a strong swimmer and diver and can get food even in deep water if it is present. Open water rather than marshes or pond edges is the source of its livelihood, and wide stretches of open water are needed for protection. The scope of the wintering grounds is limited. Fresh-water habitats are desired, although the "can" will use salt water if it is forced to do so. River channels and bays of the entire coastal regions of the United States and both coasts of the northern half of Mexico supply wintering habitats for this species.

RING-NECKED DUCK *Aythya collaris*

Description. The ring-necked, or ring-billed, duck is of special interest because of the expansion of its breeding range in the United States. Monographs on wildfowl give this duck as only casually seen or breeding in the northeast from 1900–1930, but by 1950 the breeding grounds are recorded as extending from British Columbia to Newfoundland, including several of the New England states (55 *g.r.*, 57 *g.r.*). Any waterfowl that can expand its range when the ranges of other waterfowl are shrinking deserves a second look.

The ring-necked duck is a medium-sized bird that might be described as dumpy in appearance, having a short neck and a large puffy head. The male in breeding plumage is dark-colored with a dark purple head and chest, a greenish neck and back, and a dusky-brown tail. The bill is deep blue in both sexes, having light-colored rings, one near the tip and the other at its base. The belly is light with a white crescent extend-

FIG. 18-5. Male and female ring-necked ducks.

ing upward forward of the folded wing. The wings are dusky with a pearl-gray speculum. There may be a grayish-blue bar at the rear of the speculum. The feet are bluish green. Even in a male in full breeding plumage the neck ring of chestnut seldom shows.

The female is dusky except for the white belly and light cheek patches. The bill is blue with the white ring near the tip and the white ring of feathers around the head back of the nostrils. The speculum does not show when the wings are folded.

Distribution. The breeding range of the ring-necked duck extends from the interior valleys of British Columbia to the east, including most of Alberta, Saskatchewan, and Manitoba. Breeding also occurs in the southern part of Mackenzie District. Ring-necks breed across the southern half of Ontario, Quebec, and in most of New Brunswick and the western third of Newfoundland. In the United States, breeding occurs in northern Maine, New Hampshire, Vermont, and New York.

In the Lake states, it breeds in Wisconsin, Iowa, Minnesota, and North Dakota.

The bulk of the ring-necked ducks winter along the Atlantic Coast from Chesapeake Bay to Florida and west to eastern Texas. Inland the wintering grounds extend north to Arkansas. On the Pacific Coast, ring-necks winter from northern California to the Columbia River.

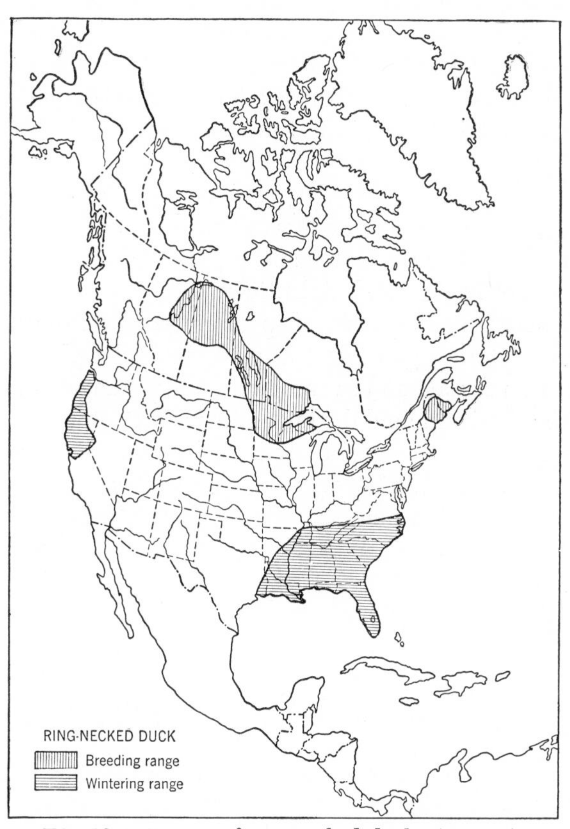

FIG. 18-6. Ranges of ring-necked ducks (41 *g.r.*).

Movements. The ring-necks start south in the fall in October with the redheads and canvasbacks but ahead of the bluebills (62 *g.r.*). Mendall (14) cites an occasion where two broods of ring-necked ducks were seen in eastern Maine the last week in August, one brood of which was unable to fly at that time. Ring-necks move into Delta, Manitoba, from the north (presumably) in October.

The northern migration takes place in the spring in March and April, ending in the southern Canadian provinces about the middle of April in the company of the lesser scaup.

The migration pattern is complex. From the Prairie Provinces the birds that move southeastward skirt the conifer belt at its south border. A contingent also returns to the breeding grounds by this route in the spring. These birds, and also those from farther east, pass east and south to Chesapeake Bay and later move on south along the Atlantic Coast. Another contingent may travel a more interior route southwest of Chesapeake Bay through Indiana, Kentucky, Tennessee, and North Carolina. Some of the birds from central and western Canada move south to the Gulf of Mexico through the Mississippi flyway. Some of these may move east along the Gulf of Mexico to the coasts of Alabama and Florida. Birds banded in Michigan in the fall are recovered in New York and along the Delaware and Chesapeake Bays regions, indicating that birds traveling from the north through Michigan travel the eastern route rather than down the Mississippi flyway. Birds which breed in the northeastern part of the United States and eastern Canada use the Atlantic flyway and winter in the south Atlantic region (5).

Courtship and Breeding. Courtship of ring-necked ducks apparently starts on the wintering grounds (55 *g.r.*). Several males may compete for the favor of a female and in the process of plumage display raise the feathers on the head and hold the tail feathers erect.

The nests are built among the reeds and over water if possible. The nest is lined with down. The eggs are greenish buff or greenish white and vary from 6 to 12 in number. The incubation period is unknown.

Habitat. Little is known about the habitat of the ring-necked ducks. According to Kortright (41 *g.r.*), they prefer marshes and sloughs to open lakes and streams and are found less commonly in open waters than other diving ducks. They are good divers, however, and may obtain food in water as deep as 40 feet.

The nests are in wet boggy places and are placed very low over the water.

On the wintering grounds these birds prefer fresh to salt water and are found in the inland marshes, ponds, swamps, and rice fields in the southern part of the United States (41 *g.r.*).

SCAUP DUCKS OR BLUEBILLS

Lesser Scaup *Aythya affinis*

Common Scaup *Aythya marila marila*

Description. The two bluebills, the lesser and common, look and appear much alike but are quite different in habits and distribution and together are quite different from the other diving ducks. Except for mature males in breeding plumage, it is impossible to tell the two species apart except by having the birds in hand where they can be measured. The color of the head and neck of the adult male of the common scaup is black. The sides of the neck are glossy dark green. In the lesser scaup the head and neck markings are the same, except that

FIG. 18-7. Male and female scaup ducks. Common and lesser scaups have much the same appearance.

the reflection of the feathers is purple instead of green. The bill and wing dimensions and weights compare as follows (41 *g.r.*):

	Bill	Wing	Weight
Lesser scaup	36–40 mm	220–233 mm	1 lb. 4 oz.–1 lb. 10 oz.
Common scaup	43–47 mm	185–198 mm	2 lb. 4 oz.–2 lb. 10 oz.

Alexander Wilson, who failed to recognize the differences in the two species, did notice that the common scaup appeared to be "much the fattest" (55 *g.r.*).

There are other differences which cannot be detected by visual inspection. The common scaup is circumpolar, having a counterpart in the European and Asiatic continents, while the lesser scaup is found only in the New World. Also the breeding and wintering ranges of the two species vary widely, as can be seen from the range maps.

The common scaup is more truly a bay duck than is the canvasback and redhead. They can stand more cold, rough weather and in many ways appear to be closely related to other true bay ducks.

Scaup are slow in developing sexually, and it is believed that some at least do not breed until the second season (55 *g.r.*).

In North America the scaup is conspicuous for its habit of rafting on the large inland waters late in the fall and winter. These rafts may consist of several thousand ducks seen on the Great Lakes and some of the other northern bodies of water, riding out a storm with little or no concern for the biting wind and low temperatures.

The scaup is a medium sized black-and-white duck. The bill is a bright blue, and the feet are blue gray. The belly is white, and outer wings and back of the male are grayish white. In the female there is a

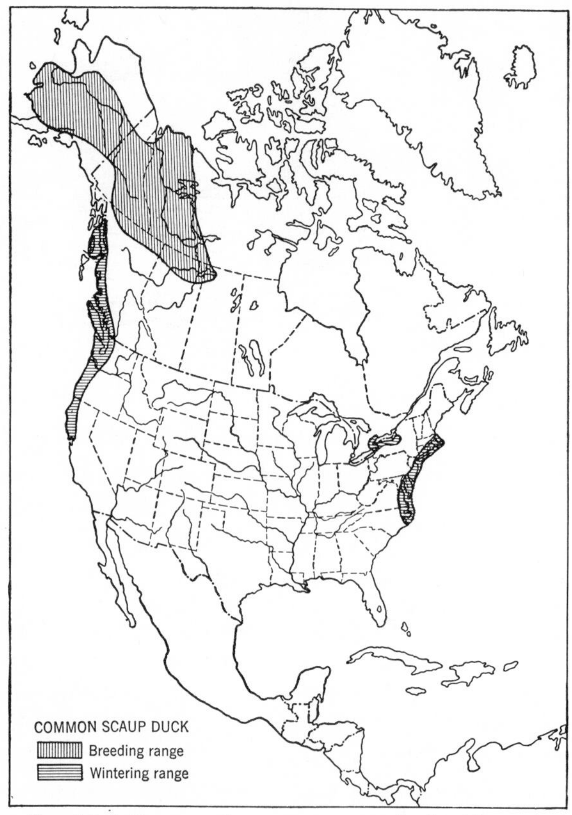

FIG. 18-8. Ranges of common scaup ducks (41 *g.r.*).

ring of white feathers between the eye and the bill. A crescent of white shows back of the folded wing. In flight the speculum shows as white with a border of black at the rear margin. There are some white feathers on the outer wing of the common scaup that are not present on the lesser scaup, thus extending the size of the white speculum in the former species.

Distribution. The common scaup thrives under severe weather conditions and as a result has both breeding and wintering groups far north of the less hardy ducks. The breeding grounds in North America are mainly in the north and west half of Alaska, the north central portion of the District of Mackenzie, a small portion of northern Manitoba, and the southern part of the District of Keewatin (1). Wintering grounds include the Great Lakes, the Atlantic Coast from Cape Cod to North Carolina, parts of the Gulf of Mexico, and the Pacific Coast from the Aleutian Islands to lower California (62 *g.r.*).

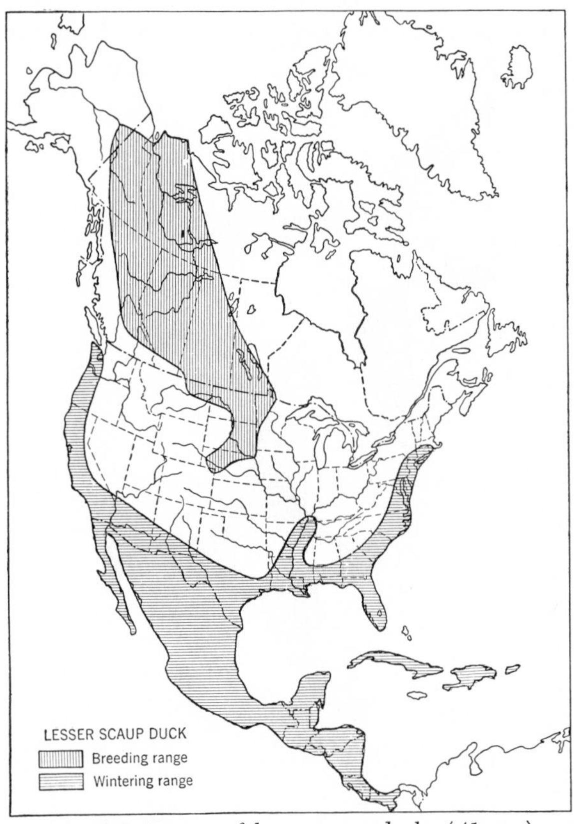

FIG. 18-9. Ranges of lesser scaup ducks (41 *g.r.*).

The breeding grounds of the lesser scaup include parts of North Dakota and Montana and the central and western parts of Canada, including portions of both the Pacific and Arctic shores. The wintering grounds include the Atlantic Coast from Maine south, and the Pacific Coast from Vancouver Island south, including the inland southwestern parts of the United States, Mexico, and the countries of Central America to the Canal Zone.

Movements. So little is known of the fall migration route of the common scaup that the limitation of knowledge rather than the facts will be the conspicuous item. Birds which breed on the west coast of Alaska move south and east across the Pacific Ocean and hit the mainland somewhere in the vicinity of Vancouver Island. From this point they move southward along the coast of Washington, Oregon, and California. The birds from northern Canada move southward over an unknown route to the Great Lakes, then eastward along the Great Lakes to the Atlantic Ocean. Whether the birds that winter along the Gulf of Mexico arrive by way of the Atlantic Coast or directly down the Mississippi

FIG. 18-10. Male and female lesser scaup ducks in flight. Note white crescent on cheek of female.

flyway is not known (1). Because scaup are late maturing, they are not ready and probably not inclined to go south early. Shortt and Cartwright (62 *g.r.*) say rafts of thousands appear several miles offshore on Lake Winnipeg and leave only when the freeze-up is imminent in November.

The spring movement north begins in February and March, but the details of the passage north are not well known. It appears that the lesser scaup move from the wintering grounds in several directions, as would be shown by the radiating spokes of a wheel from its hub. This comparison is probably not so true as is apparent because of the arrangement of the pattern of lakes and large bodies of water over the United States. The southward wintering movement may be in broad lines which move first in one direction then in another to suitable bodies of water in the path of the general direction of the flight. Without question there is a heavy eastward movement of birds from the Great Lakes through the Finger Lakes region of New York to the Atlantic Coast. Lesser scaup move westward over the mountains to the Pacific Coast and southward along the Mississippi and Central flyways. It is quite probable that the birds fan out from the Mississippi flyway as they reach the Gulf Coast and move east to Florida and south and west to Texas and Mexico. No direct evidence is available as to the routes used by the birds which go to the west coast of Mexico. The time of southern movement extends from August, when flightless birds congregate on suitable waters, to October and November when the northern lakes freeze over.

Lesser scaup reach the Canadian provinces in mid-April and spread out to the breeding grounds to the north. Hochbaum records a sex ratio of more than two males to every female at Delta, Manitoba, on the spring flights (31 *g.r.*).

Courtship and Breeding. The scaup, both common and lesser, are slow maturing and do not get at the business of courtship until late. Of the common, Phillips (55 *g.r.*) says that very little pairing has taken place when the birds leave the wintering grounds in April. As already indicated, many scaup that move north may not breed until the second year.

The mating display in both species includes pointing of the head straight up, dipping of the bill in the water, and low calls and whistles.

The nesting process begins in late May or early June and lasts through August. The nests are not far from water and may be surrounded by water or placed in small islands of vegetation or in the woody vegetation of the tundra. The scaup, unlike most of the diving ducks, seldom nest over water. The nests of lesser scaup are in cat-tails, sedges, or prairie grasses. Nests are lined with dried grass and down. Not all nests are well concealed, and several nests may be close together. Egg clutches of the common scaup are from 8 to 11 and of the lesser scaup from 9 to 15. The lesser scaup appears to be the most prolific (55 *g.r.*). Other ducks frequently use the nests of scaup to deposit their eggs. The eggs of common scaup are dull drab to olive gray and those of lesser scaup are grayish buff to a deep olive buff. Incubation of both species is given as 22 to 23 days by Phillips (55 *g.r.*).

Habitat. The scaup are among the most aquatic of the diving ducks, in fact the name "scaup" comes from the fact that these birds get much of their food from "scalps," meaning beds of mussels. All of the references emphasize the fact that these waterfowl live in or around large bodies of water.

The common scaup is definitely more hardy and also more of a salt-water species than the lesser. It is as much so as are the scoters and eider ducks (55 *g.r.*). The lesser scaup, on the other hand, breeds in a more southerly location than the common scaup, and while it inhabits both fresh and salt water, prefers the sheltered fresh and brackish waters to the open sea.

The breeding grounds of the common scaup are in the far north extending along the entire western shore of the Arctic Ocean. Here the growing season is short, the ground never thaws to more than a few feet in depth, and the vegetation is of the tundra type. This includes mosses, sedges, and many types of flowering plants. Inland stunted woody vegetation is found, including willows, junipers, black spruce, and other zerophytic shrubs. Phillips (55 *g.r.*) says the common scaup prefers dry islands for nest sites, sometimes near the water and sometimes at considerable distances from it. The nest is poorly concealed.

The breeding ground of the lesser scaup is more inland and more temperate, with a longer summer season and on better soils. The favorite nesting locations are on islands in lakes and on the grassy edges of lakes and ponds (55 *g.r.*). Sometimes the nests are over water and surrounded by water and sometimes are 50 yards inland in the prairie grasses. The nest is poorly concealed. At Delta, Manitoba, Hochbaum (31 *g.r.*) found nests in all cover types, but grain fields, thickets, brush piles, woods, and dense stands of phragmites at some distance from water were preferred. The grass-sedge-sow thistle meadow and bay meadows were the most commonly used.

The scaups are conspicuous for their rafting habits. Even during the winter, rafts of several thousand will be seen on almost any large lake in the Great Lakes region as long as the water is not frozen. Here they rest, sleep, and dive for food. The common scaups are usually found on the salt water. The wintering grounds of the common and lesser scaup are quite different. On the Atlantic Coast the common scaup is found on broad salt-water bays like Narragansett, Barnegat, and Chesapeake Bays, while the lesser scaup has its center of abundance in winter farther south on such fresh-water rivers as the St. Johns in eastern Florida.

AMERICAN GOLDENEYE *Bucephala clangula americana*

Description. The American goldeneye, or "whistler," is a spectacular black-and-white duck of medium size but not highly regarded generally by the gunner. It gets its name from the penetrating sound of the air through the wing while the birds are in flight. The American goldeneye is distributed across the continent and has a related species, the Barrow's goldeneye,[1] in the western part of North America as well as related forms in Europe and Asia.

The goldeneye is a hardy duck that occupies both inland and coastal waters. It is one of the first to start toward the breeding grounds in the spring and stays until the freeze-up in the fall.

This duck is a tree nester, so uses the wooded parts of northern North America for its breeding range.

FIG. 18-11. Male and female American goldeneyes.

The male is a short-necked duck with a large round head and a general black-and-white appearance. The head and throat are black with a green sheen or iridescence, and there is a white spot in front of the eye. The lower neck, belly, and sides are also white. There are streaks of white along the back and a large white patch on the inner wing.

The female in breeding plumage has a brown head, but no white eye spot. The white on the neck consists of a narrow ring that joins in the back. The white on the belly and the white wing spots are less distinct and smaller than in the male.

[1] Barrow's goldeneye is found along both coasts of North America from Labrador to New Jersey on the Atlantic and from Alaska and British Columbia to California on the Pacific Coast. This species is so nearly like the American goldeneye that no further details will be given.

Distribution. The breeding range of the American goldeneye extends from Newfoundland to the west coast of Alaska and includes the northern part of the United States as well as the central part of the Prairie Provinces of Canada.

Wintering areas include most of the continent where open water is available. In the east the wintering range includes most of the United

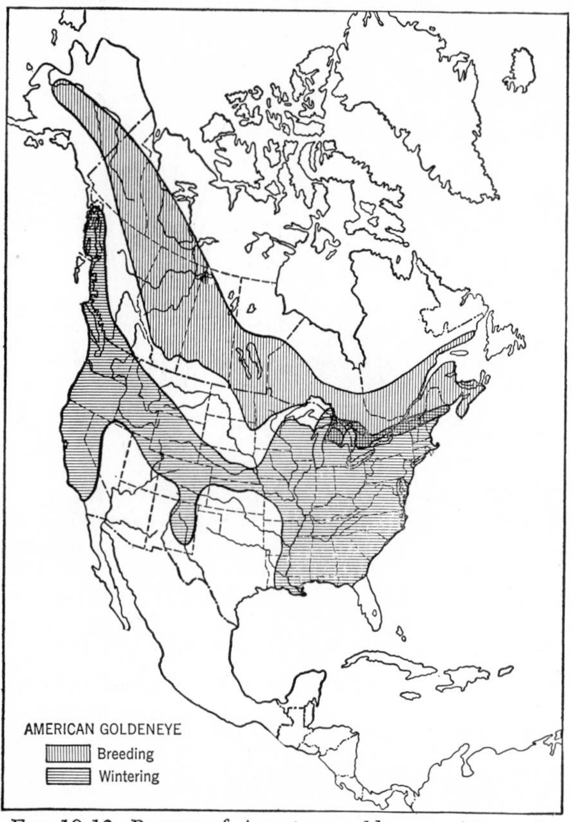

FIG. 18-12. Ranges of American goldeneyes (41 *g.r.*).

States as far west as the Mississippi River and along the western part of the continent from the Aleutian Islands to southern California (15). This species is one of the hardiest of the ducks and occupies every piece of open water.

Movements. Phillips (55 *g.r.*) speaks of the American goldeneye as an individualist. It never congregates in large groups and migrates also in small groups or pairs. Moving from the breeding grounds goldeneyes start late, waiting until the freeze-up is imminent, then moving south just ahead of severe weather in October or November. The females and young of the year come first, followed by the males (55 *g.r.*).

The northward migration in the spring appears to be a movement of small numbers of birds following in the wake of the ice. In the Connecticut Valley birds are seen on the river as early as February and March and seek out the streams as soon as the ice breaks up.

American goldeneyes are day feeders and are very restless as seen on their wintering grounds. They are very shy while on small waters or along narrow channels, and move to larger bodies of water for the night. They also move with the tides near salt water, taking advantage of the low tides on the flats and of the rise in water on the creeks at high tide (55 *g.r.*). Apparently there is a separation of some of the old males from the females and younger birds during the wintering period. These old males move out of the breeding grounds last and may choose a different wintering ground from females and young. Phillips (55 *g.r.*) is inclined to believe these old males do not go so far south as the females and young and that males are more apt to be found on salt water and females and young on fresh water.

Courtship and Breeding. The courtship of the American goldeneye is spectacular and may be termed almost violent. One antic of the male is to swing the head back until it touches the rump, then bring it forward violently. At the same time the feet are kicked out behind, sending the bird forward in a violent plunge. Several males may perform around a single female.

The nest of the goldeneye is in a cavity of some kind, usually a hollow in a tree, although they will nest in boxes placed for them. The eggs are olive green and vary from 5 to 19 in number, the average being about 10 to 12. Two or more females may lay in one nest, and the eggs may be piled in layers. The incubation period varies from 22 to 24 days (55 *g.r.*).

In southern Canada broods may be seen as early as the last of May (10).

Habitat. The habitats of the American goldeneye vary greatly. The breeding sites include wooded streams and lakes in Ontario and the northern part of the United States and the woodlands along the lakes in Canada. Wooded mountainous country satisfies the breeding-ground needs of this species wherever water is present. Old or decadent trees are necessary for nesting sites, and still water, with shallow borders, is used by the broods for feeding.

The wintering grounds may be either salt- or fresh-water habitats. Large expanses of water are preferred over small ponds, and the water adjacent to the frozen-over zone seems to be preferred. In the fall migration the smaller bodies of water are avoided if larger, open waters are available. Along the coasts the birds trade back and forth between the open water of the ocean and the tidal flats, stream estuaries, and fresh-water ponds inland.

BUFFLEHEAD *Bucephala albeola*

Description. The bufflehead is a graceful little duck with a high rounded head and a short bill. The average weight is a pound or less, and its general appearance is conspicious for its black-and-white markings. The bufflehead, or butterball, is an excellent swimmer and diver and a swift flier. It is not prized by the hunter, however, because of its small size and poor quality of its flesh.

The head and upper neck of the male in breeding plumage are dark, the feathers showing a green, purple, and violet sheen except for a patch on each side of the head, back of the eye, which is white. These patches unite across the back of the head. The back, tail, and flight feathers of the wings are black, and the speculum and some of the secondary wing feathers are white as are the feathers of the neck, belly, and narrow strips along the sides of the back. The female is more dusky than the male with a spot on the side of the head, and the breast and the belly are light-colored.

Distribution. The bufflehead is found only in North America. Its breeding range extends from the St. Lawrence River north and west of Lake Ontario to southern Alaska and the central part of Washington and Oregon. As it is a tree-den nester it seeks breeding areas where forests are present and nest dens are available. It must be assumed that large expanses within the outlines of the breeding area are without nest sites and therefore devoid of breeding birds. The need for tree cavities for nests explains the eastward extension of the range through Ontario and its presence in southern Alaska and British Columbia.

The bufflehead does not seem to mind adverse weather conditions so long as open water is available. It winters from Cape Cod south along the Atlantic Coast, in the Great Lakes region, and on the western part of the continent from the Aleutian Islands south through most of the western states to southern California and northern Mexico.

Movements. The flocks of migrating buffleheads are small, apparently mostly family parties. When flying over water they fly low, rising gracefully from the water and lighting with a splash. The fall migration is late and occurs only when forced by the necessity of keeping ahead of the freeze-up. In southern Canada this is October, and the movement south is through the coniferous forest rather than across the prairies (62 *g.r.*). At Delta, Manitoba, Hochbaum (31 *g.r.*) indicates that they are always present in the autumn but never common. Phillips (55 *g.r.*) speaks of the initial arrival of immature birds and the late arrival of the adults.

On much of its range the distance from the wintering to the breeding grounds is short. Along the British Columbia Coast, it travels inland along the river valleys (16). In central Canada, it passes north during the middle of April (62 *g.r.*).

On the wintering grounds this duck rests during the night on wide expanses of water and travels to the shores for feeding during the day.

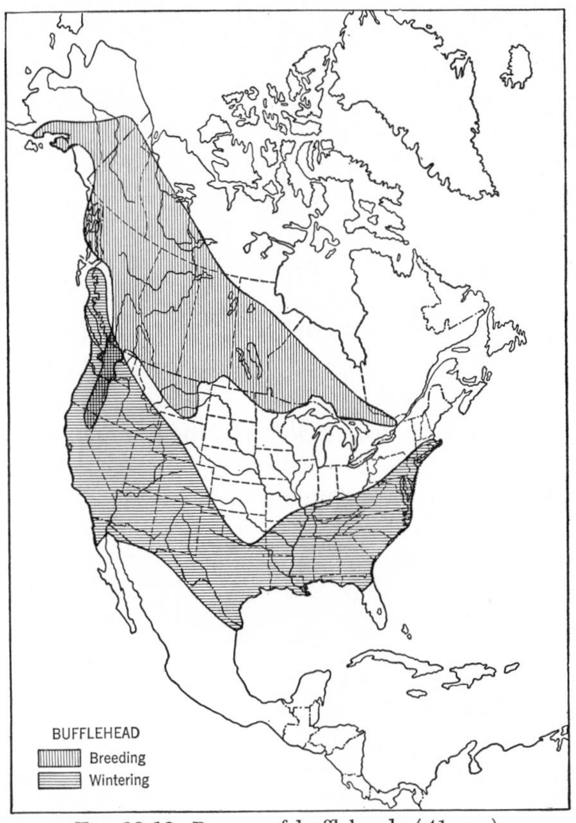

FIG. 18-13. Ranges of buffleheads (41 *g.r.*).

Courtship and Breeding. The yearling female bufflehead does not breed. According to Munro (16) these nonbreeding birds assemble in flocks with the breeding birds but later are left to their own devices as the paired birds separate out for the breeding territories. The males are both quarrelsome and covetous, first putting on a show for one female then another. One of the courting antics of the male is the snapping of the head from a prone position to an upright pose, holding the head so the bill points straight up. Courting takes place in April and May, and nesting is well under way by that time. The nest is in a cavity in a tree or a hole in a bank. Usually the tree den is a former woodpecker den at any height up to 40 feet.

The eggs are ivory yellow to pale olive buff in color and vary from 6 to 14 with the average number being 10 to 12. Incubation time is not definitely known but is given as 21 to 22 days if hatched under a hen (55 *g.r.*). In British Columbia broods appear on the water in June. The average brood in July during 2 years was 7 (16).

Habitat. The breeding habitat of the bufflehead is definitely wooded and varies with each location. In the prairies the ponds and lakes may be open, provided there is a fringe of trees somewhere near of sufficient size to provide a nest den. Farther west and north the breeding is predominantly in forested areas with rivers, ponds, and lakes supplying the range for the various activities of both the bufflehead and the other species that need forested range for breeding.

The winter range is both fresh and salt water, but wide expanses of water rather than potholes and swamp streams seem to be preferred.

NORTH AMERICAN RUDDY DUCK *Oxyura jamaicensis jamaicensis*

Tribe *oxyurini*

Description. The ruddy duck belongs to the group of diving ducks but except for this characteristic is not like the other members of the group. It is small with a short neck, a blue bill, and blue feet.

FIG. 18-14. Male and female ruddy ducks.

The male in breeding dress has a black-and-white head and throat, being black on the top to below the eye and pure white on the throat and lower sides of the head. The chest, neck, sides, and back are chestnut and the belly light. The undersides of the wings are silver.

The female is mostly dark except for the head, which resembles that of the male, and the belly which is light. On the water the light cheek patch, the short upright tail of the male, and the light-colored cheeks of the female help to distinguish this duck from others.

The ruddy duck has many of the characteristics of grebes. It dives with the wings folded, can sink into the water at will, and has the legs placed so far back it has difficulty walking on land. Of the ruddy, Phillips (55 *g.r.*) says: "Everything about the bird is interesting to the naturalist but almost nothing about it is interesting to the sportsman."

Distribution. The breeding range of the ruddy ducks includes both

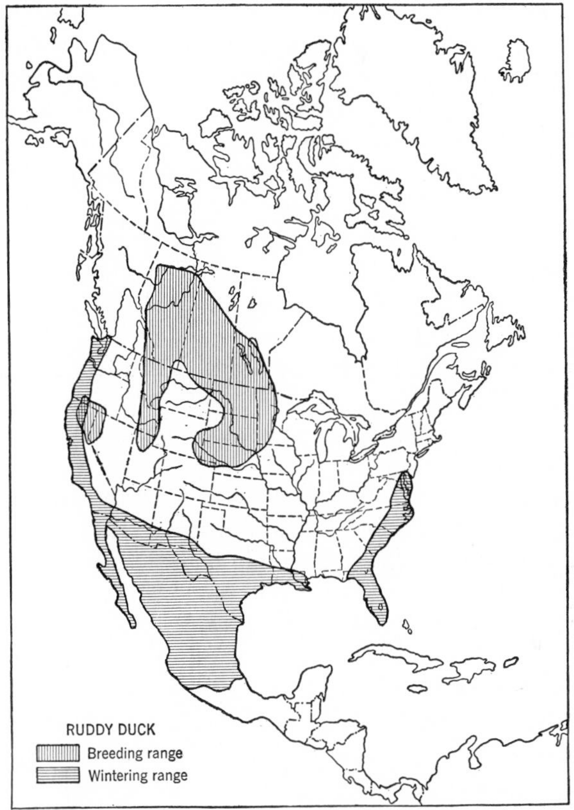

FIG. 18-15. Ranges of ruddy ducks (41 *g.r.*).

the eastern and western parts of the North American continent. They are also found from Alberta to New Mexico. In Canada the breeding area includes Ungava, Manitoba, Alberta, and British Columbia. In the United States the ruddy has been observed breeding in Maine, Massachusetts, Rhode Island, central New York, Minnesota, Michigan, Illinois, Wisconsin, Iowa, Texas, Arizona, New Mexico, and California. South of the United States breeding colonies are reported from lower California, Mexico, and Guatemala.

The ruddy duck winters along the Atlantic Coast from New Jersey to

Florida and along the Pacific from Vancouver Island to the latitude of Mexico City. Parts of the coast of the Gulf of Mexico, the southwestern states and Mexico to Mexico City are wintering grounds.

Movements. The ruddy is at home in the water but very awkward on the land. It does move overland to water if the sloughs in which it is nesting dry up (31 *g.r.*).

On the migrations away from the breeding grounds the ruddy starts relatively early, about the middle of September in southern Canada (62 *g.r.*). The migrating birds begin to arrive in Massachusetts the last of September and through the month of October. From here they move down the coast to the south Atlantic states. According to Phillips (56 *g.r.*), they go back north by an inland route, as they do not appear along the New England Coast on their spring journey to the breeding grounds.

The movement of ruddies north in the spring is not particularly early. At Delta, Manitoba, the ruddy ducks and blue-winged teal are among the latest to arrive in the April flight and the white-winged scoter is the last to arrive, coming in the second week in May (31 *g.r.*).

The ruddy migrates exclusively at night. It is a day feeder, however, according to Phillips (56 *g.r.*).

Courtship and Breeding. The courtship antics of this species are among the most elaborate and spectacular of all of the waterfowl. The bill of the male is snapped up and down against the chest and into the water, the tail is raised and lowered, and the male rushes forward toward a rival with abandon. Rough-and-tumble flights occur with other males. All these antics are part of the elaborate process of selecting a mate.

The nest of the ruddy is usually over water, where a dense growth of vegetation is available and the female can approach and leave the nest by means of water. At Bear River Marshes, Utah, the nests were found in all the plant types growing in water. The nest is often roofed over with woven materials (62 *g.r.*). Very few ruddy nests have down in them (12). The eggs are exceedingly large and are creamy or pure white. Clutches vary from 3 to 14, but 6 to 8 is the average number. The incubation period varies from 21 to 25 days but in the wild is probably about 3 weeks (31 *g.r.*). At Delta, Manitoba, the nesting period occurs from the last week in May to the first of September. Of 158 eggs inspected at Bear River Marshes, 52 per cent hatched. Sixty-nine per cent hatched in Iowa (12). The ducks are said to have a second brood, but no good evidence is available to substantiate this view.

Habitat. The breeding habitat of the ruddy duck has great variation. In the southern part of the range, where it breeds and winters in close proximity to other ducks, there is great variety in its habitat. Phillips (56 *g.r.*) says it shows a preference for fresh or brackish rather than salt water and that it prefers waters of broad extent to ponds closed in by woods.

The presence of suitable nesting cover and the need of open water for escape probably determine the extent of suitable breeding grounds for ruddy ducks. Low (12) says that vegetation available to nesting ducks bears a close relationship to water levels during the nesting season and the extent of vegetation removal by muskrats. At Delta, Manitoba, it nests in bulrush islands, bulrushes in shallow water, and cat-tails in shallow water (31 *g.r.*). Hard-stemmed bulrushes were preferred for nests at Bear River Marshes in Utah, but alkali bulrush, salt-grass, and cat-tails were used to a limited extent. Low (12) says that plants which decompose or mat below the water level in the fall and winter or shed their leaves are of little value for nest cover for the ruddy. Also 12 to 20 inches of water appear desirable below the nests, as the ruddy escapes under water rather than by flying.

The wintering range is the fresh and brackish waters of the coastal regions of both oceans and the Gulf of Mexico.

OLD SQUAW *Clangula hyemalis*

The old squaw and harlequin ducks are primarily of biological interest and not of much importance to the hunter. Both the Atlantic and Pacific winter scenes would be less picturesque and less interesting if it were not for these colorful and active members of the waterfowl family.

Description. The old squaw is a duck of the northern hemisphere, its breeding range being circumpolar and its wintering range extending down the shores of all northern continents.

The male is conspicuous because of its long thin tail and general white-and-black appearance. In breeding plumage the sides of the neck, chest, and back, including the long tail feathers, are dark, while the remainder of the body is white. The bill is black with spots of pink on the sides. The wings are reddish brown to black during both seasons.

The female is less spectacular than the male, with a short tail and buffy-brown colors on the top of the head and around the upper chest and back. There is a small spot of brown on the side of the head, and the white feathers of the body are tinged with rust. In summer more of the upper parts of the head and body are dark, but the lower chest and all the under parts and sides are white. The wings are dark brown with a tinge of tan on the edges of some of the coverts and secondary feathers. The bill and feet are steel gray.

This species is notorious for its noisy and vociferous chatter.

Distribution. The old squaw is the most northern of the ducks. It breeds in the tundra and along the borders of the Arctic Ocean along the north shores of North America, Europe, Asia, and Greenland. In North America breeding occurs along the entire northern coast from Labrador to the Aleutian Islands and includes the islands of the Arctic Coast as well as Greenland and Iceland.

The north-south extent of the breeding range is probably greater than most of the range maps indicate. On the East Coast of North America it apparently extends south as far as the St. Lawrence River and north to within a few degrees of the north pole (41 *g.r.*). Phillips (55 *g.r.*) reports stragglers as far south as Long Island Sound.

FIG. 18-16. Male and female old squaws.

The wintering range is likewise extensive. On the West Coast these ducks are found along the Aleutian chain of islands and down the coast as far south as Oregon. They winter commonly in the Great Lakes region where open water is available. On the Atlantic Coast they are found as far north as the Gulf of St. Lawrence and as far south as North Carolina.

Movements. The old squaws are among the most agile of the waterfowl. They fly, swim, and dive with the greatest of ease under the most turbulent air and water conditions. Their skill both in flight and in or on the water allows them almost complete mastery of their environment. They habitually fly to great heights and then come down like bullets, often lighting on the water with a splash. They frequently fly through waves and at other times swim and dive in the roughest of water. In the

Great Lakes, fishermen have taken them from nets 50 to 200 feet under the surface. They appear to be perfectly at home during the most severe winter storms of the North Atlantic, riding the waves or flying in the coldest weather.

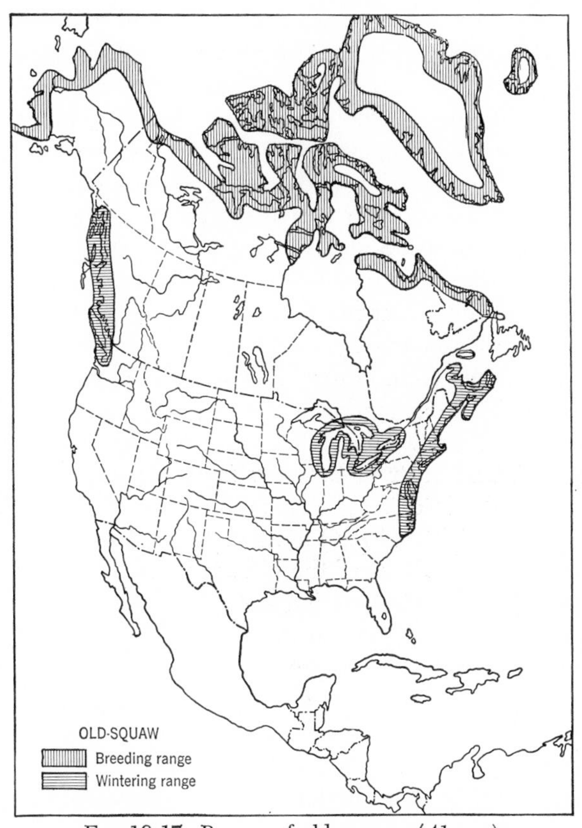

FIG. 18-17. Ranges of old squaws (41 *g.r.*).

The spring migration is early, as might be expected of so hardy a duck. They follow the weather north until the breeding grounds are reached. In the fall they stay north until severe weather and ice drives them south. During both migrations they do not hesitate to fly overland, usually following extensive groups of lakes or river systems (55 *g.r.*). The females and young migrate first in the autumn, while the adult males remain until severe weather drives them south. Along the east coast of New England the first arrivals reach Massachusetts during the first 2 weeks of October. It is suspected that some males winter farther north than females.

The daily activities of the old squaw are little known on the breeding grounds because of their remoteness but have been observed on the wintering area. They are almost entirely day feeders, and the evening flights are away from the bays and shallow waters out toward the open sea (55 *g.r.*). In the morning they return to the feeding grounds. Some birds, however, never leave the open waters. The winter flights are always over water no matter how far they have to go around to get to the open sea. Migration flights are in large flocks high in the air and often in single file.

Courtship and Breeding. The old squaw female is slow to come into breeding condition, but apparently the males are ready for breeding while still on the wintering grounds. As a result several males may be seen going through the courting activities around a single female that is ready to mate. The courtship antics consist of stretching of the head and neck and bowing before the female, as well as wild courtship flights and struggles between overzealous males.

The nest is placed on open land in grass, sometimes near but frequently some distance from water. The nest is lined with down from the female duck. The old squaw is a close sitter and covers the eggs when she leaves the nest. The clutch consists of 5 to 17 eggs, but the average is 5 to 7. The color of the eggs is a deep olive buff. Second or third clutches will be laid if the first ones are unsuccessful. Incubation time is given by Kortright (41 *g.r.*) as 24 days.

Habitat. The winter habitat of the old squaw is the open water in the northern hemisphere not too far from the ice line. The birds inhabit both fresh and salt water and seldom venture overland.

The habitat in the breeding grounds is near fresh water, in fact Phillips (55 *g.r.*) says the nests are always adjacent to fresh water. Islands are preferred for nests, probably because of the protection they give from land predators. In the land where the ground seldom thaws very deep, vegetation is more herbaceous than woody and mostly of the tundra or arctic type. Grasses, flowering plants of various kinds, and woody plants like willow, birch, and juniper are used as protection for the nests.

HARLEQUIN DUCK

Eastern Harlequin *Histrionicus histrionicus histrionicus*
Pacific Harlequin *Histrionicus histrionicus pacificus*

The harlequin duck inhabits both the Atlantic and the Pacific Coasts. In the eastern part of the continent its breeding grounds include the coasts of Labrador and Greenland. However, the western form breeds inland from the mouth of the Mackenzie River as far south as Yosemite in California.

Description. This duck is small and dark. Average males weigh less than 1½ pounds and females slightly more than a pound. The males appear blue with black wings, having white spots and streaks around the head and fore parts. The feathers under the wings are chestnut.

The female is a dark-colored duck with white spots on the front and sides of the head and a light-gray breast. The eastern harlequin is more colorful than the Pacific species which is paler and has a washed-out appearance.

Distribution. The eastern harlequin breeds on the borders of Iceland, Greenland, and the eastern shores of Baffin Island and Labrador. Winter-

FIG. 18-18. Male and female harlequin ducks.

ing grounds of this duck include Newfoundland and the North Atlantic Coast from Nova Scotia to Long Island Sound. The Pacific harlequin breeds along the islands of the North Pacific from Baikalia to Anadyr and both the islands adjacent to and including the Asiatic Coast, including Kamchatka, Sakhalin, and the Kuril Islands. On the North American Coast breeding occurs on the Pribilof and Aleutian Islands and along the coast from the Alaskan peninsula south to the United States. The interior of North America is used for breeding from the delta of the Mackenzie River south to the northern border of the United States in the vicinity of Idaho and western Montana.

Wintering grounds of the Pacific harlequin include the seacoast bordering the Pacific Ocean from northern Japan and the North Pacific islands and the West Coast of North America as far south as San Francisco (62 *g.r.*).

Movements. The spring migration of the eastern harlequin takes place in small flocks during the months of February, March, and April, depending on where they winter. The general direction of migration is north and east. The migration of the western form is mostly a movement

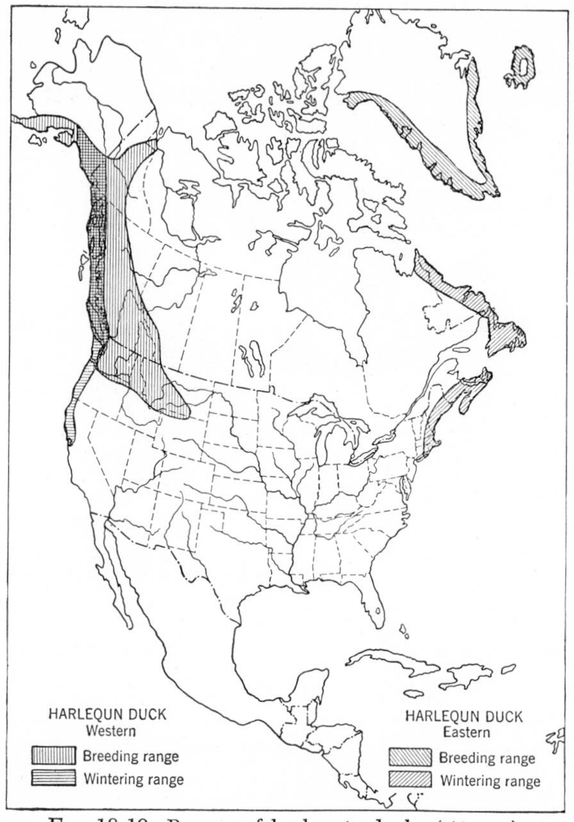

FIG. 18-19. Ranges of harlequin ducks (41 *g.r.*).

inland to mountain lakes and streams. Some of the birds have to move several hundred miles from the coast of the United States, British Columbia, and Alaska to the waters inland. This movement occurs as the weather becomes suitable for nesting. Phillips (55 *g.r.*) speaks of the migrations of the harlequin as mostly local, inland to the coast in fall and back again in spring.

The daily movements consist of flights from the open sea to sheltered coves and rocky shores in the morning and back again to the ocean in the afternoon. This duck is at ease during the roughest weather as well as among the rocks where its favorite food organisms are found.

Courtship and Breeding. The harlequin is a handsome and sociable duck, and breeding activities conform to this pattern. The males and females bow to each other, the male brings his head and bill to a vertical position and then jerks them forward with a quick movement and a sound that resembles the crowing of a rooster. He later rises high in the water with a wild flapping of wings. Much swimming around and chatty sounds accompany the breeding activities.

The nests are always near the water and usually on the ground or among rock crevices. Nests may be sheltered by scrub vegetation or in the case of the western form may even be in holes in trees.

The clutch consists of 5 to 8 eggs of cream or cinnamon-buff color. The incubation period is 25 days (62 *g.r.*).

Habitat. The wintering habitat is the open ocean and adjacent rocky shores where food in the form of shells and bivalves may be found. The harlequin is an expert swimmer and is agile on its feet in climbing around the slippery rocks in search of food.

The breeding habitat is mostly the borders of mountain ponds and streams, where swift currents and turbulent waters are the favorite swimming grounds. The harlequin has no fear of fast cold waters and finds in these all the conditions of food, water, and protection for an abundant life.

It is not the intention of the author of this book to give a summary of the material available on all the waterfowl, but mainly data on those species which are important to the waterfowl gunner.

For the sake of completeness, however, brief comments will be made on the various related species which occupy parts of the waterfowl range and which do contribute to a limited extent to the waterfowl-gunning fraternity and are of biological interest.

The eider ducks, scoter ducks, and mergansers may be considered in the above category. These are classified as follows:

Subfamily	*Anatinae*
Tribe	*mergini*

EIDER DUCKS

The eider ducks consist of the following species:

	Species
American eider	*Somateria mollissima dresseri*
King eider	*Somateria spectabilis*
Northern eider	*Somateria mollissima borealis*
Pacific eider	*Somateria mollissima* var. *nigra*
Spectacled eider	*Somateria fischeri*
Steller's eider	*Somateria stelleri*

These are all ducks of the northern part of the western hemisphere and are particularly hardy and generally coastal and arctic rather than inland and temperate.

The eiders are well known for the eider down of commerce which they produce, the fine dense feathers which cover the bodies of these ducks and insulate them against the cold winds and waters of the arctic. This down is used for filling pillows, bed coverings, sleeping bags, and for clothing. Eider down is produced in Iceland, Norway, and some of the islands of the North Atlantic. The use of eider ducks for egg and down production is being promoted in Canada. The eider, in addition to producing an excellent product in the form of down, has other properties which make it suitable for semidomestication. It nests in colonies which makes the collection of down an easy operation. Likewise, the birds appear to be temperamentally well-suited to close association with humans.

Down is gathered after the incubating female has plucked it from her own body to line the nest. Each nest is visited by the down gatherer about twice, a few days apart, and the down under and around the eggs is removed. It takes 35 to 40 nests to produce a pound of down, but a pound of this material is bulky, so it takes only a few pounds to fill a quilt or a sleeping bag. Taking of the down does not appear to interfere with the hatching process (41 *g.r.*).

Several northern European countries, including Iceland and Canada, are now engaged in the commercial production of down and the birds are legally protected from hunters for this purpose. Many birds and eggs are taken on the breeding grounds by the Eskimos, however, for food and for the skins and feathers which are used for clothing.

Description. In general the eiders are large ducks, although there are some variations between the different species. The Pacific eider is the largest, weighing on the average about 5 pounds but sometimes getting as heavy as 6. The American and the King weigh from 3 to 4 pounds and the Steller, the smallest, weighs from 1 to 2 pounds. All the eider ducks have short necks and coarse angular heads. The males in breeding plumage are bright-colored with contrasting hues of dark and light, with heads conspicuously marked with crests and eye patches and necks of pastel greens, blue, and orange. The females do not have these brightly marked feathers, all being dark brown with the exception of a few white-edged feathers on the wings. For a comparison and detailed description of the various species, see the colored prints and descriptions in the monographs in "The Ducks, Geese and Swans of North America" by Francis H. Kortright (41 *g.r.*) and Sports Afield collection of "Know Your Ducks and Geese" by Shortt and Cartwright (62 *g.r.*).

Distribution. Like so many other wildlife forms, each of the species of eider ducks seems to have been developed to fit a particular environmental situation. Why each is limited to a particular habitat and why some are more widely scattered cannot be explained. No doubt there are reasons for this habitat suitability, and perhaps we may some time be able to find the morphological and physiological limitations of each species.

The American eider seems to be the most southerly of the species listed. Its breeding grounds are all east of the 100th meridian and include the northern border of the Gulf of St. Lawrence and both the east and west shores of the northern portion of Hudson Bay. On the west side of the bay these breeding ducks extend as far south as the Nelson River.

The American eider winters along the Atlantic Coast from Newfoundland to Long Island Sound. According to Kortright (41 *g.r.*) and Phillips (55 *g.r.*), wintering takes place on inland fresh as well as salt waters and salt water around the Gulf of St. Lawrence and the north Atlantic Coast.

The King eider appears to be the most broadly distributed of the eiders, its breeding ground extending across the Arctic from the shores of Greenland west and including the islands and the continent bordering the Arctic Ocean to Norton Sound on the west coast of Alaska. The wintering grounds include the Gulf of St. Lawrence, the Atlantic Coast from Newfoundland to Long Island Sound, and the Aleutian Islands of the Pacific.

The Northern eider is a bird of the eastern Arctic and north Atlantic Oceans. It breeds along the coast of Greenland and on the islands east of the 90th meridian and winters on the south tip of Greenland and the Labrador and Newfoundland coast. It nests on fresh water.

The Pacific eider breeds on the Arctic shores of the North American continent and Alaska west of 110 degrees as well as on the Aleutian Islands. The more northern breeders move to the open waters of the Aleutian Islands to winter.

Both the spectacled and Steller's eiders breed along the Alaskan Arctic and Bering Sea Coasts from 140 degrees west to the mouth of the Yukon River. Both species winter along the Aleutian Islands.

For the sake of brevity, the details of movements, courtship and breeding, and habitat will be omitted except for the American eider.

Movements. Along with some of the other northern species of birds, the eider appears to have perfect mastery of its movements in relation to its environment. It is at home both in the air and on and in the water. In flight the American eider flies in single file or abreast in small flocks of from 20 to 100 birds. It often flies so close to the water that birds are lost to sight behind a wave.

This duck feeds on the surface or underwater as the situation demands. It is an expert diver and will go down 50 to 100 feet with ease. It uses both feet and wings in this operation. If shot at or wounded, it may swim with only its bill above water and so escape detection by virtue of being submerged.

The northern migration takes place in March, the birds flying in long lines. The adult males are said to go first, followed by the females and juveniles. According to Kortright (41 *g.r.*) the males leave the breeding grounds in June, but this seems early. The general autumn migration is late, taking place during October and November.

Courtship and Breeding. The courtship antics of the eider begin in May and June along the eastern coast of Labrador and on the islands of the North Atlantic. The male shows off in customary duck style, going through various antics and uttering numerous love calls in the process of selecting a mate.

Nests are placed on the ground in communities not far from water. The nests are made of seaweeds, sticks, and grasses and are lined with down. The nest may be open or concealed by alder, laurel, grasses, or rushes. Icelanders often build rough rock cubicles for the use of the nesting birds. A clutch of 3 to 6 eggs is laid, the shell of the eggs having a rough granular texture and colored green or brown. The eggs of the eider are the largest of the duck eggs. The incubation period is 28 days (41 *g.r.*).

Economic Status. The eider duck is a species that is on its way to at least partial domestication. Perhaps it would be more accurate to say that the eider is one wild species that serves man in its natural state and is given protection in parts of its range where the eggs and down have a high value. Phillips (56 *g.r.*) says that traffic in eider down was common in Iceland as early as the fifteenth century and indicates that new nesting sites are built to encourage the birds to nest. A suitable place on a rocky point near the sea is chosen. It must be high enough so it will not flood. A fence is built around the nest location to keep predators away. Small nest cavities are made with an open side facing the sea. Branches of brush, old eggshells, and feathers are scattered around to give the site the appearance of previous use. Decoys are placed nearby in the sea to lure the females to the spot.

Icelanders harvest both eggs and down from the nesting birds. The first clutch may be 4 or more eggs, the second 2, and the third 1 (41 *g.r.*). From ½ to 1 ounce of down is taken from each nest. The total amount of down harvested apparently depends on the price, the latter varying with the demand.

SCOTER DUCKS

Three species of scoter, or sea, ducks will be considered in this section:

	Species
American white-winged scoter	*Melanitta fusca deglandi*
Surf scoter	*Melanitta perspicillata*
American scoter	*Melanitta nigra americana*

The scoter, or "coot," is of interest to the gunner because of the more liberal season and bag allowed by law as compared to other waterfowl. Scoters could be shot from September 28 to December 31 in 1951, as compared with October 26 to December 9 for other ducks. The broader shooting regulations apply to shooting outside of harbor limits. Where other ducks were shot the season was October 26 to December 9 as for other ducks. The bag-and-possession limit for scoters was 7 daily or 14 possession limit, as compared with 4 daily and 8 possession limit for other ducks.

In former times scoter shooting was more popular and more productive than at present. It was done with decoys from a boat. Phillips (56 *g.r.*) speaks of a record take of scoters by two men in 1910 at Cohasset, Massachusetts, when 148 birds were shot in one day. A take of 237 in one day is recorded at Hyannis by this same author, but the year is not given.

While some of the coots are eaten, many are shot for sport and are never cleaned or used. The flesh of scoters has a very strong fishy taste, especially after they begin feeding on the ocean during their winter stay along the coast. Phillips says stew made from scoters shot before they have reached salt water is very tasty (56 *g.r.*). At present the common practice seems to be to use only the breast muscles and to cook them by boiling, then frying.

Description. All of the scoters are dark-colored but vary in size and head, wing, and feet markings. Generally the males are glossy black, and the females are brown. Head and feather markings vary with both species and sex. The following gives the comparison of weights:

Species	Male—average	Female—average
American white-winged scoter...	3 lb. 8 oz.	2 lb. 10 oz.
Surf scoter....................	2 lb. 3 oz.	2 lb. 0 oz.
American scoter................	2 lb. 8 oz.	2 lb. 3 oz.

Distinguishing marks of the various species are as follows:

American White-winged Scoter. The male appears nearly all black when on the water. At close range a small curved white spot shows under and back of the eye. A small spot or streak of white may show along the flank. The female is smaller than the male but has no white marking under the eye. The white streak may or may not show along the flank.

In flight both sexes show a conspicuous white speculum, and the feet appear purple or orange in color. The white-winged scoter flies in single file close to the water.

Surf Scoter. The male is glossy black except for white patches on the forehead and the back of the head. The female is brown rather than black, with light-colored (but not white) regions along the side of the head both in front of and back of the eye but below the eye level. In flight a light region shows on the belly. The feet of both sexes are orange or purple. These birds fly in irregular flocks of 20 to 40 or in larger groups during migration (62 *g.r.*).

American Scoter. The male is glossy black and the female a dark brown. The male is all black except for an orange-colored protuberance

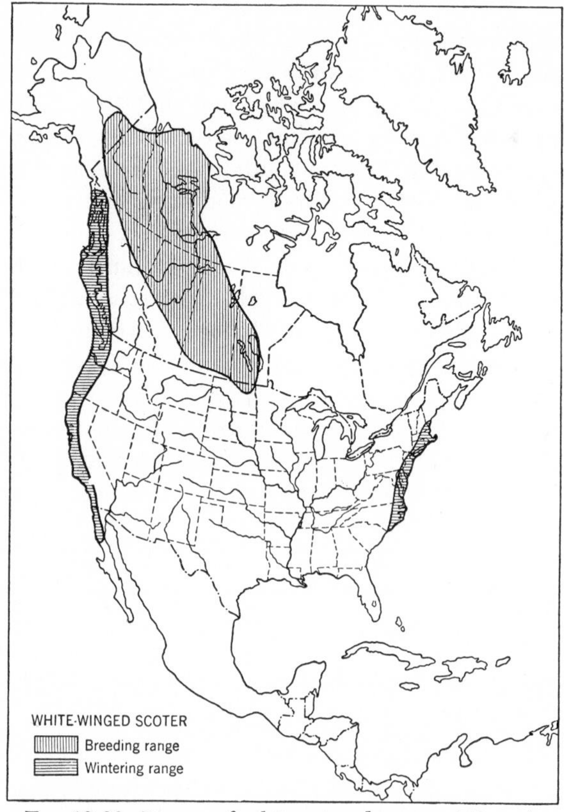

FIG. 18-20. Ranges of white-winged scoters (41 *g.r.*).

at the base of the bill. The female has a darker head and bill and shows a light patch on the throat and along the cheeks and sides of the throat and the chin. Groups of males crowd closely together with their bills pointing upward if approached on the water. This species is said to be more ducklike in appearance than the other species of scoters.

Distribution. Of the scoters, the white-winged is the most widely distributed in North America. Its breeding range includes a vast segment of the northern continent from the Yukon and Mackenzie Rivers in

Canada to the Red River of the North and including parts of North Dakota and Montana along the international border.

Breeding grounds of the surf scoter include an area along the Mackenzie and Yukon Rivers and the Arctic Coast as far south as Lake Athabaska. In width the range is much less extensive than that of the white-winged.

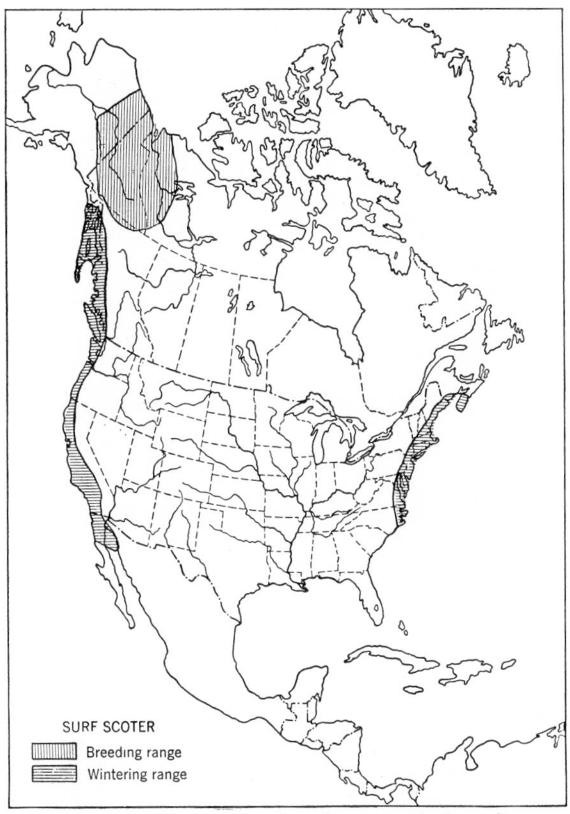

FIG. 18-21. Ranges of surf scoters (41 *g.r.*).

The breeding range of the American scoter extends in a narrow strip inland along the northwestern shores of North America from the mouth of the Anderson River around the Bering Sea to Cooks Inlet on the Gulf of Alaska.

The wintering grounds of the white-winged and surf scoters are approximately the same, extending along the Atlantic Coast from Maine to North Carolina for the white-winged and from Nova Scotia to approximately the same location for the surf scoter. On the Pacific Coast both of the above species occupy the coastal waters from Juneau, Alaska, to

Rosario, lower California. The American scoter occupies more limited wintering ranges along both coasts. On the Atlantic the winter range extends from central Maine to North Carolina and on the Pacific from Juneau to Puget Sound.

Movements. Scoters, probably a mixture of all three species, are seen in rafts along both the Atlantic and the Pacific Coasts during the winter

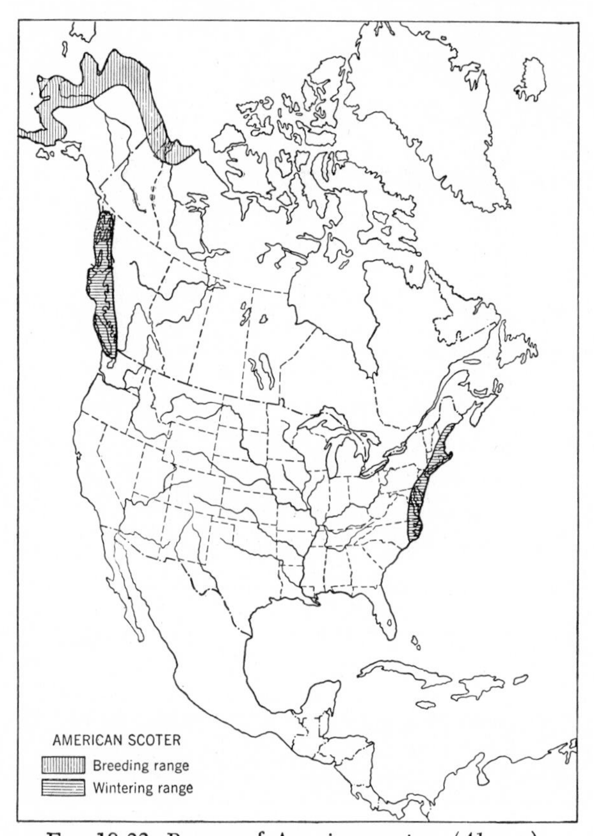

FIG. 18-22. Ranges of American scoters (41 *g.r.*).

period. The scoters seldom leave the immediate vicinity of water except during the breeding season. On the wintering grounds the movements occur during the day rather than at night. They feed during the day, moving toward the land during the early morning and back to the sea toward evening.

Both the pattern and the distances of the migrations are erratic. Nonbreeding birds may spend the summer on the so-called "wintering grounds." The birds that winter along the Atlantic Coast must move diagonally overland to the breeding grounds in northern Canada. The times of leaving New England in the spring are relatively late:

American white-winged scoter	May 12–15 (56 *g.r.*)
Surf scoter	May (41 *g.r.*)
American scoter	April and May (62 *g.r.*)

The fall flights from the breeding grounds are overland but apparently high and by long stages. Scoters are seen on inland lakes but not in as great numbers as one would expect. Hochbaum (31 *g.r.*) mentions American white-winged scoters as being not uncommon at Delta, Manitoba, in September and October and indicates that the early flights are females and young birds and the late flights are males.

Courtship and Breeding. All of the scoters move to fresh water to breed. It is probable that many of the birds do not go to the breeding grounds at all because of incapacity to breed. American scoter males are said to choose mates on the wintering grounds. Others do not. The courting display of all scoters includes the resting of the neck of the male on the water, then raising it and rushing toward the female. Diving is also part of the courtship antics (56 *g.r.*).

Nesting of all the scoters is late, occurring during June and July. Nests are on the ground and are lined with plant debris or grasses and are usually under low shrubby plants. The birds also line the nest with down taken from their own bodies. The eggs are ivory, pink, or yellow in color, and the shell texture may be pitted or smooth.

The number of eggs in a clutch and the incubation periods are as follows:

Species	Average clutch	Incubation period, days	Investigator
American white-winged	6–14	27–28	(56 *g.r.*)
Surf	5– 7	Unknown	(56 *g.r.*)
American	6–10	32–33	(56 *g.r.*)

Habitat. The wintering habitats of the scoters are the oceans and adjacent shores. The breeding habitats are not well known and neither are the details of its ecology on the flights between the breeding and wintering territories.

The scoters are much alike in their choice of winter territory, all choosing semiprotected coastal waters in contrast to the rough, windy, open sea. Phillips speaks of the scoters as coming farther into the bays and arms of the ocean than do the eiders and old squaws. All feed in relatively shallow water varying from 10 to 25 feet in depth (56 *g.r.*).

The surf scoter is more of a salt-water duck than the white-winged and black and appears to avoid small fresh-water ponds more than the others. In migration it moves along the coast before cutting inland and thus covers the distance between the wintering and breeding ranges with a minimum of contact with fresh water and land.

MERGANSERS OR SAWBILLS

The mergansers, or fish ducks, can by no stretch of the imagination be called game ducks. While they are given only passing attention by the waterfowl gunner, they do attract aggressive opposition from the fishing fraternity who consider their fish-eating habits a definite menace to the sport. Whether or not this antagonism is justified is questionable, as the mergansers may do much good in removing trash fish and thus allowing more valuable species greater space and more food (18).

The three species of fish ducks will be considered together, although they vary in many points as to habits and habitat. The male of the hooded merganser is a handsome bird. Hooded mergansers always nest in tree cavities and Americans sometimes do. The range preferences of the mergansers tend to favor the forested sections of the North American continent rather than the more open prairie lands. Of the three species the red-breasted is more of an open-land form than the other two.

The species here described are:

	Species
Hooded merganser	*Mergus cucullatus*
American merganser	*Mergus merganser americanus*
Red-breasted merganser	*Mergus serrator*

Description. All species of mergansers have long and narrow rather than the short broad bills of the ordinary duck. The bills have sharp serrations, or "teeth," which make them very effective in catching and ingesting fish. The males of the hooded and American species are definitely black and white, while the red-breasted is more of a reddish or cinnamon color. In size the hooded is the smallest and the American and red-breasted larger. The two latter are similar in weights and dimensions. Average weights of the three species are as follows:

Species	Average	Investigator
Hooded	1 lb. – 1 lb. 8 oz.	(41 *g.r.*)
American	2 lb. 9 oz. – 4 lb. 2 oz.	(41 *g.r.*)
Red-breasted	2 lb. 7 oz. – 2 lb. 14 oz.	(41 *g.r.*)

All three species have long feathers on the head that give the back of the head a "long-haired" appearance with the exception of the male hooded, where the black-and-white feathers stand straight up over the head and neck in a handsome "crew-cut" appearance.

Hooded. The head, bill, back, and wings are black and white. The sides are chestnut, and the centers of the hood, chest, and belly are light-colored. The female hooded is a drab-appearing duck with a chestnut crest and a light-colored belly.

American. The male American merganser in breeding plumage has a dark green or black head and a dark neck and back with white along the wings. The breast and belly are cream-colored, and the tail gray. The bill and feet are pink or orange. The female is a gray duck with a rusty head and neck, except the throat which is light, and with pink or orange bill and feet. The nostril of the American merganser is definitely nearer the tip of the bill than it is in the red-breasted.

Red-breasted. The red-breasted male in breeding plumage has a dark green head and a ragged, unkempt-appearing nape. There is a white ring that partially circles the neck except at the back. The lower neck is reddish-colored with dark markings. The shoulders have a black-and-white appearance, and the sides and tail are gray. The breast and belly are cream or tan, and the bill and feet are red or orange. The female appears much the same as the American female merganser.

Distribution. See range maps.

Movements. The mergansers are very active both in the air and in the water but are awkward and clumsy on land. All three species are excellent swimmers and divers and have the ability to sink out of sight into the water with no apparent effort. In the process of catching fish, these birds swim rapidly at various depths and often dive from considerable heights to catch their underwater prey.

In leaving the water or land to get into the air the hooded is the most agile, while the American and red-breasted have some difficulty in becoming air-borne. On both land and water these latter two begin their flights into the wind and help by pushing with their feet.

All of the mergansers are day feeders. The flights from the night resting grounds are early in the morning, about daylight, and the flight back to the night stands occurs in late afternoon. The hooded is said to be very active all during the day, flights up or down a river being swift and precise.

The hooded merganser flies alone or in small flocks even in migration. The flight is low and direct, the birds stretching their necks in the direction of flight.

The flight of the American is somewhat similar to the hooded, being close to the water. Flocks of both American and red-breasted are larger than the hooded, but not numerous, usually less than 50. Lines and wedges of these two species are seen during migrations. Phillips (56 *g.r.*)

also speaks of aggregations of 30 or 40 young red-breasted fish ducks seen together in late summer and autumn.

The times of migration are always a relative matter. The terms early or late are better than exact times for particular places in indicating the habits of migratory birds. In general the spring movements to the breeding grounds start early, but perhaps not so early as some of the other waterfowl. Late February appears to be the starting time for New England, March for western New York, and early April for Ottawa (56 *g.r.*).

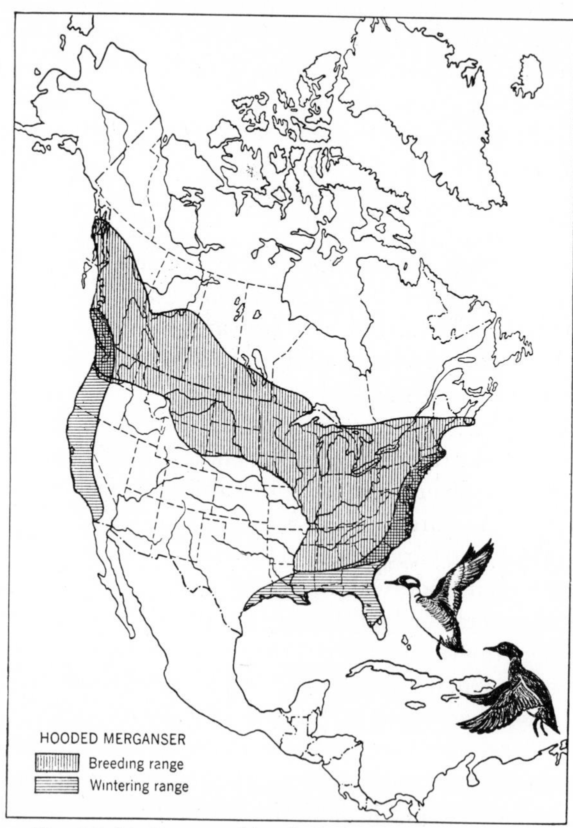

FIG. 18-23. Ranges of hooded mergansers (41 *g.r.*).

In the fall, migrations are relatively late, but there exists a differential between males, and females and young of the year. The average time when the hooded mergansers pass the area of southern Minnesota, central Iowa, and central Ontario is November (56 *g.r.*).

The American merganser is an early migrant in the spring and very late in the fall. Flocks stay as far north as there is open water and then follow the thaw north. In central Massachusetts Americans are seen on the Connecticut River as soon as the ice breaks up. The time of the movement south in the northern part of the United States is November, the females and young moving through first and the males following later.

The spring migration of the red-breasteds starts in March and April, although some even stay on the wintering grounds until May. In the fall the greatest movement is during October and November (41 *g.r.*). Some

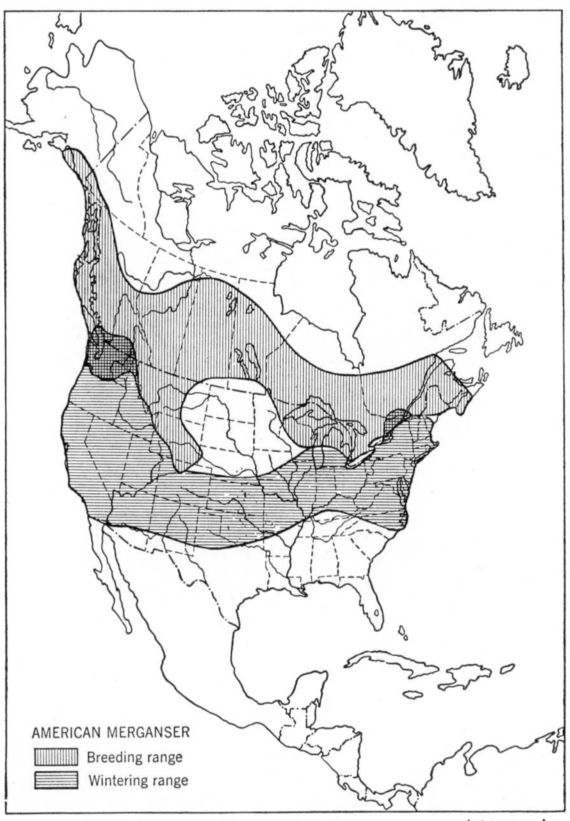

FIG. 18-24. Ranges of American mergansers (41 *g.r.*).

winter far north along the edge of the open water, but the red-breasteds are not so common here as are the Americans.

Courtship and Breeding. *Hooded Merganser.* Courtship starts early, probably on the wintering grounds. Males display before the females by swimming and maneuvering so as to display the white of the chest and the black and white of the crest to the best advantage. The head and bill are thrown upward and back as part of the courtship display. Usually there are several males competing for the favor of a female.

Nests are nearly always in hollow trees and are started very early in the southern part of the range. Nest boxes placed for wood ducks may also be used. The clutch consists of 6 to 18 eggs, but usually 10 to 12. The eggs are small, smooth, and quite spherical. Incubation takes 31 days (13 *g.r.*).

American Merganser. The males begin their mating antics early and go through an elaborate ceremony of swimming and plumage display in the presence of the female before a pair becomes mated. One of the

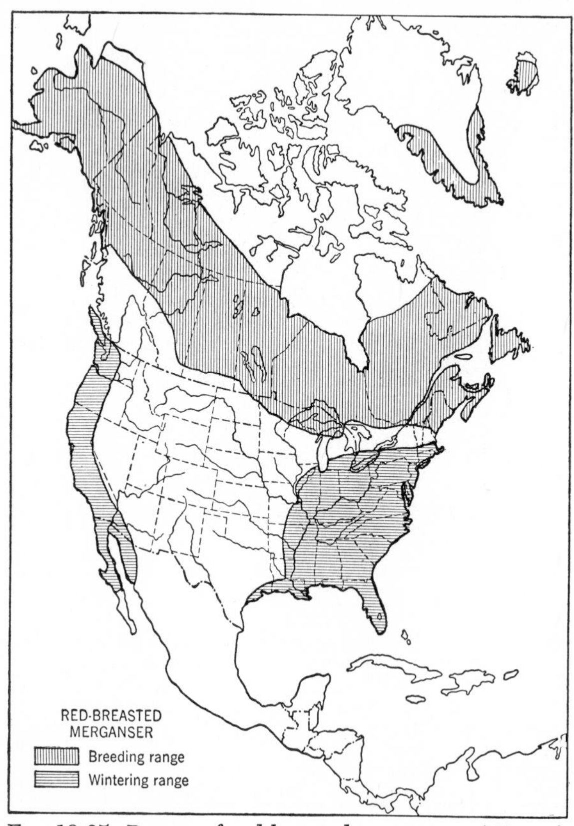

Fig. 18-25. Ranges of red-breasted mergansers (41 *g.r.*).

characteristics of the maneuver is the jet of water kicked backwards by the courting male. While the species prefers to nest in hollow trees, it does nest on the ground occasionally, but usually in situations with some overhead protection (13 *g.r.*).

The American merganser lays from 6 to 17 eggs, but the average is about 10. The color of the eggs is pale buff, and they are dull but have a strong shell. The incubation period is 28 days, according to Bent (13 *g.r.*). The young are called out, rather than carried out, of the nest by their mother.

Red-breasted Merganser. Courtship is similar to the other mergansers, usually several males going through the various maneuvers and displays for the benefit of a female. Sometimes the female responds to the attention of the male by a bobbing and dipping of the head and bill.

The nest is built on the shores of lakes and ponds, usually near but not adjacent to the water's edge. The nest cavity is hollowed out of the soil and is protected by driftwood logs or prostrate branches of trees or shrubs. The clutch consists of 8 to 16 eggs, but the average is nearer 8 to 10. The eggs are smooth and colored olive buff. Incubation lasts from 26 to 28 days.

Habitat. *Hooded.* The habitat of the hooded merganser is definitely fresh water and a wooded site. It lives and breeds inland along the wooded streams and ponds of the interior of the country and finds its food, nesting sites, and escape facilities along the streams and ponds of the central and southern portions of the continent. The hooded merganser is particularly fond of overflowed woodlands, slow streams, and woods-enclosed waters (56 *g.r.*). While it prefers a slow stream, fast-moving waters are used if the others are frozen over. Shallow rather than deep waters are probably more productive of the food preferred by these ducks.

American. The American mergansers prefer the rivers and lakes to the salt water, and as they prefer tree-cavity nests to sites on rocks or soil, could be called inland rather than salt-water birds. They prefer large streams and clear ponds with sandy or rocky bottoms to muddy waters (56 *g.r.*). This indicates the choice of habitat may be ecologically quite different from that of the hooded merganser even though both choose fresh-water sites. The American merganser sits on the rocks or rides the waves at night but does not feed during darkness. The northern edge of the breeding range appears to be the northern limit of trees large enough for nest sites.

Red-breasted. The red-breasted merganser is the salt-water relative of the sawbill clan. While it spreads inland both to feed and winter, it likes the coastal habitats and prefers large rather than small bodies of water. The nests are always on the ground, and so the breeding range is not limited on the north by lack of trees. As this species seems to prefer the larger sizes of fish and are voracious feeders, the waters bordering the seacoasts probably meet their needs to a better degree than adjacent smaller bodies of fresh water.

REFERENCES

1. Aldrich, John W. 1949. Migration of the greater scaup duck. Migration of some North Amer. waterfowl. *U.S. Fish and Wildlife Serv., Spec. Sci. Rpt.: Wildlife* 1.

2. Baillie, James L., Jr. 1946. The redhead as a breeding bird of Michigan and Ontario. *Wilson Bul.* **58**(2):111–112.
3. Bennett, Logan J. 1938. Redheads and ruddy ducks nesting in Iowa. *Trans. 3d North Amer. Wildlife Conf.* Pp. 647–650.
4. Cartwright, B. W. 1945. Some results of waterfowl banding in western Canada by Ducks Unlimited (Canada). *Trans. 10th North Amer. Wildlife Conf.* Pp. 332–338.
5. Duvall, Allen J. 1949. Migration of the ring-necked duck. Migration of some North American waterfowl. *U.S. Fish and Wildlife Serv., Spec. Sci. Rpt.: Wildlife* 1.
6. Erickson, Ray C. 1948. Life history and ecology of the canvasback *Nyroca valisineria* (Wilson) in southeastern Oregon. Unpublished M.S. thesis, Iowa State College, Ames.
7. Heit, William S. 1948. Texas coastal waterfowl concentration areas and their 1947–48 wintering population. *Trans. 13th North Amer. Wildlife Conf.* Pp. 323–338.
8. Hochbaum, H. Albert. 1946*a*. Status of the redhead in southern Manitoba. *Wilson Bul.* **58**(1):62–65.
9. ———. 1946*b*. Recovery potentials in North American waterfowl. *Trans. 11th North Amer. Wildlife Conf.* Pp. 403–418.
10. Lewis, Harrison F. 1935. Early nesting of American golden-eye (*Glaucionetta clangula americana*). *Canad. Field Nat.* **49**(4):76–77.
11. Lincoln, Frederick C. 1934. Distribution and migration of the redhead. *Trans. 20th Amer. Game Conf.* Pp. 280–287.
12. Low, Jessop B. 1941. Nesting of the ruddy duck in Iowa. *Auk.* **58**(10): 506–517.
13. ———. 1945. Ecology and management of the redhead, *Nyroca americana*, in Iowa. *Ecol. Monog.* **15**(1):35.
14. Mendall, Howard L. 1938. Ring-necked duck breeding in eastern North America. *Auk.* **55**(3):401–404.
15. Munro, J. A. 1939. Studies of waterfowl in British Columbia; Barrow's golden-eye, American golden-eye. *Trans. Royal Canad. Inst.* **22**(2):259–318.
16. ———. 1942. Studies of waterfowl in British Columbia, Buffle-head. *Canad. Jour. Res., Vol.* **20**, *Sec. D*(6), pp. 133–160.
17. Robbins, Chandler S. 1949. Migration of the redhead. Migration of some North American Waterfowl. *U.S. Fish and Wildlife Serv., Spec. Sci. Rpt.: Wildlife* 1.
18. Salyer, J. Clark, and Karl F. Lagler. 1940. Food habits of American merganser during winter in Michigan, considered in relation to fish management. *Jour. Wildlife Mangt.* **4**(2):186–219.

CHAPTER 19

Swans and Geese

Subfamily *Anserinae*
Tribe *Anserini*

The swans and geese are among the most attractive and spectacular birds found on the North American continent. Both are wild and wary and are strong fliers and usually very shy of man.

FIG. 19-1. Comparative sizes and markings of the white waterfowl, the whistling swan, snow goose, and Ross's goose.

Both swans and geese are large birds and have flesh much in demand by gunners. The swans, however, cannot be hunted legally. Geese of various kinds are open to hunting and, where conditions are favorable on the flyways, are among the most popular of the waterfowl.

Both swans and geese differ from the other waterfowl in being larger and having different structures, habits, and ecological relationships. In feeding, both swans and geese tip up in shallow water like the puddle ducks. Geese of the white-cheeked geese and brant species are less terrestrial on the whole than are white-fronted, blue, tule, and snow geese.

Likewise it is very questionable if one subspecies can be transferred successfully to a part of the country outside of its natural range. Possibly such a transfer may be successful if the process is carried on by slow, intensive management.

Swans. According to Kortright (41 *g.r.*) there are nine species of swans in the world, three of which occur in North America. One of these, the mute swan, came originally from Europe.

The scientific names of North American swans are:

	Species
Mute swan	*Sthenelides olor*
Whistling swan	*Cygnus columbianus*
Trumpeter swan	*Cygnus buccinator*

Mute Swan. The swans are all large, majestic-appearing birds that are completely white except for black or orange spots on the head. They also have dark feet.

Mute swans may live to an age of 50 to 100 years, but probably usually less than 50 years. The head tips down at an angle. The neck is arched instead of being straight. With the trumpeter swan, the neck is straight and the bill points straight ahead.

The mute swans are found along the eastern part of the continent, usually in ponds on estates, where they have been imported to give a European atmosphere to the landscape. Originally these birds came from England where they are traditionally royal birds belonging to the king and where they carry swanmarks cut in the upper mandible to indicate ownership. In London the mute swans on the Thames River still belong to the royal family and are caught and marked with the king's mark each year by swan-uppers or special officers.

Swans of different sexes and ages have special names; the male is a "cob" and the female a "pen." The young in its first year is a "cygnet" and in its second year a "grey bird."

Swans mate for life or as long as both individuals of a pair survive. The females do not lay until their second or third year and lay from 3 to 7 eggs during their first 2 breeding seasons. When mature, swans lay a clutch of 9 to 11 eggs. The nest is large and carefully constructed of vegetation or any available materials. It is always near the water, and the female assumes responsibility for the incubation of the eggs. The male stands guard over the incubating female although he does none of the actual incubating. The incubating period is 35 days or longer. Both parents care for the young, and the female is said to brood them on her back when the cygnets are young and helpless.

The mute swan is not really voiceless but gives out a hissing sound when disturbed; in the wild state in Europe it utters a call or "bark" during the breeding season.

Whistling and Trumpeter Swans. The whistling swan is native to North

FIG. 19-2. Whistling swan, the most abundant of the swans. Note the curved neck. (*U.S. Fish and Wildlife Service.*)

America and is relatively numerous. The trumpeter is a larger bird and at present very scarce, with a highly restricted range. Comparatively, the weights of the three species are as follows:

Species	Male, lb.	Female, lb.	Average, lb.
Mute swan	.....	.....	25–30
Whistling swan	12–18	10–18	14–16
Trumpeter swan	21–38	20–24	22–28

The whistling swan is the common swan of North America and is on the increase under complete protection. On the other hand, the trumpeter swan is restricted to a few hundred individuals and, while on the increase, is still in a precarious position.

Description. All adult swans 2 years or over are white. The adult mute swan has an orange bill with a dark protuberance between the bill and the eyes. The whistling swan has a dark bill and dark feet with an oblong spot of yellow just in front of the eyes. The trumpeter has a dark bill and dark feet with no protuberance and no yellow spot on the bill. With all species the young are gray in color, and the bills and feet tend to be lighter than the adults, although the young of the trumpeter is likely to have a dark bill and the young of the whistling swan may have dark feet.

FIG. 19-3. Female and male trumpeter swans. Compare the straight neck of these birds with the curved neck of the whistler. (*Roy C. Erickson, U.S. Fish and Wildlife Service.*)

Distribution. The breeding and wintering ranges of the two North American swans are quite different, a condition which probably also accounts for the great difference in the numbers of each species now in existence. The breeding range of the whistling swan is in the far north on the Arctic shore of the continent extending from Southampton Island in Hudson Bay to Kodiak Island in the Gulf of Alaska. This range is a belt of arctic shore and tundra rather than a restricted area along the immediate border of the Arctic Ocean. The wintering ranges include the shore of the Atlantic from Chesapeake Bay to South Carolina and the Pacific Coast from southern Oregon to lower California.

The ranges of the trumpeter swan are very restricted but are probably broader than was formerly suspected. In the United States it includes territory in Wyoming, Montana, and Idaho, centering around the Yellowstone National Park and Red Rock Lakes refuge. The wintering range is a much restricted part of this territory where enough open water is available to furnish feeding grounds during the cold season of the year.

Movements. Whistling swans are early migrants, leaving the wintering grounds in February and March depending on the latitude. The flights

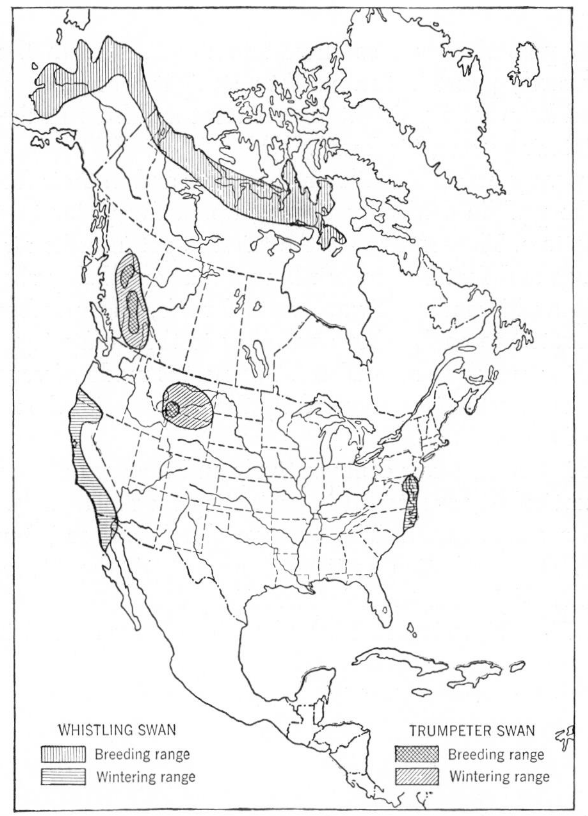

FIG. 19-4. Ranges of whistling and trumpeter swans (41 *g.r.*).

are made in small V-shaped flocks high up and in a northerly direction. Stops are made at open waters along the route where feeding and resting grounds are available. The birds arrive at the breeding grounds while ice and snow still cover the ponds and grounds, often early in May, and by June are dispersing to the nesting grounds and preparing for the egg-laying season (13 *g.r.*).

In the fall the young birds are able to fly by September, but migrations are delayed until later in October and November. Flight groups in the fall appear to be large, with as many as 500 in a single line flying south (17, 41 *g.r.*).

Apparently swans have ancestral migration routes which follow the same pattern each season. Bent (13 *g.r.*) indicates that swans which breed in northern Alaska cross the Rocky Mountains and move southward through the interior of Alaska, while those which breed in southern Alaska and Canada migrate down the Pacific Coast to the west-coast wintering grounds. From the vicinity of the Great Lakes, swans take a route southeastward to the Atlantic Coast and also south to the Gulf of Mexico and possibly some southwest to the Pacific. In the migratory flights they rarely pause but rather set a straight course for the wintering grounds and keep going. Flight is persistent and high in the air until a suitable wintering ground is found.

Swans are very graceful while on the water and in their feeding habits resemble the puddle ducks by tipping up in the water to obtain food from the bottom. They must face the wind to get into the air but by use of both wings and feet become air-borne in a remarkably short distance.

Courtship and Breeding. Swans mate for life, and members of a pair are very devoted to each other as well as to their offspring. The nest is near the water, usually on an island. The nest is made of vegetation, and the incubation process is performed by the female with the male in close attendance for protection.

The nest is a huge affair comparatively and the eggs are large, but the birds are particularly successful in protecting them. The eggs are creamy white with a smooth shell. The average clutch is 4 or 5 but may vary from 2 to 7. The incubation period is from 35 to 40 days. The eggs hatch during the last of June or the first part of July.

Habitat. The wintering habitat of whistling swans consists of open water, shallow bays, and estuaries for feeding.

The trumpeter swans stay inland mostly and are frequently hard-pressed for feeding spots during severe winters. Harrison Lewis (21) says the limiting factors for swans in Canada are the small numbers of feeding areas and the losses from lead poisoning. River habitats in Yellowstone National Park and in British Columbia and springs provide open feeding areas for the limited number of birds of this species. Possibly the limited migration urge of the trumpeter may be one reason why it is so low in numbers and so slow to recover from the verge of extinction.

General. All swans are protected in the United States, Canada, and Alaska. Some swans are killed, however, during the hunting season, both because of the similarity of young swans to geese and the urge of hunters to shoot any large, conspicuous bird. Phillips and Lincoln (57 *g.r.*) gave the number of whistling swans as 16,000 as early as 1916, and the general impression in recent years is that these waterfowl are on the increase and are in no danger, partially owing, at least, to the remote nature of their breeding grounds and partially to improved protection on the wintering grounds and during migration.

The status of the trumpeter swan is not too satisfactory. As of 1952 there were something better than 400 trumpeters in the United States, 900 in Canada, and 350 in southern Alaska (3, 21, 28). Red Rock Lakes Refuge in Montana has been set aside by the U.S. Fish and Wildlife Service where in 1935 there were only 75 birds. There has been a steady increase since that time, so now (1952) there are about 400 on the refuge (24 *g.r.*, 28). It has been stated that the capacity of the Red Rock Lakes Refuge has now (1952) reached its limit and that other means may have to be devised to keep this species on the increase (24). To help to correct this situation, the U.S. Fish and Wildlife Service recently moved 20 cygnets to Malheur Refuge in Oregon to attempt to raise trumpeters in captivity (7). This appears to be a wise move and should help to spread the species around to prevent a catastrophe.

CANADA GOOSE *Branta canadensis canadensis*

The common Canada goose is one of a group of white-cheeked geese that occupy the suitable goose ranges on the North American continent. The other seven white-cheeked species are as follows:

	Species
Central Canada goose	*Branta canadensis interior* (35, 36)
Western Canada goose	*Branta canadensis occidentalis*
Tundra Canada goose	*Branta canadensis leucopareia*
Richardson's goose	*Branta canadensis hutchinsii*
Athabaska Canada goose	*Branta canadensis parvipes*
Basin Canada goose	*Branta canadensis moffitti*
Cackling goose	*Branta canadensis minima*

From the standpoint of the hunter, the goose has great appeal. Its flesh has excellent flavor, and it is large enough so one bird will feed a fair-sized family. Geese are wary, so the shooting of one is no mean accomplishment. Because of the spectacular nature and regularity of both spring and fall migration flights, these are of interest to everyone who loves the out-of-doors.

Description. Mature common Canada geese (*B. canadensis*) are majestic birds. The head is held high, and the movements are deliberate. On the ground one or more geese of a flock keep a constant watch while the other members are feeding. The general appearance is gray or brown, although there are lighter parts that approach dull white. The neck and head are shiny black with the exception of a patch of white on the throat and cheeks. The bill and feet are black. The under parts are white or cream-colored, and the back is gray and tan. The rump and tail are black and the wings gray to brown (41 *g.r.*).

The central Canada goose is a subspecies created by a subdivision of the common Canada geese because of differences which had formerly been ignored. The revision was accepted by the committee on nomenclature of the American Ornithological Union in 1945. While the upper back and lower neck of the common subspecies is light, that of the central subspecies is darker. The upper mandible and head of the new subspecies

FIG. 19-5. Comparative sizes and markings of the Canada, blue, and white-fronted geese.

tend to be rounded or humped, while those of other geese are straight or slightly concave.

The western Canada goose (*B. canadensis occidentalis*) is much darker in appearance than the Canada goose. The western subspecies may have a white collar near the base of the "stocking." Also the white cheek patches are usually divided by a black area under the throat. Cheek patches also may be brownish or barred with dusky-colored feathers. The average weight of male western Canada geese is about a pound heavier than that of the common geese.

The tundra Canada goose (*B. canadensis leucopareia*) is smaller than the common and western but larger than Richardson's and the cackling goose. The coloration pattern is much the same as in the common Canadian goose. Average weights of male geese are 5 pounds and 2 ounces.

Richardson's goose (*B. canadensis hutchinsii*) appears much the same as the tundra goose. The average weight of males is slightly less than 5 pounds.

The cackling goose (*B. canadensis minima*) is the smallest of the white-cheeked geese, weighing less than 5 pounds and about the size of a mallard duck. Coloration is generally darker than the common, and the feathers below the base of the neck are darker than the rest of the chest, giving the effect of a less marked contrast of color between the neck and body than in the other geese. Also the white cheek patches are frequently divided by black at the throat (41 *g.r.*).

FIG. 19-6. Female goose and eggs. Note the down which with plant materials makes up the simple nest. Nests are built typically in the open, the top of a muskrat house being a favored site. (*C. J. Henry, U.S. Fish and Wildlife Service.*)

Distribution. The breeding and wintering ranges of the eight subspecies of white-cheeked geese are widely scattered over the North American continent. The Canada race winters entirely along the Atlantic Coast, while the cackling and western races winter on or near the Pacific Coast. The various other races winter in numerous locations from the Atlantic to the Pacific.

The ranges of the remaining subspecies of white-cheeked geese are given on Range Map 19.5. The cackling goose nests in northwestern Alaska. Nesting ranges of the *tundra* and *Richardson's* races are across northern Alaska and Canada. That of *interior* is the eastern shore of Hudson Bay and around James Bay. The *Canada* nests along the shores of Labrador and Newfoundland. The *Athabaska* nests in the north central part of Canada, and the *western* along the Canadian Pacific Coast from Kodiak Island to Vancouver Island. The *Basin Canada goose* nests in the central and northern part of the Great Basin.

Wintering ranges of the white-cheeked geese vary from the coasts of the Atlantic and Pacific Oceans and the coast of the Gulf of Mexico to inland locations across the southern part of the continent.

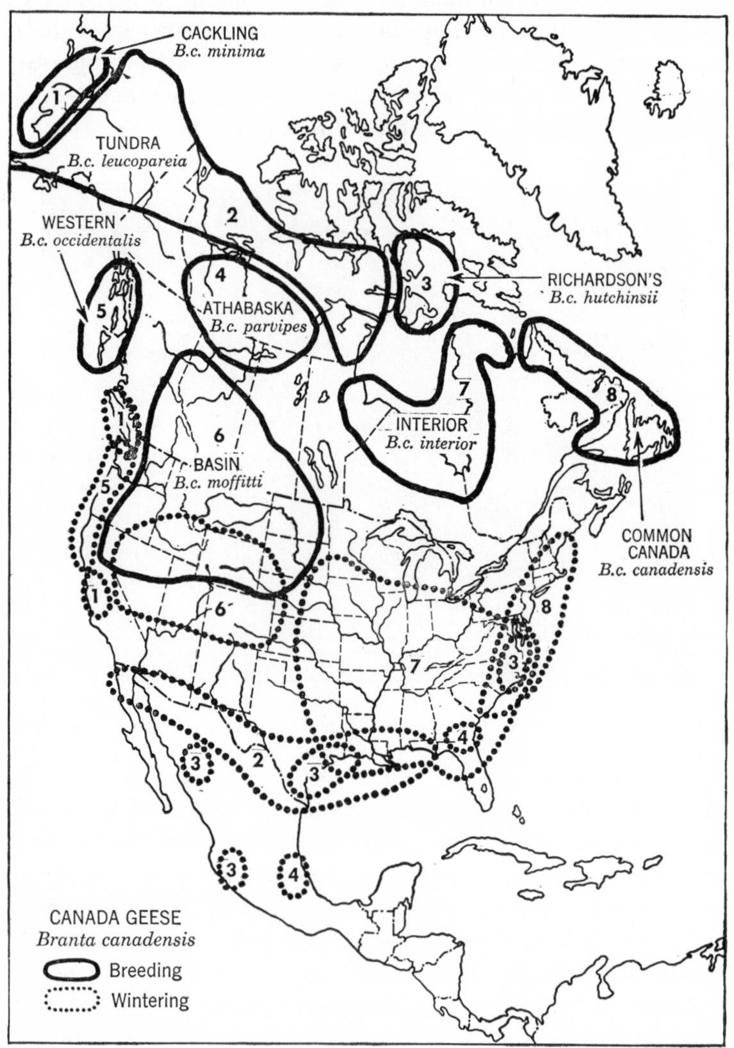

FIG. 19-7. Ranges of the white-cheeked geese. (*John W. Aldrich, U.S. Fish and Wildlife Service.*)

Movements. Movements of migrating wild geese are most impressive. A single line may extend for half a mile, with each bird in its place at a regular interval from the next. The flock may be a V formation with lines extending on each side and back of the leader. Flights may be high or low depending on atmospheric conditions and the purpose of the movement. The movements of geese are not the same as other waterfowl but rather are geared to the peculiarities of the species. All the above characteristics regulate and complicate the pattern of movements of geese.

The time of the spring migratory flight north is early and begins during February and March on the wintering grounds. The earliest movements toward the breeding grounds are by slow stages at the rate of a few miles a day, but as the season advances longer flights occur until the breeding grounds are reached. March seems to be the time of the most extensive migrations (41 *g.r.*). Returns of birds banded at Kingsville, Ontario, Horseshoe Lake, Illinois, and various other places seem to indicate that the migration north in the spring in general is west of the fall migration route. Also the spring migration north is said to be more leisurely than the trip south in the fall (14). When the breeding grounds are reached the flocks break up into pairs, each pair seeking its own nesting site and area.

During the breeding season the activities consist of watching and protecting the incubating female and guarding the young after the eggs have hatched. During the flightless period all movements must be carried on by swimming or walking, so the use of cover is more important than when flight is a possibility.

The reassembling of the flock occurs in the fall beginning in September (14). At this time family groups unite and begin a show of uneasiness as cold weather advances. By October and November the birds are on the move toward the wintering grounds. Many Canada geese move only as far south as ice and food conditions require.

Daily activities of the goose differ from those of the more aquatic members of the waterfowl group. Geese often stay on land days at a time if not disturbed and if food and water are available. If the night is spent on the water or on a sand bar distant from the feeding grounds, the trip is made after daylight, according to Arthur Hawkins, rather than at the first streaks of light as is true with most waterfowl. Daily movements are usually made in small parties (families), in pairs (no young), or singly (still unmated, or pairs where one has been lost) (10). In feeding, one or more stand guard to watch while the remainder of the family proceed to graze, if on green vegetation, or by scooping up the feed if feeding on corn or other grains.

Courtship, Breeding, and Family Relationships. Courtship begins on the wintering grounds before the beginning of spring migration. With the older birds this is the renewing of a show of attention and affection between mated pairs as the breeding impulses become stronger and with the defense of the female against attention of unmated old males or young males just coming into sexual maturity. All evidence seems to indicate geese do not become sexually mature until the approach of the second summer (20, 45 *g.r.*).

The nest sites are usually a slightly elevated land feature near or surrounded by water. Research workers seem to agree that old muskrat houses make ideal goose nest sites, although many successful nests are located on other type of terrain. On Bear River Refuge in Utah, Williams and Marshall (37) found 77 per cent of the nests within 30 feet of the water. For cover hard-stemmed bulrushes and cat-tails are

FIG. 19-8. Mated pair of Canada geese and goslings. Pairs remain mated throughout life. (*C. J. Henry, U.S. Fish and Wildlife Service.*)

favorite nesting grounds, if grass or grain fields and open water are not too far distant.

The nest is made of grass, other vegetation, or sticks and down. The eggs are creamy white in color, and the clutch may range from 4 to 10, but 4 to 6 eggs are the most common (6, 37). The incubation period is 28 to 30 days and is performed by the female (41 *g.r.*). In a study of 84 complete Canada goose nests at Bear River Refuge, 81 per cent of the eggs hatched and 6 per cent were infertile. Thirteen per cent were lost by other causes (37).

Some data are available on the average number of young produced per nest in different parts of the goose breeding area. On Gray's Lake in Idaho, an average of 4.4 goslings were produced during the 1950 season. An estimated 300 nests were present on 22,000 acres of marsh and 1,000 goslings are the estimated production (4). Because of the tendency of Canada geese to stay in family groups, additional data are available as to what happens to the young after the migration in the fall and after the pressure of hunting has operated. In comparing flock counts by several investigators, the Elders (10) found the peak of the flock counts to be 5, 6, and 7. This fits with previously stated figures of 2 adults and 4 young. Counts at Horseshoe Lake before and after hunting showed the number of the average family after the shooting season to have dropped to 4 or a loss of 2 geese from the average flock. No accounting in this calculation is made for the year-old birds that may have remained with the family group.

Habitat. Excellent information is available on the composition of the cover of at least three types of breeding grounds and shows the diversity of cover conditions desired or tolerated by various species of Canadian geese.

James Bay Area. One of the extensive breeding grounds for Canada geese is the wild forest and muskeg country around Hudson's and James Bays. Hanson and Smith (14) list five different types of muskeg from well-timbered country with only a few ponds to a type called "small-pox bog" which is practically all water. These investigators state that breeding pairs of geese are scattered within certain breeding centers and there is seldom more than one pair of geese on a given lake. Production centers are largely between the basins of large rivers where drainage is poor and the area is at least 25 per cent water.

Bear River Marshes. Williams and Marshall (37) described a goose nesting area on the Bear River Migratory Waterfowl Refuge in Utah, where 95 goose nests were found on an area of 5,000 acres. Two-fifths, or nearly half of the area, had emergent vegetation. The nesting cover types are hard-stemmed bulrush, salt-grass, cat-tails, and alkali bulrushes.

The presence of muskrat houses and the proximity of water had a definite influence on the location of nests, as more than half of the nests used muskrat houses as bases, and over three-fourths of the nests were within 30 feet of open water.

Snake River, Idaho. A study of goose nests along 40 miles of the Snake River during the summer of 1947 by the Craighead brothers revealed the following densities and conditions (6):

The nests averaged two per mile.
Ninety-five per cent of the nests were on islands.
The height of the nests above water averaged about 3 feet.
More than half of the nests were 40 feet from the water.

Wintering areas for Canada geese are found along both the Atlantic and Pacific Coasts of the continent as well as inland. A summary of these needs is given as follows:

A body of water on which the birds can rest and escape harassment by wild animals, dogs, and human beings.

Fresh water to drink. If wintering grounds are on salt water or far north, open fresh water in streams or ponds must be available.

A food supply of sufficient quantity and of good quality must be at hand. If artificial feeding is resorted to, as at Jack Miner's refuge at Kingsville, the feeding should be done at a time and place where the geese will not lose their wariness of human beings. If grains or grasses are planted for food, they should be not more than 10 miles from the resting grounds.

Resting grounds. Sand bars in large rivers or sandy shores along the ocean are ideal places for resting and preening.

Behavior Characteristics. The extreme interest of hunters in Canada goose shooting during the past decade indicates the need for a discussion of some of the characteristics of geese that are the basis of both success and failure.

Wariness versus Tameness. There is much contradiction in the condition of wariness of different geese at different places. The goose hunter is unable to get within gunshot of geese, yet at selected places and times geese will be as tame as pigeons and actually feed from your hand. Hanson and Smith (14) explain this phenomena as follows: Newly hatched geese, as compared to newly hatched ducks, are trusting and unafraid of man. Soon after hatching the behavior pattern of fear of man in geese is fixed by association with older geese which have survived because of that fear. If later these same geese are fed by man and learn to associate food with him and are unharmed by man, they lose their fear and so are subject to unusual losses because of getting too near to hunters.

Family Ties. The family relationships of geese have already been referred to under the heading of Courtship and Behavior. As indicated by Hanson and Smith (14), this characteristic no doubt has survival value under normal conditions as it allows part of the family to feed while others stand guard. Under hunting conditions, however, it may prove to be a liability when one member of a flock is killed or injured by a gunner as the rest of the family may return to the same spot. This family tie appears to be especially strong with mates during the breeding season.

Management. Hochbaum (16) has pointed out the extreme danger of completely shooting out populations from a given habitat. The slow increase of waterfowl at Jack Miner's refuge at Kingsville indicates the difficulty of using a particular habitat even under the most apparently favorable conditions (14). Certain techniques and rules are available, however, in rebuilding both breeding grounds and wintering refuges for geese.

Starting with the Correct Subspecies. Subspecies of birds have developed over a long period of time so are closely related to a given region. Start the breeding nucleus with the subspecies which belongs to the region to be managed.

Sources of Seed Stock. Both the states and Federal government are running banding traps and banding stations, so seed stock should be available in all the regions. Where goose shooting grounds are available, crippled birds can be picked up during the hunting season and nursed back to health to speed up the process of use of a refuge and to decoy in wild birds. This practice has been used successfully on many state and Federal refuges (8, 13).

Feeding forage for grazing and grains can be grown on refuges or adjacent to refuges for the purpose of feeding geese. Horseshoe Lake Game Refuge in southern Illinois consists of 3,660 acres of land, 1,200 of which are used to raise feed for geese.

Where public shooting is carried on around areas managed for geese, a buffer zone in which shooting is prohibited should surround the place where geese feed or rest. Such a zone should be at least a mile in depth and possibly more. The concentration of blinds should be regulated even beyond this zone, and daily and seasonal bag limits should be set for each locality. As with Horseshoe Lake Refuge in Illinois, a total seasonal bag limit should be set and the hunting season closed when this limit is reached (9, 27, 34).

BRANT

American Brant *Branta bernicla hrota*
Pacific Black Brant *Branta nigricans*

The brant are among our smaller geese and found only on salt water. In the past brant shooting was a favorite sport with the New England waterfowl gunner, but since the closing of spring shooting and the reduction of the eelgrass, the brant have been much reduced in numbers and brant shooting as a sport has declined (22).

The two species of brant are much alike so will be described together.

Description. Both species have dark heads, necks, and chests with the exception of a white-and-black marking on the side of the throat. In the American brant the white-and-black patches are separated by black on the mid line of the throat, but in the black brant (western brant) these markings are not separated. The American brant is light-colored along the under parts, the white terminating in a distinct line at the fore part of the belly. The dark color of the chest of the black brant extends back along the belly to the region of the legs. Both species have

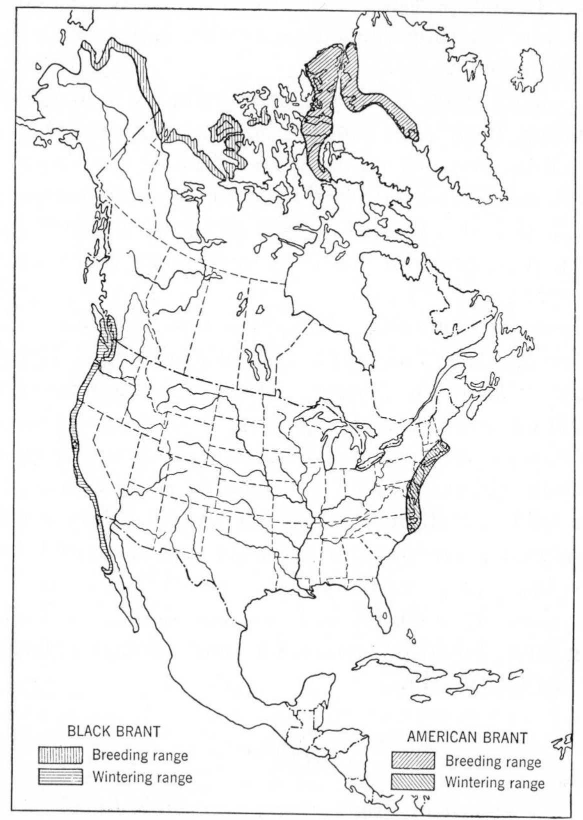

FIG. 19-9. Ranges of American and black brants (41 *g.r.*).

white underparts and back of the legs and white and dusky streaks along the sides and on the outer sides of the wings. The bills and feet are black.

The weights of the two species are about the same, each weighing 2½ to 4 pounds or slightly more when mature and fat (41 *g.r.*). Cottam *et al.* (5) give the weights of average male American brant as 3 pounds 5½ ounces and of females as 2 pounds 15 ounces. Heavy birds may weigh up to 4 pounds.

Distribution. The American brant is found along the East Coast and north Atlantic and the black species along the Alaskan and Pacific Coasts. The American brant winters along the eastern Atlantic Coast from Massachusetts to North Carolina and also in the Great Lakes (29). The breeding range is the Arctic shores of eastern North America and Greenland. Kortright (41 *g.r.*) gives the breeding locations as Southampton Island, Boothia Peninsula, Parry and Ellsmere Islands, and the west shore of Greenland north of the 70-degree parallel.

The black brant winters on the Pacific Coast from Vancouver Island to Cedros Island on the west coast of Southern California and breeds from the Parry, Banks, and Victoria Islands west along the Arctic Coast to Cape Prince of Wales (41 *g.r.*).

Movements. According to Bent (13 *g.r.*) brant do not fly in V formations but rather in long lines or irregular flocks. When traveling overland they fly high, but over the sea, which is the usual procedure, they fly within a few feet of the water. They swim well but do not dive unless hard-pressed.

The spring migration of the American brant begins along the south Atlantic Coast in February, small groups of birds starting to move northward along the coast and joining other groups. From the vicinity of New Jersey the flights are overland toward the north. A few still congregate along the north Atlantic Coast and the Gulf of St. Lawrence. Bent (13 *g.r.*) speaks of counting 60,000 in 1909, which was then believed to be practically the entire number of birds in this species.

The fall migration is the reverse of the spring movement, except that they move down the coast of Hudson's Bay on the trip south and their flight is more rapid (13 *g.r.*) Cottam *et al.* (5) say the birds pass mainly *east* of Hudson's Bay. They begin to arrive off Cape Cod the middle of October.

The flight habits and other activities of the black brant are identical to that of the American brant. The west coast birds migrate earlier than their eastern relatives, however. The main northern flight takes place in March and early April and the birds reach the breeding grounds in early June. The southward flight passes across the Bering Sea during the first half of October and reaches California in late October and November (41 *g.r.*). According to Bent (13 *g.r.*), the route south is different from the spring migration, being farther out to sea. Moffitt, quoted by Cottam *et al.* (5, 26), says the brant do not reach California in shootable numbers before November 25.

Courtship and Breeding. Presumably brant are monogamous, but this is a guess. Nests of both species are constructed on the ground of any vegetation available and down from the mothers' breasts. It is said of the two species that the black brant builds the better nest. As to behavior of mated pairs of black brant while nesting, Cottam *et al.* (5) quote Gillham as follows:

> Black brant are usually much wilder when approached on the nest than Lesser Snow Geese. The female is attended by the male, but he is not as solicitous as the male goose. He usually swims about in the vicinity but several cases were noticed where the female chased her mate away from the nest. Any other brant, duck, goose, swan, loon or gull that approached the mother brant on her island was immediately chased away. Two birds rarely nest on the same little island. The female brant quickly covers her nest with down when approached, and departs rapidly.

The general locality of nesting sites for black brant is described by Spencer (31) in western Alaska on the low tidal flats along the coast in a belt 2 to 3 miles wide, although some brant do nest on low ground farther from the ocean shore. The nest sites are on low delta islands which are built up by the floodwaters of rivers. Numerous river channels run between the islands and sand bars, and mud flats occur at the mouths of the channels. These serve as resting places for the brant. Bays where the water is clear enough provide a growth of pondweed (*Potamogeton vaginatus*) which is a food of the brant. The islands are rimmed by a natural levee adjacent to the channel, and in some cases a low beach is formed by the tides. The nesting cover, according to Cottam *et al.* (5) is soft grass (*Dupontia fischeri*), river sedge (*Carex aquatilis*), and cotton sedges (*Eriophorum angustifolium* and *E. scheuchzeri*). Mosses and lichens are conspicuously absent. The woody cover is represented by two species of willow, an erect form (*Salix alaxensis*) which is 3 to 5 feet high and a prostrate form (*S. anglorum*) which forms a low mat that provides excellent cover for brant nests and provides food in the form of catkins and leaf buds.

Cottam *et al.* (5) say the nest of the black brant is the most beautiful of all the waterfowl. Grass is used for the foundation and the nest proper is a symmetrical ring of pure down 14 to 18 inches in diameter. The colors of the down of the nest are powder blue, slate, and steel gray. The eggs are faintly glossy white or soft ivory, and the clutch is 4 to 6 eggs with the average of 5. While the vegetation has not put forth new growth when the birds begin incubation in early June, the incubating female is fairly well camouflaged and the water surrounding the nest makes travel difficult for land predators. Arctic storms and fluctuation of water levels are a constant menace to these nests which are not high above normal water levels so they may be flooded out as the water covers the low land. Kortright (41 *g.r.*) says the incubation period is about 4 weeks, but it is doubtful if anyone really knows. The female does the incubating. Because of the short arctic summer it is doubtful if brant renest. On the western shores of Alaska the young hatch during the first week of July and are flying the second week of August (31).

Numerous references have been made to the fluctuations in numbers of the brant along the East Coast of the United States. Counts on both coasts are given by Cottam (5) as follows:

Year	Totals on East Coast	Totals on California Coast
1932	......	43,946
1933	......	13,819
1934	......	29,968
1935	......	125,153
1936	48,000	66,055
1937	56,000	33,187
1938	44,000	59,520
1939	72,000	57,913
1940	94,000	75,412
1941	......	61,339
1942	......	64,703

Part of the variation of numbers from year to year no doubt is the result of shifts of the birds and possible errors of censusing. That the numbers change from year to year, however, there is little doubt. Causes for the variations may be due to failures of the nesting season or failure of eelgrass or other important foods on which the brant are so dependent.

Habitat. Brant are definitely sea geese, but because of their food habits in which vegetable rather than animal forms predominate, their flesh has an excellent flavor and as a result the brant is a favorite of the gunner. On the wintering grounds the brant stay in shallow bays and river estuaries where they can obtain their favorite food of eelgrass, widgeon-grass, and sea lettuce. The feeding is done by tipping or wading in shallow water, so the feeding periods conform with low tides on the last half of the ebb tide or the first half of the flood tide. When the water is too deep for feeding on the beds, the birds feed on floating vegetation that has been pulled loose or along the shore drift. Brant may feed in close proximity to diving ducks and also in the wake of oyster dredges where vegetation is pulled up from water too deep for them to feed in normally.

SNOW GEESE

Greater Snow Goose *Anser caerulescens atlanticus*
Lesser Snow Goose *Anser caerulescens hyperboreus*
Ross's Goose *Anser rossii*

The geese listed above are all white except the primary feathers of the wings, which are all black. Often the lower body feathers are stained brown, probably because of the mineral in the waters in which they swim. The lesser snow goose is said to be the most numerous of all of the geese on the American continent. All lesser and Ross's geese have breeding grounds on the extreme northern lands or the islands in the Arctic Ocean. The greater snow geese breed on the northwestern margins of Greenland. The three species vary somewhat in size and weight, the greater snow goose being the largest and Ross's goose the smallest.

Description. The weights of the snow and Ross's geese are given below. A table of average weights follows:

Species	Males	Females
Greater snow goose	7 lb. 7 oz.	6 lb. 2 oz.
Lesser snow goose	5 lb. 5 oz.	4 lb. 11 oz.
Ross's goose	2 lb. 14 oz.	2 lb. 11 oz.

The plumages of the greater and lesser snow geese are identical. The wing primaries of adults are black, and the primary coverts are gray. The area around the head and eyes is lightly flecked with rusty brown. In the Ross's goose the feathers are similar except the spurious wing feathers, one of which is black. Also the Ross's goose has a warty protuberance at the base of the upper mandible. The juveniles of all of these geese are darker-colored. The secondary coverts of the two species of snow geese are gray or sooty in color and the head has an area of dusky or rusty-colored feathers. The entire body covering is bluish-gray. The bill and feet are dusky rather than pink but change to pink during the first winter. The secondaries and secondary coverts of the Ross's goose are white, but the body has a gray appearance and a darker head.

Distribution. The greater snow goose is found on the eastern part of the North American continent and the lesser farther west (19). The breeding ground of the greater snow goose is given by Kortright (41 *g.r.*) as including the northern part of Baffin Island, Devon and Ellesmere Islands, and a small portion of the northwest shore of Greenland.

The breeding ground of the lesser snow goose includes the Arctic Coast from Baffin and Southampton Islands west to beyond Point Barrow on the coast of Alaska. Ross's goose breeds on a limited area just north of the Arctic circle on the 100th meridian.

The wintering grounds of the greater snow goose include the Atlantic Coast of North America from New Jersey to South Carolina. The lesser snow goose winters mainly along the Gulf of Mexico from the Mississippi River to the Rio Grande River and along the Pacific Coast in the central

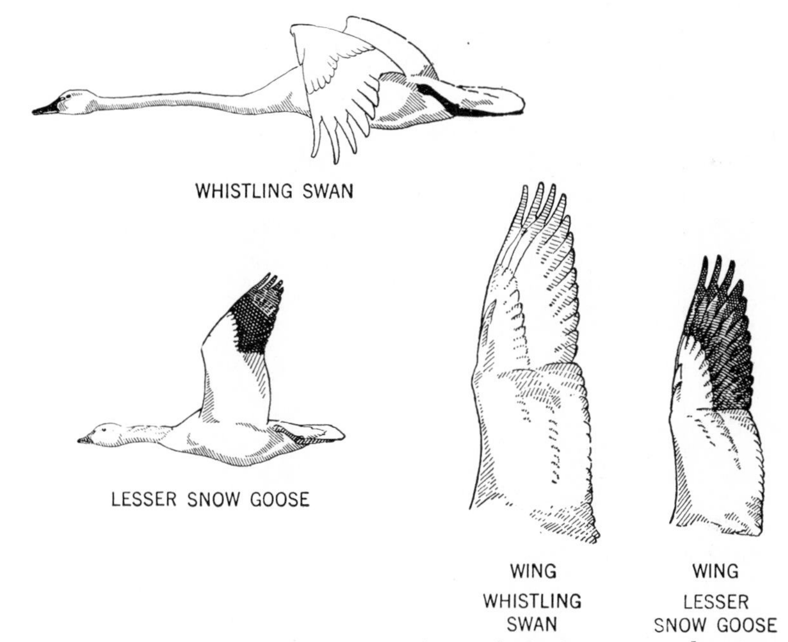

FIG. 19-10. Comparative sizes and wing markings of whistling swan and snow goose.

valley of California and from Oregon to Mexico (41 *g.r.*). Ross's goose winters in the central valley of California.

Movements. The snow geese are strong fliers and move in long lines at considerable elevation when migrating. White birds of any kind catch the eye and give the appearance of being larger than they really are. Another point of difference from other geese is their relative silence as opposed to the noisy behavior of Canada geese.

Greater snow geese, which spend the winter along the Atlantic Coast, migrate overland across New England to the Gulf of St. Lawrence and then across Labrador to their Arctic breeding ground. They arrive at the actual nesting sites in late June (13 *g.r.*). The geese leave the breeding grounds early and begin to arrive at the St. Lawrence River in early

September and congregate at St. Joachim, Quebec, a game club where they are protected and fed. It is said that practically all the birds of this species stop at this refuge both in the fall and spring. The first arrivals are adults, and the later arrivals are young of the year. In 1908 two thousand geese were counted here, but by 1952 they had increased to more than 40,000. Mr. Fremont states that the birds rest here for 2 months on each of their two yearly migrations (11).

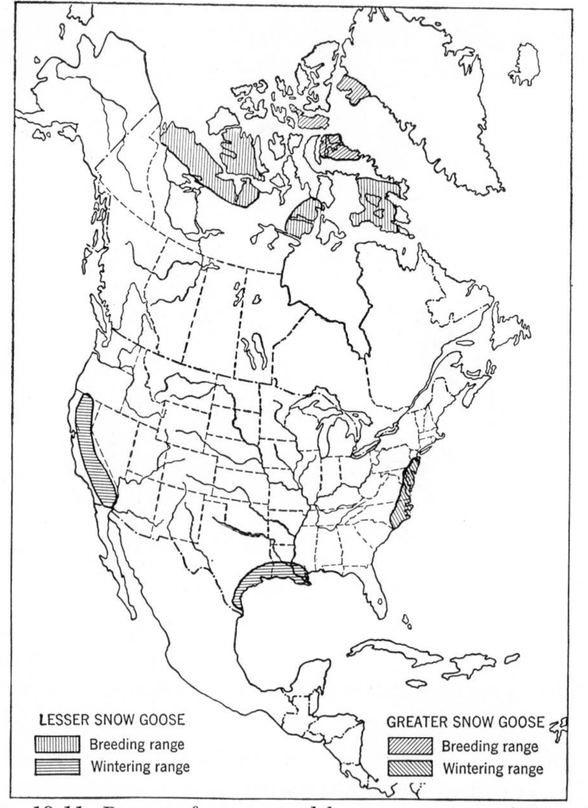

FIG. 19-11. Ranges of greater and lesser snow geese (41 *g.r.*).

Snow geese formations are long, irregular lines rather than precise V formations. Of the migrations of lesser snow and blue geese at Delta, Manitoba, Hochbaum (31 *g.r.*) says:

> In early April blue geese and lesser snow geese are always in the prairie skies; sometimes their skeins reach to all horizons. The "waveys" like the Canada geese loaf on the lake, and feed in the grain fields, now empty, except for gleanings, lingering until the second week in May before moving to their Arctic breeding grounds. Both species are rare at Delta in autumn.

Ross's goose is one of the waterfowl that moves far west of its breeding territory to winter. From the breeding grounds it moves south and west to Great Slave Lake and Lake Athabaska, then south to central and western Montana from where it crosses the mountains to the Central Valley in California (57 *g.r.*).

According to Bent (13 *g.r.*) greater snow geese leave their wintering

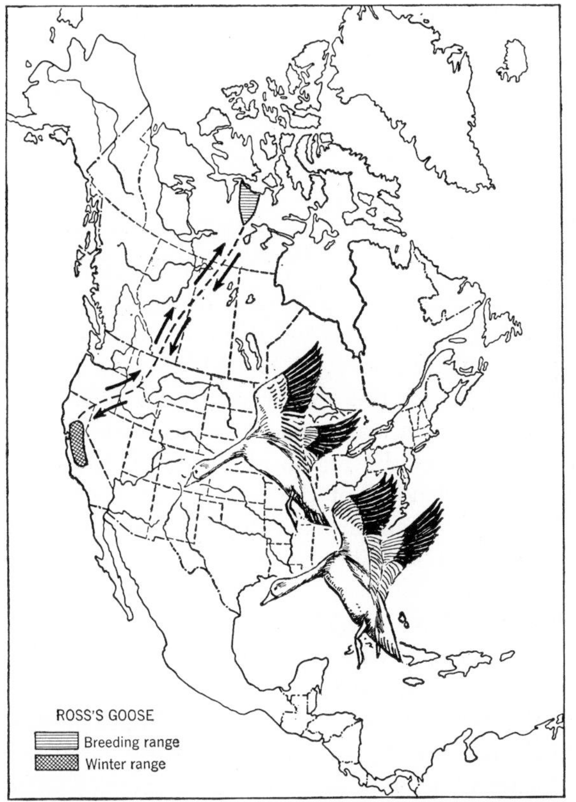

FIG. 19-12. Ranges and migration routes of Ross's goose (41 *g.r.*).

grounds in March and arrive back at Currituck Sound, North Carolina, in early December. The lesser snow geese pass through Sac County, Iowa, and Teton County, Montana, in late March and early April on their spring migration.

Courtship and Breeding. Geese, in contrast to ducks, mate for life and so do not go through the conspicuous antics of the latter annually. The young make selections of mates as they come into sexual maturity, but very little has been written of this highly interesting activity.

Kortright (41 *g.r.*) describes the nest of the greater snow goose as located in grassy swales and flats along a lake-dotted flood plain of streams. The nests are placed in depressions among the tussocks and are built up with mud, grass, and dead vegetation, and lined with white feathers and down. Of the lesser snow goose Kortright says: "The nest of the Lesser Snow Goose is situated on dry ground at the edge of a lake, sometimes at some distance from the water's edge and often three or four miles inland from salt water. . . . " A summary of the nest and incubation characteristics of the three geese is as follows:

Species	Clutch	Incubation period, days
Greater snow goose.......	6–7	28
Lesser snow goose........	4–8	22
Ross's goose.............	2–6 (4 most common)	Not recorded

The discovery of the breeding ground of Ross's goose was made on July 1, 1940, by Angus Gavin and Ernest Donovan, officials of the Hudson's Bay Company. Mr. E. F. G. White of Ottawa helped to set the wheels in motion for this discovery at the First North American Wildlife Conference when arrangements were made with the Hudson's Bay Company to explore the region of the Perry River near the 100th meridian and 50 miles north of the Arctic Circle. Charles E. Gillham had seen the geese from an airplane in 1938 and would probably have made the discovery in 1939 except for the sudden death of the pilot of his chartered plane.

Nests of all species have a thick lining of down. The eggs of all three species are ivory or creamy white but the eggs of Ross's goose are smaller than those of the other two species.

Habitat. Little more can be said of the habitats of the three geese than has already been said. The Arctic breeding grounds are all areas with a short growing season, and there is always ice within a foot or more of the surface. Sedges, grasses, and dwarf willows are predominant plants of the deltas and river borders. Where the ponds are more inland, mosses and lichens may predominate. As geese feed mostly on vegetation, land as well as water plants become an important part of the habitat.

The winter habitat is better known because of its close proximity to civilization. The Atlantic Coast is a combination of salt marshes, sand bars, brackish bays, and fresh-water estuaries. Mud flats are common. While leaves and bulbs of aquatic plants form the bulk of their food, grasses and herbaceous material on dry land are also used freely. Of greater snow geese, Howard (18) says:

Feeding is done early in the morning and late in the afternoon and also on moonlight nights. The geese feed in the marshes preferably where grass is standing in a few inches of water. Not only the leaves and stems are eaten but the stems and roots are eaten as well.

Geese spend the daytime on the water away from shore or may line up on sand bars in the sun to preen and oil their feathers. A summary of a study of goose activities along the Texas Coast by Glazner (12) indicates that Canada geese were "grazers" and the snow and blue geese were "grubbers." The trips to the feeding grounds are made twice a day, in early morning and late in the afternoon. Grasses (*Gramineae*) and cultivated crops including rice, corn, and grain sorghums made up the bulk of the goose food. Salt-grass, water cress, and panic grass were the native species most extensively used by the snow and blue geese.

The following are life-history and ecological sketches of the waterfowl not already described.

BLUE SNOW GOOSE *Anser caerulescens caerulescens*

Description. The color pattern of the blue goose may vary in the amount of light and dark coloring on the neck, breast, and belly. Normally the sexes of adults appear alike. The head is white with rusty spots scattered over the face and cheeks. The neck is white with the lower foreneck a dusky-slate color. The general body color is a dark grayish brown. The rump is nearly pure white or sometimes gray, and the belly and breast are variable. The primaries of the wings are black with gray at the base, and the secondaries are black, with some edged with gray. The bill and feet are pink. Juveniles are much darker than adults, with dusky rather than pink bills and feet. The plumage of the young changes to adult during the summer after the birds are a year old (41 *g.r.*).

Distribution. For many years the blue goose was well known on its wintering grounds along the coast of the Gulf of Mexico, but its breeding grounds were unknown. Finally, John Dewey Soper, an employee of the Canadian Department of the Interior, discovered the location of the breeding "blues" in 1929. The breeding grounds have now been established on a narrow strip of coastal plain on the eastern shore of Bowman Bay, Fox Basin, Baffin Island, as well as on Cape Kendall, Southampton Island. Some also breed several hundred miles to the west on the 100th meridian.

The wintering grounds are along a narrow strip of land on the coast of the Gulf of Mexico in Louisiana and Texas. McAtee gives the location as extending along the coast from the delta of the Mississippi to Vermillion Bay (41 *g.r.*).

Movements. Blue geese seem always to a marked degree to be associated with the lesser snow geese. It is thought the "blues" and lesser "snows" may be closely related and that they may at times interbreed (41 *g.r.*). The blue geese are noisy and gregarious birds, and all their activities are accompanied by loud honking, yapping, and barking.

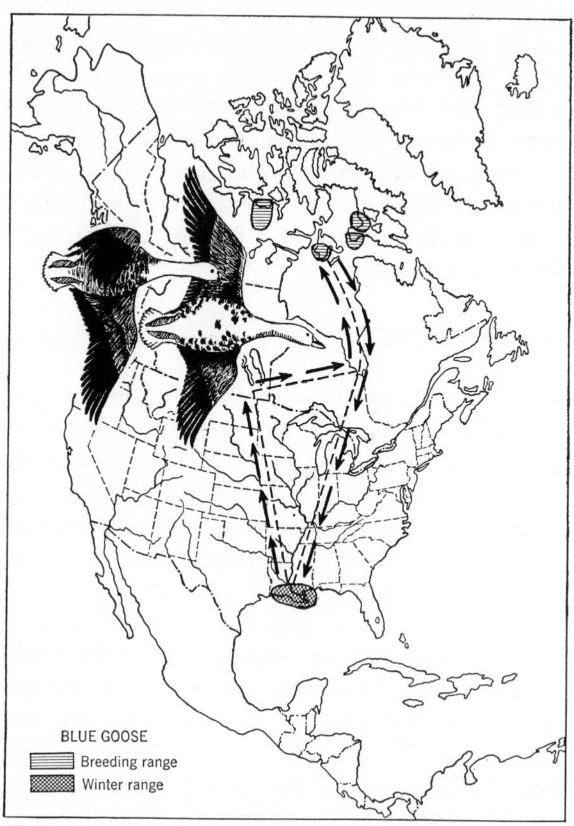

FIG. 19-13. Ranges and migration routes of blue goose (41 *g.r.*).

The fall migration begins during the first half of September. At this time the "blues" move south to the shores of James Bay where excellent feeding grounds attract them. They collect in large flocks in the vicinity of Hannah Bay where they feed heavily in preparation for their long flight to the Gulf of Mexico. The autumn migration from the breeding grounds is along the east side of Hudson's Bay and from James Bay south. Phillips and Lincoln (57 *g.r.*) say that the flight south from James Bay is practically nonstop, although occasionally flocks may stop on the sand bars of the Mississippi River in the vicinity of Memphis. This long flight and the remote and inaccessible breeding grounds have much to do with the abundance and stability of numbers of this species.

The spring migration north is a leisurely one and follows a different flight lane from the route south. The geese fly north up the valleys of the Missouri and Red Rivers to Manitoba (32), where, Hochbaum believes (31 *g.r.*), they arrive at Delta in early April. From here they move east and north toward James Bay and hence north to the breeding grounds. The extent of the flight north is 3,000 miles, 600 miles farther than the one south (41 *g.r.*).

Courtship and Breeding. So remote are the breeding grounds of the blue geese that little can be said of their breeding habits. As with the other geese, the male stands on guard to defend his mate. The nests are made of finely shredded moss and grass, lined with dead grass and down. The outside structures of the nests are large and bulky, but the inside diameters are small. The eggs are white or pale creamy white, and the shell is thick and granular. The number of eggs varies from 3 to 5. Incubation takes from 23 to 25 days and, according to Soper (30), the male takes turns at incubating. Manning, however, states he found no evidence that males ever assist in the incubation process (22, 23).

The eggs hatch late in the season because of the lateness of arrival of the geese on the breeding grounds. This arrival is about the first of June and the eggs hatch about the middle of July. The days are long and apparently juvenile food is plentiful. The young are precocious, being able to leave the nest shortly after hatching, and are able to fly in about a month. They are full-grown and ready for the migration flight by September.

Habitat. The habitats of the blue goose have been described under lesser snow geese so will not be repeated here.

American White-fronted Goose *Anser albifrons frontalis*
Tule Goose *Anser albifrons gambelli*

The white-fronted goose is often called the "laughing goose," or "grey wavey." The word "wavey" comes from the Indian word "wa-wa" which means wild goose. "Specklebelly" is also often applied to the white goose. The tule goose is the larger of the two and is more restricted in its ecological relations. Both the breeding and wintering areas of the latter are very restricted. The flesh of the white-fronted is very well flavored and no doubt furnishes a choice morsel to the Eskimos and Indians on the arctic and Greenland shores. Gunners also like the flavor and seek them whenever available.

Description. Compared to the common Canada goose, the white-fronted is small, weighing about 5 pounds. The tule goose is larger than the white-fronted by a pound or two. Average weights of the two are given below (41 *g.r.*).

Species	Male	Female
American white-fronted goose..........	5 lb. 5 oz.	4 lb. 13 oz.
Tule goose..........................	6 lb. 11 oz.	5 lb. 10 oz.

The appearance of the male and female geese is alike. The head is brownish gray with a white band around the face in front of the eyes. This is the most conspicuous identifying mark except perhaps the dark bars on the belly and chest. The general appearance of the head, neck, and body is grayish brown with the exception of the wing primaries and secondaries, which are darker brown or black. The primary coverts are gray. The breast, belly, and flanks have a ground color of white with dark splashes or bars of very dark brown or black. The bill is orange or yellow with some blue at the base, and the feet are deep yellow or orange.

The tule goose is marked like the white-fronted but may be slightly darker.

Distribution. The distribution of the white-fronted goose is broad but, except for stragglers, does not include the eastern part of the continent. The breeding grounds include the Arctic Coast of North America from the vicinity of Victoria Island to Kuskokwim Bay. Breeding in Alaska includes all the territory north of and including the Yukon River basin.

Wintering grounds include inland valleys in Washington, Oregon, and California from the vicinity of Tacoma, Washington, to the Salten Sea in southern California, a large area of western Mexico and the Gulf of Mexico Coast from the delta of the Mississippi River to the mouth of the Rio Grande.

The tule goose has a very limited area for both breeding and wintering. The breeding grounds are on islands on the shore of an unnamed lake east of the first tributary of the Perry River. It nests only a few miles distant from the nesting tule geese, but apparently the two subspecies keep strictly apart. The wintering grounds of the tule are in Central California in the valley along the Sacramento and San Joaquin Rivers.

Movements. The migrations of white-fronted geese are characterized by their noisy clatter and the great height at which they fly. Flocks fly in V formations with an old gander in the lead.

White-fronted geese are early migrants in the fall, arriving in the central Canadian provinces and the northern Pacific states during September. Some apparently linger on the breeding ground until later, however, and do not leave the northern Canadian provinces and Alaska until October and the first of November (13 *g.r.*).

Migrations toward the breeding grounds begin early, depending on the location of the wintering grounds. Nelson found the birds nesting in the Yukon valley in Alaska as early as May 27.

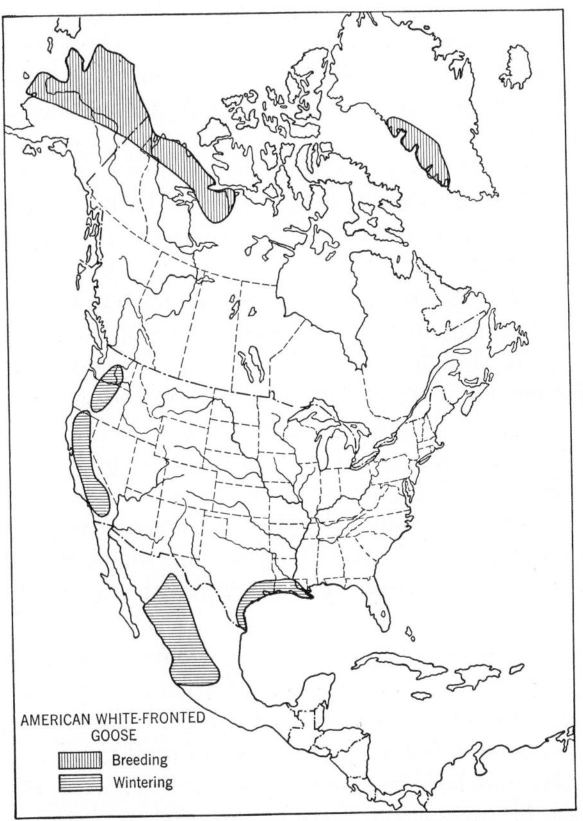

Fig. 19-14. Ranges of American white-fronted goose (41 *g.r.*).

The flight lanes of the white-fronted geese are not well described, but must be complex because of the broad extent of both the nesting and wintering territory. Some follow the north-and-south route along the Mississippi and Central Plains flyway while others cross from the Central flyway across the mountains to the West Coast. Others follow the Pacific flyway from Alaska to California and western Mexico.

The migration route of the tule goose can only be given by joining the nesting and wintering grounds. This implies a long flight which is as much east-west as it is north-south. It covers the crossing of arctic tundra, vast prairies, two ranges of mountains, and the great dry basin of the west.

Courtship and Breeding. As far as is known, the courtships of all geese follow a similar pattern. The pairs spread out to suitable nesting sites as soon as they reach the breeding grounds. Because of the far northern localities they may be delayed until ice and snow melt away, but this occurs rapidly in the latter part of May and early June. The nesting sites are along the edges of lakes or rivers. A depression is scooped out of the sand and dead vegetation is gathered around to make a nest. Down and feathers are added as the number of eggs in the clutch increases.

The size of the clutch varies from 4 to 7, but 5 or 6 is normal. The eggs are light buff or pinkish white. The incubation period is 28 days, and the male stands by to protect the incubating female, the eggs, and young (41 *g.r.*).

The nonbreeding birds and, during the summer, the molting males gather along the lakes to feed on berries and wait for the development of flight feathers. Indians and Eskimos use the eggs and capture the birds during the flightless period. The flesh of the white-fronted goose always seems to be well flavored and delicate.

Habitat. The breeding ground of the white-fronted and tule goose is the tundra. Here the seasons are short and ice is never very far below the surface. Mud is deposited by the rivers, and the ponds and lakes have springy grass-covered shores. Grasses and sedges with a few tundra willows are the predominating plants. Where the water is acid, mosses and lichens develop.

The winter habitat has great variety. Domesticated grains, grasses, and legumes add to the plants available for white-fronted and tule geese in winter and spring. Nuts and berries are available in the fall, and corn, rice, sorghum, and grasses are all found on their wintering grounds.

The habitats and behavior of the tule goose differ from those of the white-fronted in several respects. Moffit (26) says the tule goose is found only along the heavily wooded banks of the larger sloughs of Butte and Sutter Counties in California where the birds remain during the day, feeding in the small ponds in the tule beds of the surrounding marshes while the closely related white-fronted geese are foraging on the nearby grain-stubble fields.

Emperor Goose *Philacte canagica*

The emperor goose is one of the highly specialized birds of Alaska. It is used by the natives for food, being captured formerly by the use of nets during the flightless period. Ordinarily it is not seen south of the Alaskan peninsula and Aleutian Islands, but sometimes individuals stray south to British Columbia, Oregon, and California. While this is one of the most handsome of the geese, its flesh is not palatable.

Description. The emperor goose is a medium-sized bird with ashy-gray body and feathers barred with black and white. The throat and foreneck are black, while the head and rear portion of the neck are white. The white of the head and neck is likely to be sprinkled with rusty-colored feathers. This is intensified on the face and sides of the head. The tail is also white, the bill flesh-colored, and the feet yellow.

The average weights of male and female geese are given by Kortright (41 *g.r.*) as follows:

Males............	6 lb. 2 oz.
Females..........	6 lb. 4 oz.

Distribution. The distribution of the emperor goose is limited to Alaska with possibly a few scattered individuals found in winter along the Pacific Coast. The breeding range extends along the Alaskan coast from Kotzebue Sound on the Bering Strait to Bristol Bay. The wintering grounds are the Alaskan peninsula and the Aleutian Islands. It is said that the numbers of emperor geese are much reduced from formerly. In a study of the goose nesting area between the Yukon and the Kuskokwim River deltas, emperor geese constituted 10 per cent of the waterfowl population. The nesting area of the emperor, as well as that of cacklers, white-fronteds, and eiders, extends inland 12 to 15 miles from the coast (31).

The emperor goose is a marine species and finds suitable habitat along the inlets and islands of the Alaskan peninsula and the Aleutian chain of islands. The food of the species is probably aquatic as indicated by a strong flavor of fish oil in the flesh.

Movements. The distance between the wintering and breeding grounds for this species is so short that it is doubtful if the migration is anything more than a gradual shifting from one area to the other. The shift to the Aleutian Islands is more east-west than north-south but is a change from frozen to open water. As the emperor is a hardy bird, it no doubt has no fear of strong winds and rough water.

Courtship and Breeding. The emperor gander is a vigorous individual, and this vigor is reflected in the active protection of its mate and the fighting off of rivals. The nests are started in late May or early June near the water and frequently among the driftwood on the tidal beaches. At the beginning of the egg-laying season the nests are poorly made, but as more eggs are laid, more vegetation is added, and finally down from the female's breast is used for lining.

The number of eggs in a clutch numbers 3 to 8, with 5 or 6 being average. The color is creamy white and texture granular rather than smooth and shiny. The incubation period is 24 days, and the eggs hatch in late June and early July. By October the young look much like the adults. Apparently the molt of the young is continuous through the first and second summers and intervening winter (13 *g.r.*).

FIG. 19-15. Ranges of emperor and tule geese (41 *g.r.*).

Habitat. The nesting and summer habitat of the emperor goose is not so marine as that of the brant and cackling geese. Most of the lands on the nesting grounds are deltas and have been built of soil deposited at the mouths of large rivers. The land is low grass-covered flats dissected by numerous tidal streams and interspersed with thousands of small ponds. The border between the tidal fringes and the tundra supplies the sites for the summering flocks of nonbreeding birds and the nesting places for the breeding geese.

The wintering grounds consist of the rocky islands and sheltered bays of the long coast line from Alaska west to the international date line.

BARNACLE GOOSE *Branta leucopsis*

The barnacle goose is an old-world species that occasionally is seen along the eastern shores of North America. It is a handsome black-and-white goose with a white head, except a line from the bill to the eyes and a narrow cap of black which extends from the neck in a narrow pattern over the back of the head. The neck, throat, and breast are black as is the tail. The body is white; the wings, gray, white, and black; the bill and feet, black. No weights of barnacle geese are available.

The nest locations are found far north on the eastern shores of Greenland and the island of Spitsbergen. Unlike other waterfowl, these birds choose nest sites on cliffs along the sea or along high ridges.

The clutch consists of 3 to 6 pure-white eggs and the male, as is true with other geese, protects the nest.

The barnacle goose appears to be much more terrestrial than most of the other geese and prefers to feed on vegetation away from the shore. Kortright (41 *g.r.*) quotes Witherby as saying this goose is not so shy as other wild geese and tends to keep to itself rather than mingle with other species of geese.

REFERENCES

1. Aldrich, John W. 1946. Speciation in the white-cheeked geese. *Wilson Bul.* **58**(2):94–103.
2. Anonymous. 1949. Yellowstone swan census shows substantial gain. *Sci. News Letter.* **56**(9):140.
3. ———. 1950. Trumpeter swans prefer Canada, Alaska to U.S. *Sci. News Letter.* **58**(13):201.
4. Bizeau, Elwood G., and Paul E. Steel. 1950. Waterfowl production on Gray's Lake, Idaho, 1950. Waterfowl populations and breeding conditions, summer 1950. *U.S. Fish and Wildlife Serv., Spec. Sci. Rpt.: Wildlife* 8.
5. Cottam, Clarence, John J. Lynch, and Arnold L. Nelson. 1944. Food habits and management of sea brant. *Jour. Wildlife Mangt.* 8(1):36–56.
6. Craighead, Frank C., and John J. Craighead. 1949. Nesting Canada geese on the upper Snake River. *Jour. Wildlife Mangt.* **13**(1):51–64.
7. Dambach, Charles A. 1944. Trumpeter swan. *Wilson Bul.* **56**(4):220.
8. East, Ben. 1950. Canada goose can be brought back. *Outdoor Life.* **105**(2):38–40.
9. Elder, William H. 1946. Implications of a goose concentration. *Trans. 11th North Amer. Wildlife Conf.* Pp. 441–446.
10. ——— and Nina L. Elder. 1949. The role of the family in the formation of goose flocks. *Wilson Bul.* **61**(3):133–140.
11. Fremont, Charles. 1942. Reports on game conditions in the Canadian provinces: Quebec. *Trans. 7th North Amer. Game Conference.* Pp. 14–15.
12. Glazner, W. C. 1946. Food habits of wild geese on the Gulf Coast of Texas. *Jour. Wildlife Mangt.* **10**(4):322–329.
13. Hanson, Harold C. 1949. Trapping and handling Canada geese. *Ill. Nat. Hist. Survey, Bul.* **556**.
14. ——— and Robert H. Smith. 1950. Canada geese of the Mississippi flyway with special reference to an Illinois flock. *Ill. Nat. Hist. Survey Bul.* **25**(3):67–210.
15. Hewitt, Oliver H. 1950. Recent studies of blue and lesser snow goose

populations in James Bay. *Trans.* 15*th North Amer. Wildlife Conf.* Pp. 304–308.

16. Hochbaum, H. Albert. 1946. Recovery potentials in North American waterfowl. *Trans.* 11*th North Amer. Wildlife Conf.* Pp. 403–418.
17. Hole, A. 1933. Migration of swans. *Canad. Field Nat.* **47**(8):158–159.
18. Howard, William Johnson. 1940. Wintering of the greater snow goose. *Auk.* **57**(4):523–531.
19. Jeffrey, Robert. 1950. Snow goose flocks of the Skagit flats. *Game Bul.* 2(3):3.
20. Kossack, Charles W. 1950. Breeding habits of Canada geese under refuge conditions. *Amer. Midland Nat.* **43**(3):627–649.
21. Lewis, Harrison F. 1946. Management of Canada's wildlife resources. *Trans.* 11*th North Amer. Wildlife Conf.* Pp. 11–17.
22. Lincoln, Fredrick C. 1950. American brant—living bird or museum piece? *Audubon Mag.* **52**(5):282–287.
23. Manning, T. H. 1942. Blue and lesser snow geese on Southampton and Baffin Islands. *Auk.* **59**(2):158–175.
24. Marler, George. 1948. Is the trumpeter swan to remain a refuge bird? *Natl. Parks Mag.* **22**(95):22–25.
25. Mayr, Ernst. 1942. Systematics and the origin of species, Columbia University Press, New York.
26. Moffit, James. 1926. Notes on white-fronted tule geese in Central California. *Condor.* **28**(5):241–243.
27. Pirnie, Miles David. 1938. Restocking of Canada goose successful in southern Michigan. *Trans.* 3*d North Amer. Wildlife Conf.* Pp. 624–627.
28. Sharritt, Grace V. 1949. Our swans trumpet good news. *Nature Mag.* **42**(7):316–318, 340.
29. Sheppard, R. W. 1949. American brant on the lower Great Lakes. *Canad. Field Nat.* **63**(3):99–100.
30. Soper, John Dewey, 1930. The blue goose. *Canada Dept. Int. North West Territories Bul.*
31. Spencer, David L., Urban C. Nelson and Winston A. Elkins. 1951. America's greatest goose-brant nesting area. *Trans.* 16*th North Amer. Wildlife Conf.* Pp. 290–295.
32. Stiles, Bruce F. 1948. The blue goose: is it changing its migration through Iowa? *Iowa Bird Life.* **18**(1):9–13.
33. Sutton, A. M. 1931. The blue goose and lesser snow goose on Southampton Island. *Auk.* **48**(3):335–364.
34. Swanson, Gustav. 1944. Canada goose hunting at Horseshoe Lake. *Wilson Bul.* **56**(4):220.
35. Todd, W. E. Clyde. 1938. A new eastern race of the Canada goose. *Auk.* **55**(4):661–662.
36. Wetmore, Alexander, and Committee. 1945. Twentieth supplement to the American Ornithologist's Union checklist of North American birds. *Auk.* **62**(3):436–439.
37. Williams, Cecil S., and William H. Marshall. 1937. Goose nesting studies on Bear River Migratory Waterfowl Refuge. *Jour. Wildlife Mangt.* **1**(3–4):77–86.
38. ———. 1938. Survival of Canada goose goslings, Bear River Refuge, Utah, 1937. *Jour. Wildlife Mangt.* **2**(1):17–19.

SECTION FOUR

Fish

CHAPTER 20

Fresh-water Game Fish (Cold Water)

For the reader who is interested only in fish, it may be well to review the reason for the fish being placed last of the three groups: fur bearers, waterfowl, and fish. All of the animals involved are more or less aquatic in their habitat selection. Certainly the fur bearers are more dependent on dry land than are waterfowl and waterfowl are more dependent than are fish. All, including fish, are dependent on the fertility that comes from the soil and the anchorage which soil gives to plants through which the elements are changed to compounds suitable for nutrition. In addition, fish are partially dependent on plants for oxygen which may come from the plant processes and also as the home for insects and for escape cover for the young.

The discussion will include only the sport fisheries. A section on management of trout and salmon waters by Dr. Clarence M. Tarzwell will be followed by brief life-history and ecological sketches of eastern brook or speckled trout, rainbow, brown, and lake trout, chinook (king), Atlantic and sebago salmon, and smelt. The chapter on the management of warm-water fish is written by Dr. R. W. Eschmeyer, followed by life-history sketches of smallmouth black bass, largemouth black bass, pike, chain pickerel, muskellunge, yellow pike-perch, yellow perch, white perch, bluegills, sunfish, brown bullheads and crappies. A section on farm fish ponds by Dr. Louis A. Krumholz is included.

THE MANAGEMENT OF STREAMS FOR FISHING[1]

INTRODUCTION

Our tens of thousands of miles of streams, both large and small, are among our greatest natural resources. The recreational uses of streams rank high among the various stream values. Because of the pressures and strains of modern living the aesthetic and sport value of streams are of considerable public-health importance. Each year millions seek out clear, pure streams where they can picnic, fish, or just relax and enjoy the

[1] This section is contributed by Clarence M. Tarzwell.

beauty and soothing qualities of a flowing stream. Each year our 26 million licensed sportsmen enjoy many hours of sport and relaxation on small streams and rivers and in addition take several million pounds of fish. In many states recreation ranks near the top among their industries. In Michigan, the recreational industry ranks second after the great automobile industry. Commercial fishing in our streams provides a valuable supply of high protein food. The latest available catch records show a total take from the Mississippi River and its tributaries of 82,382,000 pounds of fishery products. Of this total, 37,255,000 pounds was mussel shells. In 1946, the total catch of stream and anadromus fishes, according to *Statistical Digest* 19, of the U.S. Fish and Wildlife Service, was about 551 million pounds, and valued at $37,444,000. Exclusive of the salmon, the catch was about 73,181,000 pounds, valued at $5,540,000. The value of our streams for sport fishing is many times the value of commercial fishing. It is estimated that sport fishes cost the fisherman $1 to $2 a pound when all costs are considered. Estimates of the amount spent annually for sport fishing vary from 100 to 200 times the value of the commercial catch of resident stream fishes. When the values of streams for recreation, sport, food, irrigation, power, and domestic and industrial water supplies are considered, the need for their preservation and improvement is quite evident. In the development of the country, however, a short-sighted policy has often been followed to the detriment of our streams. Since colonial times there have been great changes in ground cover and land use. The advance of civilization has brought about deforestation, drainage, and extensive and widespread agricultural use. These activities have changed the character of watersheds and environmental conditions in streams. Many of these changes have been unfavorable for fish life.

DESTRUCTION OF STREAM VALUES

The fauna which the white men found in the streams of America was the product of a long development. With the exception of the great plains a large portion of this fauna arose under forested conditions and was adapted to streams whose watersheds and banks were forested. Under those conditions floods, erosion, silting, and turbidity were at a minimum while shade, cover, pools, and spring flow were at a maximum. Swamps and marshes were common and extensive, especially in glaciated areas, and they played an important role in the ecology of the streams. In the north central states much of what is now the richest farm land was once forested swamps. About one-fourth of the state of Michigan was originally sold as swamp land.

The introduction of European civilization in the early 1600's initiated a series of changes which had by the beginning of the present century drastically changed environmental conditions in most watersheds, eliminated many streams, caused many others to become intermittent, and greatly changed conditions in the remainder.

Studies by the writer of the past and present state of different types of streams in various parts of the country have indicated that during the past 80 years man has been the chief factor in stream changes. Since the settlement of the country, several practices common to our way of life have increasingly wrought drastic and disastrous changes throughout the watersheds and in the streams. Deforestation, fire, overgrazing, drainage, poor agricultural methods, mining, irrigation, pollution, road building, construction and operation of dams, lumber drives, and stream clearances are the outstanding activities which have destroyed our streams or made conditions less favorable for fishes. The testimony of old residents has disclosed almost unbelievable changes in the character of watersheds, the stream banks, the stream bottoms, the character of the flow, and the temperature and content of the water. Streams which are now dry for part or nearly all the year, or which now carry most of their muddy waters in the spring and after heavy summer rains, were once permanent, clear streams. Many streams which are now wide, flat, and devoid of pools were once narrow with an abundance of pools and cover.

Among the various destructive forces, floods and their accompanying erosion are the most damaging to the fish habitat. Floods wash out or silt up spawning beds and destroy the fry; roll and grind the bottom materials, destroying food organisms or flushing them completely out of the stream. They wash away or cover rich, food-producing areas with unproductive materials; fill pools and destroy cover; erode the banks and widen the streams; destroy plant beds; and generally reduce fertility by washing away organic materials and mucky deposits. Outstanding causes of increased and destructive floods are deforestation, fire, unwise farming methods, overgrazing, and excessive drainage. The effects of these activities on stream habitats will be briefly discussed.

Deforestation. Lumbering, lumbering practices, fire, and the clearing of the land for agriculture are outstanding and widespread causes of altered stream environment. The effects of deforestation have been described by many investigators. Zon (42) pointed out that seepage is greater in forested areas, and more underground water is made available for spring flow in such areas than in cleared areas. This is evidenced by the fact that in all except sandy regions springs dry up when the forests are removed. Under forested conditions, the layer of humus on the forest floor acts as a huge sponge absorbing up to ten times its weight of water, which it feeds gradually to the soil beneath so that percolation is maintained at a maximum and runoff at a minimum. This high rate of percolation insures sustained spring flows which are essential for trout streams. Further, the forests break the force of the rain, retard the melting of snow, and maintain low ground temperatures. The effects of deforestation manifest themselves throughout the seasons. When the trees were removed, slash fires which generally followed lumbering operations destroyed the humus layer and exposed the mineral soil. Rains then beat directly on the soil, muddying it and filling the soil pores so that surface runoff was greatly increased and seepage decreased. Because the

Fig. 20-1. Floods have converted this stream into a gravel and rubble wash. Pools and cover have been destroyed. (*C. M. Tarzwell.*)

humus and forest litter were no longer present to check the velocity of the increased surface runoff, severe floods resulted. The accompanying decrease in seepage brought about the failure of springs or the reduction of spring flow so that the water flow of streams was greatly reduced or eliminated and the streams made less desirable for game fishes.

In trout areas the increased runoff of warm surface water coupled with the decrease of cold spring flow caused streams to become much warmer. Temperature conditions were made even more unpropitious by the removal of streamside shade which allowed the direct rays of the sun to reach the water and the stream bottom. The combination of these factors following deforestation so warmed the water of many fine streams that they no longer supported trout.

Further, floods with their accompanying turbidity, erosion, and silting limited the production of fish foods, covered rich, gravel-rubble, riffle areas with unproductive materials, filled pools, destroyed cover, eroded banks, widened streams, and produced barren flats. In addition to bringing about the deposition of large amounts of unproductive materials in the streams, forest removal also destroys the source of most of the organic matter which enriches the streams, namely, leaves, twigs, bits of bark, and forest duff and humus from the forest floor. Silt of a high organic content is essential for productivity of bottom organisms. Light-colored inorganic silt present in streams in eroded areas is unproductive. In summary, therefore, in contrasting conditions in forested and cleared areas it is evident that forest cover equalizes flow, keeps the streams cool, holds and protects the banks, enriches the stream and furnishes the source of cover and fertilizing materials; its removal increases surface runoff and floods, decreases seepage, the flow of springs and low water flow, warms the water, decreases fertility, brings about the widening of streams and the destruction of pools, shelter, and food-producing areas, and thus makes conditions untenable for game fishes and more favorable for their competitors, the excessive numbers of which limit the game fish yield. The clean cutting of the forests and fires brought about drastic changes in environmental conditions on the watershed which caused unfavorable conditions for fish in streams. Certain lumbering practices, however, were directly harmful to the habitat of stream fish.

Many streams in the Great Lakes region were cleared of all wing jams and other obstructions in preparation for the driving of logs. The lumber drives themselves were very harmful. Old river drivers state that sometimes log jams half a mile or more in length were formed, which were so tight that the stream ran almost dry before them, and the logs were pushed along by the force of the floodwaters behind the jam, gouging the stream bed and eroding the banks. The action of these jams coupled with the intermittent flooding for the timber drives, widened the streams and deposited thick blankets of unproductive sand over productive gravel bottoms. Dams built to store water for the drives eliminated streamside shade, warmed the streams, prevented fish migration, and caused sand to be deposited over extensive areas. Many Michigan streams which have been used for the driving of logs have wide sandy sections which were created by the drives. Evidence that the sand was deposited by lumbering operations is furnished by the hundreds of saw logs buried in the sand and lying directly on the former gravel bottoms. Many miles of Michigan trout streams have had their pools, shelters, and riffles ruined or rendered less productive for trout by the lumber drives. Streams which have not been driven have a great deal of natural cover, whereas streams which have been driven are wide, shallow, and have eroding sand banks which each year add immense quantities of barren sand to the stream.

Ill-advised Agricultural Practices. While clean-cut lumbering and fire have greatly changed primitive conditions in streams, clearing for agriculture and ill-advised agricultural practices have produced even more drastic and widespread changes. The cultivation of slopes, the extensive growing of row crops, clean cultivation, and excessive drainage have greatly increased surface runoff and soil erosion. The effects of the extensive drainage of areas for agricultural use and the excessive drainage of crop lands are slow-acting and not readily apparent to many. However, the removal of a large portion of the annual precipitation by surface drainage has so decreased deep seepage that in many sections of the country the water table has been lowered below the stream bottom and the streams have become intermittent and now are only open ditches carrying floodwaters after rains. The destruction of permanent streams has been especially marked in areas of clay soil. For example, the streams of southern Michigan which were originally suitable for trout are now intermittent or are capable of supporting only warm-water fish. In the northern sandy areas of Michigan there is little or no runoff even after the removal of ground cover and seepage has maintained spring flow. When streamside shade is sufficient to prevent excessive warming, streams have continued to maintain trout. Outside of the sandy glaciated areas, however, agricultural use has drastically reduced the number of streams suitable for sport fish. In the southeastern section of the country annual burning was practiced for many years, and the soil became practically devoid of humus. Extensive row cropping was also practiced year after year, and soil erosion and floods became progressively worse until recent years brought the adoption of better agricultural practices. Erosion of the red-clay soils of this area produced a turbidity which was very persistent. This turbidity coupled with floods and silting has destroyed or greatly reduced fishing values in many southern streams. During floods the streams are swept clear of sediments, while during periods of more normal flow a deposit of fine silt forms over the bottom. This silt deposit could be productive of chironomids, but it is usually swept away by high water before organisms can become well established. The result of this is that the production of bottom food organisms is poor because bottom types change so rapidly no extensive fauna can develop.

Overgrazing. In the mountainous areas of the west and the intermountain region many streams have been saved from destruction by the creation of national forests in their headwaters. However, outside the national forests land-use practices which are destructive of stream values have been widely practiced. Among these various practices overgrazing has been outstanding in the destruction of stream conditions essential for good game-fish production.

The destruction of ground cover through overgrazing brings about most of the detrimental effects caused by deforestation. Several workers (4, 11, 13, 25) have shown how the reduction of the vegetative cover by overgrazing increases surface runoff and leads to floods and erosion. In the west, where overgrazing has been severe and widespread, it has been responsible for the erosion of stream beds and banks, the destruction or deepening of stream channels, the filling of stream beds with thick deposits of sand and gravel, and the complete disappearance of many streams during the dry season.

Grazing in stream bottoms is especially harmful as the cattle tend to congregate along the stream, destroying streamside shrubs and trees and ruining the stream banks by trampling. Under these circumstances the stream banks are very susceptible to erosion by floods, and the stream is widened by bank erosion. The removal of streamside shade exposes the water to the direct rays of the sun, while the destruction of the banks and widening of the stream by floods make the water shallow and so warm it is more favorable for minnows and coarse fish than it is for trout. In many sections of the country, floods have eroded the banks to such an extent that all pools and cover have been ruined; and the greatly reduced stream, due to the decrease in spring flow through increased surface runoff, flows in a thin sheet under and around the boulders, stones, and gravel of the canyon bottom, or meanders as a braided stream over the wide, flat bottom of the gully, often entirely disappearing here and there under the sand and gravel deposited by floods. Although prominent in the west, this type of damage is not confined to that section alone, as many eastern streams have been damaged or despoiled by clearing of the stream bottoms for agricultural use and by the trampling of cattle. The clearing of stream banks in order to provide more crop land often actually results in less land for agricultural purposes. When the protective strips of trees are removed, floodwaters from crop lands often so widen the stream that much of the rich bottomland is removed. The runoff from crop land is usually so muddy it is harmful to fish life and many shifting mud or silt bars are formed. Muddy water hinders feeding of many game species and limits food production by cutting off light and smothering food-producing areas.

Pollution. Pollutants are usually classified according to their origin as domestic sewage and industrial wastes. From the biological standpoint it is desirable that pollutants be classified according to their effects on the receiving streams and their aquatic populations. From a functional standpoint all pollutants may be roughly classified into three groups: (1) inert inorganic materials, (2) putrescible or oxygen-depleting wastes, (3) toxic wastes. The first group includes material such as silt, sand, gravel, clay, mine washings, wastes from hydraulic and placer mining operations, and wastes from ore refineries and other manufacturing processes. These wastes when added to streams fill pools, cover rich food-producing areas with barren materials, increase turbidity and decrease productivity, destroy cover and plant beds, and in extreme instances completely fill the channel and obliterate flow or convert the stream into a shallow meandering sheet of water largely devoid of fish and insect life. Among pollutants of this type, materials from sheet, gully, and bank erosion are of outstanding importance. Although other types of wastes are of major importance in some areas, when the whole country is considered, the products of erosion are, perhaps, our most damaging pollutant. Under our present system of land use, only streams in sandy or forested areas are reasonably free of turbidity and materials from land erosion.

Putrescible wastes exert a variety of effects on a receiving stream, chief of which is the depletion of dissolved oxygen by the bacteria which break them down into simpler compounds. When oxygen is depleted the anaerobic decomposition of these wastes may yield toxic materials such as hydrogen sulphide, methane, or ammonia. Putrescible wastes are added to our streams from a variety of sources and in various forms such as domestic sewage and wastes from canneries, tanneries, sugar refineries, starch factories, milk and cheese plants, slaughter houses, breweries and distilleries, paper mills, etc.

When large amounts of organic materials are added to a stream, septic zones often develop which are devoid of fish life. Organic wastes, however, are subject to natural purification in the stream. In this purification process four pollutional or life zones are usually recognized. These are the zone of recent pollution or degradation in which the organic content is high but the bacteria have not yet had time to deplete the oxygen; the septic zone in which bacterial activity has used up all or most of the dissolved oxygen; the recovery zone where bacterial action is diminishing and algae are adding oxygen through photosynthesis; and the clean-water zone where conditions have improved to the extent that a normal fish population can exist.

The third group of pollutants are toxic wastes which are directly poisonous or indirectly lethal to fish. Many of these are not purified by biological processes and can be rendered safe for fish life only by dilution. This group of wastes contain the metallic ions such as lead, zinc, copper, mercury, silver, beryllium, etc., acids and alkalies, and poisonous organic materials as cyanide and the phenols.

Until fairly recent years the severe pollution of streams was largely localized in certain eastern areas. Pollution with putrescible wastes has been widespread for some time but in general the most severe and earliest pollution occurred along the eastern seaboard. Pollution, with attendant oxygen blocks and dams, has been largely responsible for the destruction or decimation of the runs of anadromous fish in the east-coast streams. Formerly there were large runs of shad up these streams. The shad fishery of the Delaware River was worth $125,000 in the early 1800's but by 1880, it had dropped to $80,000 in spite of an increase in price. In the early period of exploitation shad sold for as low as $1.50 to $2 for a hundred fish. At one time the shad fishery exceeded 50 million pounds annually. Although overfishing was undoubtedly a factor in the depletion of the shad and alewives, pollution and dams were outstanding causes.

Salmon were once very abundant in the Connecticut River, but a dam was erected in 1798 which destroyed their spawning migration. Pollution and changed environmental conditions completed the destruction in other areas. At one time the Atlantic salmon ran many of the streams as far south as the Delaware River but they are now largely confined to one or two rivers in Maine. Pollution has not been confined to the lower portions of the eastern streams. Many are polluted throughout extensive portions of their length; nor is severe pollution limited to the eastern seaboard. Steel mills, metal finishing plants, and foundries often severely pollute streams with toxic wastes. Coal-mine drainage in Pennsylvania, West Virginia, and other areas has made many streams barren. Oil wastes and salt water have polluted many streams of the southwest while pulp mills have seriously affected streams in all parts of the country. Pollution has made many streams unfavorable for fish life and has greatly reduced the productive capacity of many others.

Dams. Multiple-purpose dams are generally beneficial to fish when they are located on streams which do not support migratory or anadromous species. High dams placed on streams supporting large runs of anadromous species have generally destroyed or seriously reduced those runs. The Pacific salmon has been largely eliminated in California, and its runs have been seriously reduced in many rivers farther north.

Power dams are often harmful to the trout population through limiting spawning migrations. Often the dams are operated intermittently so that there are great fluctuations in stream flow below the dam. When this occurs, large portions of the stream bottom contribute nothing toward fish production as they are alternately covered and uncovered. Eggs laid during high water are exposed and killed during the low-water periods and often the water is entirely shut off after a large flow and fish are stranded among the bushes and in holes on the flood plain.

Other Detrimental Activities. A number of other activities have adversely affected fish production. Many fish enter unscreened irrigation ditches and are eventually destroyed in the fields. The fishing values in some streams are destroyed through the complete removal of water for irrigation or the dredging and straightening of the stream channel. In mountainous areas many streams are damaged by road-building activities. Often roads are built straight up canyon bottoms without regard to the stream, or the protection of cuts from erosion, the preservation of streamside shade, or the handling of drainage from the right of way. Widespread drainage projects have greatly affected habitat conditions for fish. The drainage of swamps, marshes, potholes, and ponds has decreased seepage, lowered water tables, increased the speed of runoff and maximum flows, and decreased spring flow and low-water flows. Excessive drainage on agricultural lands has increased surface runoff and erosion, lowered the water table, and changed once permanent streams into ditches which carry only muddy floodwaters during periods of extensive precipitation.

Beavers. Stream conditions unfavorable for trout are not all due to man's activities. The activities of beaver have altered the physical, chemical, and biological balance of many streams. Spawning migrations have been limited or prevented, or the temperature and chemical conditions of the stream so altered that spawning is unsuccessful. Spawning areas are destroyed, and winter temperatures of the water lowered so they are not favorable for the development of the eggs. Large beaver ponds on small trout streams produce unfavorable chemical conditions through the collection of large amounts of organic material (27). By spreading the water over considerable areas, beaver dams have killed much timber valuable for shade and for holding the banks of the stream. When beavers become numerous on small feeders, their dams are often placed so close together that the entire stream is impounded. In such streams the water temperature often becomes too high for trout, and the entire flow is at times consumed by increased evaporation and seepage so that the stream disappears. On a small feeder one dam may raise the temperature as much as 16°F. When these dams remain in place for considerable periods, a series of marshy terraces or beaver meadows is formed and the stream vanishes. On larger streams, beaver activities usually result in the deposition of great quantities of dark, mucky material and the destruction of the banks and streamside shade trees. After extensive beaver occupation many fine, narrow, well-shaded, gravel-bottomed streams are converted into wide, shallow, open streams having a soft, unproductive bottom with little or no cover and no valuable pools or riffles. In Michigan, streams which have had extensive beaver occupancy are usually widened, are deepest in the center and shallow at the sides, and have sand bottoms and environmental conditions that are usually more favorable for bullheads, minnows and suckers. These fish usually become dominant in the stream, and the trout yield is drastically reduced. Since the streamside shade is destroyed and the streams made wider and more open, predator pressure is increased. Also the parasite index generally becomes greater in beaver ponds.

In the mountainous regions of the West, beavers are generally regarded as beneficial. Often their dams help to stabilize the flow of streams and store water which can be used for irrigation. The effects of beavers in mountainous regions are quite different from those in the lowlands of the east. Since there are many natural barriers to fish migration in mountain streams, the barriers caused by beaver dams are not so serious as in the flat streams where fish migrate considerable distances. Because most mountain streams are cold and have a steep gradient, beaver ponds are not large and so do not produce a dangerously high water temperature. As floods are frequent, injurious chemical conditions seldom occur. In this type of stream, beaver ponds furnish resting places for the large trout and often furnish refuges during periods of low water.

However, some beaver dams do have harmful effects even in the western part of the country. When an area is flooded by beavers, the vegetation is killed and a soft, silty deposit is laid down. When the dam goes out, this silty material is not resistant to the floods common to the region and the whole ponded area is eroded. The excessive cutting activities of the beaver destroy trees and shrubs required to hold the soil and extensive erosion results. The burrowing of the bank beaver is directly responsible for the widening of many streams. When beaver dams are placed in comparatively flat-bottomed canyons, the streams are eroded and widened by the water going around the end of the dam to form a new channel. This occurs constantly, as beaver dams are usually flat on top and have no flood spillways. Breaking the stream up with a number of channels in this manner is undesirable both from the standpoint of erosion control and trout production.

From the foregoing discussion it is evident that the activities of man have greatly changed environmental conditions on most watersheds. These changes have drastically reduced the mileage of streams suitable for fish and have rendered much of the remainder unproductive. While this destructive process has been going on the numbers of fishermen have been steadily increasing. It is evident, therefore, that in so far as possible damaged streams should be restored to productivity and all managed to serve the best interests of the public.

STREAM MANAGEMENT

General Considerations. The management of streams for fishing is a relatively new science, and it is still in the process of development. Ideas, methods, and procedures are changing rapidly, and much remains to be learned before stream management can be placed on a sound basis. As now understood, the objectives of stream management are to provide at reasonable cost the maximum amount of the most desirable sport and commercial fishing consistent with the productive capacity of the waters and to utilize the resource fully, but on a sustained-yield basis, for sport and commercial fishing. In general, it is conceded that sport or recreational fishing should take precedence over commercial fishing, but often each can be carried on without damaging the other, and in some instances commercial fishing may benefit the sport fishery. It is no longer possible for anglers to look upon sport fish primarily as a source of food. Their recreational value is many times greater than their food value. Management plans should be developed, therefore, to provide healthful and enjoyable sport for as great a number as possible. This obligation is not fulfilled if the crop is harvested at the beginning of the season and the later fishermen fish without success. The fish manager should endeavor to spread the fishing throughout the season.

Those who have undertaken the management of streams have undoubtedly heard stories of the good old days when the streams were teeming with huge fish and it was an everyday occurrence for a fisherman to take several dozen fish. Many of these stories may be true, but it is well for the fish manager, when judging the quality of past fishing, to make some allowance for the enthusiasm that is usually associated with piscatorial retrospection. Further, there is a tendency among fishermen to forget the days they returned empty-handed and to remember only the large fish and the unusual catches. Also, it should be remembered that in the intervening years most streams have changed greatly and they may no longer be capable of supporting such fish populations or they may have become more suitable for other species of fish. It is well to consider that it might not be good management practice to attempt to reestablish or build up populations of fish which were once abundant. In fish management, as in any other business, the impossible or unprofitable should not be attempted. Although large private clubs having great financial resources may establish and maintain, for a time, certain desired species in a stream not well-suited to them, such projects are sooner or later abandoned and nature reasserts herself. The effective manager works with and not against nature. He follows no hard and fast rules but takes all the facts into consideration and continually keeps abreast of changes, be they physical, chemical, or biological. His management plan is dynamic and is not based on sentiment. He does not manage a stream for brook trout when it is better suited for brown trout, just because he has a sentimental feeling for brook trout. He does not attempt to restore or establish trout in a stream which is better fitted for smallmouth bass. In making such decisions he is not entirely governed by physical conditions but takes into consideration established fish populations, the interactions of groups of species, and dominant species. No species can be managed separately, because the entire fish population must be considered as an organic unit and so managed. Further, the objectives of management often are different for different regions and different streams, and the objectives for private streams are not the same as those for public waters. The ideal situation for carrying out a management program is where the entire watershed can be managed as a unit.

In public waters preference should not be given to any one type of fishing. Bait fishing may be beneficial in some trout streams as it removes the large cannibalistic fish. Although large fish are desirable, a water will support more moderate-sized fish which will provide more fishing for the public. It requires much more food to produce 100 pounds of 20-inch fish than it does to produce the same weight of 10-inch fish, other conditions being equal.

In order to attain the final objectives of fish management, it is essential that aquaculture be studied and developed in a way comparable to the development of agriculture. A long-time program which will include research on all phases of the problem is needed to place aquaculture on a basis similar to agriculture. Further studies must be made on life histories, habits, habitat requirements, competitor-predator relations, parasites, and diseases. Management embraces not only production but also the proper harvesting of the crop. Correct harvesting of the crop is difficult to attain because only limited control can be exercised over the harvester, the man with the rod, and the harvestable crop is not always known.

Many of the past efforts directed toward fisheries management have been ineffective and some have been actually harmful. Management methods were put into use without determining their over-all effects. Until quite recently fisheries management has had a slow, somewhat varied, and unbalanced development. At times certain procedures have been credited with values out of all proportion to their true worth and have been carried on almost to the exclusion of other methods. Recently the tendency has been to inquire into the real value of all practices and to use only those which actually contribute to the achievement of the desired results. A brief review of the efforts and methods used in the past for the improvement of fishing will probably be helpful in judging the value of various management procedures.

Growth and Development of Fish Management. Prior to the early 1800's introductions of fish were made by the transplanting of adults or eggs. It is believed the Chinese were the first to plant eggs. The artificial propagation of trout was first undertaken in Europe. Stephan L. Jacobi fertilized trout and salmon eggs in 1741 and carried on fish culture in

Germany. Pioneer fish-cultural operations were undertaken in this country by Theodatus Garlick, who successfully carried on artificial fertilization of trout eggs in 1853. Seth Green initiated modern trout culture in his New York hatchery in 1864. During the 1870's artificial propagation and stocking of trout increased greatly in scope and popularity and spread to many sections of the country. Pond fish culture and the propagation of the *Centrarchidae* was undertaken late in the century and expanded greatly in the early portion of the present century under the leadership of Dwight Lydell.

The great upsurge in fish-cultural activities was brought about by a marked falling off of game-fish populations in the more settled portions of the country. This depletion was a gradual process that developed with the changing of environmental conditions in watersheds. As the tide of civilization moved westward lumbering, fire, drainage, grazing, agricultural use, industrial development, and pollution steadily and inexorably changed the character of watersheds and environmental conditions in streams and lakes. Although these changes were fairly slow in some areas, by the middle of the last century sport fish and particularly trout were decreasing at an alarming rate in some sections, and it became clear to many anglers that the supply of fish was not inexhaustible. The angler's apprehension over the depletion of the fish was heightened by increases in fishing pressure due to more abundant and better transportation, more leisure time, and the greater popularity of outdoor recreation and fishing. While much concern was expressed over the great increase in fishing clubs, resort hotels, and summer vacationists who penetrated even to the remote areas, little thought was given to the practices causing changed environmental conditions and their results.

Thus, in early efforts to maintain the fish supply, the chief cause of much unsatisfactory fishing, unfavorable environmental conditions, was largely ignored, and overfishing was stressed as the cause of the poorer angling. This belief tended to oversimplify the problem and led to purely artificial and arbitrary measures for the maintenance of fishing. Great stress was laid on stocking and restrictive legislative measures, but little or nothing was done to control the causes of undesirable habitats or unbalanced fish populations in the streams. Creel limits, size limits, and finally closed seasons were initiated and progressively made more restrictive as the forces of depletion and the effects of unbalanced populations continued to operate.

The last quarter of the nineteenth century was a period of reckless and random efforts to introduce foreign species (19). Exotics were planted in all types of habitats, often to the detriment of the native species or the kind of fishing it was desired to encourage (15). Between 1878 and 1886 the carp was broadcast over the country with results which are known to almost everyone. This fish has, through its destruction of plant beds, muddying of the water, and competition for food and space drastically cut game and pan fish production in many areas. The tench (*Tinca tinca*) was introduced at about the same time as the carp, but it did not thrive, and apparently little good or bad resulted from its introduction. Continued and persistent efforts were made to establish the landlocked salmon (*Salmo salar sebago*) in lakes throughout the country. No results were obtained from these efforts other than the waste of large sums of money and the depletion of the original source of supply. Efforts were also made to establish the Pacific salmon in many areas without avail.

Some very good initial results were obtained from the introduction of some species into new areas. In 1871 the shad was transported to the West Coast. They have done quite well there. The introduction of the brown trout has been quite successful in many areas, especially those in which environmental conditions have been changed and the water has become warmer. The brown trout is more resistant to high temperatures and is a better forager than the brook trout. The brown trout, however, is harder to catch, and it grows poorly in cold streams.

The introduction of new species has been most successful where they have been planted in fishless waters, as the placing of trout in the fishless, high mountain lakes. Good results have also been obtained in the stocking of new species in areas where environmental conditions were becoming less suited for the native species. The introduction of black bass, sunfish, bullheads, and catfish to the west has produced fishing in some waters.

It was these successes which created confidence in stocking as a tool for the maintenance of fishing and led to the routine propagation and stocking of native species for the preservation of fishing. During the 1870's the artificial propagation of native species increased greatly in popularity and spread so rapidly that by 1880 fish-cultural operations were being carried on in one form or another in practically every state. Rainbow trout were propagated and planted throughout the East, brook trout were introduced into western streams, and some of the black spotted trout, particularly the one from the Yellowstone region, *Salmo clarkii lewisii,* were planted throughout the intermountain region. Because these plantings were made without regard to environmental conditions in the streams or the fish population already present, they met with varying degrees of success.

Because of these intensive fish-cultural operations, many have mistakenly come to consider fish propagation and stocking as being synonymous with fish conservation or management. Hatcheries have been publicized as the solution to every depletion problem, and among certain portions of the fishing public, faith in fish culture has grown to such proportions that the continued despoliation of the environment and the fishery resources seems to cause no considerable alarm. Many anglers believe that all fisheries problems are of one type and can be solved simply by planting more fish.

In the past, little attention was given to the environments into which the fish were placed, and no effort was made to determine the fish population which was already in the water being stocked. Usually no definite stocking budgets were made prior to planting, and the number and kind of fish stocked was governed by the number and kind available. Often trout were placed in waters which were unsuited to them or which were already overstocked, and competitor-predator relations were largely ignored. Introduced fish have in many streams replaced more valuable native species or have so hybridized with them that the breeding stock has actually been reduced, and fishing made poorer rather than better. Many fishermen desired to take a great variety of species in a single water and had the mistaken idea they could add bass, perch, pike, and sunfish to a trout water and harvest an equally large crop of each. These warm-water fish were, therefore, stocked in many trout waters. They grew fairly well until they eliminated the trout. After that, owing to the cold water and the absence of food, they grew very slowly or stunted. Thus, the stocking of these fish resulted in the elimination of trout and produced no fishing in return. Many small brooks which will produce a fair crop of trout are worthless for the production of warm-water species. Although some plantings have been harmful and some have been beneficial, the great majority have been more or less neutral; the stocked fish simply did not establish themselves or produce any fishing. There have been instances where a water has received periodic heavy stockings of one species, while another unstocked native species has continually made up practically the total catch. In view of these facts it is not surprising that waste and inefficiency have characterized many restocking programs, and it is not strange that doubling and tripling the number of fish propagated and planted has failed to halt the progressive deterioration of fish populations in many streams.

Because the failures were usually attributed to too small a planting and the successes were widely advertised, the popularity of stocking steadily increased. The hatchery program was greatly expanded during the first third of the present century. Fish culture became a big business, with production facilities costing many millions. During 1936, according to Earle (8), the Federal government planted 2,749,573,970 fish, and 37 of the states planted a total of 3,280,908,534 fish. Even though the hatchery program had been carried on for many years, little or no effort was directed toward determining the effectiveness of the program. Most hatchery men and officials considered their job completed when the fish were dumped into the water. Little attention was paid to the fish after planting, and the success of the stocking program was judged by the number of fish reported as hatched and planted rather than the number later taken by the fishermen. In the 1930's, however, several workers began to investigate the value of artificial propagation and stocking. They found that the stocking of fry and fingerling trout was of little value because very few survived to reach the fishermen's creel. Shetter (29) found that returns from plantings of fingerling trout did not exceed 1.6 per cent and varied between 0.01 and 1.6 per cent. Many other workers confirmed these findings. As summarized by Schuck (28), the recovery of legal-sized trout planted in the fall varied from 1 to 4.7 per cent, while the highest survival of planted fingerlings over 1 year was 6.3 per cent. The survival of naturally spawned trout was considerably greater, the survival from fingerlings to yearlings being estimated at 52 per cent for brook trout, 18 per cent for brown trout, and 14 per cent for rainbows. Stocking just before and during the season was found to be most effective in the production of fishing. This procedure, however, is expensive and can be carried out only on a small scale.

Investigations of populations of warm-water fish revealed that many waters receiving annual plantings of pan fish were already overstocked with these species and the fish were stunted. Further, unstocked waters were found to have excessive populations. Because of their great reproductive capacity and competitor-predator relations, there is little reason for stocking most members of the family *Centrarchidae* in waters where they occur naturally.

Because the decline in fish populations was attributed to one cause, overfishing, it is only natural that restrictive legislation should have been adopted as a means of conserving the fish supply. Although seasons, creel limits, and size limits have been beneficial in many instances, especially in regard to trout, they were often of little or no value and in some situations were actually harmful. Most regulations were adopted on opinion of someone in authority; they were not based on research findings, and their over-all effects were not known. In general they were adopted for the protection of trout fishing, as the demand for this type of fishing was great and the supply was limited. Later they were extended to cover the warm-water species. Many states adopted legislative restrictions simply because other states had done so. Seasons, creel, and size limits have no value for the warm-water species when only a small portion of the crop is harvested or the fish are overpopulated and stunting. In this instance conservation would consist in increasing the take in all ways possible. Regulations cannot take the place of a suitable environment. All regulations should be kept to a minimum, and they should not be put into effect until they are shown to be beneficial.

During the second and third decades of the present century, the groundwork was laid for environmental control and improvement and a more realistic stream-management policy. The role of the forests in controlling runoff and stream flow, and the harmful effects of fire, lumbering, overgrazing, unwise land use, and their attendant, erosion on the watershed, were stressed by many workers (2, 7, 13, 26). In the 1920's some workers began to stress the importance of a correct environment for trout (5, 14). Several English investigators and gamekeepers pointed out the importance of advantageous surroundings and the value of a knowledge of the requirements of trout (1, 24). Preliminary work in environmental improvement was begun in Michigan by Dr. Jan Metzelaar in the late 20's. More intensive investigations were undertaken in the same state in 1930 (35), which had as their purpose the devising and testing of means for improving the trout habitat in streams. These studies were continued and gradually expanded (17) until 1933, when trout-stream improvement received a great impetus by being taken up as a project by the various relief agencies.

By the end of 1934, almost every state which had any trout water at all was carrying on some form of trout-stream improvement. During the next few years history repeated itself, and artificial devices placed in the stream bed were overemphasized and credited with an importance out of all proportion to their true value, as had been done with artificial propagation and restrictive legislation. Habitat improvement by the introduction of barriers became somewhat of a fad during the years 1934 to 1938. Because of this rapid increase in popularity and the urgency of relief spending, much of the work carried on during this period was done by inexperienced men who were not adequately acquainted with the environmental requirements of trout or the causes of unfavorable stream conditions. Most of the improvement efforts were confined solely to the building of dams, deflectors, and covers. Land-use practices on the watershed which had originally caused the unfavorable conditions in the streams were largely neglected or not recognized as being the cause of the decline in trout populations. Further, structures which had been devised to meet conditions in certain areas were installed in streams for which they were not suited and were used in an indiscriminate manner with little appreciation for the problems involved. Thus, the high expectations of most fishermen were not realized, and many came to the conclusion that habitat betterment was of little value. This is indeed unfortunate, because the provision and preservation of a suitable environment is essential for fish production. The maintenance or creation of a favorable environment is basic to an inland fisheries-management program. It is now realized, however, that while the physical and chemical environments are of great importance, attention must also be given to the biological environment, the species of fish and other organisms present, their relative abundance, and their influence on one another in the particular situation.

Further, it should be recognized that in the maintenance of fishing in streams no one method, whether it be regulation, artificial propagation, environmental improvement, or population control, is sufficient in itself. Fisheries management, as it is now understood, may include all these in their proper proportion plus the restraint or control of parasites, diseases, and predators, and perhaps the introduction of exotics. These phases or activities should be united into a single well-coordinated effort under efficient executive control to meet the variety of conditions in the waters under management.

Formation of Management Plans and Procedures. The objectives of stream management have been outlined. It should be realized, however, that only an approach can be made toward these goals, because there are so many interacting factors involved and these are changing so constantly that no static condition can be established. In streams, erosion, silting, floods, or drought may alter the habitat, the food supply, or the fish population at any time. It cannot be emphasized too strongly that each stream is a problem in itself and must be dealt with individually. The ends to be obtained often differ, because what may be most desirable in one locality or under one set of conditions may be of secondary importance elsewhere. The results desired in private waters are usually entirely different from those which will give greatest satisfaction in public waters. It is well to recognize also that tastes or customs in fishing vary throughout the country. An effort should be made to satisfy as many personalized tastes in fishing as possible; dry-fly, wet-fly, bait fishing, plug casting, trolling, and the old cane poles must all be considered.

The methods of utilizing or harvesting the crop are very important. Game fish can no longer be regarded merely as a source of food because their value for sport and recreation far exceeds any possible food value. Healthful and enjoyable outdoor exercise for as many anglers as possible throughout the fishing season should be the aim in fisheries management.

The activities connected with the formation and operation of a management program may be grouped under three headings: administrative, investigative, and operative. Administrative functions include the coordination of research and operational programs, the interpretation and presentation of research findings to the general public, the education of the public in the principles of good management, and the securing of funds and legislative action essential for the carrying out of the program. Research and operational activities are interdependent, and after a program is set up they are carried on concurrently and continuously. The several investigations and procedures involved in the formation and operation of a stream-management program may be roughly grouped under four headings: (1) the determination of the life history and habitat requirements of the important stream fish; (2) the ascertaining of existing environmental conditions in the streams, the determination of the cause or causes of the complex of conditions which tend to limit fish production, and the designating of environmental conditions which must be restored; (3) the devising and carrying out of methods and procedures for restoring or maintaining environmental conditions essential for fish production; (4) the management of the fish population so that the productive capacity of the water is utilized for the desired species of fish. In brief, the fish manager must know the life history, habits, and habitat requirements of a species of fish before he can provide those environmental conditions which are conducive to the growth, survival, and reproduction of that species. Further, he must learn what factors in the stream environment are unfavorable, and thus limiting production, and the conditions in the watershed which have brought them about. The next step is to devise, develop, test, and utilize methods or procedures for eliminating the harmful environmental conditions in the stream and for restoring those environmental factors essential for a good yield of the desired species. In addition, populations of predator, coarse, and forage fish must be controlled in so far as practicable so that the productive capacity of the stream can be utilized by the desired species.

Life History and Habitat Requirements of Fish. Considerable is now known of the life history, habits, habitat requirements, and ecology of the more important game, pan, and food fish. Information on these subjects can, therefore, be gained by a survey of relevant literature. Pertinent information of this type on the important species is a prerequisite for the detection of limiting factors in the aquatic environment and the devising of methods for meeting the requirements of the fish. Essential requirements for most stream fish can be roughly grouped under four headings: (1) suitable water supply, (2) adequate spawning facilities, (3) abundant food supply for all age groups, (4) accessible shelter for all sizes of fish. These requirements for several species of fish are briefly described in the sections on fish habits, requirements, and ecology.

Determination of Factors Limiting Production. When data have been assembled on the life histories, habits, habitat requirements, and interrelationships of the various species, the next step in the formation of a management program is a survey of the waters under consideration to determine present habitat conditions and to discover any deficiencies in the aquatic environment which are preventing or hindering fish production. In this connection, it cannot be too strongly emphasized that the success of any survey will be largely dependent upon an understanding of the requirements of the fish, since all limiting factors cannot be detected if the essentials for growth, reproduction, and survival are not understood. A survey should consider not only the stream but the entire watershed, as a knowledge of past and present conditions in the watershed is required for an understanding of the causes which have produced the existent environmental conditions in the stream.

GENERAL RECONNAISSANCE SURVEY

When undertaking a survey of a stream or streams, usually the first procedure is a general reconnaissance of the area to obtain information on the topography, the soils, forest cover, agricultural uses, erosion, floods, industrial use, pollution, precipitation, and the location of towns and roads. This should be supplemented by a study of the available literature on the characters and features of the watershed. Geological and hydrographic reports and surveys often contain much of interest, as do soil surveys and ground-water studies. Data on floods, normal and low water flow, springs, location of the water table, erosion, silting, the soils, and their chemical content are all important. Much can be learned from the study of various types of maps such as topographic, geological, hydrographic, soil, agricultural and industrial use, and forest-cover. Often there are extensive reports on surveys of domestic and industrial pollution which give the location and sources of pollution, types of pollution and polluting substances, and the areas affected.

Old residents can often supply useful information concerning the history of fishing in the area and the changes which have taken place on the watershed and in the streams. Alert, local fishermen can usually point out changes in the watershed which have altered the general environment and the fish habitat, such as the lowering of the water table; the drying up of springs; severe land erosion due to fires, lumbering, or grazing; severe floods; stream erosion and silting; clearing for agriculture; unwise farming practices; irrigation, drainage, mining, industrial, and urban development. Special attention should be given to the reports of all past fishery surveys, stocking records, statistical reports on sport and commercial fishing, and past and present fishing regulations. The attitude of the general public on present fishing conditions, trends of the fishery, the results of past regulations, and the need or desirability of present or future regulations should be considered with care.

The correlation and interpretation of the data secured from these various sources will give the investigator an idea of the past and present state of the watershed and will enable him to determine the cause of many unfavorable situations in the streams of the area. Financial restrictions usually limit the amount of survey work, and intensive studies cannot be carried out on all streams. The extensive survey should provide data for a usable classification of the streams into groups according to the characteristics of the watershed or the particular needs of the stream. Then intensive studies can be made on representative streams in each group or class so management plans can be devised for all the streams in the various groups.

Intensive Survey. The intensive survey of a stream includes a study of physical, chemical, and biological conditions. In the investigation of physical factors the following should be considered: type of stream and valley; variation in width and depth; source of water; length, altitude, gradient, and total fall of stream; velocity of current; average flow and fluctuations in flow; erosion; silting; abundance, flow, and temperature of springs; turbidity, color, and temperatures of the water; falls, dams, diversions, and other barriers to migration; height, character, and state of banks; kind and amount of streamside shade; type, frequency, and extent of riffles, pools, and flats; kinds and amount of shelter; extent and types of stream-bottom materials; and species and abundance of aquatic vegetation. There is a considerable range in the chemical content of stream waters, and a general knowledge of the dissolved gases is desirable as at times the oxygen content may become low; this usually occurs in polluted streams. The waters of some springs are deficient in oxygen or are entirely without oxygen, while some contain large amounts of carbon dioxide. In the West, some streams have a total alkalinity which may at times become high enough to adversely affect fish life. Total alkalinity, phosphorus, and nitrogen are basic factors influencing the productivity of a stream, and a knowledge of their form, amount, and availability is of value to the fisheries manager. Basic streams flowing from limestone areas which have some phosphate are much more productive than streams from regions of granitic or volcanic rock. The lack of an adequate supply of available phosphate is the outstanding cause of low yield in many streams. If sufficient phosphate is available in the watershed and throughout the stream, there will be no deficiency of the necessary nitrogenous substances, for their production is largely dependent upon the availability of phosphate.

A thorough knowledge of the spawning facilities is of major importance. The location, extent, suitability, and accessibility of spawning beds or areas; the temperature of the water throughout the year; ice action; floods and silting; turbidity; the presence of springs or spring seepage; and the nearness of sufficient desirable food and cover for fry and fingerlings should be taken into account.

Obviously the food supply of a stream is of outstanding consequence, for in the final analysis it is food which determines the pounds of fish that can be produced in a stream. During the 1930's, great stress was laid on quantitative counts of stream-bottom organisms for the expressed purpose of determining the carrying capacity of streams. Although the carrying capacity might be determined by such studies, it has not been accomplished as yet, and such studies are not recommended to the fisheries manager as a method for determining the carrying capacity. The needed information can be obtained much more easily by growth-rate and population studies. Studies of the bottom fauna are desirable, however, to gain a general idea of the production of different stream-bottom foods, the species of food organisms present, and the relative productivity of the different stream-bottom materials. This can be accomplished without such extensive studies as would be required for the determination of carrying capacity. General examinations should also be made to determine if food suitable for all age groups of fish is available throughout the various seasons.

The productivity of different bottom types varies considerably (36). Areas in which silt has collected are usually productive of chironomids and other small organisms which are suitable food for the young fish. Plant beds are very productive of insect life, and a rubble-gravel bottom which is covered with *Fissidens* or some other water moss usually harbors large numbers of caddis flies and mayflies. Rubble-gravel bottoms are usually most productive of bottom foods in trout streams, while shifting sand bottoms are least productive.

In the larger and slower streams plankton constitutes an important food source. The young of most fish depend on it for their food, and some fish feed on plankton during their entire life. Forage fish, many of which feed largely on plankton, constitute a very important food of black and white bass, pike, saugers, walleyed pike, and crappies. A general knowledge of the abundance of the various types of foods is of great assistance to the fish manager in setting up a management program.

Intensive surveys provide an opportunity to learn more concerning the life history of important species. Gaps in existing knowledge may be filled by studies of spawning, food, and shelter requirements. Migration studies are also of importance in the formulation of management programs. Migration may be determined by means of fin clipping, tagging, weirs, fish traps, and counting weirs. Studies of the effects of barriers to migration are of prime importance in the management of anadromous species.

It is also desirable to determine the extent and importance of pollution in the stream. Sources of pollution should be located, the character and amount of their waste determined, and the extent of the septic and recovery zones ascertained. Studies should also be made to determine the effects of pollution on the fish population and other organisms of commercial or recreational importance.

The abundance of beavers and the effects of their activities on fish production should be studied. Data should be collected on unfavorable temperature changes, undesirable changes in chemical conditions (27), reductions in the food supply (34), barriers to spawning migrations, detrimental changes in the composition of the fish population, the destruction of streamside shade, and stream erosion. Such data are essential in carrying out a program for beaver control.

There are a number of studies which should be carried on continually in order that changes in conditions may be detected, the effects of the management program evaluated, and the necessity for additional or different management procedures determined. These investigations are determination of fishing pressure, census of fishing, growth-rate investigations, and fish-population studies.

Determination of Fishing Pressure. Counts of fishermen have been used to determine total fishing. It is usually impracticable to make daily total counts of all fishermen. Some counting method must, therefore, be devised which will provide data from which the total number of fish can be estimated (41). Haphazard, periodic, random, or stratified random counts may be used. Generally, fishing goes in cycles, being heaviest in the spring and on week ends. It is also heaviest in accessible areas and near centers of population. Temperature, rain, clouds, wind, and the season all affect the amount of fishing. The quality of fishing is of great importance in controlling the amount of fishing. Because of these variables it is difficult to adequately sample the fishing in large areas. Several methods may be used for making the counts, such as airplanes, boats, checking approach roads, or a combination of methods.

Census of Fishing. Several methods have been used to census sport fishing. These include franked census cards for individual trips, voluntary depositing of census cards at established stations, census by game wardens, census of the catch of selected expert fishermen, annual report at time of buying fishing license, census by fishing clubs, or census by hired census takers. Experience has shown the latter method produces the best results, but its cost may prohibit its use. For determining the catch of commercial fishermen, voluntary monthly reports on prepared blanks, annual reports at time of license renewal, or required monthly reports on prepared forms have been used. In general the latter method is the most successful. The census of commercial fishing should furnish information on the type of gear used, the catch of each type, the total catch, the species taken and their relative abundance in the catch of each type of gear, the catch per unit of effort or unit gear per time interval, and trends in the fishery.

The creel census of sport fishing should be planned to provide data on type of fishing (boat, bank, or wading), tackle or bait used, number and weight of total catch, species taken and their relative abundance in the total catch, time fished, and catch per hour. A creel census will indicate successful fishing methods and baits, rate of catch from year to year, and the decline or increase of various species in the catch. It also shows the average number and weight of fish in the catch and increases or decreases in the average weight of the fish taken. Information of this nature when combined with data from the fishermen count (39) provides data on the total removal and the catch of the different species, trends in the fishery, the effectiveness of various management programs, and the need for other management methods.

Growth-rate Studies. These studies are now generally made by means of scale readings (6, 18, 21). They show the relative abundance of the various age groups in the population, the rate of growth, adequacy of the food supply for different age groups or species, and trends in growth or the effects of management procedures. They also provide data valuable in the setting of size limits, stocking, and other management procedures.

Fish-population Studies. Knowledge of the fish population is of outstanding importance for the formulation and prosecution of a management program. A variety of methods has been used for the counting of fish or the estimation of fish populations. Methods used include visual counts, netting, tagging and recapture (22), seining of fish from screened areas of stream, collection or counts of fish by means of electric shockers (23) or electric seine (12), diversion of streams from certain sections (33), and poisoning (20, 39).

Population studies are perhaps the most important tool available to the fisheries manager. When combined with removal or yield studies, they furnish much data needed for the regulation of the fishery, such as creel limits, seasons, size limits, and stocking. They indicate the species present; the total population, and thus the carrying capacity (if fishing is not heavy) as well as the relative abundance of each species; the percentage of the weight of the total population comprised by each species; the abundance of each size group; the number of legal fish of the desired species; and trends in the fish population. Population studies also give valuable information on the relative sizes of the various species and their habitat preferences, their reproductive potential, the success of spawning, and the survival in the various age groups. Combined with food studies, they indicate competitor-predator relations and the species in need of encouragement or control. All four studies furnish much data needed for the increase of the desired species and the harvesting of the crop on a sustained-yield basis.

The surveys as outlined will give additional information on the habits and life history of the fish as well as valuable information on the various organisms with which they are associated. They will also indicate the present condition of the aquatic habitat and the practices which make life untenable for game fish as well as outline the problems and show what undesirable situations must be overcome if the fish supply is to be maintained at a high level. When the data from the surveys are grouped, analyzed, correlated, and interpreted, they will provide information essential for the classification of waters, the determination of needed environmental improvements, and the management of fish populations.

Management Methods. Fisheries-management activities are largely of two general types: environmental improvement and population management. To date environmental-improvement activities have largely been confined to trout streams. Therefore, the various environmental-improvement methods and improvement structures which are described are primarily for trout streams. Many of them are, however, applicable to warm-water streams.

ENVIRONMENTAL IMPROVEMENT

The general objectives of environmental improvement are (1) to maintain a water supply which is relatively constant and pure yet productive, (2) to keep the temperatures of the streams within such a range that they are conducive to growth, survival, and reproduction of the desired fish, and yet are of such a range that disease and competitors are kept in check, (3) to maintain adequate and suitable spawning areas for each species and to keep open the migration routes for them, (4) to afford pools, shelter, and protection for all age classes of the desired fish, (5) to insure food supplies for these fish and the organisms on which they feed.

When undertaking environmental improvement it should be realized that it is not feasible or economically desirable to restore every stream to its former condition for the purpose of fishing. For example, many former trout streams are no longer habitable for trout because the area has been developed for agricultural use and they have become intermittent or too warm for trout. It should be further recognized that some streams are now submarginal and they do not warrant extensive expenditures for the restoration of fishing. In addition, many streams have been so altered that their restoration would require impractical or undesirable changes in the watershed. However, much can be accomplished through the application of conservation practices which are carried out for the benefit of other resources. Forest management, the regulation of grazing, and the adoption of sound agricultural methods, although designed to bring about other ends, will be of benefit to fishing through their effects on the watershed.

In so far as possible, the fish manager should aid any program for the control of floods. Correct agricultural practices can be an effective means for stream protection, while poor agricultural practices can be the greatest menace to the even flow and productiveness of streams. Improved pastures, contour plowing, strip cropping, crop rotation, terracing, cover crops, fertilization, and the removal of critical areas from cropping all serve to prevent runoff, increase seepage, and prevent soil erosion. In several sections of the country the regulation of grazing is essential for the maintenance of an adequate ground cover and the protection of stream bottoms. Restoration of ground cover through the regulation of grazing has reduced floods and soil erosion as indicated by experiments conducted on the Wasatch Plateau in central Utah (25).

Stream-bottom fencing against cattle is a valuable means for the maintenance or restoration of a stream. The strip fenced off on each side of the stream need not be very wide, and water gaps can be built at intervals for stock. In a fencing program careful consideration should be given to initial costs plus subsequent maintenance as compared to other methods, such as reduced stocking and better distribution of the stock to secure comparable results. Fencing of stream bottoms in the Southwest by the U.S. Forest Service has been very beneficial. When coupled with the control of grazing, it has resulted in the reestablishment of stream banks, streamside shade, pools, shelter, and food-producing areas. A good growth of trees and shrubs along a stream will hold the banks against even severe floods when they are of infrequent occurrence. In addition, this border of trees furnishes shade which keeps the stream cool and contributes drift food and fertilizing materials, while the roots of the larger trees cause the formation of pools along the bank and furnish cover. Trees and shrubs also add greatly to the beauty of the stream and the enjoyment of the angler. If streamside trees do not appear naturally, improvement can be hastened by planting. When stream-bottom planting is carried on to protect the banks in unfenced sections, an effort should be made to select plants which are nonpalatable to stock or otherwise resistant to grazing.

The various methods of erosion control now in use, such as terracing, the building of check dams in gullies, spreading, planting, etc., are of benefit to streams through the reduction of surface runoff. Improved road-building methods such as sloping and sodding banks, disposing of runoff so erosion is not produced, and building the road back from the stream so there is a strip of trees left along the stream are all practices which tend to reduce the harmful effects of road construction.

The present impoverishment of many of our streams has resulted from a series of changes in the watershed which have developed over a considerable period of time. The restoration of proper habitat conditions by the correction of situations on the watershed will likewise require considerable time. However, this is the only means of securing relatively permanent improvements, because for a real cure we must treat the cause and not the effects which are manifest in the stream. After the programs for the control of floods, the prevention of erosion, and the restoration of vegetative cover have been initiated, it is often desirable to speed up the recovery of the streams by certain practices carried out in the streams themselves, and by the installation of improvement devices known as barriers.

The effective improvement of streams by the use of barriers demands detailed information on the requirements of the fish and the factors which are limiting production. Meeting the needs and overcoming the deficiencies of each type of stream requires considerable experimentation and the evaluation of the results produced by each type of structure used. Further, it should be borne in mind that streams in each section of the country present different problems which require specific remedies. Even streams which are similar should sometimes be treated in entirely different ways. For example, a cold-spring feeder flowing into a trout lake or a large trout stream could be improved as a nursery, whereas, if it flowed into a nontrout lake or stream, it would be developed as a habitat for adult trout. For best returns the improvement plan for any one stream should be fitted into the unit management plan for the entire stream system so no one section is developed at the expense of another. Thus, although by making the water of a cold headwater stream warmer and deeper by damming improves fishing in the headwaters, it is not always a desirable practice as it often reduces the mileage habitable for trout farther downstream. Such practices are difficult to prevent when various portions of the stream system are owned by different individuals.

Improvement of Trout Streams. In so far as possible a stream should be developed into a self-sustaining biological unit so that it supplies all the requirements of the trout. In carrying on environmental-improvement work a proper balance should be maintained among the essential requirements of the trout, and one should not be developed at the expense of another. The creation of more spawning beds, pools, or shelters than are needed may be definitely harmful and reduce productivity. An overabundance of young may lead to stunting by increasing the population beyond the food supply, while an overabundance of pools may reduce food production as pools are usually not as productive as riffles. Moderation should be practiced especially in the construction of pools by dams or deflectors.

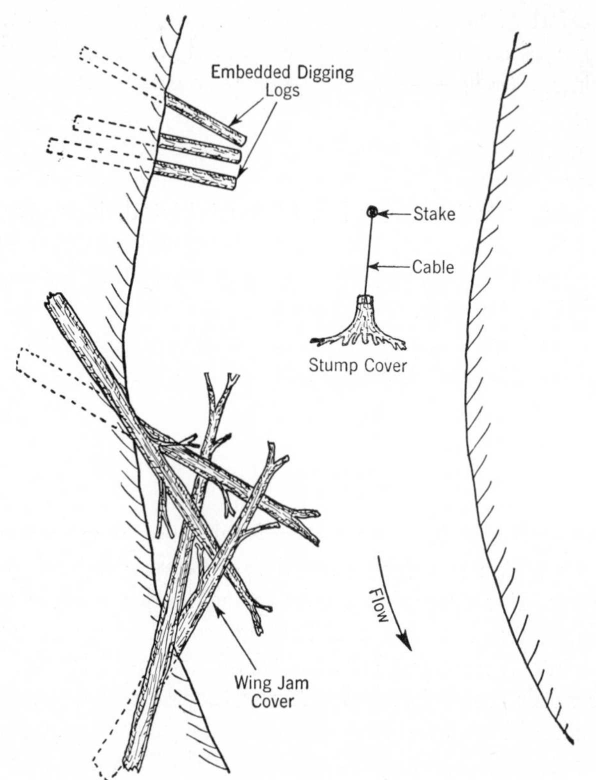

FIG. 20-2. Pool-forming devices. (*C. M. Tarzwell.*)

In the construction of dams, deflectors, and shelters, there are certain procedures which are considered desirable. Generally, it is best to work downstream, as materials can be floated down from structure to structure and advantage can be taken of the changes in the stream flow for the planning and placing of succeeding structures so all can be united into an efficient unit. When building dams, however, it is best to work upstream so the extent of the ponded water can be noted and adequate provisions made for the necessary riffle areas. It is desirable to install structures during periods of low water as defects are more apparent at

Fig. 20-3. Triangular crib deflectors are especially beneficial during floods. (*C. M. Tarzwell.*)

Fig. 20-4. A boulder deflector in a Michigan trout stream. (*C. M. Tarzwell.*)

that time and construction is easier. It is essential, however, that flood stages be kept constantly in mind. Banks should be protected against erosion; adequate food spillways should be provided on dams; and deflectors should be placed so they will not cause bank erosion at high-water stages. All structures should be made strong enough to withstand the highest floods which occur in the stream. Though it is desirable to

Fig. 20-5. Rock dams in a trout stream furnish fine pools and fit naturally into the surroundings. (*C. M. Tarzwell.*)

occasionally create refuges for fish, generally such structures should be built so they do not prevent fishing.

From the standpoint of natural appearance and cost it is advisable, whenever possible, to use only natural, locally occurring materials for the construction of the barriers. Each structure should be fitted into its and shrubs near the stream should not be cut or injured, but advantage should be taken of all natural objects occurring in the stream or on the banks to make the structure stronger or to blend it with the natural surroundings and the stream banks disturbed as little as possible. Trees surroundings. In building stone structures, use the largest boulders which can be found or moved into position. When dams are built remove trees and shrubs which will be killed by flooding. Stakes can be concealed by cutting them off beneath the water surface. All dams and deflectors should be kept low; and covers placed under water whenever possible. These practices are especially important in streams having high flood crests and considerable ice action.

The blending of the structures with the surroundings is very difficult in stream sections which are not wooded. If wires, cables, spikes, and driftpins are used they should be hidden from view. It is well to leave the bark on logs and to hide axe and saw marks. Structures which extend above water can be given a more natural appearance by placing sod on them. This practice is of value only where floods are not severe.

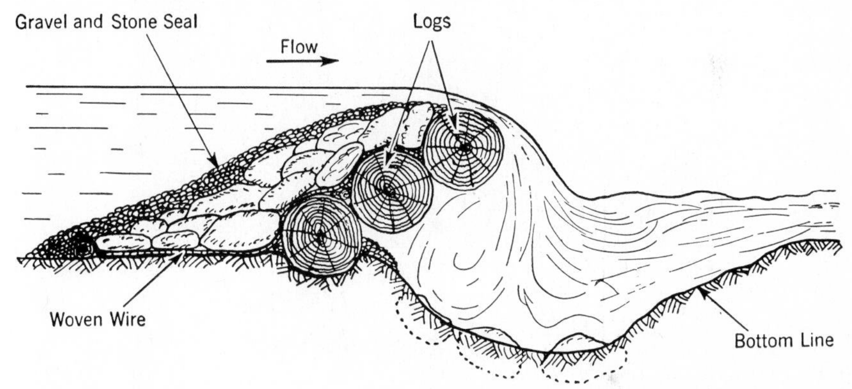

FIG. 20-6. Cross section of a log dam at spillway. (*C. M. Tarzwell.*)

The various types of structures which are used for trout-stream improvement may be classified as dams, deflectors, and covers. Many types have been designed for experimental purposes, but only a few have proven successful. It has been found that structures which are suitable for one type of stream are entirely unsuited to another. Detailed descriptions of the various dams, deflectors, and covers will be omitted because of lack of space.

Improvement of the Water Supply. Although the character of the water supply is largely determined by the watershed, certain modifications can be made by the encouragement or planting of streamside shade. Sections of streams exposed to the sun's direct rays may be improved by planting willows or other trees along the banks. In addition, an effort should be made to utilize all spring water to best advantage. Springs and short spring feeders can be led to the main stream in narrow, direct channels so they reach it while still at a low temperature.

If these channels are long or unshaded they will also be benefitted by streamside plantings. When cooling the water is in order, no dams which spread the water should be built and old dams should be removed.

If a stream is too cold for good trout growth and it is advantageous to make it warmer, dams can be built to spread the water and expose it to the sun. The creation of backwaters and quiet water areas not only increases the temperature but also develops the area for food production and tends to fertilize the stream by the addition of organic material. This is especially helpful in mountain streams where the water is tor-

FIG. 20-7. Log dams held in place and banks protected by toed-in boulders. (*C. M. Tarzwell.*)

rential or uniformly swift. Important sources of fertility in trout streams are the leaves and litter from the forest floor which fall into or are washed into them. Deflectors are very effective in collecting and holding these organic materials and converting them into mucky bars. Huge piles of leaves which collect behind deflectors in the fall are converted into mucky bars rich in food organisms within a period of a few months.

Headwater dams for the storage of flood waters and their controlled release during the dry periods have been beneficial in the mountainous regions of the west. These dams are usually built at the outlets of mountain lakes or at the lower ends of mountain meadows so that a relatively low dam has a large storage capacity. In California such dams have prevented damaging floods and have provided flow throughout the dry season in streams which formerly went dry. Trout production has been greatly increased in this way. Some streams have sink holes which may, during the low-water stages, take the whole flow of the stream. It is sometimes possible, by fluming the stream around these holes, to make several miles of fishing water.

Spawning Facilities. Where sand and silt have covered spawning beds, they can be washed away by means of deflectors concentrated in deep bars on their downstream side. Through the concentration of these materials extensive gravel areas which are suitable for spawning purposes can be uncovered. Even a small amount of silt tends to smother trout eggs. Where the bottom is very firm or the gravel has been cemented together by the secretions of blue-green algae, deflectors can be used to break up the bottom materials and form gravel bars suitable for the construction of nests. Whenever possible, barriers to spawning migrations should be removed to insure access to the spawning areas. If the large fish are prevented from moving upstream by spreads or silt and sand flats, one channel may be kept open by means of V deflectors. Jams, old lumbering dams, and beaver dams that hinder migration can be removed if such removal is beneficial. Sometimes it is feasible to arrange the materials at or near rapids or low falls so trout can pass over them. Although it is possible to blast some falls to enable trout to get over them, this practice is not suggested for it destroys the scenic value of the stream and may remove a barrier to migration which has value for the management of the fish population. Falls often serve the useful purpose of separating the species in the stream and preserving the headwaters of the stream above the falls for the favored game species or for a native species which it is hoped to preserve. When streams become warmer, natural barriers to migration are especially beneficial as they keep predator and competitor species, such as perch, pickerel, bass, and minnows, out of the section of stream above them. Dams can also be used for this purpose.

In private waters where intensive management is sought, several practices not applicable to public waters may be used. If suitable gravel beds are not available, spawning beds may be formed by placing gravel in the stream near springs, in spring feeders, or in the headwaters. The gravel used should be clean and vary in size from that of a pea to a hen's egg. The proportion of the various sizes should be such that the trout eggs are given protection without being crushed. If plants do not become established on the bars below the deflectors, they may be planted. Watercress was successfully established in Gamble Creek, a private stream in Michigan, and it is probable that the establishment of several other species could be hastened by plantings. An adequate food supply for all the bottom organisms must be available if trout are to make a good and uniform growth. Among the various groups of organisms which serve as food for trout, the stream-bottom insects are of outstanding importance. The streams should be so managed that they will provide conditions which are more conducive to the growth, survival, and reproduction of aquatic insects.

Food. Because studies of bottom fauna in trout streams have shown that some bottom types are more productive than others, a logical approach to the problem of increasing food production is to preserve or supply more of the productive bottom types. Investigations conducted in Michigan and elsewhere over a number of years (36) have furnished data on the relative productivity of stream-bottom types. In Michigan it was found that sand is the least productive kind of bottom, while plant beds are the richest. A considerable range in the amount of food was found in beds of the different species of aquatic plants. *Chara* and *Eleodea* beds contained the largest volume of food organisms per unit area, but watercress and white-water buttercups were also rich. Gravel and rubble bottoms, when covered with *Fissidens* moss, are next in order of yield. Whenever this moss is present on the rocks, large numbers of aquatic insects are found. This is true not only for coarse gravel, but also for medium and fine gravel. This moss provides an adequate resting and attachment place for those insects which depend on the current for their food. Many *Hydropsyche caddis* are found in it, as are many of the may-flies and the species which prey upon them. In general, the plant beds, the swift rubble-boulder riffles which have *Fissidens* moss, the mucky flats, and the gravel areas are the most productive, while sand, silt, mud, and bedrock are unproductive. Sand and light-colored inorganic mud are especially barren. According to the averages found in the Michigan studies, a gravel-rubble bottom with *Fissidens* moss was about 140 times as rich as sand and about twenty-four times as productive as marl (36). When sand is mixed with the various other materials, the resultant yield is dependent upon the amount of sand present, the more sand the less food. In the north branch of the Au Sable River in Michigan, it was found that coarse-gravel bottoms had more than eight times as much food as the sand-and-gravel bottoms. Even a very little sand can reduce production, for it fills all crevices and covers many areas suitable for the attachment of insects.

Deflectors and dams may be used in a number of ways to provide the bottom types which are best for aquatic insects. By the use of deflectors an unproductive blanket of sand may be concentrated into deep bars so that the gravel bottom is exposed. Organic materials which settle out in the lee of deflectors form a mucky deposit over these bars and bring about a very favorable situation for certain *Oligochaeta*, several chironomids, numerous caddis fly larvae, and the burrowing mayflies, *Hexagenia*. Because these organisms and many others found in these mucky deposits directly utilize the partially decayed organic matter, there is a quick turnover of food materials and a large bottom fauna in these areas. If these mucky areas persist from year to year, they are many times as productive as sand, clay, mud, marl, bedrock, or silt bottoms, and they rival in richness the rubble-gravel bottoms. Plants very often become established on these mucky flats and further improve food conditions as they provide food and shelter for many kinds of organisms.

In mountainous areas dams can be used for the production of mucky bottoms in much the same way as deflectors are used in the north central states. When so utilized, they may increase basic productivity by the collection and retention of organic materials such as leaves and forest litter, which otherwise are constantly being carried downstream and lost. These organic materials are suitable for direct utilization by several trout-food organisms. If wide, quiet, mucky areas can be created, microcrustaceans, amphipods or scuds, small mollusca, and the larvae of *Diptera*, especially chironomids, will be produced. These are the food of trout during the fry stage.

In predominately gravel-bottom areas there is an increase of bottom organisms in the riffles around the ends and below deflectors. This is due in part to the removal of sand and fine gravel from the coarse gravel which is more productive and in part to the acceleration of the current. The forms which predominate in these areas are certain species of mayflies and the *Hydropsyche caddis*, which largely depend on the current for their food. To a certain extent, an increase in current velocity enables them to strain more water and obtain more food in a given time. Notable increases in the bottom fauna have been found in the vicinity of deflectors. In a section of the east branch of the Black River in Michigan which was intensely improved, counts of bottom organisms made before and after the installation of the barriers indicate a significant increase in the population of bottom organisms. Such increases, however, are possible only where sand bottoms can be partially replaced by gravel riffles and mucky flats. Although the various structures can materially assist in the increase of the food supply, the control of floods and other adverse agents by the management of the watershed is the best means for maintaining or improving food conditions.

Attention should be devoted to drift foods, since during the summer season they provide as much as two-thirds of the total consumed by trout 4 to 10 inches long. Although sunlight is needed to promote the growth of algae and many other organisms, streamside trees are desirable, as Needham (51 *g.r.*) found almost twice as much drift food per unit area in wooded sections of stream as in open stretches. Deflectors can be used to concentrate drift food into a narrow channel and direct it over a pool or along a cover where it can be more fully utilized by the trout.

In England trout keepers have devoted considerable time to the culture of snails, as well as to the planting of vegetation and aquatic insects. It appears that snails are not so important in this country as they are in many of the more sluggish streams of England. Although watercress is a valuable source of food and cover in headwater areas, it will usually be found naturally in all areas suitable for it. This principle is also applicable to the planting of insects and other bottom-food organisms. Since snails are hosts for certain stages of many fish parasites, their introduction might be distinctly harmful.

The introduction of forage or other fish into trout streams usually results in the reduction of the trout population. Pike, pickerel, sunfish, bluegills, bass, perch, ling, suckers, and bullheads should never be placed in trout waters, and every effort should be made to keep them out or remove them if they are present. Minnows should not be introduced into trout streams as food for trout, especially if the streams are at all warm. While the large trout may benefit from the minnows, they will do so at the expense of the fry, as the minnows compete with the latter for food. If there is a superabundance of minute food, both fry and minnows can get along, but the danger lies in the great reproductive powers of the minnows. In cold streams, trout and minnows are not incompatible, but where the streams are warm, conditions are reversed and favor the minnows instead of the trout; the former increase out of all bounds, dominate the stream, and compete with the young trout to such an extent that the trout yield of the stream is reduced. Some of the highest trout yields on record were secured from streams which contained only trout (37).

Shelter. Various shelter and pool-forming devices have been described. Shelter for trout has two principal purposes: (1) it slackens the current so the trout can rest and do not have to continually swim to maintain their position, (2) it gives protection from enemies of land, air, and water. Numerous well-spaced pools and covers are required if all food-producing areas are to be utilized. If a stream has but a few pools, all the trout are crowded into a limited area and the competition for food is severe. Trout do not usually forage far from shelter, and if there are few pools only a portion of the food will be utilized. An increase in the number of pools and shelters in such a stream will, if correctly spaced, increase the carrying capacity of the stream by allowing the trout to forage over all the food-producing areas. Pools and shelter can be used to balance the relative numbers of trout. If the young are very abundant, the older trout can be encouraged by producing more deep pools and cover; but if the young are scarce, they can be favored in the construction of shelters.

Control of Bank Erosion. The erosion of stream banks has deposited immense quantities of sand and other materials in our trout streams. These materials have drifted downstream, filling pools, destroying shelters, covering food-producing areas, and forming wide, shallow, open flats not suited to trout production. In the sand plains of the Great Lakes region, the erosion of the stream banks is especially noticeable. Studies

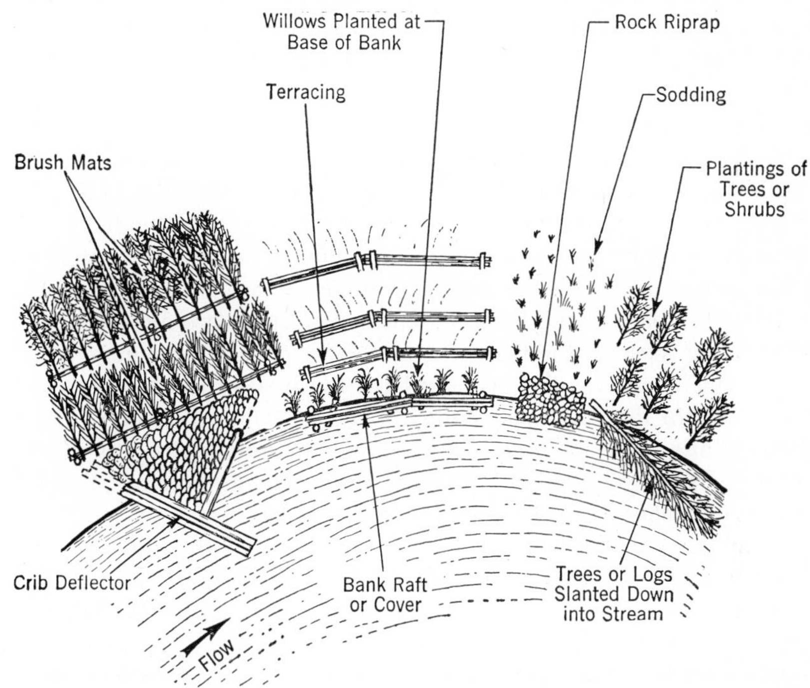

FIG. 20-8. Methods of erosion control on high banks. (*C. M. Tarzwell.*)

of bottom organisms and trout populations have shown that shifting sand bottoms, produced by bank erosion in these areas, are very barren.

Controlling bank erosion on most of the trout streams of the country is definitely related to flood control. Although this is true to a certain extent in the trout streams of the north cenral states, it appears that additional measures are necessary in that area. Direct control of these banks is required, for sand is continuously added to the streams during normal flow by erosion at the waterline. Although the large sand banks are more spectacular, attention should be given to all banks. Large boom covers and bank covers are of value for the protection of banks at bends. Deflectors are effective for directing the current away from the banks and producing quiet water along their base. Often bank covers can be combined with deflectors for added protection, or retaining walls of poles and brush held with stakes may be used. These combinations of structures have been successful in stopping bank erosion and in creating mucky bars and plant beds. Deflectors used for bank erosion are built higher than usual so floodwaters will not pass over them. This is essential because if floodwaters go over them a condition is created which actually increases bank erosion. The triangular crib deflector is one of the best structures for the protection of the base of eroding banks. These deflectors can be made very strong and yet be built to the desired height. The logs forming the crib are mortised at the apex of the triangle and held with driftpins. These structures are embedded into the bank almost as far as they extend into the stream. Numerous crosspieces are required to give strength to the structure, and it should have a bottom to hold the rocks in place in case it is partially undermined. If a long deflector is needed, the logs of the upper face can be extended.

Erosion of high sand banks has been found to be due to the action of frost, wind, and rain on the slope as well as to the erosive action of the stream at the base of the bank. Extensive landslides are often caused by the breaking loose of the frozen surface layer of sand. The action of the stream which removes the material from the base of the bank is chiefly responsible for the continued sliding of the sand into the water. As sand has a definite angle of repose, it continues to slide as long as material is removed from the base of the bank. It is apparent, therefore, that both the base and slope of the bank require protection.

Several means may be used for the protection of the base and slope of banks. If the most critical area, the base of the bank and that just below the water level, is adequately protected, extensive work on the slopes is not required, for when the base becomes stable, slipping may be expected to cease, and vegetation will have an opportunity to recapture and hold the slopes. One of the best methods of bank protection, when stones are available, is to riprap the bank from below the water level to slightly above the high-water mark. Trees, logs, and brush can be slanted down from the bank into the stream in such a way that they deflect the current and protect the bank. The use of trees in this way has proven to be the cheapest and yet one of the most successful ways of stopping bank erosion. Often muck bars and dense plant beds form along the bank below these trees.

If, when the base is protected, additional protection to the slope is needed, several methods can be used. Various grasses, shrubs, and trees suitable to the area may be planted, or the bank may be sodded with native or other grasses especially adapted to conditions encountered on the bank. When using trees and shrubs, it is often advisable to plant some quick-growing resistant plant which will hold the slope for the first year until the trees and shrubs can become established. Sweet clover is good for this purpose. Terracing may be used on the slope, but it is an expensive practice and may not be entirely practicable, for when the holding walls decay, erosion may begin again.

One of the best methods for holding the slope is a covering of brush. The brush is laid on the slopes with the butts down and is held in position by a pole placed across the butts and secured by stakes driven into the slope. When laid in this manner the branches of the brush hold the sand and prevent blowing, washing, or sliding. If available, some species of evergreen mixed with hardwood brush should be used for this purpose. If the base of the bank remains stable, this brush furnishes adequate protection for the slope until vegetation becomes established.

MANAGING THE FISH POPULATION

The objective of the fisheries manager is to supply sufficient fish of suitable size for the angling public. This is a very difficult and sometimes impossible task, for not only has the amount of fishing water been steadily reduced during the past century, but the number of anglers has steadily increased. Fishing pressure is therefore many times greater on the remaining streams, and in certain areas the demand exceeds the productive capacity of the waters. It is essential, therefore, that the remaining streams be preserved, developed, and fully utilized for those species of fish which they are best fitted to produce. Not only must the productive capacity of the stream be brought to a maximum through the preservation or restoration of environmental conditions on the watershed and in the stream, but also it is essential that this productivity be utilized for the increased yield of the desired species. This can best be accomplished through control of the composition of the fish population. Such control, however, is often a difficult task.

Any action taken in a stream should be well considered since it is liable to be far-reaching owing to the interdepedency of all life in the stream. In the past we have tended to think of fish management only in terms of one species. This is biologically wrong, since one species cannot be managed separately and without regard to all the other species present. The interrelation and influences of all species on any one species are important elements of the biological environment which govern the yield and standing population of any and all species. In fisheries management we must deal with and manage fish populations and not individual species. Each species must be considered in relation to the total population and management practices adjusted accordingly. Conversely, our idea of standing crops, annual turnovers of residual populations, and yields should also be fitted into the concept of the management of populations. Although the total yield of any body of water is more or less fixed quantitatively by the productivity of the water and soil of the watershed, the percentage which each species constitutes of the total population is not fixed or constant. Under good management the total fish population, and thus the total yield, will be so controlled that the productive capacity of the water will be utilized to the fullest extent possible for the production of those species most desired for economic and recreational purposes. For example, if a given water can support 500 pounds of fish per acre, and of this poundage 85 per cent is carp, carp suckers, gars, dogfish, and gizzard shad, it is apparent that a reduction of these species and an increase in the game fish will bring greater recreational returns. Thus under management the desired species are encouraged in all ways possible, while the weed or rough species are controlled by all means at hand.

Stocking, regulations, various cropping methods, predator-competitor control, and total removal by poisoning are methods used for the control of fish populations. Population problems in cold and warm waters are sometimes quite similar, but they may be quite different. In large warm streams, especially those which have been impounded, very often only a portion of the annual fish crop is harvested. In trout streams, however, a large portion of the annual yield is removed during the first few days of the season. Regulation of the take and other management procedures must, therefore, be different for these two types of waters.

Stocking. The stocking of exotic species of trout has been common practice in most trout streams of the country. Annual stockings of fingerling and legal-sized trout have been made in many streams. In some areas the exotic species have become established and are providing considerable fishing. In other areas they have not survived and have provided little fishing in spite of large annual stockings. In some areas hundreds of thousands of trout of one species have been stocked, while the native unstocked species has continued to furnish most of the fishing.

Recent investigations (32) have shown that very few fish which are planted in the fall winter over to reach the fisherman's creel. One investigator found that fall planting of legal-sized trout gave a return of 1 per cent, whereas a spring planting gave a return of 19.6 per cent. Spring and summer plantings of legal-sized trout give the best returns. Most of the planted trout which are caught are taken within a month after planting. For best returns legal trout should be planted at intervals of not more than a month throughout the summer. Such put-and-take stocking is costly, and natural reproduction which is much more successful than stocking (28) must be relied upon to produce the majority of the fishing.

The success of plantings is inversely proportional to the numbers of native trout already present. The greatest success has been obtained when trout were stocked in fishless water, such as the high mountain lakes of the west. Rainbow trout should be planted in streams directly accessible to large waters. If streams end in uninhabitable areas or the trout cannot return, they will be lost. Waters ending in irrigation diversions, power diversions, polluted areas, or warm water will not give good return from rainbows. Rainbow trout use streams as nurseries and streams tributary to lakes may become overstocked with young to such an extent that they are stunted. Under such conditions the native species are driven out, and fishing is largely destroyed. Rainbow trout are perhaps the most suitable species for planting in cold lakes having feeders that dry up in the fall. Since they are spring spawners, they can utilize the tributary streams which would not be available to fall-spawning trout.

Overstocking of trout sometimes occurs when large numbers are planted in areas which are already fully stocked with young. In such instances stunting results; there are many fish just below the size limit, and legal-sized fish are scarce. Some control of the various size groups is essential. Very often when this situation occurs the fishermen demand the planting of more trout. However, if growth-rate studies show very slow growth no plantings should be made, size limits might well be reduced, and creel limits increased.

Although large fish are much sought after and may be encouraged in rich streams, or streams in remote areas, they are not so desirable as medium-sized fish in heavily fished waters. A larger number of moderate-sized fish can be produced in a comparable area, and they will thus furnish fishing to a greater number of anglers. Many small streams are not suitable for the production of large trout. In general the size of trout varies with the type of stream and the size of the pools.

Under certain conditions of changed environment the stocking of exotics may be beneficial. Brown trout can withstand somewhat higher temperatures and more turbid waters than brook trout. Further, they are better foragers and more difficult to fish out.

The stocking of exotics is a procedure which should be well considered because it is difficult to foresee all the biological consequences of such introductions. Minnows and suckers should not be placed in streams where they do not occur naturally. Many of our best trout streams are now overrun with suckers and minnows, and pike, pickerel, bass, bluegills, perch, and sunfish are not uncommon in many formerly good trout streams. Although overfishing for trout is one of the things which allows these fish, especially minnows and suckers, to become established in trout streams, it is not the main factor. Changed environmental conditions which make the stream less favorable for trout and more favorable for the other fish is the main cause of this shift in species which has occurred in many of our streams. In some instances undesirable species have been established by introduction. Pike, perch, bass, and sunfish should never be introduced into trout water. Although they may thrive for a time and replace the trout, they themselves produce little fishing. In the cold and small trout streams they grow slowly and never attain a desirable size. The result is that after a time there is no fishing where formerly there was good trout fishing. We have many streams which are so small that they will not support any game fish except trout.

Pike are especially bad for trout streams, as they can live in cold waters and they are very successful predators of trout. In England much time is devoted to the control of pike. They are seined, speared, and snatched. Efforts are also made to destroy them and their eggs at spawning time.

The purpose of management is not merely to increase the number of fish in an area. Very often it is necessary to decrease the number of fish. An optimum condition is one where there is a desirable balance between the numbers of the different species of fish. If a stream is fully stocked, as it usually is, even though the desired species are not abundant but coarse fish are, it is difficult to increase the number of the desired species. Overstocking leads to dwarfing, an increased mortality, and less desirable fishing.

Members of the family *Centrarchidae* have a high reproductive potential. The sunfish are especially successful in the establishment of large populations. In the majority of instances there is no justification for stocking these fish. Many streams which have been stocked in the past were already overstocked and the fish were stunting. Excess pan fish populations should be discouraged because they are a very important enemy of the bass during the nesting period. When bass comprise a small portion of the total population it is very difficult and usually economically unfeasible to increase their numbers by stocking. The small number stocked when compared to the total native fish population is like a drop in the ocean. Further, even though huge numbers were released, they would have little effect because there is a very small survival of hatchery fish when they are placed in competition with a native population which is already overstocked. The wise procedure is to control or utilize the competitor-predator species. The natural reproduction of warm-water fish is usually adequate. Their numbers are limited by the environment and population pressure and not reproductive capacity. In a new water the survival ratio is high, but when the stream is fully stocked the ratio becomes very low. It is this low survival ratio which makes the stocking of fingerlings in such waters an economically unsound procedure.

Regulations. Regulations are a management tool used to spread and equalize fishing, to manage fish populations, and to insure maximum use consistent with maintenance of the breeding stock. They are a means to an end and not an end in themselves. They should be kept to a minimum and not be placed in effect until the need for them and their utility are clearly demonstrated. Regulations vary from state to state, which is desirable when these variations meet special needs. In reality regulations should seldom be uniform throughout any one state. They should be designed to meet the needs of each individual water, and thus it is conceivable that the regulations for two streams which are close together geographically might differ considerably.

The kinds and amount of regulation should be determined by the productivity of the water, size of stream, species of fish present, character of the fish population, and fishing pressure. A concerted effort should be made to determine what regulations provide for the best utilization of the aquatic resource before they are put into effect.

A variety of regulations have been used; some limit and define the methods for taking sport and commercial fish and thus limit the removal from various areas. Others place restrictions on tackle, prohibit the sale of game fish or designate hours for fishing. The regulations in most common use are closed seasons, creel limits, and size limits. Because of differences in productivity, species of fish, growth rates, and reproductive capacity, the regulations for warm and cold water are necessarily different.

When demand and removal may exceed the production, as it often does on trout waters, closed seasons are desirable. The length and time of the season varies for different species but the open season should occur, if possible, during the most pleasant time of year and it should be when the fish are in the best condition. The best season for spring and fall spawners differs. The season for spring spawners usually should not open until they have completed spawning and have recovered their condition. However, the season should not be such that it largely prevents harvesting the fish. For example, in the Great Lakes area the rainbow trout use many of the streams as nurseries. The adults return to the lakes before the season opens so they are not utilized and many of the young migrate down to the lakes before reaching legal size. Thus they use the space and food in the stream and destroy fishing for the native species without providing any in return. In such instances a special open season would be desirable to allow the capture of the adults when they are in the streams.

Creel limits are usually necessary to spread the fishing throughout the season. They also must be kept low where stocking is relied upon to provide a portion of the fish, because stocking with legal-sized fish is a costly procedure. Psychologically a small limit for trout is best. Anglers try for the limit and like to tell of catching the limit. An angler feels much better about catching the limit of 5 than he does when he takes 10 fish when 15 is the limit. When he takes the limit there is always the implication he could have caught many more if he had been allowed to do so. As fishing pressure increases and areas suitable for trout decrease, it may be necessary to encourage the fishermen to catch but not to creel their fish.

Size limits may be detrimental if they are set too high. Often there is a great abundance of trout just under the size limit. In some streams where productivity is low a large size limit prevents the harvesting of the crop. However, size limits should not be too low, as then they result in the throwing back of small fish when larger ones are taken. If most of the population is small, the size limit should be lowered. Limiting fishing to the daylight hours may be harmful if there is an excess number of large trout which feed largely at night.

In marginal streams where the population is maintained by stocking and the fish can live only a portion of the year, it should be planned to fish them out early in the season. Regulations should not protect the predators or competitors of the trout. Although the taking of minnows by seine is prohibited in most trout waters, in many streams their removal would be beneficial. Further, if minnows are used for bait it is advantageous to take them from the stream in which they are to be used because in this way the addition of undesirable species is avoided.

In some areas, especially in the south, closed seasons for warm-water streams may not be needed. They cannot be justified where only a fraction of the available annual crop is harvested. Further, closed seasons may be detrimental because they prohibit fishing when the best catches can be made, and they thus limit the utilization of the crop. Creel limits are often undesirable for the same reason. In northern waters, however, they may be beneficial to fishing in general. Under good management creel limits are determined by fishing pressure, the productive capacity of the stream, and the total annual yield. The fundamental principle of creel limits is to limit the rate of removal so fishing can be enjoyed over a longer period of time by a greater number of fishermen. If only a portion of the crop is harvested there is no reason for such regulations.

Size limits are difficult to justify and are often harmful. They should be put into effect in each water only after a specific need for them has been shown. When a water is overstocked with stunted sunfish, size limits are distinctly detrimental as they prevent utilization and tend to protect a group of fish which compete with the black bass and limit their production. In impounded areas of streams where sunfish are overabundant, a commercial fishery for them may be desirable, and their use as bait should be allowed. Some species of sunfish, which never reach a desirable size, often occur in great numbers and exert a detrimental influence on game species.

In some large warm-water streams where commercial fishing is prohibited and sport fishing is popular, the food and coarse fish increase greatly in abundance and limit the production of the game species. In such instances commercial fishing for the nongame species should be encouraged. Such fishing will allow the utilization of a resource which otherwise is being wasted and may benefit the sport fishery. In some instances a commercial fishery for sunfish and crappies is desirable. Investigations show (22) that in some impoundments these species are not fully harvested and they tend to stunt. Harvesting of the crop promotes rapid growth, reduces the total number, and tends to increase the size. In Reelfoot Lake, where a commercial fishery was prosecuted for the sunfish, they were much larger and in better condition than they were in surrounding waters where commercial fishing was prohibited. Commercial fishing may serve as a tool to improve sport fishing (40).

Proper regulations are basic to fish management. However, before even the best regulations can be effective, the public must believe in them and be in favor of them. Keeping the public fully informed as to the need and value of all regulations is essential to a management program. Regulations themselves do not grow fish, and their mere enactment does not constitute management.

Control of Predators and Competitors. The control of rough or weed species is an outstanding problem of the fisheries manager. In many streams of the country the coarse species make up a large percentage of the total weight of the fish population. Good management indicates that these undesired species should be reduced in number and kept in control by all means possible, while the desired species are encouraged by all available means.

Common fishery practices run counter to good agricultural practices. For many years in handling the fishery it has been customary to pull out the carrots (game fish) and leave the weeds (coarse species), instead of cutting out the weeds and encouraging the carrots. The result has been that the weeds have taken over not only the space between the rows but also the space where the carrots had been. Under such conditions it should be readily seen that it is difficult to establish carrots (game fish) by broadcasting a few seeds. An extensive commercial fishery is one means of keeping the food and coarse species from entirely dominating the fish population. The food fishes—catfish, drum, and spoonbills—have a ready market, and there is some sale for carp and buffalo. If only these species are taken, however, even a more difficult problem may arise as the shad, carp suckers, dogfish, gars, and suckers may increase in abundance. Many of these can be taken in commercial fishing operations, and if the fishermen can realize some return for handling them they may be willing to carry on a fishery for them. These fish and the waste from the food fish can be used for the production of oil and fish meal. There is a great demand for fish meal for use as poultry feed, and there is a market for low-melting-point oil.

Some control over the species composition of fish populations can be secured by creating environmental conditions which are more favorable for the desired species. Some species are most readily controlled at spawning time. Spawning concentrations of fish may be eliminated, fish may be prevented from reaching spawning areas, or nests and eggs may be destroyed.

Trout have a host of enemies which prey on them in different ways and at different times. Ducks, water hens, grebe, water ouzels, and kingfishers take fry and fingerling trout, while otters, minks, and 'coons take larger fish. However, the otter and mink may perform an actual service by the removal of the old, weak or diseased trout. The most destructive bird enemies are the loon, American merganser, heron, fish hawk, and kingfisher. These are all enemies which have existed as long or almost as long as the trout, and the trout have continued to exist in large numbers at least until civilization interfered with the natural conditions. Changed environmental conditions have increased the importance of some predators. In some situations control of these is essential.

With changes in environmental conditions, fish formerly associated with the trout or introduced into trout streams have become important predators or competitors. As long as streams remain cold, conditions favor trout and they can maintain themselves as the dominant fish, but when the streams become warm, pike, pickerel, perch, bass, ling, and sunfish may enter the stream and limit or destroy the trout. These fish should never be planted in a trout stream, and when they gain entrance efforts should be made to control or destroy them. In the streams of this country suckers, cottus, chub, dace, and several other species of minnows were the fish most commonly found with trout. While under natural conditions these fish were never very abundant, they have since the warming of many streams become the chief competitors of the trout. When the streams become warmer, environmental conditions become less favorable for trout and more desirable for suckers and minnows, so that these fish become dominant in the stream and reduce the numbers of the trout. Although the minnows serve as forage fish for the trout, they should never be introduced into a trout stream, as they compete directly with the young trout for food and space.

Population studies show that the warmer trout waters support larger standing-fish populations than do the cold streams. In some instances the population is several times as large. However, in these warm waters trout comprise only a small portion of the total fish population, whereas they are dominant in the fish populations of the cold streams. Thus, while the warmer, more productive streams have larger fish populations, the cold streams have larger standing populations of trout. It is believed that trout populations may be limited in the warm waters by competition with the suckers and minnows for food and space. The minnows and small suckers compete directly with the young trout for food, and the large suckers compete with the trout for space in pools. One of the largest recorded annual yields of trout was taken from a stream where trout were the only fish present (38).

Where possible, it is desirable to utilize the greater productivity of the warmer trout waters for the production of trout by eliminating the other fish. Where trout streams have become warmed to such an extent that they are overrun by minnows, suckers, sunfish, pike, ling, and bass it is perhaps desirable to eliminate all fish by poisoning and restock the stream with trout. Such a procedure is feasible only in stream sections above falls or where a dam can be built to prevent the weed species from migrating back into the stream. Some method must be devised for the control of weed species, because in many streams they are the principal factor limiting trout yields.

When poisoning is impractical, electric shockers or seines can be used to remove the coarse fish and assist in their control. It should be realized, however, that such thinning of the population of minnows, suckers, and other weed species will result in an increased growth rate and a larger percentage of survival.

There are several advantages in having trout streams stocked only with trout. When this is accomplished the total food production in so far as it is available can be used by the trout. Further, the anglers may be allowed to take all fish except those needed for reproduction without fear of competitor species encroaching on the trout habitat. Such removals will result in a young, fast-growing population which makes the best utilization of the food supply and provides the best fly fishing.

MANAGEMENT PROBLEMS

The carrying out of a management program presents problems not encountered in stream surveys and the formulation of the program. Lack of funds often hampers the work on state and Federal lands. Further, the potential value of streams for recreational purposes is not universally recognized. Because of this situation, and because a large portion of stream mileage is in private ownership, much of which is not interested in the management of streams for fishing, there are many obstacles to fisheries management.

Good land-use policies are fundamental to the maintenance of favorable stream environment. Favorable watershed conditions are rarely attained, however, as a planned endeavor. They have more often been a by-product of the acquisition and maintenance of forest lands. The diversity of ownership along streams, the lack of knowledge of stream requirements and of their dependence on conditions in the watershed, and the lack of funds have greatly hampered real progress in the management of streams for fishing.

The ideal situation from a management standpoint is one in which the entire stream can be managed as a unit. Future developments in stream management are dependent upon advances in our knowledge of the environmental requirements of the fish, an understanding of the essential factors which are lacking, and the development of effective methods for remedying deficiencies. Future advances are also dependent upon public support for the program. Education and psychology play an important part in the furtherance of a management program. To effectively put its program into operation, a fisheries agency should have a strong educational unit which cooperates closely with sportsmen's organizations and the press, radio, and television stations.

The fish-management program must have the understanding and active endorsement of the landowners and the interested public if it is to be successfully prosecuted. This should be kept constantly in mind as a basic policy guide. A well-informed public is *the* necessary basis for progressive management programs. Progress will not be rapid until the public becomes sufficiently well-informed and interested to demand the use of good management practices, or until the conservation departments gain the confidence of the public and are granted discretionary powers. Effective fisheries management requires a competent, conscientious manager with the knowledge, the means, and the power to act.

REFERENCES

1. Armistead, W. H. 1920. Trout waters, management, and angling, A. and C. Black, Ltd., London.
2. Bates, C. G., and A. J. Henry. 1928. Forest and streamflow experiment at Wagon Wheel Gap, Colorado. *U.S. Monthly Weather Rev., Sup.* **30**:1–79.
3. Belding, D. L. 1929. Water temperature and fish life. *Trans. Amer. Fisheries Soc.* **58**(1928):98–105.
4. Bennett, H. H. 1934. Soil erosion studies. *U.S. Dept. Agr. Yearbook.* Pp. 321–323.
5. Brown, Ernest C. 1923. Adjustment of environment vs. stocking—to increase the productivity of fish life. *Trans. Amer. Fisheries Soc.* **52**(1922): 131–145.
6. Creaser, Charles W. 1926. The structure and growth of the scales of fishes in relation to the interpretation of their life-history, with special reference to the sunfish, *Eupomotis gibbosus. Univ. Mich. Mus. Zool. Misc. Pub.* **17**.
7. Dana, S. T. 1916. Farms, forests, and erosion. *U.S. Dept. Agr. Yearbook.* Pp. 107–134.
8. Earle, Swepson. 1937. Fish culture is big business in the United States. *Prog. Fish Culturist.* No. 41 (July, 1937), pp. 1–29.

9. Ellis, M. M. 1937. Detection and measurement of stream pollution. *U.S. Bur. Fisheries Bul.* **48**:365–437.
10. Embody, G. C. 1922. Concerning high water temperatures and trout. *Trans. Amer. Fisheries Soc.* **51**(1921):58–64.
11. Forsling, C. L. 1931. A study of the influence of herbaceous plant cover on surface run-off and soil erosion in relation to grazing on the Wasatch Plateau in Utah. *U.S. Dept. Agr. Tech. Bul.* 220.
12. Funk, John L. 1949. Wider application of the electrical method of collecting fish. *Trans. Amer. Fisheries Soc.* **77**(1947):49–60.
13. Hall, William L., and H. Maxwell. 1910. Surface conditions and stream flow. *U.S. Dept. Agr. Forest Serv. Cir.* 176.
14. Hankinson, T. L. 1922. The habitat of the brook trout in Michigan. *Papers Mich. Acad. Sci., Arts, and Letters.* **2**:197–205.
15. Henshall, James Alexander. 1919. Indiscriminate and inconsiderate planting of fish. *Trans. Amer. Fisheries Soc.* **48**:166–169.
16. Hewitt, Edward R. 1934. Hewitt's handbook of stream improvement. The Marchbanks Press, New York.
17. Hubbs, Carl L., John R. Greeley, and Clarence M. Tarzwell. 1932. Methods for the improvement of Michigan trout streams. *Mich. Dept. Conserv. Inst. Fisheries Res. Bul.* **1**.
18. Joeris, Leonard. 1950. Fish growth rates read directly from the projected scale. *Prog. Fish Culturist.* **4**(12):209–210.
19. Kendall, William Converse. 1924. The status of fish culture in our inland public waters and the role of investigation in the maintenance of fish resources. *Roosevelt Wild Life Bul.* **2**(3):204–351.
20. Krumholz, Louis A. 1950. Some practical considerations in the use of rotenone in fisheries research. *Jour. Wildlife Mangt.* **14**(4):413–424.
21. Lowry, Edward M. 1951. A monograph for rapid back-calculation of fish lengths. *Prog. Fish Culturist.* **13**(4):199–204.
22. Miller, Lawrence F. 1951. Fish harvesting in two TVA mainstream reservoirs. *Trans. Amer. Fisheries Soc.* **80**(1950):2–10.
23. Morris, Robert W. 1950. An application of electricity to collection of fish. *Prog. Fish Culturist.* **12**(1):39–42.
24. Mottram, J. C. 1928. Trout fisheries, their care and preservation. Herbert Jenkins, Ltd., London.
25. Reynolds, R. V. P. 1911. Grazing and floods: A study of conditions in the Mante National Forest. *U.S. Dept. Agr., Forest Serv., Bul.* 91.
26. Roth, Filbert. 1906. The fisherman and reforestation. *Trans. Amer. Fisheries Soc.* **13**:164–168.
27. Salyer, J. Clark. 1935. A program of beaver management. *Amer. Wildlife.* **24**(3):39, 47, and **24**(4):56, 62–64.
28. Schuck, Howard. 1948. Survival of hatchery trout in streams and possible methods of improving the quality of hatchery trout. *Prog. Fish Culturist.* **10**(1):3–14.
29. Shetter, David S. 1939. Success of plantings of fingerling trout in Michigan waters as demonstrated by marking experiments and creel censuses. *Trans. 4th North Amer. Wildlife Conf.* Pp. 318–325.
30. Shetter, David S., O. H. Clark, and Albert Hazzard. 1946. The effects of deflectors in a section of a Michigan trout stream. *Trans. Amer. Fisheries Soc.* **76**(1946):248–278.
31. Shetter, David S., and A. S. Hazzard. 1939. Species composition by age groups and stability of fish populations in sections of three Michigan trout

streams during the summer of 1937. *Trans. Amer. Fisheries Soc.* **68**(1938):281–302.
32. ——— and ———. 1941. Results from plantings of marked trout of legal size in streams and lakes of Michigan. *Trans. Amer. Fisheries Soc.* **70**(1940):446–468.
33. Shetter, David S., and Justin W. Leonard. 1943. A population study of a limited area in a Michigan trout stream September, 1940. *Trans. Amer. Fisheries Soc.* **72**(1942):35–51.
34. Sprules, William M. 1941. The effect of a beaver dam on the insect fauna of a trout stream. *Trans. Amer. Fisheries Soc.* **70**(1940):236–248.
35. Tarzwell, Clarence M. 1932. Trout stream improvement in Michigan. *Trans. Amer. Fisheries Soc.* **61**(1931):48–57.
36. ———. 1937. Experimental evidence on the value of trout stream improvement in Michigan. *Trans. Amer. Fisheries Soc.* **66**(1936):177–187.
37. ———. 1938*a*. Factors influencing fish food and fish production in southwestern streams. *Trans. Amer. Fisheries Soc.* **67**(1937):246–255.
38. ———. 1938*b*. An evaluation of the methods and results of streams improvement in the southwest. *Trans. 3d North Amer. Wildlife Conf.* Pp. 339–364.
39. ———. 1942. Fish populations in the backwaters of Wheeler reservoir and suggestions for their management. *Trans. Amer. Fisheries Soc.* **71**(1941): 201–214.
40. ———. 1945. The possibilities of a commercial fishery in the TVA impoundments and its value in solving the sport and rough fish problems. *Trans. Amer. Fisheries Soc.* **73**(1943):137–157.
41. Tarzwell, Clarence M., and Lawrence F. Miller. 1943. The measurement of fishing intensity on the lower TVA reservoirs. *Trans. Amer. Fisheries Soc.* **72**(1942):246–256.
42. Zon, Raphael. 1908. General relations of forests and streams. *U.S. Inland Waterways Comm. Prelim. Rpt.*, pp. 505–513.

CHAPTER 21

Life Histories and Ecology of Cold-water Fish

Scientists have been studying fish and fish habitats for many years, but most of the written descriptions of their results have been very technical and often too complicated for the layman or even the elementary student of biology. Also, the reports have not been readily available.

Other circumstances have contributed to the confusion in the fisheries field. Even simple terms like "pond" and "lake" have not been clearly defined. Also fish have been called by so many different names that anyone not familiar with the local terminology is at a loss to know what is being discussed. For example, a "horned pout" in New England is a "bullhead" in Wisconsin. A walleyed pike from Lake Champlain becomes a yellow pickerel in Michigan and a jack salmon in Tennessee. The scientific names clear this all up for the technical man but not for the layman. You can hardly blame the fisherman for shying away from a name like *Esox masquinongy* for the musky or *Cristivomer namaycush* for the lake trout.

The great number of factors involved in a water habitat makes both the environment and the activities of fish difficult to understand. This is of concern to the technician as well as the fisherman as it helps to determine how, when, and where fish can be taken. This book attempts to describe some of these difficulties in terms which the beginner or layman can understand. The following items are taken up in an attempt to build a suitable background for the beginning fisheries manager and the intelligent fisherman.

What fish are found where?
Why are some fish large and some small?
Why do fish bite sometimes and not at other times?
How can we tell the age of fish?
How can we tell whether a body of water is productive?

The following discussion should clear up some of these points:

What Fish Are Found Where? Fish are a crop just as cattle and poultry are a crop. Fish are different from chickens and cattle, however, in that their temperature fluctuates with the temperature of the water in which they live, whereas the chickens and cattle keep their temperatures at about a constant degree regardless of the surroundings. Fish demand a certain amount of oxygen in the water in order to survive. The air in which higher animals live has a constant amount of oxygen present at all times. The oxygen in the water varies.

Waters such as rivers and ponds change as they pass from "youth" to "middle" and "old" age. As these changes occur water may be suitable or unsuitable for certain species of fish. Also water may be fertile or nonfertile and because of this nutritional condition may carry a small amount (weight) of fish.

A young river is one that forms the drainage of high or rugged lands. As a result it moves rapidly with many falls or riffles as it moves down the steep gradient. It is usually cool and well aerated. It is likely to have a good oxygen content for the salmonoid fish, especially if there are many rapids along its course.

After a river has time to cut down its banks and the high land becomes worn flat, it becomes slow, warm, and choked with weeds. Gradually the warm-water fish such as suckers, yellow perch, and bullheads take over.

Because fish react to water temperature and oxygen content, they will attempt to go where the water is suitable. This may be near the top or at lower depths in a lake. Likewise fish move to satisfy their food requirements. Also they may move even hundreds of miles to leave their eggs in locations where the conditions are suitable for incubation and development of the young.

The conditions and changes that take place in water make up the science of limnology. These changes follow the seasons as well as changes in the weather. Even the passing of a cloud over the sun may change the temperature of the water. The wind helps to aerate the surface water and causes it to move about. Earle Douchette (15) describes clearly the changes and conditions that occur in a northern lake in a little book called "Fisherman's Guide to Maine." He says:

> We must remember these facts—the water reaches its greatest density at 39 degrees fahrenheit; consequently it is heavier than it would be if it were either warmer or cooler; that, except for two very brief periods during the year, the water in the lake is never the same temperature from top to bottom—the heavier water is on the bottom and the lighter on the top, much like cream in a milk bottle; that cold water has the inherent ability to contain more dissolved oxygen than warm water.

In the winter the temperature under the ice is 32 degrees. It gets progressively warmer—and heavier—as it goes downward until at the bottom it is close to 39 degrees.

When the ice leaves the lake a highly interesting—and little known—phenomenon takes place. Gradually the sun, beating down on the surface, heats the water downward until at last it is the same temperature, about 39 degrees, throughout. When this happens even a moderate wind creates water currents that will roll the water completely from top to the very bottom of the lake. Guides then say that the lake is turning. At this time—and the phenomenon occurs again just before the fall freeze—the water from top to bottom is all the same temperature, and the same weight and the same oxygen content.

This condition lasts just a few days, for, as the sun gets warmer and warmer, the lake slowly progresses to what is called the summer stagnation stage.

At the height of this period—usually in July or August—the lake is separated into three layers, each with its individual characteristics.

The upper layer, or *epilimnion,* extends in large lakes to a depth of from 18 to 25 feet and is uniformly warm: the temperature 25 feet down will not be more than two or three degrees cooler than the surface water.

The middle layer, or *thermocline,* extends downward from 10 to 20 feet below the bottom of the upper layer. Here we experience a remarkable drop in temperature. At the top of this layer the water may be 75 degrees and at the bottom only 50. The lower layer, or *hypolimnion,* extends from the bottom of the thermocline to the bottom of the lake and contains more water generally than the other two layers combined. The water throughout this layer is cold, generally about 50 degrees at its top and about 44 at the lake bottom.

Here then we have a warm and a cold layer of water separated by a layer that acts as a buffer between the two. The thermocline acts much as a hydraulic cushion. Its greater—and increasing—density prevents the wind from rolling the lighter surface water down to any great depth.

Now let's see how this affects the fish. In general cold-water fish cannot tolerate water that is warmer than 75 degrees. On the other hand, extremely cold water is not conducive to their well being. Fish are cold-blooded creatures: their body temperature varies with the temperature of the surrounding water. Thus the metabolism of the fish rises and falls with the water temperature. In the winter it takes them a week or more to digest a meal that they could digest in a day in the summer. Anyone who has looked at a fish scale under a microscope will realize the truth of this statement. . . .

The ideal water temperature for cold-water fish is between 50–65 degrees. When they are in water of this temperature they are comfortable, they have a sense of well-being and *they feed voraciously.*

But we must not forget there is another factor involved. The cold water fish need about 6 parts per million (6 ppm) of dissolved oxygen in the water in which they live.

So to find the best fishing, we must fish in water of the right temperature and where the oxygen supply is sufficient. During the stagnation period (summer period) this place is in the thermocline.

Why Are Some Fish Big and Some Little? All fish are little when they are hatched. But some fish grow to a larger size than others. Many lake trout grow to 20 or 30 pounds, but brook trout never do. Some fish which have inherent possibilities of growing large do not if space or food is lacking. Thus we have female brook trout in some New England streams that, because of lack of food or because of extremely cold water, will lay eggs and live their entire lives and never get beyond the length of 5 inches. These are the "stunted" fish that are so much talked about by fishermen. The only solution for too many fish or too little food is to either decrease the number of fish or increase the amount of food. In farm fish ponds the food may be increased by adding fertilizer to the water, just as food for cattle in a pasture is increased by adding fertilizer to the soil.

Why Do Fish Bite Sometimes and Not at Other Times? I realize this is a most dangerous point to discuss. So many factors are involved that all the points cannot be covered.

To bite, fish must usually be hungry. An exception to this may be salmon which may strike at a lure because of being annoyed. Fish will not feed if the temperature of the water is not right for them.

Fish have daily and seasonal feeding habits and foods. Some fish, as the brown trout, feed more freely at night than during the day. Also, fish must be in the zone of water where you are presenting your bait. This is anywhere in a pond during the turnover (spring and fall) or in the thermocline during the summer. Exceptions may be lake trout or smelts which are likely to be in the bottom zone.

Fish will change their habits seasonally depending on what they are feeding, so you must present them with bait of the same kind or that looks enough like it so they will think it is the same. Also, fish do not feed if they are frightened, so your bait must be so presented that it (or you) does not scare them. Also the movement that you give a bait or fly has a lot to do with whether the fish strike or not.

How Can We Tell the Age of Fish? The age of a fish is important for a number of reasons. The purpose of stocking and the end product of natural production are to give some fisherman a legal-sized fish of good quality at a price he can afford to pay. The longer it takes to produce legal-sized fish naturally, or the greater length of time artificially reared fish must spend in fishing waters to reach catchable size, the greater is the cost and the greater the chance that a predator and not the fisherman will get it. Rapid growth usually indicates fertile waters and suitable numbers of fish. Thus the determination of age of a fish is important. Fish ages are commonly determined by studying scales taken under a microscope from the side of a fish. Scales are built up by the addition of layers or *circuli*. Where these layers are close together or show as broken or discontinuous patterns, a winter period of slow or lack of growth is indicated. This zone is called an "*annulus*." Ordinarily annuli are marked with Roman numerals as O, I, II, III, etc., and indicate the number of winters each fish has lived. Where fish are taken in

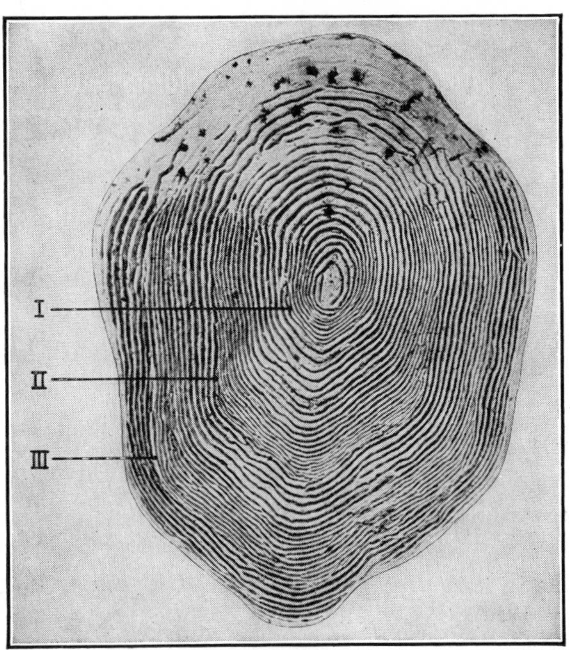

FIG. 21-1. Magnified scale of a 10-inch brown trout in its fourth year. Scale shows three annuli, I, II, III. (*Institute of Fisheries Research, Ann Arbor, Michigan.*)

the early part of the year they are given credit for a complete annulus at the edge of the scale, even though it is not yet completed (28).

How Can We Tell Whether a Body of Water Is Productive? Many methods have been used to test the productivity of water, but none is too satisfactory. Chemical analysis may give the mineral content or enough oxygen to sustain the various species of fish. A very simple method of determining fertility is to note the vegetation growing in a pond or stream, but this abundance may also prohibit the production of a satisfactory fish population. Quantitative bottom samples of insects or other invertebrate animals give some indication of fertility as will the quantitative measure of plankton. All of these are indicators, but one alone or all may not tell the story of how fruitful the water is for producing desirable fish. Water may be highly fertile and productive, but all of the power of this fertility may be expended in a growth of stunted fish of an undesirable species.

One of the most satisfactory measures of the productiveness of a body of water is the capture and classification of some of the fish which grow there. In a stream a sample of fish can be netted out or "shocked" by the use of electricity and some of the fish measured, weighed and scales taken. With the results of these data a close estimation can be made as to the fertility and productivity of the stream or pond. Many small fish of advanced age may indicate too many fish or conditions where the fertility never reaches the desired species. The age-size table given with each species shows average but probably not maximum growth for these fish. Where a particular kind of fish is not present in the sample, it may indicate that some necessary condition for the well-being of that species is lacking or that there is some deficiency in the method of collecting.

COLD-WATER FISH[1]

Taxonomy of the Game Fish. The fish that will be discussed in the following pages are classified as follows:

Class: Pisces

Family: *Salmonidae*	Genus	Species
The chars		
Eastern brook trout	*Salvelinus*	*fontinalis*
Lake trout	*Cristivomer*	*namaycush*
The salmon		
Rainbow trout	*Salmo*	*gairdnerii*
Brown trout	*Salmo*	*trutta*
Atlantic salmon	*Salmo*	*salar salar*
Sebago salmon	*Salmo*	*salar sebago*
Pacific salmon	*Oncorhynchus*	
Sockeye, red, or blueback	*Oncorhynchus*	*nerka nerka*
Chum	*Oncorhynchus*	*keta*
Pink or humpback	*Oncorhynchus*	*gorbuscha*
Spring, chinook, king, tyee, quinnat	*Oncorhynchus*	*tshawytscha*
Coho or silver	*Oncorhynchus*	*kisutch*
Family: *Osmeridae*		
Smelt	*Osmerus*	*mordax*

EASTERN BROOK TROUT *Salvelinus fontinalis*

Description. Many reasons can be given for the popularity of trout fishing. Brook trout live in a beautiful and inspiring environment.

[1] Nomenclature for the fishes will be according to Walter H. Chute and Committee. 1947. A list of common and scientific names of the better known fishes of the United States and Canada. *Amer. Fisheries Soc. Pub.* 1.

Usually it is clear and cold and has a variety of quiet pools and turbulent rapids. Such a setting makes an ever-enjoyable and interesting picture. The sea trout, or salters, of the north Atlantic Coast and the "coasters" of Lake Superior and Lake Nipigon are all forms of this versatile fish.

Classification and general location of various forms of char in North America are as follows (34, 44):

Class: Pisces

Family: *Salmonidae*	Genus	Species	Distribution
Eastern brook trout	*Salvelinus*	*fontinalis*	General
Lake Sunapee trout	*Salvelinus*	*aureolus*	Lake Sunapee, N.H.
Rangeley Lake, or blueback trout	*Salvelinus*	*oquassa*	Rangeley Lake, Maine, and a few Canadian lakes
Dolly Varden (salmon trout) of Alaska, western char or bull trout	*Salvelinus*	*malma spectabilis*	Northern California to Alaska east to Alberta and Montana
Great Lakes trout, gray trout or togue	*Cristivomer*	*namaycush*	Northeastern United States west to Montana; Canada and Alaska

The eastern brook or speckled trout is one of the most beautiful, as well as one of the most popular of the fresh-water game fishes. The body color is a mottled green above and orange below. The spots on the sides are orange to red, centered on a larger whitish-colored halo, both of which are imposed on the darker background. The markings above are olive-colored vermiculations on a darker background, while the lower fins have a white line towards the front. The tail is nearly straight across, hence the term "squaretail."

Age, Size, and Growth. Brook trout vary in size, shape, and form depending on the condition of the waters in which they grow. Very large brook trout are the exception rather than the rule, but trout up to 3 pounds or more in weight are not too uncommon in fertile lakes or large rivers. Dymond (17) records a brook trout taken on a line from Nipigon River which weighed 14½ pounds. Size related to age is about as follows. Fish reach a total length of 2 to 4 inches at the end of the first growing season and 4 to 8 inches at the end of the second. From here on the growth is about 2½ to 3 inches per year if sufficient food is available (51, 52).

Weight and condition of brook trout vary with the size of the body of water in which they grow, the temperature of the water, and the amount of food available. Hoover (33), however, states that lack of food may not be the limiting factor, believing that low temperatures may prevent the utilization of food.

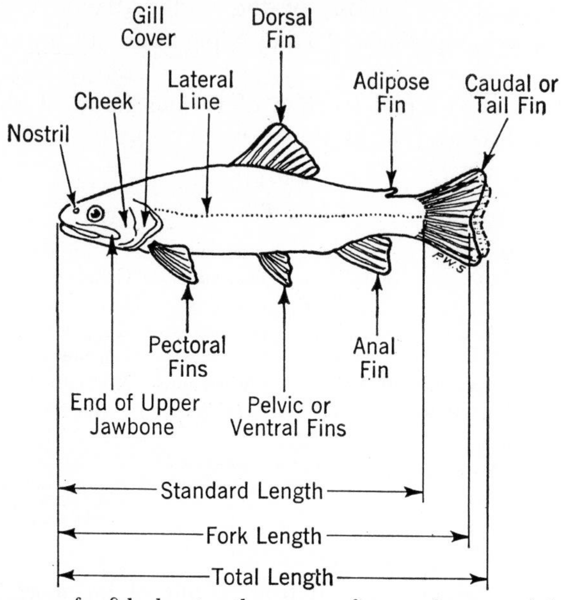

FIG. 21-2. Diagram of a fish showing the names of external parts and different length measurements.

Cooper (14) gives the total lengths[2] and weights of speckled trout in six bodies of water in the Rangeley Lake district of Maine as follows:

Table 21-1. Age and Size of Eastern Brook Trout (14)
(Basis 405 fish)

Age in growing seasons, Jan. 1	Total length, in.	Total weight, oz.
1	4.2	
2	8.4	4.8
3	10.0	5.9
4	12.1	11.4
5	14.8	22.7
6	18.1	47.2
7	20.7	60.1

[2] Total length (T.L.) is the distance from the tip of the head (jaws closed) to the tip of the tail with the lobes compressed so as to give maximum possible measurement. Fork length (F.L.) is the length from the tip of the snout to the end of the rays in the center of the caudal fin. Standard length (S.L.) is the length from the tip of the snout to the end of the vertebral column. (From Karl F. Lagler. 1950. Studies in fresh water fishery biology, J. W. Edwards, Ann Arbor, Mich.)

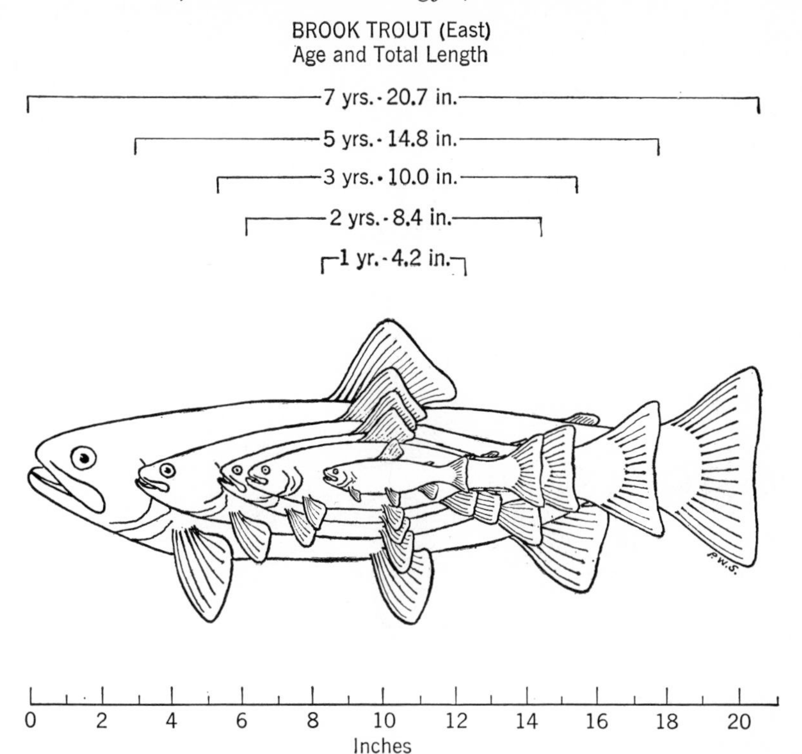

Fig. 21-3. Length and age relationship of the eastern brook trout from eastern waters (14).

A compilation of the age and size of brook trout is given for the western part of the continent by Rawson (49).

Table 21-2. Approximate Total Length of Western Brook Trout in Relation to Growing Seasons
(Basis 60 fish)

Age in growing seasons, Jan. 1	*Total length, in.*
1	4.4
2	7.8
3	10.3
4	12.5
5	14.4
6	16.0

Fishermen frequently talk about the fine appearance of wild or native trout versus the poor color or pallid appearance of hatchery-reared

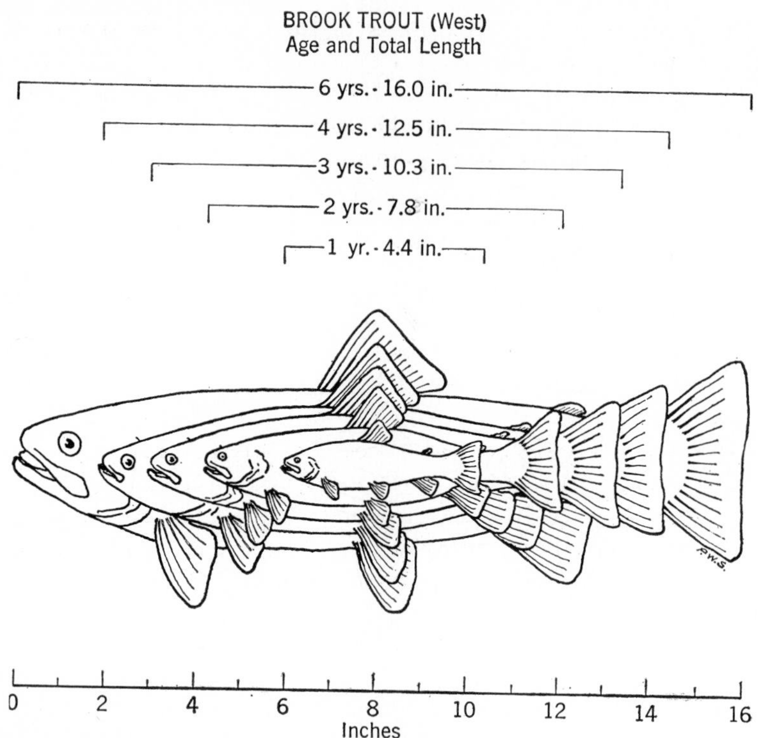

FIG. 21-4. Length and age relationship of the eastern brook trout from western waters (49).

("liver fed") fish. Of the differences in color of wild trout, Ricker (51) has the following to say:

> Differences in colour can usually be correlated with the type of water in which the trout is found. In streams and ponds of southern Ontario trout are brightly coloured, with clearly defined spots on the sides and a definite pattern above. In soft waters of the north, the sides have a dusky cast and the back is much more nearly black, a condition which reaches its fullest condition in the tea-brown waters of bog streams. In lakes the back is often greenish with well-defined vermiculations, the sides and belly are bright silver with pale spots, the fins are not a particularly bright red. In the sea this condition is intensified and the spots are sometimes almost or completely obscured.

The color of the flesh of wild fish varies from white to bright pink or deep salmon. In comparing wild and hatchery trout for palatability, Baeder *et al.* (3) say wild trout have deeper color, better flavor, and lack the condition called "tacky" or "sticky" which is found in hatchery trout. The flesh of wild trout also holds together better.

Distribution. Originally brook trout were limited to the eastern part of North America. Since all species of trout have been reared in captivity, either eggs or fish have been distributed to practically all waters of the continent that are suitable for them. In general they are found in waters of glacial soils or where rocky strata produce springs. Also forest growth, bogs, or swamps tend to keep the water temperature within their tolerance range (32 to 70°F.), unless of course the source of the water is from snow. Good trout waters are not usually found in heavy-clay or black-prairie soils.

Habits. The movements of eastern brook trout are quite local. During the day, if the sun is bright, the trout will lie in the seclusion of a deep hole or under a stream bank where they can watch what is going on out in the more exposed parts of the stream. It appears also that they get out of the main current so as not to have to fight it. If a choice morsel of food comes floating past or something drops on the surface of the water near them, they usually move out to capture it. During early morning or as the sun goes down in the evening, the fish may move to the more shallow parts of the stream to feed among the rubble or gravel. Sometimes this movement is upstream, sometimes down, but never far from a deep hole, a submerged log, or overhanging bush.

In a pond the pattern of movement is modified. When the water temperature is suitable, the fish may move from one place to another wherever food becomes available, as with a hatch of insects. At other times deep holes, springs, or other suitable spots are sought. The reaction to light is also apparent with pond fish. Any disturbance or unfamiliar object will cause them to seek shelter.

Spawning. Brook trout migrate toward the headwaters of streams to spawn in late October and November. The number of eggs laid by a female varies with her age. Year-old trout may lay 150 to 250 eggs; 2-year-olds, 350 to 600; and older fish, 500 to 2,500 (16 *g.r.*). Spawning locations sought are gravel bottoms in spring-fed tributaries. Pond-locked brook trout seek gravel beds where the spring waters seep through the gravel, but Cooper (14) indicates lake spawning is of minor importance. The age of spawning for the brook trout varies, beginning usually with the second year, but it reaches full development at the third year (14, 59). The male arrives over the beds first and is followed later by the female. The female digs a bed in the gravel where the water is swift and clear. As the eggs are laid, the males fertilize them and the pair move upstream, depositing eggs as they go and covering those downstream. The eggs remain in the bed until spring. Losses of eggs may be caused by predators, smothering with silt, or being washed away by floods.

Food. Brook trout fry and fingerlings eat plankton, midges, and other insect larvae (29), while the adults prefer insects, shrimps, and forage fish. Needham (44) lists the following foods eaten by eastern brook trout in central New York: mayfly nymphs, 30.1 per cent; caddis fly larvae and pupae, 44.7 per cent; stone fly nymphs, 3.5 per cent; fly larvae and pupae, 15.8 per cent; beetle larvae, 2.8 per cent; crayfish and scuds, 1.1 per cent; and miscellaneous, 1.9 per cent.[3]

Large trout feed mainly on vertebrates, mostly small fish. In order to produce a supply of food for large trout a type of forage fish which will not grow too large for the trout to take and which is vigorous enough as a species to keep ahead of the feeding habits of the predatory trout is desirable. Smelt fit these requirements in a large cold body of water where oxygen is available in the deeper parts of the lake.

Habitat. Brook trout live in a wide variety of waters as well as general surroundings. The brooks of the mountains or woodlands of the eastern part of the continent are known to all. Natural lakes or ponds and both man-made ponds and beaver flowages are used if springs or streams keep the water sufficiently cold.

Good trout water must have suitable protective cover in one form or another. On streams and rivers cover consists of deep pools, undercut banks, brush, and logs. It is possible to describe the environment for fish by setting maximum limits for chemical and physical properties, as temperature, hydrogen ion concentration, dissolved oxygen, and dissolved carbon dioxide. It is difficult to define these limits precisely, however, since the various factors are interrelated. For example, the amount of oxygen consumed by the fish and the minimum amount of dissolved oxygen which will barely support life vary with the temperature, pH, and dissolved carbon dioxide. For this reason, recent investigations have given greater emphasis to the study of fish populations as indicators of the suitability of water habitats, rather than depending on physical and chemical measurements of samples of the habitat. The presence of the fish and evidence of its reproducing itself are good contributing evidence in the evaluation of the habitat for a particular species.

Physical and Chemical Limits. The reader should keep in mind the limitations mentioned above when applying the figures given in this and the following habitat descriptions.

The brook trout is not found in streams where the water temperature is much over 68°F., with 57 to 66° being a safe range. They may survive temperatures from 75 to 81°F. for short periods and may live in ponds where the temperature is well over 68°F. if the water is well aerated and competitors are not numerous (21). If trout are accustomed to temperatures of less than 57°F., they tend to seek warmer waters. If accustomed to temperatures of 57 to 66°F. they tend to "stay put." If temperatures go higher than 66°F. they attempt to find cooler waters.

[3] Total of percentages does not equal 100. Data are given as originally published.

Even though trout will live in waters of higher or lower temperatures than the above, their body processes are not at optimum. Thus if the waters in a pond are cold, the fish feed in the shallows, but as the temperature rises above 68°F. they cease normal feeding and seek cold spring holes or cool water of tributary brooks (21, 22).

The fact that brook trout require a high oxygen content in water is well known. According to Fry (21) and Graham (22), waters that have reached air saturation are probably optimum. Fry (21) observes that speckled trout can exist in waters containing 0.9 ppm at 50°F. temperature and 1.6 to 1.8 ppm at 68°F. Cooper (14) suggested an oxygen content of 5 parts per million as a safe minimum. Carbon dioxide in water should not be greater than 40 ppm, according to Hoover (29), but Fry (21) indicates high CO_2 content has little or no effect on speckled trout. A range of 5.0 to 9.0 on the pH scale (acid intensity) is satisfactory (14).

Miscellaneous. It is the opinion of the author that the virtues of the brook trout have been much overrated. It is relatively easy to catch, often taking a poorly concealed hook and with crude fishing techniques. Perhaps this should be rated as a virtue as it encourages many inexperienced people, especially children, to fish. It is quite intolerant of unfavorable conditions, as high temperatures or polluted streams. It is also subject to a higher degree of loss due to predators or other unfavorable conditions associated with economic uses of land than are the other trout.

The brook or speckled trout has no peer in the minds of many fishermen. At his insistence it has been stocked in almost every type of water in existence, in some places where the returns do not at all justify the cost and effort of stocking. Cooper (14) says it is biologically unsound to stock brook trout in lakes and ponds until the fish are 6 to 8 inches long and that fry should be planted only in suitable tributary streams. If a lake has no such streams, the fish should be held in the hatchery until they are 6 to 8 inches long or of legal size.

The matter of stocking trout in the fall versus in the spring has been the subject of numerous arguments by sportsmen for the past 100 years. Studies have been carried on with marked fish in several places, comparing the returns from both the east and west, which show the following facts:

1. There are tremendous losses of trout during the winter period for fish up to 18 months of age. These losses vary from 60 to 85 per cent of the population (47).

2. Hatchery-reared trout sustain heavier losses than naturally spawned fish (47).

3. The returns of all plantings of artificially reared trout are low and

therefore costly. In one Michigan river the fall tagged fish gave a return of 1.0 per cent, and the spring planted fish returned 19.6 per cent (27, 56, 58).

LAKE TROUT *Cristivomer namaycush*

Description. Various names for the lake trout include Mackinaw trout, longe, and togue. In the Lake States Mackinaw or lake trout is used most commonly, but in Canada and New England the use of "togue" or "gray trout" is customary. The lake trout is a char, belonging to the same group of fishes as the brook trout as far as classification is concerned. This classification is based on a detail of the anatomy of the two fish (teeth on the vomer which is a part of the upper jaw of a fish) rather than on the similarity of the habits or places where each live. Both species have very small scales and similar demands for cold water with an abundance of oxygen.

The lake trout has the distinction of being both a sport and a commercial fish. In the northern Great Lakes and Canada thousands of fishermen spend many hours trolling for "lakers." The size of the fish and the excellent quality of the flesh make the sport both exciting and worthwhile. Hundreds of deep lakes in the northern part of the United States and Canada yield good catches of Mackinaw trout each year.

The general method of fishing for lake trout is by the use of wire lines with large wabbling spoons and large hooks trolled deep. Commercial fishermen take the fish with set lines or by the use of gill nets. In the spring just as the ice goes out they can be taken with a fly near the surface. The most dramatic and catastrophic occurrence in the history of fisheries is the destruction of the lake trout in the lower Great Lakes by the lamprey eel that came from the Atlantic Ocean through the Welland Canal.

The lake trout is the least colorful of the trout. It is deep gray above and along the sides and white below, with round pale spots sometimes tinged with pink. The shape of the body is troutlike, with a pointed head and the body about four times the length of the head. The scales are small, and the tail is forked. These fish are frequently very fat but have excellent-flavored flesh. Baked, fried, or broiled lake trout is among the choice morsels of the epicure.

Age, Size, and Weight. Lake trout live in a cold and somewhat infertile environment. They are therefore slow to mature and live to get both old and large if nothing disturbs their life span. Fry (19, 20) reported the oldest specimens taken from the Algonquin Park lakes as 17 years old and referred to a fish of this species from Great Bear Lake which was 37 years old.

Weights and lengths of lake trout vary with the size of the lake, the

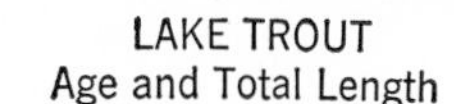

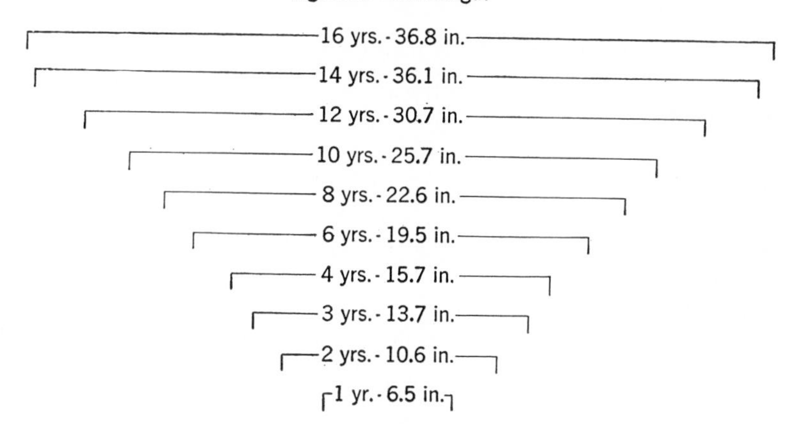

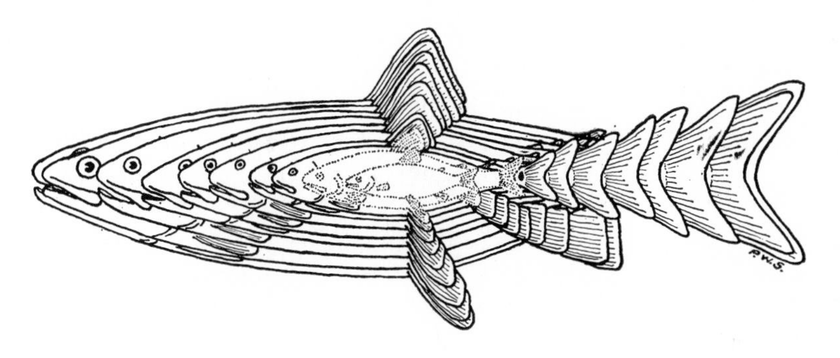

FIG. 21-5. Length and age relationship of the lake trout (19).

amount of food, and the length of time the fish have escaped capture. Fry (20) shows a fish taken at Bear Island, Timagomi, Ontario, that weighed 32 pounds, but the length is not given. Lake trout taken from Lake Superior often weigh 20 to 25 pounds and are 36 to 40 inches long. Carlander (16 *g.r.*) gives the weight-length (T.L. in inches) as follows:

Table 21-3. Lengths and Weights of Lake Trout, Great Lakes Region (19, 20)

Total length, in.	*Weight, lb.*
15	1.0
20	2.4–2.6
25	5.4–5.5
30	8.6–9.2
35	14.9
40	22.3

Distribution. Lake trout are found in suitable waters in the United States and Canada south as far as southern New England, and west across New York and Canada including the Lake states to Montana, and north and west including the lakes connected with the Yukon basin in Alaska (44). Practically all the trout species that are raised in captivity have been planted in waters outside of their natural range, so the range has been considerably expanded during the past 50 years. J. H. Wales (65), in an article on the trout of Castle Lake in northern California, shows pictures of 9- and 17-pound Mackinaw trout taken from the lake. This was no doubt beyond the natural distribution range of lake trout.

Habits. Movements of lake trout may be limited by the oxygen supply and the temperature of the water. The fact that Mackinaws can be taken on the surface at some times of the year indicates that shallow water

Table 21-4. Age and Length of Lake Trout from Ontario (19, 20)

Age in growing seasons, Jan. 1	*Total length, in.**	*Age in growing seasons, Jan.* 1	*Total length, in.**
1	(6.5)	10	25.7
2	(10.6)	11	27.7
3	13.7	12	30.7
4	15.7	13	32.7
5	17.4	14	36.1
6	19.5	15	36.3
7	21.3	16	36.8
8	22.6	17	37.4
9	23.9		

* Figures in parentheses are estimated from curve.

does not restrict them if other conditions are suitable. The average preferred temperature for this trout is about 50°F. (19, 20).

Spawning. Lake trout do not breed until 4 to 7 years old (29, 54), reaching maturity at a certain age rather than a particular size, according to Fry (19, 20). In Ontario lakes the females are 6 to 7 years old before they are able to spawn. Males mature slightly earlier than females. As a result some trout are spawning at 15 to 17 inches, and others at this size are immature.

Lake trout females as a class produce a small number of eggs. The number of eggs produced by Ontario trout weighing from 6 to 25 pounds is 6 to 14 thousand per fish; the smaller-sized trout produce relatively less (16 *g.r.*). Eddy and Surber (22 *g.r.*) give the number of eggs produced by 16- to 20-inch females as 1,500 to 2,300 eggs.

Lake trout spawn on clean gravel or rubble bottom, and the eggs are left to cling to the rock particles. Currents of water keep the spawning area free from mud and bathed with fresh water. In Seneca Lake in New York the spawning season begins in late September and lasts through October. The spawning location is 100 to 200 feet deep according to

Royce (54). Eddy and Surber (22 *g.r.*) give the time of spawning in Lake Superior as the latter part of September to December and in inland lakes as the time when the ice closes over, usually in early November. The temperature of the water on the spawning beds at the time the eggs are laid is not known exactly but the spawning act occurs at approximately the time of the water turnover. It is earlier in the shallow lakes and later in the large ones according to Royce (54). An exception appears to be Seneca Lake in New York where the maximum depth is 625 feet and spawning starts in September. Surface temperatures in Seneca Lake taken from September 29 to October 17, 1941, showed a variation from 57 to 62°F. (54).

One or more males attend the female during the spawning act, and the peak of spawning is from 5 to 9 P.M. A high percentage of eggs are fertilized, and the survival of eggs to hatching also seems to be high. The temperature may range from 50 to 32.5°F. without injury. The time of incubation is about 140 days at 36 to 37°F. (18).

Food. Lake trout grow slowly and continue to grow for many years. The waters in which they can survive are likely to be infertile and contain a minimum of food organisms. Likewise smelts (and possibly other lake trout) are about the only species of fish able to survive in water suitable for lake trout.

Young lake trout feed on plankton, insect larvae, and nymphs (29). In the Great Lakes trout smaller than 15 inches long feed on insects, crustaceans, and mollusks as well as on fish. With trout over 15 inches long the diet consists of smelts, chub, shiners, trout perch, yellow perch, sculpins, and suckers (29, 64).

Habitat. The entire life of a lake trout is spent in large bodies of water and usually in the deeper parts of the lake. It is intolerant to warm water, so spawning lake trout appear on sandy bars to spawn only after the water has cooled in the fall. They may also appear in shallow water in the spring before the water has had time to warm up. Scant vegetation and large areas of gravel and rocks on the bottom are characteristic of young lakes suitable for lake trout. Low temperatures and abundant oxygen are found in lakes only where there is a minimum of weed growth, a condition which results from waters that lack fertility. Thus the lake trout grows slowly because of the conditions that limit its existence.

Physical and Chemical Limits. *Temperature.* Preferred temperatures 50 to 60°F. Will tolerate 65°F. (22 *g.r.* 29).

Oxygen. Minimum 4 ppm. Eddy and Surber (22 *g.r.*) say "abundant oxygen" is needed in the deep part of the lake. Greater oxygen concentration than 4 ppm is probably more desirable.

pH range. 6 to 9. May not be important but most lake trout waters are acid.

Carbon dioxide. Estimated under 20 ppm (29).

Depth. Part of the lake should have a depth of 100 feet or more with the deeper water well oxygenated. Smaller lakes with less depth may carry lake trout because of cold springs in the bottom or drainage from cold bog swamps. Such lakes are likely to carry only the lake trout that can be supported by the limited cold water and a suitable oxygen supply during the warmer periods in the summer.

Miscellaneous. Fishing for lake trout is a thrilling sport. Small lake trout up to 10 pounds may be caught by trolling from small boats along the rocky shores of northern Lake Huron, Lake Michigan, and Lake Superior. Cruisers are used to get into the deeper waters of these lakes, and the lures are trolled deep. Usually the lure is a large metal spinner with a large hook attached. This is trolled just off the rocks at a slow pace. The line may be a large cotton one weighted with a pound or two of lead, as a strong line is needed because of catching the lure on the rocks. A popular type of gear is a braided Monel metal or copper line or a solid copper line. The rod is short, and the line is taken up on a large, direct-acting reel. When a fish strikes it is likely to give two or three struggles and then come to the surface like a heavy log. In smaller lakes lighter gear may be used. A nylon line with a lead core is satisfactory. A boat rod and a multiple deep-sea reel may be used where the water depth is not more than 100 to 200 feet.

RAINBOW TROUT *Salmo gairdnerii*

Description. Usually rainbow trout fishing begins in early spring after the fisherman has had a long inactive winter season during which he has

FIG. 21-6. A rainbow trout. The western forms are called steelheads and cutthroats. The rainbow trout is an outstanding game fish. (*R. D. Robinson, Ontario Department of Lands and Forests.*)

conditioned both himself and his gear for the season ahead. When the season gets under way any kind of trout will be attractive, but if the water is high and discolored and the weather is cold, brook and brown trout may refuse to cooperate. As rainbows are inveterate travelers and spawn under natural conditions in the spring, spawners may be moving up the larger streams adjacent to large lakes where the fish have spent the winter. No moment in life can be more thrilling than the one in

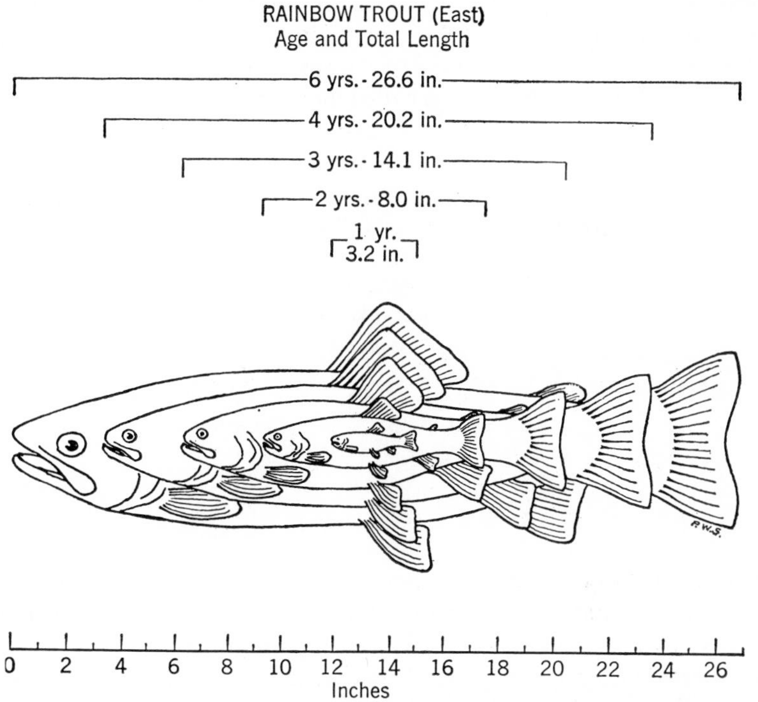

FIG. 21-7. Length and age relationship of the rainbow trout from eastern waters (24).

which a large spawning rainbow trout takes the lure of a hopeful and courageous fisherman who has cast his lures in spite of cold winds and high, snow-filled water.

Various forms of the rainbow trout are found throughout North America. Some of the common forms follow: (44)

Class: Pisces

Family: *Salmonidae*	Genus	Species	Distribution
Rainbows	*Salmo*	*gairdnerii*	Most of North America; remains in fresh water.
Steelhead	*Salmo*	*gairdnerii*	Has access to ocean.
Golden	*Salmo*	*aqua-bonita*	Kern River, California, planted in high mountain streams of West.
Cutthroat	*Salmo*	*clarkii*	Rivers of interior basins of northwestern United States.

Rainbows are said to be the best fighters in the trout group. They are well-suited to turbulent waters, so perhaps get their fighting qualities of necessity from the type of habitat they live in.

Steelheads are rainbows that spend part of their life in the ocean, usually 2 or 3 years, before returning to fresh water. In general, all rainbows are inclined to migrate rather than to remain in one location.

The red stripe along the side is the most conspicuous marking of the rainbow. The background is likely to be light, with markings of black spots. The fins do not have the color markings of the brook trout. In weight, resident river rainbows vary from ¼ to 3 pounds, but the sea-run steelheads may weigh a great deal more, usually from 3 to 12 pounds (44).

Age, Size, and Growth. The size of rainbow trout in relation to age varies with water temperature, length of the growing season, and food available. Selected age groups are as follows:

Table 21-5. Age and Size of Rainbow Trout from Michigan Waters (24)
(Basis 329 fish)

Age in growing seasons, Jan. 1	*Total length, in.*
1	3.2
2	8.0
3	14.1
4	20.2
5	22.4
6	26.6

A study of steelhead trout (*Salmo gairdnerii*) caught in Tillamook County, Oregon, shows the extent of variation of size in relation to age. These fish, which live in the ocean and migrate up the streams to spawn, were exceptionally large (2 to 3 feet), reflecting the effect of the rich food supply found in the sea (60).

Distribution. The rainbow trout was originally a western species, but during the past hundred years has been distributed in the form of eggs or fish to almost every point of the world. It does well where large rivers that are reasonably cold and clean run into large lakes or the ocean. In many localities fisherman still net the migrating steelhead for commercial purposes, but gradually the greater value of these fish for sport is being recognized and legal restriction placed on their capture and sale.

Habits. The rainbow trout are the most unstable of the various trout species. They prefer to move downstream to larger waters but may move up streams adjacent to the ocean and to large lakes to breed. They have been planted in many ponds, but as yet there is no good evidence to show they ever breed in other than tributary streams.

Spawning. Needham (44) gives the spawning time as February to

June. Swollen or silt-loaded streams seem to be no deterrent and in fact may be a stimulant to start the spawning run. A strain of rainbow trout has been developed that spawns from October to February (22 *g.r.*). The age of spawning is 2 or 3 years. The males are more likely to spawn at an early age than are females.

The redd, or nest, is dug by the female in the gravel at the lower end of a pool where water pours over the nest. The eggs are usually covered

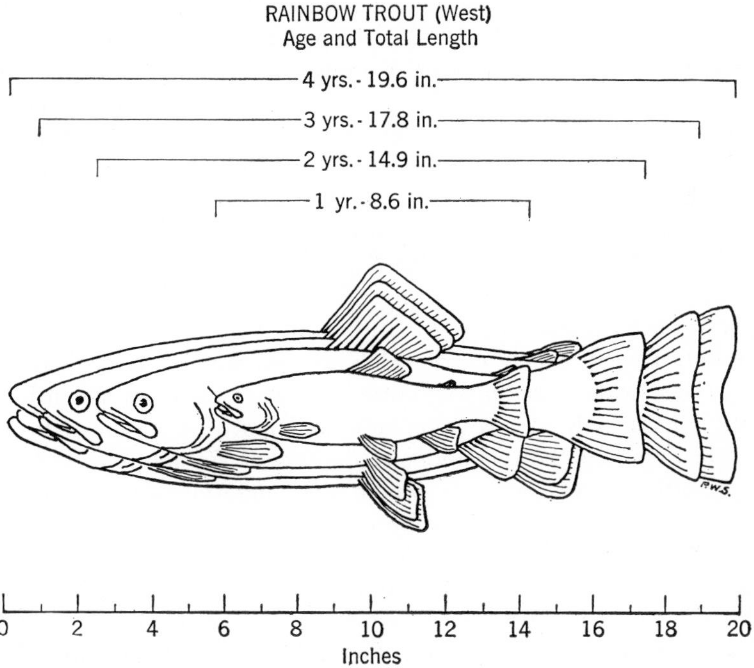

FIG. 21-8. Length and age relationship of the rainbow trout from western waters. (*C. McC. Mottley, Trans. Amer. Fisheries Soc.* **62:** 144–151.)

by several inches of gravel. Several nests may be prepared by one female, according to Needham (44). One or more males are usually in attendance to fertilize the eggs but take no part in the preparation of the nest. A mature female may lay as many as 6,400 eggs, with about 1,000 to 1 redd. Carlander (16 *g.r.*) gives the number of eggs as ranging from 200 to 9,000, but most of the fish listed produced less than 3,000 per female. Desirable water for spawning is usually shallow, from 4 to 6 inches deep. At a mean temperature of 38.3°F. the eggs hatch in 103 days, and at 60.8°F. in 18 days (18). Rainbow trout and steelheads return to the sea or lake after spawning, so may spawn for several years.

Food. The food of young rainbow trout depends on the kind of organisms in the streams in which they live. In fact, trout up to about 8 inches in length depend on invertebrate organisms, mostly insects, for their food. Cooper (13) lists larval stages of such insects as mayflies, caddis flies, stone flies, midges, dragonflies, damsel flies, and some of the beetles, as well as fresh-water shrimps or amphipods, as most frequently found in streams. Older fish depend on mature insects that drop on the water from bordering vegetation, as well as fish and other vertebrates.

The food of rainbow trout no doubt varies as to whether they live in a river or a lake and also depends on the locality. Leonard and Leonard (40) analyzed the stomachs of 322 rainbows from Birch Lake, Michigan, and found the two most important groups of food for these trout were aquatic insects and fishes. Insects accounted for 23 per cent of the total volume and fishes 43 per cent. The remaining 34 per cent consisted of miscellaneous items. Of the fish taken, forage species made up the larger part of the diet of both rainbow and lake trout. Yellow perch and centrarchids (bass and sunfish group) occurred but seldom. Rainbow trout took very little surface food except during June when the burrowing mayflies were emerging and during October and November when land insects were consumed.

Habitat. Rivers which carry rainbows are usually large, turbulent streams, but wide variation in these properties exists as the fish may use the stream only at spawning time and move up or down to more desirable water for the remainder of the season. Rainbows may be resident in either rivers or lakes where the migrating activity does not operate. Under these conditions the waters need to be cold, with a maximum of 83°F. and well aerated.

The rainbow is very versatile and seems to do well under a wide range of conditions, but the one where it is most nearly at home is a large stream of relatively constant flow which has a temperature of 65 to 75°F. and many swift runs over rubble and coarse gravel with deep pools and escape covers. It is said that there are two strains of these fish, the resident river or pond strain and the ocean or lake-river strain. The ocean-run fish have developed to larger size, some reaching the enormous weight of 42 pounds (44). River residents are much smaller, weighing 2 to 5 pounds.

Physical and Chemical Limits. *Temperature.* Summer maximum water temperatures of 83°F. have already been given for the rainbow. Temperatures much less than this, varying from 55 to 75°F., are optimum. Cooper (13) sets the maximum temperature of ponds for all trout at 75°F. because of the competition of warm-water species which live in the upper and warmer parts of a pond.

Oxygen. Rainbows' requirements in ponds are the same as for brook and brown trout.

pH range. The pH range (acid intensity) should be 5 to 9 on the pH scale. Trout can tolerate more acid than most other game fishes. According to Cooper (13), a low pH in deep water reflects low oxygen and high carbon dioxide content, which trout and salmon cannot tolerate.

Carbon dioxide. Under 0.20 ppm (29).

Game Status. Usually fishing is done in large streams adjacent to the ocean or in large lakes. Rainbows are also caught in ponds on submerged bait, either natural or artificial. Where rainbows are hooked in streams the fight is enhanced by the currents and by large pools where the fish have the advantage of plenty of space in which to operate. The fact that rainbows leap out of the water more than other trout adds interest to the battle.

Miscellaneous. There is some confusion on the part of the layman as to the use of various names for trout that have some similarity to rainbow trout but are called by different names. The following species are given and described briefly to clear up this confusion.

Common rainbow trout (*Salmo gairdnerii*). This trout is the common form of trout with the red band along the sides.

Steelhead trout (*Salmo gairdnerii*). This trout is a sea-run or salt-water trout that spends part of its life in salt water and may migrate long distances up fresh-water streams to spawn.

Cutthroat trout. (*Salmo clarkii*). This trout is also called the black spotted trout. It has bright-colored streaks along the lower jaw and a greater degree of spotting. It originally was found in the streams that flow into the Pacific Ocean from northern California to Alaska. In the West Coast streams it migrates a shorter distance than the rainbow trout. Cutthroat trout have been planted inland and behave much like lake-run rainbows.

Other Species. Trout of the rainbow type also include Kamloop trout, *Salmo kamloop;* Rio Grande trout, *Salmo spilurus;* Piute trout, *Salmo seleniris;* and golden trout, *Salmo aqua-bonita.*

Stocking of Rainbow Trout. Many sportsmen and fish administrators have pondered the questions of what size, when, and where to stock rainbow trout. The conclusions of the New York biological survey are perhaps as good as can be arrived at.

They (rainbows) become sexually mature at the end of the third year counting from the time the eggs are laid in April. Those kept in the spring water of the State hatcheries may spawn at varying times from December to April, but wild rainbows in New York streams spawn principally during April. Young rainbows planted in the smaller streams, whether cold ones suitable for brook trout or the warmer ones containing browns, generally remain there until sometime during the second year after which they migrate downstream. During the second year many of them ranging in size from 6 to 8 inches are legal size for angling. The migrants may or may not leave the stream apparently depending upon their size and summer temperature of the water to which the stream is tributary and the presence or absence of barriers (waterfalls or serious pollution), the latter preventing their return even if it is otherwise possible. If it is possible for them to return they do so toward the end of the third and subsequent years in March and April, and at this time may range from 15 to 24 inches long, thus furnishing excellent sport (1).

A set of rules for stocking rainbow trout based on the habits of the fish should be about as follows:

1. If stocked in a river, the water should be tributary to a larger body of water where the fish can grow to maturity and with no barriers, such as falls, dams, or pollution, to prevent the return of the fish.
2. If stocked in a pond, there should be tributary streams without barriers and suitable for spawning.
3. Provisions should be made regarding fishing regulations so the fish have a chance to spawn naturally at least once before being exposed to angling pressure.

BROWN OR LOCH LEVEN TROUT *trutta*

Description. The brown, or German brown, trout was introduced into the United States from Europe. Through plantings it has been spread to most of the trout waters of the world and is an excellent addition to the American fauna. It is a hardier fish than the brook trout and stands a higher temperature as well as slight amounts of pollution. According to Needham (44), the brown trout is not a good fish for the cold waters of the western mountain lakes, however. Also, because of its feeding habits, a few large browns in a lake will deplete the stocking of fingerlings of other trout and may thus destroy the benefits of stocking with fry.

Brown trout stand up well under heavy fishing pressure. They are very shy, and the larger fish feed mostly at night on minnows, thus making their capture difficult.

The brown trout is a less colorful fish than either the brook or rainbow trout. Its color is light brown or yellow with fins a dull yellow or white. The scales are larger than the brook trout, and the spots on the sides are dark with a few orange or yellow spots mixed with the darker ones. The tail is square, even more so than the "squaretail," but does not carry the orange color of brook trout.

Age, Size, and Growth. Brown trout frequently grow very old and large. Eddy and Surber (22 *g.r.*) speak of males weighing over 12 pounds taken from Lake Superior at Knife River. Needham (44) records a 12-pound brown taken from the Merced River in Yellowstone National

Park and a 16-pound specimen taken from Arrowhead Lake in southern California. Few brown trout are taken that are over 5 pounds, however, and most of the browns taken by fishermen are under a pound.

Table 21-6. Age and Size of Brown Trout from Crystal Creek, New York (55)
(Basis 872 fish)

Age in growing seasons, Jan. 1	*Total length, in.*
1	3.1
2	5.7
3	7.6
4	10.2
5	11.6
6	14.0

Distribution. The energy with which sportsmen demand the planting of artificially reared fish would insure their distribution in almost every possible type of water. Needham (44) indicates their extensive distribution by citing their presence in such widely separated waters as Neversink and Beaverkill Rivers in New York State and the Merced, American, and Feather Rivers in California. They are found in Lake Superior along the Minnesota shore and in suitable waters along the Appalachian mountains. Eddy and Surber (22 *g.r.*) call attention to the fact that brown trout are natural successors to the brook trout. No matter how much we decry the undesirable nature of an exotic species as compared to a native species like the brook trout, the fact remains that because of land use in many streams the brook trout is gone forever. In such waters the brown trout may find a suitable habitat. It is better to have the brown trout than no trout at all.

Habits. The habits of the brown trout are quite similar to those of brook trout. Inhabiting larger bodies of water no doubt has some influence on movements which would not be true of the "brookie." Likewise the larger fish appear to be more shy and wary than the brook trout. As the fish get larger, there is a tendency to feed more at night and to concentrate on minnows rather than insects and other types of food. This modifies their activities somewhat. Studies of tagged fish indicate that there is very little movement of the fish from season to season.

Spawning. Like the brook trout, browns spawn in the fall during October and early November (44). Streams sought for spawning may be spring-fed feeders or larger tributaries from 6 inches to 2 feet in depth. Thus brown trout find suitable spawning grounds farther downstream than do the brook trout.

The eggs are deposited in gravel and at temperatures of 57°F. take 30 to 33 days to hatch. Spawning browns usually move downstream again to the larger bodies of water after spawning.

Food. The food of brown trout is quite similar to that of brook trout, no doubt owing to the similarity of their habitats. Some differences do appear, however. Raney and Lachner (48) studied the foods of released brown trout in a stream 2, 16, and 42 days after liberation during the period from August to November. Aquatic animals made up the food of these trout to the extent of 82, 86, and 79 per cent respectively. Most of the food was of insect origin but a few earthworms, spiders, and isopods were eaten.

In a study of the foods of brown trout from 5 to 12 inches long during May, June, and July, Needham (44) gives the following results:

Table 21-7. Foods Eaten by 46 Brown Trout*

Class of foods	No. found in 46 stomachs	Per cent of total
Mayflies	1907	79.3
Caddis flies	230	9.5
Two-winged flies	61	2.5
Earthworms	51	2.1
Slugs	30	1.3
Beetles	28	1.2
Ants, bees, wasps	22	1.0
Stone flies	17	0.7
Leaf hoppers	17	0.7
Crayfish and scuds	15	0.7
Fish, salamanders	9	0.3
Grasshoppers	7	0.3
Miscellaneous	10	0.4
Total	2404	100.0

* Location of origin of the trout was not given.

The author of the above table makes the observation that while 251 brook trout ate 716 mayflies, of which 180 were adults, 46 brown trout took 993 adult mayflies. This would indicate that brown trout feed more at the surface than brook trout (44). The general opinion is that brown trout feed more and more on other fish as they advance in size and age. They are cannibalistic, so feed on their own kind as well as on other fishes, including trout. Hence it is unwise to stock large browns in waters that are suited to brook trout.

Habitat. As already indicated, the brown is a hardier fish than the brook trout and will stand water conditions that are beyond the tolerance of brooks. Some turbidity, higher water temperatures, and slight amounts of pollution may be present in brown trout waters.

Physical and Chemical Limits. Hoover (29) suggests a water temperature of 75°F. and a summer extreme of 81°F. under New Hampshire conditions. Variations in pH range may be from 5 to 9, and oxygen minimum may run as low as 4 ppm. Carbon dioxide should not be greater than 20 ppm. The brown trout reaches its maximum development in the lower reaches of good-sized streams and under these conditions temperatures are comparatively high and food is plentiful. Such rivers may be quite open but must contain enough deep holes and sheltered spots to furnish protection to a few large fish. For maximum production of large fish, streams should have an abundant supply of minnows. This means numerous shallow weedy edges and enough slow-moving water so that small fish have ample insect food and protection. While brown trout may live

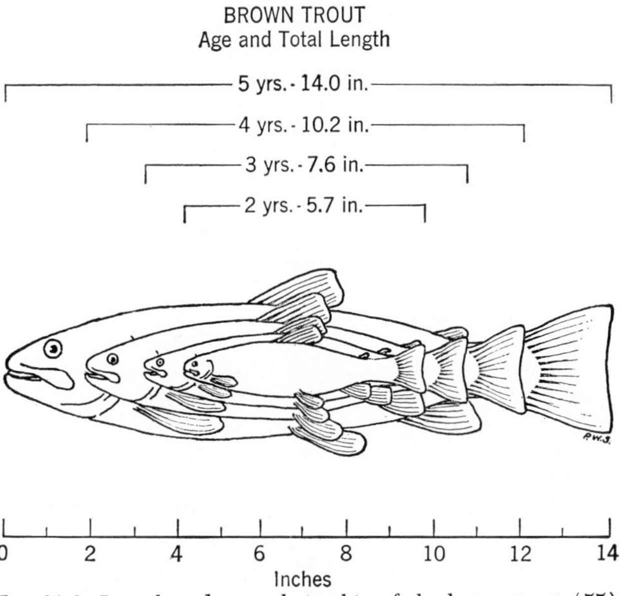

FIG. 21-9. Length and age relationship of the brown trout (55).

and grow to large size in both rivers and lakes, it has been pretty well demonstrated that border-line trout streams in the lower reaches of river systems are the places where they achieve greatest usefulness and probably highest total production.

Miscellaneous. Much controversy continues as to what species of trout is best to plant in various waters, what sizes of fish can be planted most economically, and at what time during the year the fish can be stocked to the best advantage. Needham (44) has summarized the size and species in a very brief and direct table which is given on page 448.

All the evidence seems to indicate that chances of survival in a stream habitat are low for both naturally and artificially reared trout and that hatchery-reared stock has a poorer chance of ending up in a fisherman's creel than do the naturally produced fish. When fishermen realize the

Table 21-8. Waters Recommended for Planting Trout of Various Sizes (44)

Size of fish	Eastern brook trout	Brown or Loch Leven trout	Rainbow trout
Advanced fry to 2-in. fingerlings	Cold headwater brooks or tributaries and ponds or lakes lightly fished and affording ample shelter.	Small warmer streams, lakes, or tributaries with ample shelter and lightly fished, if already well established here.	Smaller tributaries of streams preferably with unobstructed access to deep, cold lakes or to the ocean. Lightly fished streams with ample shelter.
3–5-in. (2) fingerlings	Moderately and heavily fished cold-water ponds, lakes, or streams lacking predaceous warm-water species and where food supply is rich.	Moderately and heavily fished streams and lakes where already well established.	Moderately and heavily fished lakes and streams, preferably with access to deep, cold lakes or to the ocean; wide rugged mountain streams.
6-in. or larger (3) yearlings or older	Upper portions of cold streams and lakes intensively fished near recreation centers or large cities and towns.	Heavily fished, warmer, quieter main reaches of streams where already well established near recreation centers or large cities and towns.	Large streams and lakes heavily fished. Preferably "white-water" mountain streams near recreation centers or large cities and towns.

excessive cost of hatchery fish in terms of fish caught, they will probably be more sympathetic to attempts at improving fishing by other methods (27). Where the base cost of legal (7-inch) trout is 35 cents, the cost of trout to the fisherman is much greater. In Michigan only 1 brook or rainbow trout was recovered to 4 put in the stream, and 1 of 8 brown trout released was recovered. This means the actual cost of trout in the creel varied from $1.40 to $2.80 apiece (27).

THE SALMON FAMILY

Description. All the salmon belong in the family *Salmonidae*. This includes two North American genera, the *Salmo* or Atlantic salmon, and the *Oncorhynchus* or Pacific salmon. There are two subspecies of Atlantic salmon, the true sea-run Atlantic salmon (*Salmo salar salar*) and the landlocked form (*Salmo salar sebago*). Both of these fish are found in a somewhat restricted part along the Atlantic seaboard from southern New England north and including Labrador.

The Atlantic Salmon *Salmo salar salar* and *Salmo salar sebago*

Description. Atlantic salmon have been an important item of food since the discovery of North America and are still considered a choice food. While the Atlantic salmon fisheries of the United States have shrunk to a very low point, this species is highly important as a sport fish. In the Canadian provinces it is important both for sport and for commercial purposes. In season fresh salmon can be found in most of the markets of the northeastern part of the United States at the present time. Formerly the Atlantic salmon ran up the Hudson, Connecticut, and all of the larger rivers along the coast. Overfishing and barriers in the form of dams, pollution, and destruction of the breeding grounds have reduced the runs in the United States to a few rivers in Maine where these fish are hanging on precariously.

The landlocked or Sebago salmon is found in only a few fresh-water lakes in the east and a few locations in other New England states, including Sebago Lake in Maine, and in New York. Both the true Atlantic salmon and the landlocked form are excellent sport fish and are eagerly sought by fishermen wherever they appear.

The Atlantic salmon is one of the most spectacular of the sporting fishes and at the same time combines high quality of flesh and sufficient size to make it one of the finest of commercial fishes. Formerly to fish for this prize a fisherman had to be wealthy enough to spend several weeks at a camp in eastern Canada and to belong to an exclusive salmon club. Now if one has an old jalopy and lives in the New England area, he can go to the eastern part of Maine during the latter part of May and June and obtain fairly good salmon fishing in several streams along the coast. By a systematic program of artificial rearing and planting of salmon in these streams, runs or tribes have been established in ever-increasing numbers. The program has been further aided by clearing the streams of obstructions and protecting the spawning grounds. Landlocked salmon have also been planted in many waters in northern New England. Where pond conditions are suitable and good spawning tributaries are present, they become self-sustaining. In ponds which do not have suitable spawning tributaries the fish may be reared to fair size and planted in ponds where they may grow larger and can be harvested by fishermen.

Atlantic salmon, while in the ocean, are graceful, streamlined fish, colored blue above with dark markings on the sides and white on the under parts. When in breeding condition in fresh water, the fish are beautifully colored with blue on the back, yellow on the belly, and orange-and-black spots on the sides. The male, often called a "cock or jack," has a markedly hooked lower jaw.

So many terms are used to describe the various age, breeding, and environmental phases of the Atlantic salmon that it seems desirable to give them for reference here. The following definitions are taken from Dow (16):

Alevin. Term used in describing the young fish from the time of hatching until the yolk sac is absorbed, usually about 6 weeks.
Fry. From the end of the alevin stage until toward the end of the first summer.
Parr. From the fry stage until the young fish are preparing to migrate to the sea; in the Penobscot this is 2 or 3 years of age.
Smolt. Parr which have assumed a silver coating and are migrating to the sea.
Grilse. Fish which as smolt have spent the balance of the summer, a winter, and part of the second summer in the sea; an adolescent salmon.
Salmon. Generally classified as a fish that has spent two or more years in the sea.
Kelt. A salmon that has spawned and has not yet returned to the sea.

The landlocked salmon are much lighter colored than sea-run fish, having a less intense blue color on the back and fewer orange-colored markings on the sides.

Age, Size, and Growth. Kendall (39) gives the size of Atlantic salmon as varying from 10 to 80 pounds in weight. Dow (16) gives the weights of 24 recently caught sea-run fish as varying from 7 to 15½ pounds. These fish were from 1 to 4 years old but mostly 2 and 3 years old.

The length of Atlantic salmon varies with the time spent in fresh or salt water and with age. Table 21-9 shows this variation.

Table 21-9. Age Related to Total Length in Inches of Atlantic Salmon in Fresh Water as Compared to Time Spent in Salt Water (From Raymond Dow (16) and Harry A. Goodwin*)

Fresh water		Sea	
Age in growing seasons, Jan. 1	Total length, in.	Years in sea	Total length, in.
1	1.9–2.0	1	15.5–21.0
2	4.3–4.8	2	24.0–33.5
3	6.1	3	34.0–35.5
4	6.8	4	36.0–37.0

* Harry Allen Goodwin. 1942. The Atlantic salmon in the Dennys river. Unpublished M.S. thesis, University of Maine, Orono.

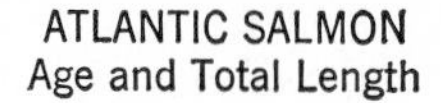

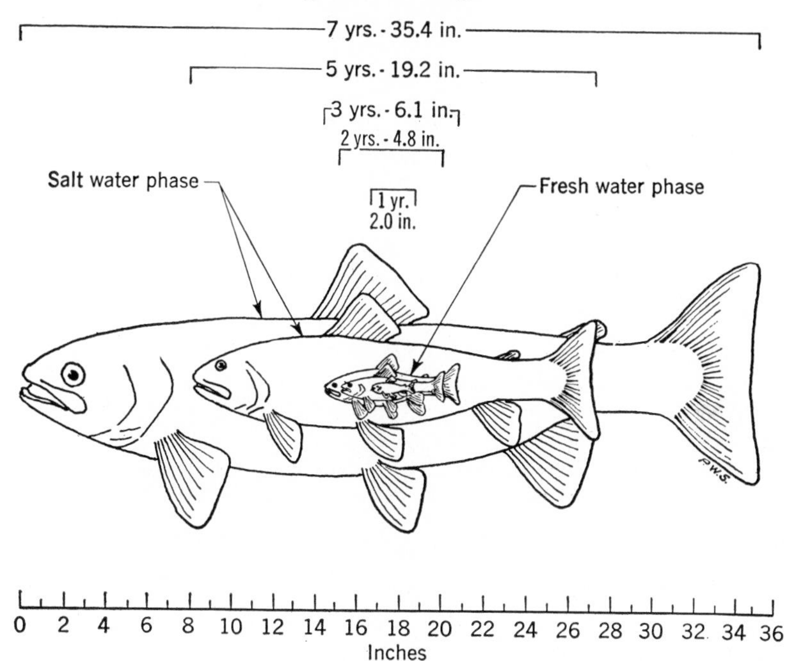

FIG. 21-10. Length and age relationship of the Atlantic salmon. Note the more rapid growth rate in salt water (16).

Sebago or landlocked salmon attain a maximum length of 20 to 30 inches and a weight of 6 to 10 pounds.

From these data and that found in Table 21-9, it is obvious that salmon grow much faster in the sea than in fresh water. For example, salmon that have spent 1 year in fresh water and 2 in the sea are about 26 inches

Table 21-10. Age-Length Relationship of Landlocked Salmon from Maine (14) (Basis 105 fish)

Age in growing seasons, Jan. 1	*Total length, in.**
1	(3.8)
2	(7.6)
3	11.4
4	15.2
5	18.6
6	21.0
7	23.3
8	21.4 (25.2)
9	22.7 (27)

* Figures in parentheses are values extended from curve.

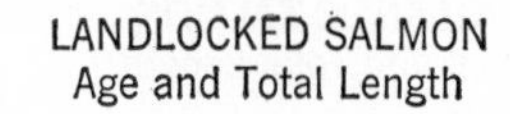

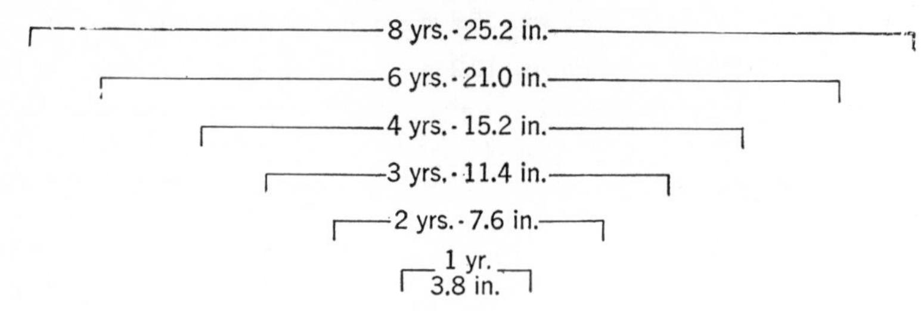

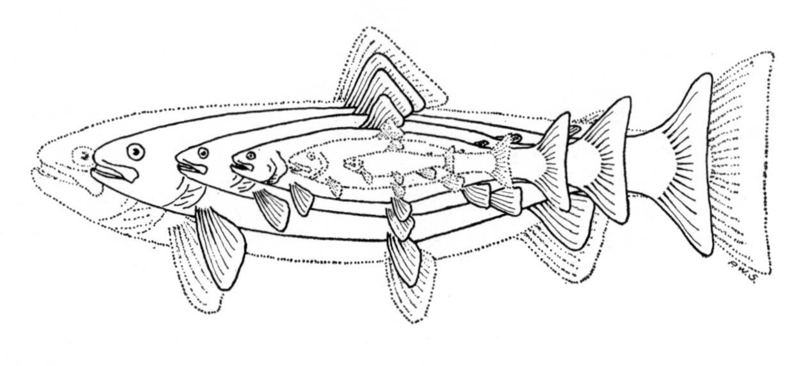

FIG. 21-11. Length and age relationship of the landlocked salmon (14).

Table 21-11. Growth of Atlantic Salmon from Calculated and Measured Total Lengths from Two Rivers in Maine

Time spent in salt water, years	Total length, in.	
	Penobscot River (16)	Dennys River*
1 (age 2–5 years)	15.5–21.0	
2 (age 4–6 years)	26.5–30.3	24.0–33.5
3 (age up to 8 years)	35.4	34.0–35.5
4 (age more than 8 years)	....	36.0–37.0

* Harry A. Goodwin, M.S. thesis.

long. Even though they have spent 4 years in fresh water and 2 in the sea (6-year-old fish), they are still only 28.7 inches long.

Distribution. The extreme limit of sea-run salmon along the Atlantic Coast was formerly the Hudson River in the north. Within recent years stray salmon have been taken in the lower reaches of the Connecticut

River, and attempts are being made to reestablish these fish in the Connecticut by planting fry in suitable nursery streams in the watershed. Atlantic salmon continue to run or have been reestablished in many Maine rivers including the Penobscot, Narraguagus, and the Dennys.

The distribution of the landlocked and Pacific salmon is widespread in the rivers and ponds of eastern United States. These fish have been distributed widely from hatcheries and also from spawn taken by commercial salmon fishermen.

A perusal of the fisheries survey reports of the New England states shows the following:

Connecticut. One report of an Atlantic salmon in the Connecticut River in 1949,[4] not found in ponds (63).

Vermont. No data, probably several lakes and ponds suited to landlocked salmon.

New Hampshire. Many ponds and lakes in which landlocked salmon are present (66).

Maine. Sebago Lake (It is from this lake the landlocked salmon took its name.) Also many lakes which have deep water with at least 5 ppm of dissolved oxygen and temperature maximum not higher than 70°F. in the deep water with smelts present.

Canada and New York. The watersheds flowing into Lake Ontario have streams which carry Atlantic salmon and ponds supporting landlocked salmon (12, 13, 41).

Habits. *Atlantic Salmon.* These fish have a most interesting and complicated habit in relation to their life cycle. Contrary to the western forms, the Atlantic salmon does not die after the spawning act but goes on out to sea to prepare for another spawning season. Half of the salmon's life is spent in the sea after 1 to 5 years spent in fresh water. In the sea the fish winter on the seaward slopes of the ocean beyond the 100-fathom line just out of reach of the harp seal (39). From the various records given by Kendall it would appear that sea-run salmon roam the ocean far from shore and fresh water, seeking food wherever it is available. This may be 20 to 50 miles from shore or in the Gulf Stream and offshore currents of the Arctic ocean. Feeding is voracious if growth is an indicator. A wide variety of sea animals have been recorded as eaten by these fish.

During late winter and early spring the fish that are approaching reproductive maturity come in toward the shore and presumably the river of their origin. White (67) states that the presence of parr and milt in a

[4] 1949. Daniel Merriam, and Jean Ives. The capture of an Atlantic salmon (*Salmo salar salar*) in the Connecticut River. *Copeia.* No. 3, pp. 220–221.

stream probably guides the migrating breeders to a stream, especially if they have not spawned in that stream before. There is no particular time of year when the fish ascend rivers; some fish may be present at any time. In the salmon rivers of the North Atlantic the main runs seem to occur during the late spring and early summer from March to June. Huntsman (35, 36) suggests the use of water from upstream dams as an incentive to start salmon runs and for the maintenance of fishing.

Some of the fish that run into fresh water are ones known as grilse, which have spent one winter in the ocean but are found in fresh water along with the larger (and probably older) salmon. Grilse appear in the spawning rivers in the later part of the summer and in Europe, at least, males outnumber the females (38).

The matter of the feeding of salmon in fresh water has been a subject of lively controversy for generations. Many texts on salmon state the salmon does not feed in fresh water. Kendall (38) indicates that while he believes the tendency to feed is lessened as the fish approaches spawning time and that the food intake in the fresh water is much reduced, there is nevertheless a certain amount of feeding by salmon as they move away from the ocean to their spawning grounds.

Spawning grounds of Atlantic salmon may be hundreds of miles inland or just above tidewater. The early-run salmon occupy the upper waters and the late-run the lower waters. The spawning grounds are in shallow, swift-running water over bottom which consists of coarse gravel and loose stones from 2 to 8 inches in diameter. The majority of the beds are near the bank where the flow of the water is broken. The depth of the water may be 6 to 48 inches. A hollow is made in the bed of the stream, and the eggs are covered with from 6 to 12 inches of coarse stones.

The female lays the eggs and has a male in attendance to fertilize them (6). Hatching takes from 90 to 100 days at 40 to 45°F. and up to 192 days if the water is excessively cold. The spent spawners or kelts do some feeding, but the feeding that takes place after spawning is not abrupt or ravenous. Many fish do not survive to spawn a second time (10).

After salmon eggs hatch the young fish live and feed in the waters of the nursery stream for a period of 1 to 3 years. Belding (8) states that the age at which the parr becomes a smolt and leaves the river is determined by the rate of growth. This in turn is determined by the temperature of the water it grows in, its fertility, and the rate of flow. The size of the stream and whether it flows through ponds or lakes on its way to the sea also affect rate of growth and age at the downstream migration of salmon parr. Apparently the time of passing toward the sea is from July to December (38). As they approach the lower reaches of the rivers, they take on a silvery color and become smolts. After some time in brackish water they pass out to sea on the spring flood (42).

Landlocked Salmon. The habits of the landlocked salmon appear to be much less complicated than those of its sea-run cousins. The adult fish live in the larger bodies of water, roaming the various parts of the lake or river at such times as the water temperature will allow and to locations where food is available. During the early spring landlocked salmon will take bait, or rise to a fly, or can be caught by trolling. Kendall (39) speaks of catching a salmon on a fly near the surface when others nearby were catching them near the bottom in 70 feet of water. Fishing in the lakes of Maine is good in May, June, and September.

The food of landlocked salmon consists of any of the numerous small fish forms that are found in fresh-water lakes. Invertebrate forms used by salmon include ants, beetles, spiders, moths, grasshoppers, and other insects. Salmon also eat newly laid trout eggs (39). Of the feeding by salmon in Maine Lakes, Cooper (13) has the following to say:

> Larger trout and salmon feed mostly upon small fishes and, in Maine lakes, the smelt is the only small fish which is abundant in deep water during the summer. Thus the smelt is an absolute necessity to the production of large landlocked salmon and is probably also important to large brook trout and lake trout.
>
> The food of young salmon is mostly insects. This stage of the life is spent in the spawning river and conditions are usually suitable here for insect production. Clean cold water and plenty of boulders insures anchorage for insect larvae and protection from the main force of the current.

The landlocked salmon may spend 1, 2, or 3 years in a stream before migrating to a lake. Cooper (13) in a study of 82 salmon in seven different locations showed only one that had moved out of the spawning stream after one growing season and also only one that had stayed there longer than 2 years.

The spawning of landlocked salmon takes place in the fall during the months of September and October. There is no early-season movement to the spawning beds as is true of the Atlantic salmon. The spawning stream must be clean and cold and have ample gravel beds. The movement upstream seems to be stimulated by a rush of water such as would be caused from the opening of a dam gate or by a rainstorm. During the spawning run and spawning process the salmon feed little or not at all. Spawning ends near the last of October or the first of November.

Habitat. *Atlantic Salmon.* The habitat needs for Atlantic salmon include the following: a relatively large stream that flows into the ocean, headwater streams that are clean, cold and have suitable bottoms for spawning, and free access between the spawning and rearing areas and the ocean. This means no dams or barriers or, if dams are present, fishways suitable for fish going both up and down stream. Streams must be free from pollution.

Spawning areas must be clean, cold, and well-shaded. They should be sufficiently free from predatory fish and other predators so a suitable number of eggs hatch and young salmon survive (6, 7). Young salmon stay in the stream habitat until they are 2, 3, or 4 years old.

Adequate protection should be given to fish so they are not destroyed in the power generating wheels at the various dams in a river. Destruction can be prevented by the installation of electrical barriers at the points of water entrance to power stations.

Protection from fishermen, both commercial and sport, must be given so a sufficiently large number of fish are allowed to spawn. Where artificial production of young salmon is used to supplement natural production, taking of eggs from commercially caught fish may aid the restoration of these fish. Commercial operations must be regulated, however, if the salmon decline is not to continue.

Atlantic salmon fry planted in some of the streams of Ontario have reached the smolt stage, but whether they will return to the stream after their stay in Lake Ontario is not yet known (41).

Landlocked Salmon. Past experiences seem to show that compared to the total number of water bodies in the eastern United States and Canada, those suitable for landlocked salmon are not too plentiful. Tributaries must be clean, cold streams with many gravel or rubble beds and not too many trout or other predatory fish present. Killing of some of the unwanted population and screening the outlets from new runs may be means of reducing predatory species (23).

Physical and Chemical Limits. Lakes suitable for landlocked salmon are described by Cooper as follows (13):

1. *Cold water.* Deep cold lakes or lakes where warm-water competitors are absent. Maximum temperature limit of 70°F.

2. *Oxygen.* At least five parts per million of dissolved oxygen. For maximum results much more than 5 ppm.

3. *pH* (acid intensity). Variation of 6.0 to 9.0, but best above 6.0. Low pH reflects low oxygen and high carbon dioxide which trout and salmon cannot tolerate.

Miscellaneous. Much pressure has been used by sportsmen to develop new runs of Atlantic salmon and to add landlocked salmon to ponds as an addition to better fishing. Success in the revival of salmon streams in Maine is demonstrated by the salmon fishing now found in the Narraguagas and Dennys Rivers. The reestablishment of Atlantic salmon in a large stream involves a long process and untold cost and effort (53). The job is about as follows:

1. There must be an unimpeded water route from the ocean to the spawning area. If dams are present, fishways suitable for salmon must be built. This may involve considerable expense.
2. Streams must be reasonably clear of pollution from the spawning stream to the ocean.
3. Agreements between states must be such as to assure uniform protection to migrating fish.
4. Control of waterflow over the dams must be such as to prevent drying up or overheating of the water in the river during the time fish are using it.
5. There must be suitable spawning streams that are not overcrowded with other types of salmonoids or other predatory fish.
6. A source of salmon eggs and hatchery facilities must be available over a period of years until the run is established.
7. Finances and technical skill must be available and the sportsmen must be prepared for a long period of waiting for the final results.

The establishment of landlocked salmon in suitable waters is a much simpler process, but much money and effort has been wasted in trying to establish them in places where conditions are unsuitable. New York State has been studying the problem of suitable places for the production of landlocked salmon and has outlined the process as follows: (25, 26, 43).

1. Lakes suitable for landlocked salmon appear to be of a northern type, as far north as the Adirondacks in New York and north of the Massachusetts-Connecticut line. The water must be of sufficient volume to maintain a maximum temperature of not more than 70°F. It should be of such quality as to support smelts. Histories of former salmon or smelt runs are good indicators.
2. There must be tributary streams which are free from silt and other pollution. These streams must have long stretches of gravel runs for spawning.
3. Waters for salmon must be free from competitors. Preventing spawning runs of other fish may be accomplished by screening the streams where the fish enter. The electric shocker can be used to remove fish which are not wanted.
4. There must be sufficient brood fish and hatchery facilities to keep the project going until natural reproduction is established.
5. The legal size of salmon should be kept at a point where the fish will have a chance to spawn at least once before being legal game to the fisherman. Greeley suggests a legal limit of 20 inches and 2 fish per day per fisherman (25).
6. In case a suitable lake is available but without spawning streams, fish of large size can be supplied from hatcheries for further growth in

the lake and subsequent fishing. Salmon grow slowly in hatcheries so this procedure is expensive.

Chinook Salmon *Oncorhynchus tschawytscha*

Description. On the West Coast Chinook salmon have a number of common names including king, spring, tyee, and quinnat salmon. It is typically a Pacific slope fish, where it hatches in fresh water and migrates

FIG. 21-12. Western salmon exhibit remarkable feats of jumping waterfalls in their journey from salt water to their spawning grounds in western rivers. (*George B. Kelez, U.S. Fish and Wildlife Service.*)

to the Pacific Ocean. Where barriers prevent its normal passage to the spawning grounds it is transported by truck (47). Millions of Chinook salmon eggs are sent to East Coast hatcheries where they are hatched and planted in landlocked lakes. On the Pacific Coast, Chinooks reach 50 pounds or more in weight and are important both commercially and for sport.

Distribution, Habits, and Habitat. Chinook salmon mature in from 3 to 8 years. After fighting their way to the headwaters of the large cold streams of the Pacific Coast, these fish spawn and then generally die. The run begins in July and may last until October. The nests are in gravel much like those of trout and are built by the female. When the fry are about an inch and one-half long they begin their journey down the river toward the sea. While in fresh water they feed on insects, crustaceans, mollusks, and other aquatic organisms.

West Coast or Chinook salmon have been planted in many eastern waters, and at first these plantings were considered successful. In both Maine and New Hampshire the original stocks have died out without successfully reproducing themselves. Planting of Chinook salmon may be considered a failure in New England.

AMERICAN SMELT *Osmerus mordax*

The smelt is a beautiful, slender, silvery fish that is closely related to the salmon family but is of small size and has been given very little attention except fishing. In the spring it is found in all the fish markets in the eastern part of the United States and is listed on the menus of many restaurants. The smelt has fine-flavored flesh as would be expected of a fish of its exacting environmental requirements.

The spectacular nature of the spawning runs of smelt and the fact that they feed during the winter makes them an excellent species for ice fishing and helps to add to their over-all value. For example, Smeltlania is a corporate town on ice, a village of ice fishermen off the shore of Boyne City in Lake Charlevoix, Michigan. A mayor and other town officials are elected, and city ordinances are enacted. No less exciting and spectacular is the regulated taking of smelt from Cold Creek in the town of Beulah, Michigan, where lights are strung along the stream and the area roped off for the smelt-dipping season. Here in a little tributary stream the fish travel upstream to the extent of occupying every inch of water when the run gets under way. The run begins at about 11 o'clock at night. At a given signal the waiting fishermen jump into the stream with nets, bushel baskets, and even bird cages to net some of the moving smelt. The rest of the night is spent in drying out, getting the blood back into circulation, and eating fried smelt. Thousands of dollars are spent for travel, lodgings, and food in this one small village for the privilege of taking part in this unusual sports activity. Regulated smelt dipping is also practiced in other states including Maine where the legal take is 4 quarts per person (14).

Ice fishing for smelt is less spectacular but no less exciting. Each little shack is a haven against the winter cold where a fisherman or two can swap stories, smoke, and escape the pressure of modern life. All of this is in addition to the silvery reward of a dozen or more smelt nibbling on a submerged bait. Its value as a forage fish in salmon waters may far outweigh its value for fishing.

The smelt has been described as a salmon which has never grown up.

It has two dorsal fins, one rayed and the second a small fatty fin near the tail. Many forms live in the sea and run up fresh-water streams to spawn. The sizes of the different races vary, some being small and others attaining a length of from 8 to 12 inches or larger. As smelt are carnivorous, many fears have been expressed as to the danger of their feeding on the young of other and perhaps more desirable fishes such as whitefish and lake trout.

The food of smelt is not well known, but probably consists of many species of water animals including insects, invertebrates, fish eggs, and small fish. Of food found in the stomachs of smelts taken from Sebago Lake, Maine, from May to September, (38) smelt was the item most commonly found. Beckman (5) lists small fish, scuds, and insects for winter-caught fish.

Except during the breeding season, smelt live in the cold parts of a lake where oxygen is sufficient and the temperature is not far above 50°F. Bottom conditions in these lakes are likely to be rocky rather than muddy, as much decaying vegetation would probably deplete the supply of oxygen.

The breeding runs occur from April 1 to May 15 in most of the northern territory. At first a few fish are found in the breeding stream and gradually more and more fish appear until a climax of almost complete occupancy is reached. After this the runs drop off until only a few fish are found in the stream. In New Hampshire the brook is never above 60°F. during the spawning runs (31). The nature of the bottom where smelt spawn is given by Kendall (38) as sand, fine gravel, and pebbles. The number of eggs laid by a female varies from 1,700 to 27,000 (4). The hatching time of the eggs is given as approximately 10 days, the exact time depending on the temperature of the water (31).

REFERENCES

1. Anonymous. 1927. A biological survey of the Oswego River system. *N. Y. State Conserv. Dept. Ann. Rpt.* 17, *Sup.*
2. ———. 1937. South Africa land of outdoor sports. *British World.* **3**(10): 14–17.
3. Baeder, Helen A., Peter I. Tack and Albert S. Hazzard. 1945. A comparison of palatability of hatchery reared and wild brook trout. *Trans. Amer. Fisheries Soc.* **75**:181–185.
4. Baldwin, N. S. 1948. The American smelt, *Osmerus mordax* (Mitchill), of South Bay, Manitoulin Island, Lake Huron. *Trans. Amer. Fisheries Soc.* **78**:176–180.
5. Beckman, William C. 1942. Length-weight relationship, age, sex ratio and food habits of the smelt (*Osmerus mordax*) from Crystal Lake, Benzie County, Michigan. *Copeia.* No. 2, pp. 220–224.
6. Belding, David L. 1934*a*. The spawning habits of the Atlantic salmon. *Trans. Amer. Fisheries Soc.* **64**:211–218.

7. ———. 1934*b*. Cause of the high mortality in the Atlantic salmon after spawning. *Trans. Amer. Fisheries Soc.* **64**:219–224.
8. ———. 1935. Observations on the growth of Atlantic salmon parr. *Trans. Amer. Fisheries Soc.* **65**:157–160.
9. ———. 1936. Atlantic salmon parr of the west coast rivers of Newfoundland. *Trans. Amer. Fisheries Soc.* **66**:211–224.
10. ——— and J. Arthur Kitson. 1934. Spring-run and fall-run Atlantic salmon. *Trans. Amer. Fisheries Soc.* **64**:225–230.
11. Cobb, Eben W. 1933. Results of trout tagging to determine migrations and results from plants made. *Trans. Amer. Fisheries Soc.* **63**:308–318.
12. Cooper, Gerald P. 1939*a*. A biological survey of the waters of York County and the southern part of Cumberland County, Maine. *Maine Dept. Inland Fisheries and Game, Fish Survey Rpt.* 1.
13. ———. 1939*b*. A biological survey of thirty-one lakes and ponds of the upper Saco river and Sebago lake drainage systems in Maine. *Maine Dept. Inland Fisheries and Game, Fish Survey Rpt.* 2.
14. ———. 1940. A biological survey of the Rangeley Lakes, with special reference to trout and salmon. *Maine Dept. of Inland Fisheries and Game, Fish Survey Rpt.* 3.
15. Douchette, Earle. 1951. Fisherman's guide to Maine, Random House, New York.
16. Dow, Raymond W. (No date). Atlantic salmon of the Penobscot River. Unpublished manuscript, Bangor, Maine.
17. Dymond, John R. 1923. A provisional list of the fishes of Lake Nipigon. *Univ. Toronto Fisheries Res. Lab. Pub.* 12.
18. Embody, G. C. 1934. Relation of temperature to the incubation periods of eggs of four species of trout. *Trans. Amer. Fisheries Soc.* **64**:281–292.
19. Fry, F. E. J. 1949*a*. Statistics of a lake trout fishery. *Biometrics.* **5**(1): 27–67.
20. ———. 1949*b*. Lake trout in our inland waters. *Sylva.* **5**(3):3–13.
21. ———. 1951. Some environmental relations of the speckled trout (*Salvelinus fontinalis*). *Proc. Northeast Atlantic Fisheries Conf.* (Mimeographed report.)
22. Graham, J. M. 1949. Some effects of temperature and oxygen pressure on the metabolism and activity of speckled trout, *Salvelinus fontinalis*. *Canad. Jour. Res. Sec. D, Zool. Sci.* **27**:270–288.
23. Greeley, John R. 1932. The spawning habits of brook, brown and rainbow trout, and the problem of egg predators. *Trans. Amer. Fisheries Soc.* **62**:239–248.
24. ———. 1933. The growth rate of rainbow trout from some Michigan waters. *Trans. Amer. Fisheries Soc.* **63**:361–371.
25. ———. 1947. Keys to landlocks. *New York Conserv.* **1**(4):16–17, 30.
26. ———. 1948. Four years of landlocked salmon study. *N.Y. State Conserv. Dept. Div. Fish and Game, Fish and Wildlife Inform. Bul.* 2.
27. Hazzard, Albert S. 1947. A look at Michigan trout fishing. *Mich. Conserv.* **16**(3):8–9, 10.
28. Hile, Ralph. 1945. Standardization of methods of expressing lengths and weights of fish. *Trans. Amer. Fisheries Soc.* **75**:157–164.
29. Hoover, Earl E. (No date). Preliminary biological survey of some New Hampshire lakes. *N. H. Fish and Game Dept. Survey Rpt.* 1.

30. ———. 1936. Contributions to the life history of the Chinook and land-locked salmon in New Hampshire. *Copeia.* No. 4, pp. 193–198.
31. ———. 1937. Biological survey of the Androscoggin, Saco and coastal watersheds. *N. H. Fish and Game Dept. Survey Rpt.* 2.
32. ———. 1938. Biological survey of the Merrimack watershed. *N. H. Fish and Game Dept. Survey Rpt.* 3.
33. ———. 1939. Age and growth of brook trout in northern breeder streams. *Jour. Wildlife Mangt.* **3**(2):81–91.
34. Hubbs, Carl L., and Karl F. Lagler. 1941. A guide to the fishes of the Great Lakes and tributary waters. *Cranbrook Inst. Sci. Bul.* 18.
35. Huntsman, A. G. 1934. Factors influencing the return of salmon from the sea. *Trans. Amer. Fisheries Soc.* **64**:351–355.
36. ———. 1945. Freshets and fish. *Trans. Amer. Fisheries Soc.* **75**:257–266.
37. Jahoda, William J. 1947. Survival of brook trout in water of low oxygen content. *Jour. Wildlife Mangt.* **11**(1):96–97.
38. Kendall, William Converse. 1927. The smelts. *U.S. Bur. Fisheries Soc.* 1015.
39. ———. 1935. The fishes of New England. The salmon family. Part 2—The salmons. *Boston Soc. Nat. Hist. Mem.* Vol. 9, No. 1.
40. Leonard, J. W., and F. A. Leonard. 1946. An analysis of the feeding habits of rainbow trout and lake trout in Birch Lake, Cass County, Michigan. *Trans. Amer. Fisheries Soc.* **76**:301–314.
41. McCrimmon, Hugh R. 1948. The reintroduction of Atlantic salmon into tributary streams of Lake Ontario. *Trans. Amer. Fisheries Soc.* **78**:128–132.
42. McFarland, William Landram. 1925. Salmon of the Atlantic, Parke, Austin & Lipscomb, Inc., New York.
43. Merrill, Arthur. 1936. Salmon restoration, Department of Conservation, Division of Fisheries and Game. (Mimeographed report.)
44. Needham, Paul R. 1938. Trout streams, Comstock Publishing Co., Inc., Ithaca.
45. ———. 1947. Survival of trout in streams. *Trans. Amer. Fisheries Soc.* **77**:26–31.
46. Nesbit, Robert A., and J. Arthur Kitson. 1937. Some results of trout tagging in Massachusetts. *Copeia.* No. 3, pp. 168–172.
47. Parker, Lewis P., and Harry A. Hanson. 1944. Experiments in transfer of adult salmon into Deer Creek, California. *Jour. Wildlife Mangt.* **8**(3): 192–198.
48. Raney, Edward C., and Ernest A. Lachner. 1941. Autumn foods of recently planted young brown trout in small streams of central New York. *Trans. Amer. Fisheries Soc.* **71**:106–109.
49. Rawson, Donald S. 1940. The eastern brook trout in the Maligne River System, Jasper National Park. *Trans. Amer. Fisheries Soc.* **70**:221–235.
50. Ricker, William E. 1930. Feeding habits of speckled trout in Ontario Waters. *Trans. Amer. Fisheries Soc.* **30**:64–72.
51. ———. 1932*a*. Studies of speckled trout (*Salvelinus fontinalis*) in Ontario. *Univ. Toronto, Fisheries Res. Lab. Pub.* **44**:68–110.
52. ———. 1932*b*. Studies of trout producing lakes and ponds. *Univ. Toronto Fisheries Res. Lab. Pub.* 45, pp. 112–167.
53. Rounsefell, George A. 1944. The effect of natural and artificial propagation in maintaining a run of Atlantic salmon in the Penobscot River. *Trans. Amer. Fisheries Soc.* **74**:188–208.

54. Royce, William F. 1951. Breeding habits of lake trout in New York. *U.S. Fish and Wildlife Serv., Fishery Bul.* 59.
55. Schuck, Howard A. 1943. Survival, population density, growth, and movement of the wild brown trout in Crystal Creek. *Trans. Amer. Fisheries Soc.* **73**:209–230.
56. Shetter, David S., and Albert S. Hazzard. 1942. When shall we plant keeper trout? *Mich. Conserv.* **11**(4):3–5.
57. Siegler, Hilbert R. 1948. Adaptability of brook trout. *Jour. Wildlife Mangt.* **12**(3):326–327.
58. Smith, Lloyd L., Jr. 1940. The results of planting brook trout of legal length in the Salmon Trout River, northern Michigan. *Trans. Amer. Fisheries Soc.* **70**:249–259.
59. Smith, Osgood R. 1941. The spawning habits of cutthroat and eastern brook trout. *Jour. Wildlife Mangt.* **5**(4):461–471.
60. Sumner, F. H. 1945. Age and growth of steelhead trout, *Salmo gairdnerii* Richardson, caught by sport and commercial fishermen in Tillamook County, Oregon. *Trans. Amer. Fisheries Soc.* **75**:77–83.
61. Surber, Thaddeus. 1933. Rearing lake trout to maturity. *Trans. Amer. Fisheries Soc.* **63**:64–68.
62. Swartz, Albert H. 1942. Fisheries Survey Report. *Mass. Dept. Conservation, Div. Fisheries and Game.*
63. Thorpe, Lyle M. 1939. A fishery survey of important Connecticut lakes. *State Bd. Fisheries and Game. Bul.* 63.
64. Van Oosten, John, and Hilary J. Deason. 1937. The food of lake trout (*Cristivomer namaycush namaycush*) and of lawyer *Lota maculosa* of lake Michigan. *Trans. Amer. Fisheries Soc.* **67**:155–177.
65. Wales, J. H. 1946. Castle Lake trout investigation first phase: Interrelationships of four species. *Calif. Fish and Game.* **32**(3):109–143.
66. Warfel, Herbert E. 1939. Biological survey of the Connecticut watershed. *N. H. Fish and Game Dept. Survey Rpt.* 4.
67. White, H. C. 1934. Some facts and theories about Atlantic salmon. *Trans. Amer. Fisheries Soc.* **64**:360–362.

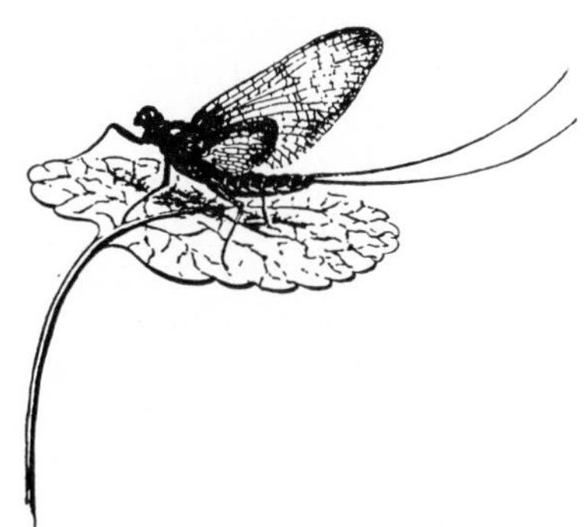

Justin W. Leonard

CHAPTER 22

Lake and Pond Management[1]

In a rudimentary way, lakes and ponds have been managed for centuries; Orientals practiced carp farming long before America was discovered. In its broader aspects, however, fish management in lakes and ponds is still in its infancy and far behind agriculture and forestry. It is less advanced than trout-stream management, which has received considerable emphasis in recent years.

The techniques of fish management in lakes and ponds are changing rapidly, and any discussion of these would soon be obsolete. For this reason, this chapter will be devoted mainly to a discussion of the basic problems involved. Many of these problems also concern stream management, but it is assumed here that the comments refer mainly to lakes, ponds, and reservoirs.

A few decades ago, fish management was relatively simple. It consisted chiefly of passing some regulations, often with little factual evidence on which to base them, and of stocking with hatchery-reared fry or fingerlings. When local sportsmen were dissatisfied with their angling success, a new regulation, and a load of hatchery fish restored contentment. There was one major drawback to the old methods of fish conservation. Angling seldom improved as a result of these "conservation" methods! The methods did furnish the angler with a psychological "lift," and often this was all that he needed. So long as fishing pressure was low, these methods sufficed.

Now, within a few decades, the entire angling picture has changed. The people, as well as the fish, have been prolific. Because of a much higher human population, better travel facilities, and an increase in leisure, the fishing pressure has increased tremendously. There are now over 15 million license buyers. Since many people, especially children, do not need a license, we may assume that about one person in eight now engages in fishing to some extent. The increase in fishing pressure is shown in a survey made by the U.S. Fish and Wildlife Service, (30)

[1] This chapter is contributed by R. W. Eschmeyer, Sports Fishing Institute, Washington, D.C.

which shows an almost threefold increase in license buying during the period 1932 to 1947. A portion of this increase may be attributed to changes in regulation, requiring licenses where none were needed before; most of it, though, can be attributed to increased fishing pressure.

Fishing Licenses Issued in the United States

Year	Resident	Nonresident	Total licenses	Revenue
1932–1933	4,553,441	304,617	4,858,058	$ 6,775,370
1933–1934	4,602,446	253,499	4,855,945	6,586,810
1934–1935	4,710,771	410,549	5,121,320	7,009,009
1935–1936	5,277,431	555,017	5,832,448	8,002,887
1936–1937	6,254,478	667,109	6,901,587	9,309,949
1937–1938	6,751,811	684,366	7,436,177	10,220,788
1938–1939	7,111,545	746,730	7,858,275	10,837,168
1939–1940	7,131,649	799,505	7,931,154	11,227,504
1940–1941	7,151,754	852,280	8,004,034	11,617,841
1941–1942	7,501,688	921,530	8,432,218	10,731,040
1942–1943	7,283,777	744,897	8,028,674	10,024,329
1943–1944	7,208,569	621,908	7,830,477	9,840,073
1944–1945	7,522,373	757,859	8,280,232	10,580,311
1945–1946	9,975,618	1,093,099	11,068,717	15,003,796
1946–1947	11,155,766	1,464,698	12,620,464	22,667,301

In 1932, there were about 5 million license buyers; in 1950, the purchases increased to about 15 million. With this decided increase in fishing pressure, the old conservation methods were no longer adequate. Angling success had declined rather decidedly, indicating that semi-indiscriminate stocking and arbitrarily made regulations are not the answer to our fish-management problems.

Fact-finding programs have now been initiated in many states. These are demonstrating why the former methods of fish conservation have been inadequate, and they are responsible for the gradual improvement in fish-conservation programs.

A major handicap exists in this change to more modern fish-management methods. A very big percentage of the license money continues to be used for stocking; consequently, there are too few funds for promoting the other fish-management activities. In the survey by the U.S. Fish and Wildlife Service, referred to above, the cost of operating state-owned hatcheries in 43 states was about 10½ million dollars (31). Income from fishing licenses for 44 states was recorded as about 19 million dollars. Over half the license money was used for stocking, yet there was evidence that a fair percentage of this stocking served no useful purpose!

Even though progress has been slow because of the overselling of one of the management tools (stocking), new fish-management concepts are gradually gaining recognition. Many state fisheries programs are on an increasingly realistic basis.

The major problem which confronts the fish manager is easily diagnosed; a solution to this problem has not yet been effected. The problem is simply this. Fishing pressure is increasing constantly. However, the waters continue to produce only a limited poundage of fish. Research has demonstrated that only a portion of this fish crop can be harvested by the angler. Consequently, in many areas, our individual share of the available fish resource has become very small—too small to be attractive. We have reached the point where demand has exceeded supply. In many localities, our waters simply can't produce enough fish to meet the demand.

What can be done to meet the ever-increasing demand for satisfactory fishing? This is the one big question in the mind of the fish conservationist. This chapter is an attempt to answer that question as it relates to lakes, ponds, and reservoirs. The reader may safely assume that the question will not be answered completely. This should be considered simply as a very brief evaluation of the various fish-management tools now available to the fisheries manager. The more important management tools, as listed by Eschmeyer (11), are (1) developing an attitude of fishing for fun—not for meat, (2) regulations, (3) stocking, (4) environmental improvement, (5) population manipulation, (6) creating demand for the less desired species, (7) creating more fishing water.

POINT OF VIEW

Before discussing these tools, we need to present, as clearly and emphatically as possible, an all-important basic concept. Failure to recognize it has been responsible for many of our misunderstandings about fish conservation. The important point is this: Our fishing waters are really aquatic pastures. The management of our aquatic pastures and their "livestock" doesn't differ greatly from the management of our land pastures and the animals which graze them. Some anglers who are rational about our land pastures continue to expect miracles from their aquatic equivalent. However, we cannot be too critical of the angler; many fisheries workers have made the same error.

The differences in our thinking about the two kinds of pastures are best illustrated by using several pairs of "news items," all fictitious:

Sportsmen and business men are still talking about that big planting of bass made on Round Lake last Monday. The two truckloads of bass, furnished by the Fisheries Service, were planted by members of the Rod and Gun Club. John Jones, president of the club, and for many years an outstanding sportsman, was instrumental in obtaining the big shipment of a thousand bass, all over 6 inches long. "Think of what this will mean to Center City," says Mr. Jones. "Two years from now Round Lake will be putting out lots of bass. Our 16,000 acres of excellent fishing water will be an asset to any community."

Friends of Joe Jones will be sorry to hear that he has been taken to a prominent psychiatrist for examination. The move was definitely decided on by Mrs. Jones after noting her husband's peculiar activities last week. Says Mrs. Jones, "Joe came home from town last week with 2 ounces of timothy seed. He spent a full day going over our whole 2,000-acre pasture land, scattering a few seeds here and a few seeds there. When he finally came in for supper, he was really happy, saying that he planted that old pasture from stem to stern and that next year we'll be rich. I really don't know what happened to him."

The average reader would be sure that Joe Jones needed the psychiatrist. He would know that 2 ounces of hayseed would be of little benefit to a 2,000-acre pasture. The reader would fail to realize, however, that the stocking of Round Lake had much in common with the planting of the hayseed, that the stocking of one small bass per 16 acres would probably not perceptibly influence the population of bass already present. However, John Jones would very probably be considered an intelligent public-spirited sportsman, even though the stocking may have been insignificant and even though the bass may have introduced tapeworm or some other parasite to the Round Lake fishes.

Here is another comparison:

Last week the Sportsman's Club drained its rearing pond and planted the whole output, 50,000 bluegill fingerlings, into Loon Lake. In making the plant, John Brown, secretary of the club, stated that Loon Lake was overfished, that no 15-acre lake could hold up under the strain without help. He mentioned that Loon Lake now contains a lot of small bluegills but that only by heavy stocking each year can it be expected to have a large number of big ones. The whole town takes its hat off to that energetic, progressive, and community-conscious organization—our Sportsman's Club.

Wallington Green died last night at the County Farm. News of his death calls to mind certain of his eccentricities, especially the one which preceded his arrival at the County Farm, and which was more or less responsible for his transfer from his fine farm on Greenville Pike to the County Institution. Green, it may be recalled, conceived the idea that he was going into the beef-raising business in a big way. He bought up 40 yearling steers to put in his 10-acre pasture, which normally took care of 6 milk cows. Green's experiment didn't do so well, so the next year he decided to do a real job. Since 40 steers failed to put on fat (in fact most of them died), he bought twice as many and put them in the 10-acre pasture. That fall, Green lost his farm and became a resident of the County Institution.

Folks laughed when they recalled Mr. Green's experiment, but they agreed with the editor that the Sportsman's Club was really doing things on Loon Lake. Yet, planting more bluegills in any of the many lakes where fishing is poor because of overpopulation by bluegills differs little from the farmer's experiment.

Elmer Doe, noted fish expert from State University, rendered Green County a real service last night when he talked to a large audience of sportsmen and members of various civic organizations. "I realize," said Professor Doe, "that Central Reservoir means everything to your county. If you can have good fishing as well as power from this 30,000-acre reservoir, you will indeed be a prosperous county. You know all too well, though, that the land drained by the reservoir is some of the poorest in the state. Any county agent can tell you that it's low in phosphorous. Your reservoir produces few fish for the same reason that the land it drains raises little corn. If you want lots of fish you must double the phosphorus content of the water."

Never a slow starter, Green County got busy this morning. Over a thousand dollars has already been raised to buy phosphate fertilizer for Central Reservoir. A committee has been named to contact the Fish and Game Department and one of the Federal agencies about getting funds for several thousand tons of fertilizer, in fact, the goal is 5,000 tons. Several prominent citizens have suggested that Round Island henceforth be called Elmer Doe Island.

When Fred White, Jr., sold out and returned to Chicago last week, the big White Ranch passed into new hands after being in the White family for over a half century. When he died four years ago, Fred, Sr., left his son several thousand head of cattle, one of the biggest ranches in the state and a neat nest egg. Rumor has it that Fred, Jr., lost it all because Fred's wife, a Chicago girl, talked him into an experiment. Remembering the lush hay fields and pastures of the Illinois prairie, Mrs. White saw no reason why the range should not be fertilized and made to produce grass like the Illinois farm land. The Whites mortgaged their holdings to buy all the fertilizer they could for the range. Several train loads were distributed. The range showed some improvement but not enough. Agricultural representatives had tried to discourage the experiment, realizing that the Whites could not buy enough fertilizer to change their thousands of acres of ranch into rich and highly productive soil.

It is now well understood that some land is marginal or submarginal for agriculture, but the fact that some water may be marginal or submarginal for fish production has received comparatively little popular consideration. Too, methods which may be practicable on a small truck farm may not be feasible on a large ranch, and methods of increasing fish production on small lakes may not be usable in the management of large waters. The sportsmen of Center City and the White family displayed similar intelligence. They both tried to apply truck-garden methods to big areas, forgetful of the immense expense involved in making this change.

The several fictitious news items are obviously somewhat exaggerated, but it is true that we take a far more rational attitude toward farming than toward "fish farming." The student who hopes to specialize in fish management would do well to have a good background in farm management. If he learns to apply the same kind of logic to his fisheries problems that he would apply to his farm-management problems, he will have less difficulty in finding the proper solutions.

FISHING FOR FUN

The poundage of "livestock" which an acre of water can produce is limited, and only a portion of this poundage can be harvested by hook and line. Small, heavily fished waters cannot possibly supply enough fish to furnish meat for the thousands of anglers who use these waters. Here we have only about three alternatives: (1) we can stock heavily and repeatedly with catchable-sized fish, (2) we can drastically shorten the open season, (3) we can allow fishing for fun only, greatly limiting the number taken home but not the number caught.

The first alternative is very costly even for trout; for warm-water fish the costs are prohibitive. Limiting fishing to a very few days provides little angling. The third alternative is undoubtedly the most desirable—allowing fishing at nearly all times but for fun only.

Actually, we no longer need to fish for meat as our ancestors did. Meat is available. We can purchase it much more cheaply than we can catch it. But with the ever-increasing tempo of living, we do need to relax. Fishing is the favorite form of mental relaxation for several million Americans. The success of an angling trip need no longer be measured by the number of fish in the creel or on the stringer—there are more important criteria.

This change in emphasis calls for a readjustment in our thinking. The fish manager should not hesitate to drastically reduce the take where facts demonstrate that such action is desirable. But he should be reluctant to impose long closed seasons, except where there is evidence that these are desirable. Waters which are closed to fishing do not provide angler relaxation. In so far as our sport fishery is concerned, our emphasis now is on human conservation—not on meat production.

Unless preceded by a long and effective educational program, a drastic reduction in the take will be unpopular with the angler. Taking home the catch, displaying it to friends (if its size warrants such display), and eventually eating it are still very important aspects of the average fishing trip. The number of anglers who fish only for fun is still small, though it increases each year.

There are many instances, of course, where fish of some species should not be returned to the water because of danger of overpopulation or because these species are not harvested adequately. Though there are many exceptions, returning most of the game, but keeping most of the pan fish, may generally be considered preferable.

REGULATIONS

Our fishing regulations, like our other management tools, are aimed at providing a maximum number of successful fishing trips without injury to future angling, and at providing a fair distribution of our fish resources. In imposing these regulations, we should remember that fishing for relaxation is now much more important than fishing for meat. The angler should be permitted to enjoy fishing as much of the time as possible, even though we may need to greatly limit the number of fish which he may take home.

Most fish belong to all residents of the state. For this reason and because of their recreational value, the proper place for commercial fishing in the fish-conservation picture is very clear. The meat fisherman with his effective gear should be permitted to take those species of fish which are not harvested by the anglers. In some instances, he may improve sport fishing by doing so. However, where sport fishing and commercial fishing are in direct competition, the latter should receive secondary consideration.

The most important regulation is the one limiting fishing to hook and line. This angling equipment gives maximum enjoyment to the fisherman, and it is sufficiently ineffective to assure a reasonably fair distribution of our fish resources. There are instances, of course, where more effective equipment is needed to harvest some species, especially where these compete with the more desirable species.

In addition to limiting most fishing to the use of hook and line, the fish conservationist may need to impose other regulations such as closed seasons, creel limits, size limits, etc. In the past our tendency has been to overrestrict fishing, but the move is now in the opposite direction, and there is a good possibility that it may go too far.

Size limits are gradually being discarded, especially on those fish which tend to become too abundant. The limits were originally imposed to assure at least one successful spawning before the fish was permanently removed from the water. We now know that fish are prolific and that only a few brood fish are needed to produce all the young fish which a lake or pond can support. In special instances, however, a size limit may be desirable for the big game-fish species. Even in these instances, though, there is one drawback to having size limits. The experienced angler who handles the fish carefully usually doesn't want the little ones and automatically returns them, whereas the angler who is mainly interested in catching meat often injures the fish when he catches it.

Creel limits should be low enough so that the average angler can occasionally "catch his limit." However, they should be reasonably high for fish such as perch, sunfish, and bullheads, which tend to become overabundant. Where the limits are so low that anglers frequently catch their limit, the fishermen tend to discard fish from their creel or stringer as the limit is approached, in the hope of catching bigger fish to replace them. These discarded fish will often be dead or dying when "released."

The closed season is now being studied extensively. Present indications are that a closed season may not be needed on the bigger waters and in areas where fishing pressure is light. It will probably be needed, though, for the bigger game-fish species in many areas. Investigators are showing that the big species such as northern pike, walleyed pike, and bass, are more harvestable than the pan fish—that anglers can remove a given percentage of these fish from a lake or pond more easily than they can remove an equal percentage of pan fish. Since these bigger fish tend to keep the pan fish reduced in numbers (by eating them), we may expect overpopulation with pan fish to become an even greater problem as fishing intensity increases. It appears, therefore, that a closed season on the bigger fish species may be highly desirable; because of the danger of overpopulation of pan fish, the tendency will probably be toward less protection for these species.

The regulation question is now receiving considerable study; as a result, the fishing restrictions are much more realistic and more effective than they were a few decades ago.

STOCKING

Stocking, long the major fish-conservation tool, is gradually being relegated to its proper position. There is a place for hatcheries in the fish-management picture, but stocking is only one of the various management tools, and it is secondary in importance to several others.

There are three distinct categories of stocking: (1) introducing species not already present, (2) planting small fish (fry or fingerlings) of species already present, (3) planting fish of catchable size.

Introducing species not already present has been helpful in many instances; it has also been harmful. Anglers normally want those species introduced into their favorite waters which are not already present. Where these species do not compete for food with the desirable fish already established in the water, or where the species are definitely superior to those already present, this introduction may be desirable, provided the waters are suitable for the species to be introduced. Where there is no direct competition for food, the introduced species may be expected to increase the per-acre yield. But if we have direct competition, the introduced species, if it succeeds, must do so at the expense of the other fish. Anglers who know that it would be unwise to introduce horses in a pasture already grazed to capacity by cattle, have often failed to appreciate the improbability of a lake or pond producing big numbers of each of a variety of competing species. As observed in a number of studies, stocking with fry and fingerlings of species already present has generally been unsuccessful. However, where conditions are suitable for the species, but not for reproduction, some plants of small fish have been successful. The general failure of such stocking is understandable when we realize that fish are extremely prolific. A bass may lay 10,000 eggs, a walleyed pike 50,000. Under suitable conditions, a big percentage of these eggs hatches. Returning to our land-pasture equivalent—if cows had from 10,000 to 50,000 calves each, placing another truck load of calves into a well-populated pasture would not increase the cattle population appreciably.

An interesting study was made some years ago on a Michigan lake (6). Here the nests of four species of fish were marked and counted. Then the fry were removed from a number of typical nests. The estimated number of fry produced in the 14.9-acre lake was 164,000 bass, 46,000 rock bass, 1,518,000 common sunfish, and 6,610,000 bluegills! There were 648 nests and presumably twice this number of adults. Of the 8,338,000 fry produced, not more than 2,000 or 3,000 could have reached adulthood; the lake could not have supported more than this number. Survival of 1 per cent of these fish would have been disastrous.

We can see why stocking with little fish might not be helpful; in fact we can see, too, why overpopulation with pan fish might be a serious problem. Stocking with catchable-sized fish in big numbers definitely increases the catch. Here the problem is an economic one. The average trout creeled from plantings of catchable-sized trout costs well in excess of 50 cents. The average license fee, if used entirely for rearing trout, would pay for very few fish—far fewer than the license buyer would expect to catch. Stocking with catchable-sized warm-water fish is much more costly; in fact, it is so costly that few of these fish are stocked.

In general, stocking will continue to be a fish-management tool, but planting small fish usually contributes little or nothing to angling, and planting with catchable-sized fish is too costly to be practiced on a large scale.

ENVIRONMENTAL IMPROVEMENT

This subject is so broad, and the field still so unexplored, that the improvement methods which have been used cannot yet be evaluated. We know, for example, that brush shelters will tend to concentrate young fish, but this increased protection might not be desirable, especially if the species protected are pan fish, which may overpopulate the lake or

FIG. 22-1. Treatment of a weed-choked lake to remove vegetation with sodium arsenate. Aquatic plants may become so dense as to interfere with fishing. (*Institute of Fisheries Research, Michigan Conservation Department.*)

pond. We know, too, that bass and sunfish use the gravel for spawning where it is provided for that purpose. But we do not know whether or not better hatching results from this "improvement" in spawning areas. We also know that slabs placed on the bottom in shallow water will be used for spawning by bluntnosed and fathead minnows. But here, too, we do not know what the improved spawning conditions for these minnows mean in terms of a greater number of successful fishing trips.

There are instances where environmental improvement in the form of increased food supply has been very helpful. For example, a fluctuating southern reservoir furnished poor fishing for a number of years. The fish population consisted mainly of largemouth and smallmouth bass, and stunted bluegills. Because of winter drawdown, bottom insects were scarce. The insect-eating bluegills had little food. The adult bass probably found young bass more available than bluegills as food, and probably kept their own numbers reduced by eating the young bass. Gizzard shad were introduced. The young shad thrived on the plankton which was readily available regardless of winter drawdown. Crappie were introduced. Their fish-eating habits made this species more suitable than the bluegills as pan fish.

Within a few years, a rotenone sampling showed that young shad were numerous and that bass were much more abundant than formerly and were in good condition. Fishing improved decidedly because of the introduction of a new food chain. The food chain consisting of insects to bluegills to bass was unsatisfactory because of the weakness of one step (insect)s in this chain. When it was changed to "plankton to young shad to bass and crappie," the fishing improved decidedly because all steps in this chain were well represented. A change in the food chain may be expected to improve many other waters where the habitat has been changed because of impoundment or some other reason.

Proper fertilization with manure or commercial fertilizer has also greatly improved production in some small waters draining moderately unproductive soils. On the big waters, though, extensive fertilizing is impracticable because of the cost.

Eventually, environmental improvement may play an important role in the management of lakes and ponds; for the present, we are handicapped in using this tool, because usually we are still unable to identify the limiting factors and we still know too little about the needs of the various species of fish.

POPULATION MANIPULATION

Managing our fish populations will eventually be a very important part of the fish manager's work. Anglers have been harvesting certain species extensively, to the advantage of the less desirable ones. What has been done is equivalent to taking only certain plants from a field and making no effort to control the other plant species. This activity may eventually cause the "weeds" to become dominant.

There is another problem. If some species become too abundant, they become stunted and fail to reach a desirable size.

If we are to have successful angling, there must be a reasonable balance between predator and prey. If the forage is too abundant, our baits cannot compete satisfactorily. If there is too little forage, the fish cannot thrive.

Our biggest problem at present seems to be overpopulation with pan fish. This problem will probably be even more widespread as fishing intensity increases. It seems that the bigger predators such as bass, walleyed pike, and northern pike are more easily harvested by angling than the pan fish species. Reduction in the numbers of big predators leads to too great a survival of such species as perch, bluegills, and bullheads.

Several methods of controlling the pan fish may be used, though all have limitations. One is to protect the big predatory species by closed seasons, and by having low creel limits for these fish. At the same time, creel limits for the pan fish should be high, and the closed season, if imposed at all on these species, should be a short one. Unless the waters are fished very heavily for pan fish, regulation alone will probably not prevent overpopulation in some instances, but the proper regulations will help.

Partial removal of overabundant populations is gaining more and more recognition as an effective management procedure. It can be accomplished by seining, netting, or by local use of chemicals. If the water is clear so that the spawn can be located, destruction of the eggs is also effective. Eventually, fish-culturists will be spending more of their time keeping populations of pan fish reduced by destroying spawn or young and less time raising pan fish for stocking. On some waters, a reasonable balance can best be restored by draining them, or by complete removal of all fish with chemicals, followed by the reintroduction of the proper species in reasonable numbers. This method is a drastic one, of course, and in areas with a short growing season, the waters might be of little value to angling for several seasons unless catchable-sized fish are reintroduced.

The fish manager may need considerable patience in explaining to an angler that fishing is poor because there are too many fish!

There are other aspects to the population-management problem, such as removing rough fish by commercial gear where these are too abundant. Our objective in managing the fish is to produce a maximum number of fish of desirable size and species, and to keep the balance between fish and food at a point where food is adequate to furnish good growth of the fish, but not so abundant that it prevents the angler from harvesting a substantial portion of the available crop.

CREATING DEMAND FOR THE LESS DESIRED SPECIES

In the past, the fighting qualities of a few species, such as bass, muskellunge, and trout, have been widely publicized. Most magazine articles and newspaper accounts concerned these species. Fishing pressure for these kinds has increased, partly because of their fighting qualities, but also partly because of the publicity which they have received.

Since the big game fish are more easily harvested than many of the other species, and because these big predators are needed to keep pan fish under control, this advertising has probably contributed considerably to the overpopulation problem. Fish managers now recognize the importance of harvesting the other species too, both because of the contribution which these fish can make to angling, and because of the need for keeping these species reduced in number.

Fortunately, the anglers are realizing more and more that species other than those mentioned above are willing to resist capture when hooked. On light tackle the bluegill is an excellent fighter. So are fish such as the carp, the channel catfish, and the dogfish.

An increasing number of articles in outdoor magazines now centers on fishing for bluegills, crappie, catfish, white bass, and other species. The demand for so-called "less desirable" species is much greater than it was a few decades ago. The belief that only trout, bass, and muskellunge are worth catching is no longer held by a big percentage of the anglers, though continued emphasis should be placed on the importance of catching fish of the "less advertised" species.

CREATING MORE FISHING WATER

If there is a big demand for beef, that demand can be met partly by raising improved strains of beef cattle and by improving our pastures. But if the demand is really great, we will meet it mainly by increasing our acreage of pasture. In many areas where fishing waters are few and where the fishing pressure is heavy, even doubling the production of fish would not satisfy the demand. In these areas, the chief method of meeting the increased angling demand is obvious—we can meet it only by increasing the acreage of fishing water. In many localities the creating of more fishing water is probably the most important management tool.

There are three important kinds of "new" water: (1) farm fish ponds, (2) fishing lakes, (3) reservoirs created mainly for other purposes.

Farm fish ponds are being built so rapidly that no reliable estimate of their number is available. Fully a third of these are used for the production of fish as well as for stock watering or other purposes. Altogether, the number of ponds used partly for fishing probably exceeds 100,000. These ponds are capable of yielding a large poundage of fish. Usually less than 5 acres in area, the ponds are easily managed, especially those which can be drained. Farm ponds are discussed separately in another chapter.

In the farm fish pond program, emphasis has been on furnishing meat for the farmer. Usually, though, ponds used only by the farmer are underfished. Emphasis should preferably be on using the fish as a cash crop by permitting anglers to fish the ponds for a daily fee.

A number of states are now using some of their income from licenses to build state-owned fishing lakes, usually ranging in size from 50 to 200 acres. One such lake in Tennessee yielded as high as 120 pounds of fish per acre. In 1948, this 65-acre lake (Bedford Lake) supported 6,437 man-days of fishing and yielded as average catch of 1.2 pounds per individual fishing trip.

Sportsmen's clubs might well consider the building of fishing lakes as important club projects. Because of the contribution of fishing to health, municipalities should give serious consideration to this important project. Fishing lakes will also support other recreation, such as swimming and duck hunting.

The big reservoirs, which are becoming increasingly abundant, have various effects on angling. Some have provided only mediocre fishing, but others have given greatly improved angling. The water-supply reservoirs of San Diego, California, are a good example of the latter. These waters now support about a hundred thousand man-days of fishing annually. Records have been kept of the fishing and fish catch for over 20 years. The city charges adults a 50-cent daily fishing fee.

The TVA reservoirs provide another example of greatly increased fishing. Here there has been about a hundredfold increase in fishing on storage waters over fishing in the reservoir areas before impoundment. On the Tennessee itself, the estimated increase is twentyfold to thirtyfold. Here in the fiscal years 1949 and 1950, the tail waters immediately below the nine dams on the Tennessee have supported about 670,000 man-days of angling per year; the entire TVA reservoirs have supported fully 2 million fishing trips annually. Here the average spring catch, based on creel census, is estimated at about 3.6 pounds per man-day of angling. This is probably well above the national average, perhaps several times as high as the average for fishing on all waters in the United States.

Some reservoirs which have provided poor fishing can be improved by introducing the proper species and a new food chain; others can be improved if the water levels are managed partly for the benefit of angling, especially at spawning time. Some reservoirs will undoubtedly continue to furnish poor fishing for one reason or another. If, when reservoirs are contemplated, the fishery interests receive full consideration, these reservoirs may play a very important part in the fish-conservation picture.

EVALUATING THE TOOLS

Some of the seven tools mentioned above are more important than others. Several will make a much more significant contribution to fish management when we learn how to use them more effectively. Briefly, the present status seems to be about as follows:

Fishing for fun. The idea of fishing for fun instead of for meat will make slow progress. A long and effective educational program must be conducted before this idea gains general acceptance.

Regulations. Fishing regulations are improving rapidly and are based more and more on factual evidence. Excellent progress is being made in the use of this tool.

FIG. 22-2. Brush shelters being installed through the ice of a northern lake. These shelters help to concentrate game and pan fish and are a substitute for aquatic vegetation. (*Institute of Fisheries Research, Michigan Conservation Department.*)

Stocking. Stocking is still greatly overemphasized but is gradually assuming its proper role. In this field there is need for more education and more fact finding.

Environmental improvement. This field has not progressed rapidly because too little is known about fish populations and fish ecology. More research is needed.

Population manipulation. This will probably become one of the most important management tools when more information becomes available. We now recognize some of the significant problems, the most important of which is probably overpopulation with pan fish. Here, too, more research is needed.

Creating demand for the less desired species. This calls for an effective educational program. Considerable progress is being made in this field.

Creating more fishing water. This is the most important management tool in areas where fishing waters are not abundant. In this field progress is excellent.

An examination of the above evaluation suggests several bottlenecks. If these tools are to be "sharpened," we need more research and a more effective educational program. There is a third bottleneck. No matter how good the tools are, they will still be ineffective in the hands of men who are unskilled in their use or ignorant of their limitations. In some instances, improvement of personnel must precede improvement in management methods. Under separate headings we discuss briefly (1) the fish manager, (2) fisheries research, (3) education.

THE FISH MANAGER

Comments made several years ago (11) about the fish manager still seem to apply:

Fish managers today are much better qualified and equipped than they were 10 or 20 years ago. Because of their varied backgrounds, however, they still fail to conform to any set pattern. The top fish management executives in our state set-ups usually stem from quite varied backgrounds. Some have had a background of college fishery training. They recognize management principles and the need for fact-finding, but they tend to forget that fish conservation involves fishermen as well as fish. They are inclined to have a much better understanding of fish behavior than of human behavior.

Then there are those who do understand the angler, those who got where they are because they know people, including the "right" people. They usually have fewer public relations problems than the college-trained man but they sometimes forget about the fact-finding program and the need for basing fish management on scientific fact.

A third group of executives has come up through the fish-cultural ranks. Such a background promotes a practical down-to-earth viewpoint, an understanding of fish-rearing techniques, and a sympathetic bend toward the demands of sportsmen. But at the same time it breeds faith in the myth that fish conservation must revolve around the hatchery; it makes one suspicious of any fact-finding program that might dispel that myth.

There are exceptions of course. Some formally trained fishery workers do recognize the significance of the human element. Some managers who have gained their position by virtue of knowing people realize that both fish and fact-finding enter the conservation picture. And some former fish-culturists can see the hatchery in proper perspective. The fact that these exceptional individuals are increasing in number speaks well for the future of fish management.

The trend in recent years has been away from the political appointee and toward the formally trained fish manager. It is following the pattern set by the older professions. The campus-trained manager, though, may find the trail a rough one because of his inadequate training. His formal education will have consisted of a variety of courses in biology, including, perhaps, a course or two in fish taxonomy and in fishery biology. He will probably have had no schooling in several equally important subjects—notably human behavior, business administration, and salesmanship. He may find that formulating a reasonably sound fish-management program is much easier than administering it, or selling it to the angling public.

We may assume that eventually fish management will be conducted mainly by the formally trained fish manager, just as medicine, dentistry, and law are now practiced by the trained professional men in these fields. This change cannot become general, though, until the trained fisheries manager can demonstrate that he can do more than the untrained individual to bring about better fishing. In many instances, he has not yet made this demonstration. Here there has been another bottleneck. The student's training has been highly inadequate, though it is improving.

Usually the formal training of the fish manager has consisted mainly of a background in general courses in biology together with a course or two in fisheries biology. This has hardly qualified him to serve as a fish manager, though it is a part of the training which a fish manager needs. There are at least four other fields in which the fish manager needs training. These are, very briefly:

1. *General conservation.* The manager should have a thorough background in general conservation to appreciate the importance of other fields of conservation to his own field. Soil conservation, forestry, etc., are all related to the fish conservation picture. Without the proper use and conservation of our other resources, sport fishing will cease to exist. Fishing for sport is practiced only where a high standard of living prevails. In areas where the resources have been dissipated, sport fishing is almost unknown. Chinese fisheries workers, for example, have one major problem—providing meat for undernourished people.

2. *Human behavior.* The embryo fish manager will soon discover that his most difficult problems will be with fishermen rather than with fish. He needs an understanding of both fish and fishermen. Yet, his training is generally limited to studying only one of these two. This defect in training has handicapped the profession greatly.

3. *Business management.* Fish management has become big business and now calls for the use of business methods. In business, for example,

the importance of taking inventory and of keeping close check on sales records is recognized. Yet, in many states we have made little effort to learn what kinds and amounts of "goods" (fish) are available to the angler and what part of the available supply of "goods" the angler is using.

4. *Salesmanship.* The fish manager must be able to sell his program and his methods to the public, and selling ideas and concepts to the angler is one of the most important parts of the fish management.

In return for this extensive training, the fish manager can expect to receive a low salary and plenty of grief. But he has the satisfaction, too, of knowing that he can contribute to the most important kind of conservation—human conservation.

RESEARCH

The research conducted by the practical fish-management agency should be directed toward providing a maximum number of successful fishing trips without injury to the fish supply, and toward a fair distribution of the fish resources. When we keep this objective firmly in mind while evaluating some of the various kinds of research, a more realistic fact-finding program usually results.

Some programs are very important but contribute very little to an early improvement in fishing. This includes life-history studies, species-distribution studies, general surveys, parasite studies, and many other kinds of research. These are important, but they might best be left to the campus while the fish manager confines his attention to some of the more immediate problems.

The investigator should preferably give consideration to the proper place of stocking in fish management, to learning what regulations are most desirable, and to discovering how the population can be managed so that the water will provide a maximum number of the fish of desirable size and species.

The conducting of these several types of basic study on a few representative waters may be especially helpful:

1. *Creel census.* This will show trends in the fishing and in the catch. A study of these records will often give valuable clues.

2. *Population studies.* Sampling the population in a representative area, by seining, netting, or use of rotenone, will demonstrate changes in the population itself, and will show whether or not reproduction and survival have been satisfactory.

3. *Harvesting studies.* These demonstrate, roughly, the extent to which the fish population is being used by the angler. By marking a representative number of fish and noting what percentage is taken by the angler,

we can discover whether the anglers are using only a small part of the crop or whether they are using most of it. This information will help in formulating regulations. This kind of study has shown, for example, that the bigger predatory species may be more harvestable than the pan fish, a very significant factor in the overpopulation question.

4. *Growth determination.* These studies, conducted from year to year, will show whether or not food is adequate. If growth is exceptionally rapid, we may assume that the water could support more fish of the fast-growing species, but if growth is slow, we can generally assume that the food is inadequate. Factors other than food enter the picture, but changes in growth of fish in a given water generally reflect changes in abundance of food. Ideally, food should be abundant enough to permit fairly rapid growth, but it should not be so plentiful that our lures cannot harvest a fair percentage of the fish population.

Often a combination of several of these studies may answer our problems. For example, even though fishing in the tail waters on the Tennessee is very extensive, and is increasing, it is very probably not excessive. Normally a number of questions would be raised regarding this very heavy fishing. Should the fast waters immediately below the dams be closed to fishing entirely? Should there be a closed season? What about stocking or fish ladders?

The evidence below one dam suggests that even though fishing increased greatly for several years, the catch per trip also increased (creel census). This would not occur if most fish were being caught. Harvesting studies in the reservoir immediately below the tail water show that only a very small percentage of the fish population is being caught. Population studies show that spawning and survival are satisfactory. Limited-growth studies show fairly fast but not exceptionally rapid growth. All evidence, therefore, suggests that the heavy year-round fishing in this tail water is doing no harm.

We might prepare a long list of other kinds of studies which might be made, but where funds are limited, we must learn for representative waters what is available in the way of fish resources and what is being utilized. These are basic to our other studies. At this early stage in fish management our big problem is still to learn how to diagnose the "ailment"; once we learn to diagnose the troubles, remedies will probably be forthcoming.

EDUCATION

In our educational programs, three points should be stressed. If we can get the average angler to accept these points as basic conservation concepts, fish management will progress much more rapidly and the remainder of the educational program can be "sold" much more easily. The points are these:

1. Fishing should be regarded as a way to relax; it should no longer be directed toward getting meat for the table. The number of trout in the creel, or bass on the stringer, should no longer be a criterion of our angling success. With the continued increase in population and leisure time, our waters cannot supply enough meat. They can, however, supply an endless number of man-days of healthful and badly needed relaxation—if we will fish more for fun and less for food.

2. Lakes and streams are really pastures. Fish are a crop. We must take the same rational viewpoint toward aquatic pastures that we take toward land pastures. Basic productivity is a major factor; some aquatic pastures are more productive than others. Aquatic pastures too can be overgrazed and overstocked. Selective harvesting without control of the "weed" species cannot operate to the advantage of the angler. Soil must be kept on the land, and out of the lakes and streams; the medium in which our aquatic "livestock" lives is water. The belief that our aquatic pastures can produce endless quantities of "livestock" is obviously ill-founded.

3. The job of managing these publicly owned aquatic pastures, and of insuring continuous crops to their thousands of owners, should be in the hands of experienced fishery managers. The job is a complicated one, involving an understanding of fish, fish habitat, and humans. Medical problems are handled by experienced doctors; legal problems are placed in the hands of lawyers; we take our farm problems to the county agent or the crop specialist. It follows then that fishery-management matters should be handled by those best qualified by training and experience to handle them.

GENERAL COMMENT

In this chapter we adhered rather closely to a discussion of some of the principles involved in lake and pond management; there has been no comment on method. The field has not yet progressed far enough to permit a general discussion of methods. We could, of course, discuss current methods of raising and planting hatchery fish. But here the important question is still: How helpful is the stocking program in providing an increased number of successful fishing trips? Or we might discuss the matter of installing brush shelters to protect young fish, but we still do not know under what conditions the shelter might contribute to a greater fish catch. Our immediate need is one of learning how to apply the various tools, and learning their values and limitations. We are still in the "what to do?" stage which must precede the "how to do it" stage.

Progress is being made, though, and there are now a number of instances where fish management has actually improved the fishing.

REFERENCES

Literature with which the fisheries worker should be familiar includes the following:

Transactions of the American Fisheries Society. Official publication of the American Fisheries Society. (Annual.)
Transactions of the North American Wildlife Conference. Contains papers on both fish and game. (Annual.)
Journal of Wildlife Management. Official publication of the Wildlife Society. Chiefly on game but contains some papers on fish. (Quarterly.)
Copeia. Official publication of the American Society of Ichthyologists and Herpetologists. Of interest primarily to taxonomists but contains some papers of interest to fish management. (Quarterly.)
The Progressive Fish Culturist. Prepared by the U.S. Fish and Wildlife Service. (Formerly monthly, now quarterly.)

Transactions of the various state academies of science contain numerous papers of value to fish management. Many important contributions appear in the monthly or bimonthly publications of state conservation departments or state fish and game units.

Among the general survey reports which are of interest to students of fish management are the following:

New York Biological Survey Reports, by Emmeline Moore *et al.*
Maine Fish Survey Reports, by Gerald P. Cooper.
New Hampshire Survey Reports, by Earl E. Hoover *et al.*
A Fisheries Survey of Important Connecticut Lakes, by Lyle M. Thorpe *et al.*

REFERENCES

1. Adams, Charles C., and T. L. Hankinson. 1928. The ecology and economics of Oneida Lake fish. *Roosevelt Wild Life Ann.* **1**(3 and 4): 235–548.
2. Beckman, William C. 1940. Increased growth rate of rock bass, *Ambloplites rupestris* (Rafinesque), following reduction in the density of the population. *Trans. Amer. Fisheries Soc.* **70**:143–148.
3. ———. 1950. Changes in growth rate of fishes following reduction in population densities by winterkill. *Trans. Amer. Fisheries Soc.* **80**:82–90.
4. Bennett, George W. 1943. Management of small artificial lakes. *Ill. Nat. Hist. Survey Bul.* **22**(3):357–376.
5. ———. 1947. Fish management—a substitute for natural predation. *Trans. 12th North Amer. Wildlife Conf.* Pp. 276–286.
6. Carbine, W. F. 1939. Observations on the spawning habits of centrarchid fishes in Deep Lake, Oakland County, Michigan. *Trans. 4th North Amer. Wildlife Conf.* Pp. 275–287.
7. Carlander, Kenneth D. 1950. Handbook of freshwater fishery biology, William C. Brown Co., Dubuque, Iowa.

8. Cooper, Gerald P. 1940. Some factors of importance in a stocking policy for trout and salmon lakes. *Trans. 5th North Amer. Wildlife Conf.* Pp. 165–169.
9. ———. 1948. Fish stocking policies in Michigan. *Trans. 13th North Amer. Wildlife Conf.* Pp. 187–193.
10. Cottam, Clarence. 1949. Further needs in wildlife research. *Jour. Wildlife Mangt.* **13**(4):333–341.
11. Eschmeyer, R. W. 1949*a.* Recent advances in fresh-water fishery management. *Trans. 14th North Amer. Wildlife Conf.* Pp. 207–224.
12. ———. 1949*b.* The status of legal restrictions in fish conservation. *Proc. Internatl. Assoc. Game, Fish, and Conserv. Commrs. Conv.* (38th Convention). Pp. 11–18.
13. Gabrielson, Ira N. (editor). 1950. The fisherman's encyclopedia, Stackpole Co., Harrisburg, Pa.
14. Greeley, John R. 1949. Habitat improvement. *Proc. Internatl. Assoc. Game, Fish, and Conserv. Commrs. Conv.* (38th Convention). Pp. 18–23.
15. Harkness, W. J. K., and F. E. J. Fry. 1942. Game fish management in Algonquin Park lakes. *Trans. 7th North Amer. Wildlife Conf.* Pp. 398–404.
16. Hubbs, Carl L. 1937. Fish management; looking forward. *Trans. Amer. Fisheries Soc.* **66**:51–55.
17. ——— and R. W. Eschmeyer. 1938. The improvement of lakes for fishing, Michigan Department of Conservation.
18. Johnson, Raymond E. 1949. Maintenance of natural population balance. *Proc. Internatl. Assoc. Game, Fish, and Conserv. Commrs. Conv.* (38th Convention). Pp. 35–42.
19. Kendall, William C. 1924. The status of fish culture in our inland public waters, and the role of investigation in the maintenance of fish resources. *Roosevelt Wild Life Bul.* **2**(3):205–351.
20. Lagler, Karl F. 1949. Studies in freshwater fishery biology. J. W. Edwards, Ann Arbor.
21. Langlois, Thomas H. 1941. Two processes operating for the reduction in abundance or elimination of fish species from certain types of water areas. *Trans. 6th North Amer. Wildlife Conf.* Pp. 189–198.
22. Moyle, John B., Jerome H. Kuehn, and Charles R. Burrows. 1950. Fish–population and catch data from Minnesota lakes. *Trans. Amer. Fisheries Soc.* (1948). Pp. 163–175.
23. Pelton, John Z. 1950. Three years of liberalized fishing at Lake Alma, Ohio. *Trans. Amer. Fisheries Soc.* **80**:64–69.
24. Ricker, William E. 1943. Creel census, population estimates and rate of exploitation of game fish in Shoe Lake, Indiana. *Investigations of Indiana Lakes and Streams.* Pp. 215–253.
25. ——— and John Gottschalk. 1941. An experiment in removing coarse fish from a lake. *Trans. Amer. Fisheries Soc.* **70**:382–390.
26. Rose, Earl T. 1949. A fish population study of Storm Lake. *Proc. Iowa Acad. Sci.* **56**:385–395.
27. Rounsefell, George A. 1946. Fish production in lakes as a guide for estimating production in proposed reservoirs. *Copeia.* **1**:29–40.
28. Smith, Lloyd L. 1949. Effectiveness of modern fish management practices: planting. *Proc. Internatl. Assoc. Game, Fish, and Conserv. Commrs. Conv.* 38th Convention. Pp. 42–48.

29. Swingle, H. S. 1950. Relationships and dynamics of balanced and unbalanced fish populations. *Ala. Agr. Expt. Sta. Bul.* 274.
30. Tunison, A. V., S. M. Mullin, and O. Lloyd Meehean. 1949*a*. Survey of fish culture in the United States. *Prog. Fish Culturist.* **11**(1):31–69.
31. ———. 1949*b*. Extended survey of fish culture in the United States. *Prog. Fish Culturist.* **11**(4):253–262.
32. Westerman, F. A., and Albert S. Hazzard. 1945*a*. For better fishing, Michigan Conservation Department.
33. ———. 1945*b*. For better fishing, Michigan Conservation Department.

Clayt Seagears

CHAPTER 23

Farm Fish Ponds[1]

INTRODUCTION

One of the most recent developments in the field of fisheries management is the farm fish pond. Although such ponds have been advocated since the early part of this century, they have really come into their own only during the past two decades. Most of these ponds are relatively small bodies of water ranging in size from a fraction of an acre to several acres in extent; the average size is probably somewhat less than an acre. The topography of the land and the amount of money available for construction purposes are two of the primary factors governing pond size.

Since the beginning of the twentieth century, well over 1 million small ponds have been built in the United States (1). These ponds have largely been built under the auspices of the U.S. Soil Conservation Service, the Agricultural Adjustment Act, or some other Federal or state agency. The great majority of these ponds have been constructed for providing water for livestock, poultry, orchard spraying, fire protection, irrigation, etc. In such ponds use for fishing and recreation has been secondary. However, a relatively small but growing number of ponds have been built solely for fishing and other recreational purposes. Apparently the only factor that limits the number of ponds that could ultimately be built is the availability of satisfactory sites.

A great many of the ponds that have been built only for water storage are unsuitable for fishing. Storage ponds that are used for irrigation in Colorado, California, and other western states are unsuitable for fish because of the extreme fluctuations in water level. Many such ponds are drained dry by the end of the growing season. Furthermore, many of those ponds are highly alkaline and are thus unsuitable for fish production.

Even though there are such exceptions, most ponds are capable of supporting at least a limited amount of fishing if properly managed. In

[1] This chapter is contributed by Dr. Louis A. Krumholz, Indiana University, Bloomington.

the proper management of any pond there is more to consider than just the fish. The pond itself is of great importance. For Indiana, Krumholz (7) has outlined the following features to be considered in good management of ponds for fishing (Fig. 23-2). Such features are applicable to ponds in any part of the United States.

1. The watershed should be large enough to maintain the water level in the pond even during long periods of drought. It should be maintained in good permanent cover so that silting will be held to a minimum.

Fig. 23-1. Farm fish ponds such as this provide food, recreation, water for livestock, and fire protection. (*L. H. Binnie.*)

2. The construction of the pond should follow sound engineering principles. The earth fill and spillways should be laid out by an individual experienced in the use of surveying instruments. The operator of the earth-moving equipment should know what he is supposed to do, and how to do it.

3. The pond should be fenced off so that it is inaccessible to livestock. If given access, livestock will trample the pond edges; such trampling will in time lead to serious erosion problems, and the pond will remain muddy.

4. The area inside the fence should be planted to vegetation that will hold the banks. Native sod grasses and wildlife cover plantings are suitable.

5. The original pond edges should be maintained. Any small tears in the sod spillway or earth fill should be repaired as soon as they are discovered.

6. The pond should be large enough and sufficiently deep so that desirable kinds of fishes will be able to maintain their numbers and reach sizes large enough to be attractive to anglers.

7. The pond should be stocked with the proper numbers of a desirable fish or combination of fishes. Any such stocking should be based on ex-

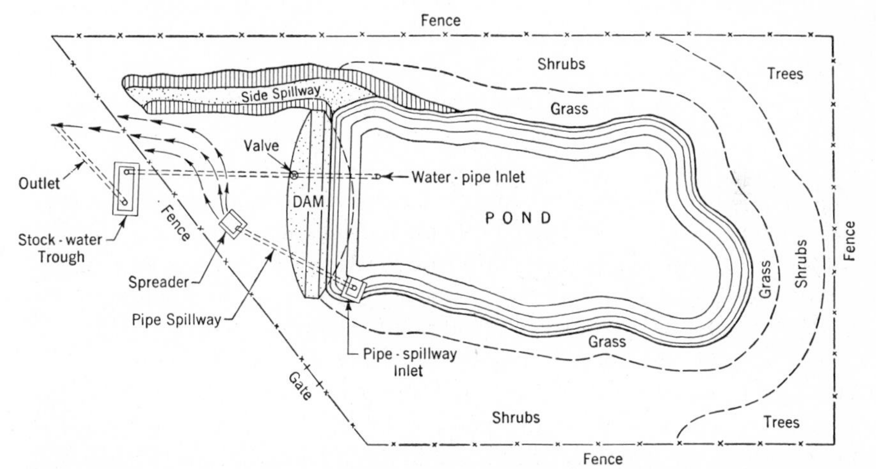

FIG. 23-2. Farm pond layout. Diagrammatic drawing of a properly constructed pond. The pond area should be adequately fenced from livestock, and provision made for proper installation of earth fill, core trench, and spillways. The area inside the fence should be properly planted to wildlife food and cover. Access to the pond area is provided by a stile over the fence. (*From U.S. Soil Conserv. Serv. Leaflet* 259.)

perimental evidence for the particular part of the country in which the pond is located.

8. The pond should be fished intensively and the crop harvested.

POND CONSTRUCTION

The small artificial pond consists of four main features as outlined by Freyburger (3, 4, 5, 6): the watershed, the earth fill that impounds the water, the impounded water itself, and the spillways. Here the small pond refers to bodies of water no larger than 2 or 3 acres. However, in larger ponds the same four features are present, but the advice of a competent engineer well versed in matters of pond construction should be sought.

Some of the commonest errors in pond construction are (1) the selection of a cultivated or badly eroded watershed that produces too much runoff to be handled by the spillway (ponds built in such areas may silt in as much as 10 per cent per year); (2) failure to determine whether the subsoil materials are tight enough to hold water (such underlying materials as gravel, limestone, etc., are usually incapable of holding water); (3) dependence upon sod spillways alone to take care of the excess runoff from the watershed (sod spillways tend to deteriorate under prolonged exposure to running water and should be supplemented by a spillway of more substantial materials); (4) trees and brush should not be allowed to grow on or near the earth fill (roots from such plants penetrate the fill and form passageways for seepage).

The Pond Site. One of the best sites for a pond is a broad, flat-bottomed draw with rather steep side slopes. The underlying soil should preferably be of heavy clay, clay loam, clay mixture, or some other impervious material that extends at least 3 feet below the deepest part of the pond. Such an ideal location, however, is not always available. Satisfactory ponds have been built on hillsides, the upper ends of long draws, or in practically every kind of location where there is a natural depression. In an area where there are tight subsoils and rolling topography it is possible to construct good ponds almost anywhere.

The size of the pond is largely determined by the topography and size of the watershed. All trees and stumps in the proposed pond area should be removed when the pond is built. Tree stumps in ponds do not afford much shelter for fish life and are a major hazard to swimmers. Further, if the owner anticipates seining the pond for fish, any stumps on the pond bottom will be in the way.

For best results the entire watershed should be kept in some kind of permanent cover such as grassland or ungrazed timber. If, however, it is necessary to cultivate part of the watershed, it should be terraced before construction on the pond begins and should be maintained under long-rotation crops. Such land should never be planted in row crops as their cultivation is conducive to erosion. Under no circumstances should the area below the lowest terrace be cultivated. That area should remain in permanent grass cover.

The pond area should be protected from livestock by an adequate fence and should be planted to wildlife cover and food plants. Any pond that is properly fenced and planted is attractive to wildlife. Many songbirds will nest in the area, and ducks and other migratory waterfowl may use the pond as a stopover during migration. Muskrats, raccoons, and other fur bearers may enter the area and, if properly handled, may become an extra source of revenue.

Size and Depth of Pond. Ponds that are expected to produce good fishing should be at least 5 or 6 feet deep in the middle. Such measurements will usually provide depths of 8 or 10 feet near the fill. The minimum surface area should not be less than $\frac{3}{10}$ acre, but it is much more desirable to have a fishing pond $\frac{1}{2}$ acre or larger in extent. Such features as the location and size of the spillways and the limits of the earth fill and core trench (keyway) should be laid out before any earth is moved.

Earth Fill, Core Trench, and Spillways. Earth fills for most ponds can be built with any suitable earth-moving equipment, such as slip scoops, bulldozers, tractors with rotary scrapers, or more elaborate machinery.

First of all, the entire area to be covered by the earth fill should be scraped clean to a depth of 6 inches to insure a good solid footing for the fill. All stumps, trees, brush, or other debris must be removed. A core trench, or keyway, must be placed beneath the fill. That trench, when refilled with impervious soil material, cuts out all old animal burrows and prevents seepage at the line of juncture between the undisturbed earth and the fill. In laying out the stakes for the fill the upstream side should have a slope of three to one, and the downstream side two to one. If either slope is less than the one recommended, sloughing will likely occur and the fill will be weakened. The top of the fill should be at least 8 or 10 feet wide. Any earth used in constructing the fill should be impervious to water and should be thoroughly compacted as it is brought in.

If any mechanical spillway other than the sod waterway is to be installed, the trench for the pipe or trickle tube should be dug as soon as the core trench is filled to a level with the surrounding soil. The pipe should be laid in undisturbed soil to prevent settling and placed at the end of the fill opposite the sod spillway. Then as the earth fill is built up, the pipe will be thoroughly compacted into the fill.

In completing the fill, the center should be brought to a crown 10 per cent higher than the end abutments. Thus any settling that may occur will not result in a low area in the center. Too little material in the fill is a far more serious mistake than too much. As soon as the fill is completed, it should be mulched and seeded with oats and native sod grasses. Here the oats will act as a nurse crop until the permanent grasses take over. One good heavy rain on a newly constructed and unprotected fill will cause considerable damage.

MANAGEMENT OF PONDS FOR FISHING

Suitability of Ponds for Fish. Most ponds, even quite small ones, are suited to fish life, provided they are not too shallow. If a pond is too shallow, the fish may die because of a decrease in oxygen content of the water to a point below the level at which the fish in question can live. Such an oxygen deficiency may occur during the winter under an ice and snow cover, or during the hot, still days of late summer. There are no fixed limits for water depth of a pond; but unless there is a reasonable area of water deeper than about 5 feet, it may not be suitable for desirable species of fish.

The oxygen and temperature requirements of various kinds of fishes differ considerably. For instance, the trout require a much higher minimum concentration of oxygen together with a much lower temperature than do the bullheads. Somewhere in between these lie the optimum requirements for the sunfish and black bass. Thus temperature of the water and its ability to carry dissolved oxygen are important factors limiting the kinds of fish that can be successfully grown in a pond.

Another factor to be considered is turbidity. Most fishes that are desirable for ponds feed largely by sight; permanently muddy ponds usually produce only inferior, slow-growing fishes and can scarcely be made to afford good fishing. Any pond intended to provide good fishing should be fenced from livestock and, if swimming is done in it frequently, some means of getting into and out of the water without roiling it should be provided.

If a pond will support fish life at all, it is very likely to hold too many. The rate of growth of fish in any pond is largely governed by the amount of food available. That food supply usually remains more or less constant year after year. In general, the rate of growth of the fish present in any pond is inversely proportional to the size of the population. A relatively few fish in a pond will grow more rapidly and will usually reach larger sizes than will a large number of fish in the same pond. Thus it is desirable not to have a pond overcrowded with fish, because under such conditions of overpopulation the fishes become stunted and will seldom reach desirable sizes for angling.

Selection of Species of Fish for Stocking. When stocking any pond with fish for the first time, it is necessary to assure the establishment of a breeding population. Surber (10) in West Virginia and Krumholz (8) in Indiana, using largemouth bass and bluegills in combination, have shown that the initial ratio of stocking has little or no effect on the future stability of the population. Thus any thought toward the future "balance" of the fish population should largely remain with the selection of the kinds of fish to be planted. The ideal combination is one in which all the kinds involved will constantly contribute to the fisherman's catch. Further, the kinds chosen should preferably not be in direct competition with each other for food. None of the kinds selected should be so much more prolific than the others that they will eventually become so numerous as to crowd them out. In some instances only a single kind of fish in a pond may be desirable. That kind should be one that will not become so numerous as to eventually overpopulate the pond and become stunted.

In selecting fishes to be used in stocking ponds, there are several criteria on which to base recommendations. These criteria are concerned primarily with the biology of the fish involved and should be proved by actual field tests in the part of the country in question. Whenever possible, native species should be used. Fish not native to the area may not live up to expectations and, in fact, may turn out to have a high nuisance value.

1. The fish should be desirable as food fish and provide sport for the fisherman.

2. The food requirements of the fish should be such that the natural supply of food in the pond can maintain a reasonably good fish population without additional feeding.

3. The fish selected should be able to spawn successfully and reproduce in adequate numbers to maintain the population without additional stocking in later years.

4. The fish population should reach some sort of satisfactory "balance" so that individuals of each kind present will grow to desirable sizes without overcrowding and consequent stunting. Any kind of fish that is unable to compete successfully with others in a pond should not be introduced.

5. A great many different kinds of fishes native to the section of the country in question satisfy one or more of the above criteria but only relatively few will meet all four. Planting any kind of fish, even though desirable for one reason, if found undesirable for another, should be avoided.

In practice, the greatest difficulties are encountered in the fourth requirement listed above. Such fishes as the bluegill, the redear sunfish or shellcracker, the green sunfish, the yellow perch, one of the bullheads, and many others, although highly prized by anglers in various sections of the country, should never be placed in ponds by themselves. For example, a new pond stocked with only a few hundred fingerlings of any one of those species will provide good fishing within about a year after stocking. Because of the abundant food supply and virtually no competition, they will grow rapidly. In the second year, however, those fish will usually spawn, even in a strictly mud-bottomed pond, and fill the pond with many thousands of fry. Those young fish will compete with each other and to some extent with the adults for food and neither the young nor adults will grow to any extent. As the numbers of fish increase, the individual food supply becomes diminished and the fish become stunted. Even such stunted fish will continue to reproduce, even though to a limited extent, and further aggravate the situation. Thus the first fish placed in the pond may be the only ones that will ever be worth fishing for, and from that time on the pond will contain only runt fish.

There are, however, certain kinds of fish that, in particular cases, will afford continued good fishing over the years when stocked by themselves. In New York State, workers (9) have found that either brook, brown, or rainbow trout, either alone or in combinations, exhibited a growth superior to that of any of the warm-water species studied. Although the trout did not reproduce successfully in any of the ponds observed, it was felt that restocking on an annual or biennial basis might not be a serious problem since the size of the population could be kept under control. In Indiana, either the rock bass, largemouth bass, or spotted bass (Kentucky bass) have maintained satisfactory growing populations for at least 4 years when stocked by themselves. In such instances the adults prey upon the young to a great enough extent so that they keep their population numbers down. However, enough young survive to replace the adults that are caught out. Hybrid sunfish have also been stocked alone with reports of varying success. Those fish have a distinctly unbalanced sex ratio greatly in favor of the males. With only a few females present to lay eggs the size of the population is automatically kept at a minimum. However, it is too early to know whether or not such a population can maintain itself over a period of years without restocking. Channel catfish, too, have been tried with some success. Here, as in the case of the trout, restocking may be necessary unless some sort of spawning facilities are provided.

Where combinations of two or more kinds of fishes are used for stocking a pond, the generally accepted procedure is to stock predaceous fish along with nonpredatory species. The first such combination recommended was that of the largemouth bass and bluegill as suggested by Swingle and Smith for Alabama ponds (12). Although that combination was not necessarily the best one, it was the only one that had been tested on a large scale at the time. Because they had no better information, many state and Federal agencies followed those recommendations, and many thousands of ponds in many sections of the country were stocked with that combination. Even though the bass-bluegill combination has been the most popular, it is not producing the desired results in some localities. In New York (9), Illinois (1), Indiana (8), and other states workers have reported that the bass-bluegill combination has not proved satisfactory. However, it apparently is the best combination found so far for the southeastern states and has enjoyed limited success in other areas (13).

The theory behind stocking predatory and nonpredatory species of fish together is sound, but until actual field tests are made any combination propounded may not be suitable for any particular area. In Indiana, for example, it was found that the bass-bluegill combination did not work, either because the bluegill was too prolific, or because the bass was not a good enough predator, or both. After trying out several combinations, it was found that, on the average, the bass-redear sunfish combination was much better. Also it was found that either the largemouth bass or the spotted (Kentucky) bass was satisfactory as a predator in combination with redear sunfish. The redear was not so prolific as the bluegill in that area and did not overpopulate the ponds in which it was stocked. Perhaps the redear was less prolific because in that area it was near the northern limit of its natural range and its reproductive potential was accordingly lower. Again, in Montana it was found that when the bass-bluegill combination was tried, the bluegills overpopulated the ponds. There, however, when northern pike were introduced into such a pond, they apparently took over a good share of the predation on the bluegills with a resultant better "balance" of the population. Unfortunately, northern pike could not be used in southern Indiana because they apparently could not tolerate the high summer temperatures.

As mentioned earlier, the basic principle behind an economical and efficient policy for stocking ponds with fish for the first time is the introduction of only sufficient numbers to assure their establishment in the pond. In general, only a very few fish will suffice. If, however, the pond owner wants to begin fishing within a year after stocking, it is necessary to stock more so as to make the fishing worth while. If a matter of a hundred or so of each kind of fish is stocked for each acre of pond surface in the initial planting, they will usually reach sizes large enough for angling within a year after planting. Even though fished for diligently, there is little chance that all of those fish will be caught; always enough will remain to spawn.

One of the principal advantages of using small numbers of fish in an original planting is that they are much more easily transported. The essential feature in stocking any body of water is that the fish get there in good condition.

From the foregoing discussion it is evident that any fish-stocking policy should be based on sound research carried out in the area in question. Just because a combination is very successful in one section of the country is not necessarily proof that it will work out in another. Climatic and physical conditions of the environment in different parts of the country are decidedly different, and fish as well as most other animals will react differently under different conditions.

Another recently popular use of ponds is for the raising of bait minnows. Although many commercial dealers have built elaborate plants for raising minnows, there is still an apparent shortage of fish available as bait for the continually growing number of sport fishermen (2). The kinds of minnows that can be raised in an ordinary pond are limited, but such species as the fathead minnow, the golden shiner, the bluntnose minnow, and others can be raised successfully. Usually only ponds with a dependable water supply can be used. Here, the entire crop is harvested annually by draining the pond and removing all the fish except the required number needed for breeding stock the following years.

Harvesting the Crop. There is little point in going to the expense and trouble of building a pond and stocking it with fishes if that crop is not going to be utilized. The ideal way of harvesting the fish crop is by steady fishing. There is little or no danger of overfishing, as it has been found that it is virtually impossible to catch many more than half of the legal-sized fish in any pond at any time. As the larger fish are being caught, the smaller ones are continually growing up and replacing them. The fish population in any body of water is one that can be continually harvested, whereas most game birds and mammals can properly be cropped over only relatively short periods of time.

Ordinarily, at least half of the total weight of any fish population can be harvested annually without having any detrimental effect on the capacity of the population to maintain itself. In fact, the experimental evidence at hand indicates that such a harvest is highly desirable, as it allows more food for the fish that remain and thus they can grow faster. The size of the crop that can be harvested can best be determined by experimental evidence on the ability of the waters in the particular region in question to support fish life.

For those who wish, a pond can be partially drained so that part of the fish may be removed and used. Such a drawdown should never be attempted in the warm summer months or during the dry season because the fish may die in the shallow water before the pond refills. Perhaps late October or November is the ideal time for most sections of the country, as the temperatures are cooler and the pond will soon be refilled by forthcoming rains. In any event, the pond should be kept full during the warmer months of the year to promote good growth.

Removal of Undesirable Fishes. When a pond has already been stocked with undesirable fishes, or is overpopulated with many otherwise desirable fish, it is usually advisable to remove them all and start afresh. This cannot be done by hook and line fishing or by seining. The most practical method is to drain the pond dry. Such draining is easy if the pond is equipped with a drainpipe. If not, the water can be removed by a centrifugal pump. If any of the fish present at the time of draining are to be used in restocking, care should be used in selecting the fish to use. Just because any individual fish is large is not reason enough in itself to return it to the pond. When starting over in any pond, it is best to treat it just as though it were being stocked for the first time.

In some instances chemicals have been used with considerable success in eliminating fish populations from small bodies of water. Rotenone, copper sulfate, DDT, and some others have given the best results. Inasmuch as copper sulfate and DDT are toxic to many other animals besides fish, they frequently wipe out virtually all animal life in the body of water treated. Rotenone, on the other hand, is a near specific for fish in the concentrations recommended and kills only a minimum of other kinds of animals. In the use of toxic substances in any body of water, extreme care should be taken and the use of that substance should be cleared with the proper authorities.

POND FERTILITY AND FERTILIZATION

Generally speaking, the natural fertility of any body of water, and consequently its ability to support a fish population, is directly dependent on the fertility of the watershed and the nutrient materials that are available. Some soils are much more fertile than others, and the fertility of land differs from one part of the country to another. Soils in the prairie lands of the midwestern "corn belt" are much more fertile than those in many other parts of the nation. Further, there may be considerable difference in the fertility of the soil in different counties in any one state and, for that matter, even in the different townships and sections of each county.

In some sections of the United States the innate fertility of the soil is so low that ponds built in that area are not able to support a sufficiently large fish population to provide good fishing except on a very limited scale. In other areas, however, the soil is so fertile and fish can be produced so rapidly that it is difficult to harvest them adequately with ordinary hook-and-line methods. For instance, in Alabama it was found that ponds could support only from 40 to 200 pounds of fish per acre (the average is probably less than 100) on the natural food supply. In Illinois, on the other hand, well over 1,000 pounds of fish per acre were recovered from some lakes following chemical treatment. There the average for a number of lakes was over 500 pounds per acre. However, by treating the Alabama ponds with an inorganic fertilizer, the over-all productivity of the ponds was stepped up to a point at which they would support from 500 to 600 pounds per acre.

Thus it is apparent that, if properly done, the application of fertilizer to a body of water will increase its ability to support fish even to a point at which it may be more than doubled. Fish do not eat the fertilizer. Rather, the nutrient materials contained in the fertilizer become dissolved in the water and are utilized by the microscopic plants known as algae. Because of the increased supply of nutrients, the algae (phytoplankton) multiply very rapidly, thus affording more food for the minute animals such as water fleas, small crustaceans (collectively known as zooplankton), insect larvae, etc., that are present in the pond. Again, because of the increased food supply, these zooplankton grow faster and reproduce more rapidly, thus supplying more food for the

Fig. 23-3. Fertilizing a farm fish pond. This practice produces large fish in a shorter time. (*Gordon Webb, U.S. Soil Conservation Service.*)

young fish in the pond and also for some of the plankton-eating adults, such as bluegills. The small fish in turn furnish food for the larger predatory species, such as the bass. Here it is evident that the increase of nutrient material in the water has set off a sort of chain reaction that is manifest all along the entire food chain from the microscopic algae to the large predatory fish.

However, in many instances where the soil has an innate high fertility, the application of fertilizer does not result in an increase in only the phytoplankton used as food. Rather there is a very sharp increase in the growth of the filamentous algae that produce huge, dense mats at the water surface. Such algae do not serve as food for fish and are extremely objectionable to swimmers, anglers, and others seeking recreation. Unfortunately, there is no way known to determine whether the algae that will become most abundant following the application of fertilizer will be the more desirable kinds that serve as food for the zooplankton and other animals present or the highly undesirable filamentous kinds that contribute very little to the diet of fish and have a high nuisance value. Furthermore, once such undesirable algae have become abundant, it is very difficult to get rid of them. Even the algae that are desirable from the standpoint of fish production are frequently undesirable for swimmers, as they make the water soupy green or brown in appearance following the application of fertilizer. Thus the use of fertilizers for increasing fish production seems to be justifiable in some parts of the country but not in others.

Because the application of fertilizers to pond waters frequently brings in a heavy algal "bloom," it has been suggested that fertilization be used to control undesirable vegetation. Such a recommendation is based on the theory that the minute algae become so numerous following fertilization that they will shade out rooted plants, thereby making it impossible for the latter to maintain themselves.

The use of fertilizers is sometimes attended with serious disadvantages. Fertilization of waters in some parts of the country may directly contribute to a marked deficiency of the oxygen content of the water. Following a period of rapid reproduction of any kind of algae, these plants may die in very large numbers. As they die and decompose, they use up large quantities of dissolved oxygen, thereby depleting that element in the water. Such an oxygen depletion is frequently the cause of mass mortality among fishes during the hot summer months. Plants liberate oxygen through photosynthesis only during the day. As darkness falls and oxygen production stops, the continued decomposition of the dead plants uses up all the available oxygen in the water, and the fish suffocate. Furthermore, the kinds of fish usually most desirable to the angler are the ones that suffer first from oxygen deficiency. Such fish as trout are extremely susceptible; bass and other sunfish are perhaps next in line, and such hardy fish as bullheads are most resistant. Such oxygen deficiencies may occur during the winter months under the ice as well as during the hot, still days of late summer.

The advantages and disadvantages of fertilization of waters for increasing fish production may be summarized as follows:

Advantages of Fertilization. 1. Fertilization increases the annual growth of fish in a pond and hence the potential annual yield.

2. If a pond currently contains a stunted fish population, it is possible by fertilizing properly to obtain good-sized fish at least temporarily.

This, however, may be followed by increased reproduction and a return to the overcrowded condition in spite of continued fertilization.

3. Under certain conditions fertilizers can be used to control the growth of submerged aquatic vegetation.

Disadvantages of Fertilization. 1. Fertilization causes the water of a pond to become greenish or brownish and opaque due to the presence of innumerable tiny algae. This condition may be objectionable to swimmers and, because of the odor, to persons who have their homes nearby. In certain parts of the country continued fertilization frequently leads to the formation of filamentous algal mats that literally cover the pond surface and render it useless for fishing and other recreational purposes.

2. By increasing the total organic content of the pond, it is made more susceptible to oxygen deficiency with a consequent loss of fish. Such oxygen deficiencies usually occur during late summer or during the winter under a cover of ice and snow. Shallow ponds are particularly susceptible.

3. It may restrict or prevent the growth of rooted aquatic plants. This is a disadvantage where waterfowl and/or muskrats are desirable.

4. Fertilization of ponds is expensive—from \$20 to \$25 per acre per year at the maximum rate recommended.

5. Once fertilization of a pond is begun, it must be continued. Once the fish population has become adjusted to the higher level of fertility, a change to a lower one is likely to result in severe stunting.

Many of the disadvantages of fertilization vanish, of course, when a pond is cropped completely each year. Thus the person who raises bait minnows or goldfish for commercial purposes invariably uses fertilizers, as do state and federal hatcheries in raising young fish for distribution. The use of fertilizers in such programs invariably assures better survival, and the young fish reach a more uniform size.

When contemplating the use of fertilizers, it must be kept in mind that any increase in the production of fish in the pond must necessarily be followed by a comparable increase in the harvest. Different ponds will react differently to similar applications of fertilizers. If the productivity of a pond is increased through fertilization and the extra crop of fish is not harvested, stunting will occur in all probability on a much greater scale than in an unfertilized pond.

Application of Fertilizers. When fertilizing a pond to increase the productivity, either organic or inorganic fertilizers can be used. Of the former, cattle manure seems best. It is frequently applied early in the spring at a rate of about one ton per acre of water surface. It should be spread out into the pond as far as possible. If the winter ice cover is sufficiently thick, the manure may be placed on the ice and it will settle to the pond bottom when the ice melts.

If inorganic fertilizer is to be used, the kind recommended for the watershed is probably the most suitable. Applications should be made at approximately monthly intervals from the first warm weather of spring until about September. The maximum desirable rate is 100 pounds of fertilizer per acre of water surface for each application. In addition, it is helpful to add about 20 pounds of agricultural limestone per acre. The fertilizer should be scattered out in the shallow water to a distance of about 10 feet from shore. The amount of fertilizer and the frequency of application may be adjusted downward if the water is naturally fertile. A simple and reliable test for fertility is the color of the water; if it is greenish or brownish in color from algal growth, there is no need for additional fertilizer. Such color should not be confused with muddiness. Muddy ponds do not profit from fertilization because the sunlight cannot penetrate the water and promote the growth of algae. Further, the fertilizer itself may be adsorbed by the tiny clay particles and rendered useless.

It is of little value to fertilize a pond that has a good flow of water through it continually. Here, most of the nutrient materials will be lost in the overflow and thus cannot be utilized in the pond. If a pond is temporarily muddy because of rain, the application of fertilizer should be postponed until the water clears. During high water much of the fertilizer would be washed downstream anyway.

TROUT PONDS[2]

Numerous ponds suitable for trout have been in use in the northeastern part of the continent since colonial times. These are the mill ponds that were built for water-power purposes and are still operating as a water supply, for power, and for fishing. Still greater potential exists for trout ponds in much of the forested area, where small ponds can be constructed adjacent to streams with controllable water intakes and screened overflows. Likewise, many undeveloped sites exist adjacent to springs where the water is relatively cold and constant, thereby meeting the requirements for suitable trout habitats. The usually accepted requirements for reproduction of the resident fish in these ponds is sometimes present, as where the pond is fed by bottom springs or is supplied by a brook suitable for spawning. Where there are no

[2] Very little data are available on trout ponds. With this in mind, these pages will contain suggestions only, included to stimulate work in this field. This discussion is by the author and is compiled from the brief literature available on this subject.

facilities for spawning, the fish can be stocked periodically from outside sources, so this limitation is not as serious as it would appear. Saila[3] indicates that in New York State trout ponds are less complex than ponds for warm-water fish, and the ponds are generally successful as indicated by the excellent quality of the fishing.

Conditions necessary for successful trout ponds include a suitable water supply, sufficiently low water temperatures, sufficient oxygen, and proper management.

FIG. 23-4. "What is so rare as a day in June?" (*U.S. Soil Conservation Service.*)

Water Supply. Many natural springs are present in the rolling, wooded parts of the Northeast. Frequently large springs have been utilized for commercial or public trout culture, but many unused springs still exist. Where the spring has good volume, especially where a pond can be built to cover the spring site, there is a good chance that the pond will furnish suitable conditions for natural reproduction in the gravel beds surrounding the spring. Usually spring water is low enough in temperature to be suitable (less than 75°F.) for trout, but if the volume is low, the pond may warm to a temperature above the tolerance level of these fish.

Brook or stream sources of water are more frequent but more difficult

[3] Saul B. Saila. 1952. Some results of farm pond management studies in New York. *Jour. Wildlife Mangt.* **16**(3):279–282.

to manage. Such a water supply will need to be led through a bypass to the adjacent pond. In this case a means of control of volume is needed as well as screens on both the inlet and outlet. A small, cold, tributary trout stream leading directly into the pond may be ideal by supplying a constant source of fish for the pond.[4]

Water Temperature. The lethal temperature for trout is 77.5°F. For all practical purposes it may go slightly higher, but for safety it should be not greater than 75°F. Shade around the pond, deep holes, or bottom springs may prove to be safety factors for ponds otherwise not having a suitable condition of temperature.

Oxygen Content. Trout require a high oxygen content in the water, usually more than 5 ppm. High oxygen content is usually found in well-aerated water coming into the pond, although some gets into the water through air contact with the pond surface or through wind action. A cold supply of well-aerated brook water is an ideal way to keep the oxygen content sufficiently high for the resident fish.

Pond Management. Of the trout species, brook trout appear to be the most desirable for pond culture. They tend to remain in one location, grow rapidly, and are short-lived. Three hundred fingerlings (2 to 5 inches long) per surface acre are suggested as about right for stocking, and it makes little difference whether they are stocked in the spring or fall. Fall stocking of fish of this size will usually insure 7-inch trout the next summer.[5]

The usual plan of stocking is to place a suitable number of fish in the pond, allow them to grow to legal size, then fish them out and start over. As already indicated, some ponds are self-perpetuating because of the presence of natural breeding conditions, but mostly the fingerlings or eyed eggs have to be supplied from outside sources.

Yields of up to 90 pounds of trout per acre are possible, and inexperienced fishermen may successfully harvest the crop.

Fertilization of trout ponds is not practical, because the movement of water carries the fertilizer beyond the pond borders.[6] Fertilizer in slow or stagnant ponds may be a liability rather than an asset, as it would tend to encourage plant growth and add organic matter to the pond which may reduce the oxygen content.

Saila[5] says the stocking of trout in New York ponds is likely to be more successful than the bass-bluegill combination that is used so successfully farther south.

[4] Frank C. Edminster. 1947. Fish ponds for the farm. Charles Scribner's Sons, New York.

[5] Saila. *Op. cit.* Frank C. Edminster. 1952. Fish pond management. *U.S. Soil Conserv. Serv., Tech. Ser.* 64, *Biol.* 6A.

[6] Gustave Prevost. 1945. Third report of the biological bureau. Game and Fisheries Department, Province of Quebec.

REFERENCES

1. Bennett, George W. 1948. The bass-bluegill combination in small artificial lakes. *Ill. Nat. Hist. Survey Bul.* **24**(3):375–412.
2. Dobie, J. R., O. L. Meehean, and G. N. Washburn. 1948. Propagation minnows and other bait species. *U.S. Fish and Wildlife Serv., Circ.* 12.
3. Freyburger, Edwin. 1946. The farm pond. *Ill. Wildlife.* **1**(4):5–6.
4. ———. 1946. II. The farm pond. *Ill. Wildlife.* **2**(1):4–7.
5. ———. 1947. III. The farm pond. *Ill. Wildlife.* **2**(2):9–11.
6. ———. 1947. IV. The farm pond. *Ill. Wildlife.* **2**(3):6–8.
7. Krumholz, Louis A. 1950. Indiana ponds, their construction and management for fishing, Indiana Department of Conservation.
8. ———. 1950. New fish stocking policies for Indiana ponds. *Trans. 15th North Amer. Wildlife Conf.* Pp. 251–267.
9. Saila, Saul B. 1950. A survey of farm fishpond possibilities in New York, Cornell University Conservation Department. (Mimeographed.)
10. Surber, Eugene W. 1949. Results of varying the ratio of largemouth black bass and bluegills in the stocking of experimental farm ponds. *Trans. Amer. Fisheries Soc.* **77**(1947):141–151.
11. Swingle, H. S. 1949. Some recent developments in pond management. *Trans. 14th North Amer. Wildlife Conf.* Pp. 295–312.
12. ——— and E. V. Smith. 1942. Management of farm fish ponds. *Ala. Agr. Expt. Sta. Bul.* 254.
13. Toole, Marion. 1946. Utilizing stock tanks and farm ponds for fish. *Tex. Game, Fish and Oyster Comm. Bul.* 24.

Michigan Conservation

CHAPTER 24

Fresh-water Game Fish (Warm Water)

The warm-water game fishes are less specialized in their requirements than are the cold water species and are therefore more widely distributed. The tolerance of some species, as the bullhead, is so great as to allow them to live under a wide variety of conditions to the degree that they will even stay alive in a wet gunny sack for several days. Also, some of the species, as the bluegill and yellow perch, will bite so readily on a baited hook that it takes little or no skill to catch them. The group as a

FIG. 24-1. Warm-water fish abound in habitats such as this southern lake. (*Peter J. Van Huizen, U.S. Fish and Wildlife Service.*)

whole, however, are both interesting and valuable for the pleasure they give to many anglers or the very young who are just getting interested in fishing. Vast quantities of delicious and nutritious flesh are produced by the various species in the "aquatic pastures" of the country.

Some of the species in the warm-water group have special qualities, both as to the condition of a suitable environment and the skill it takes to catch them. Bass, for example, have courage, beauty, and excellent food properties. For some unknown reason the smallmouth bass is held in higher esteem by fishermen than the largemouth. The "musky" or muskellunge has no peer for fighting properties, and the sport of "musky" fishing is highly specialized.

The classification of the warm-water fishes described in this section is as follows:

Class: Pisces

Family: *Centrarchidae*	Genus	Species
Smallmouth black bass	*Micropterus*	*dolomieu*
Largemouth black bass	*Micropterus*	*salmoides*
Spotted bass	*Micropterus*	*punctulatus*
Pumpkinseed sunfish	*Lepomis*	*gibbosus*
Bluegill	*Lepomis*	*macrochirus*
Crappie	*Pomoxis*	spp.
Family: *Esocidae*		
Chain pickerel	*Esox*	*niger*
Northern pike	*Esox*	*lucius*
Muskellunge	*Esox*	*masquinongy*
Family: *Percidae*		
Yellow perch	*Perca*	*flavescens*
Yellow pike-perch	*Stizostedion*	*vitreum vitreum*
Family: *Ameiuridae*		
Brown bullhead	*Ameiurus*	*nebulosus*
Family: *Serranidae*		
White perch	*Morone*	*americana*

SMALLMOUTH BLACK BASS *Micropterus dolomieu*

Description. As a sport, bass fishing has few peers. It is enjoyed from about July 1 through the remainder of the year in the North and during all of the months of the year south of Mason and Dixon's line. The bass fisherman is often as much of a purist as is the angler for trout or salmon. The places where bass live are more variable than for trout and salmon, as they include the Great Lakes and other large rocky- or sandy-bottomed lakes, as well as muddy or weedy lakes and ponds, warm, sluggish rivers, and artificial impoundments.

The smallmouth black bass is a solid, deep-backed fish that lives in clear, swift streams or in sand- or rock-bottomed lakes. Its color is deep bronze, green above and white or yellow below. The eye has a pink or red cast, a characteristic which is lacking in the largemouth bass. The lower jaw extends beyond the upper jaw and the maxillary, or jaw extends to the center *but not beyond* the back of the eye. In the young there are dusky spots on the sides which appear united into vertical dark bars. According to Hubbs and Bailey (36), the base of the caudal fin is yellowish, the middle is black, and the outer edges of each lobe are light-colored.

Age, Size, and Growth. As with other fishes, the size of smallmouth black bass varies with its age and with the numbers of bass and other fish in a given unit of water as well as the extent of the growing season. In the vicinity of Lake Ontario, which is the center of distribution of

FIG. 24-2. The smallmouth black bass, a fish of cool lakes and rivers with sandy or rocky bottoms. (*Wisconsin Conservation Department.*)

this fish, it is about 2 inches long at a year old and 10 inches long at the end of 5 growing seasons. The following table gives the age-length relationship for Ontario waters:

Table 24-1. Age and Length of Smallmouth Black Bass from Four Ontario Lakes (63)
(Basis 250 fish)

Age in growing seasons, Jan. 1	Total length, in.	Weight, oz.
1	1.9	
2	4.3	0.5
3	6.9	3.3
4	8.0	5.2
5	10.0	10.5
6	10.7	12.5
7	12.0	17.8
8	12.4	18.8
9	13.5	23.5
10	14.2	27.8
11	15.2	34.2
12	15.7	50.8
13	15.1	33.0
14		
15	16.6	47.0

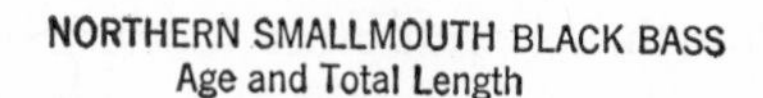

NORTHERN SMALLMOUTH BLACK BASS
Age and Total Length

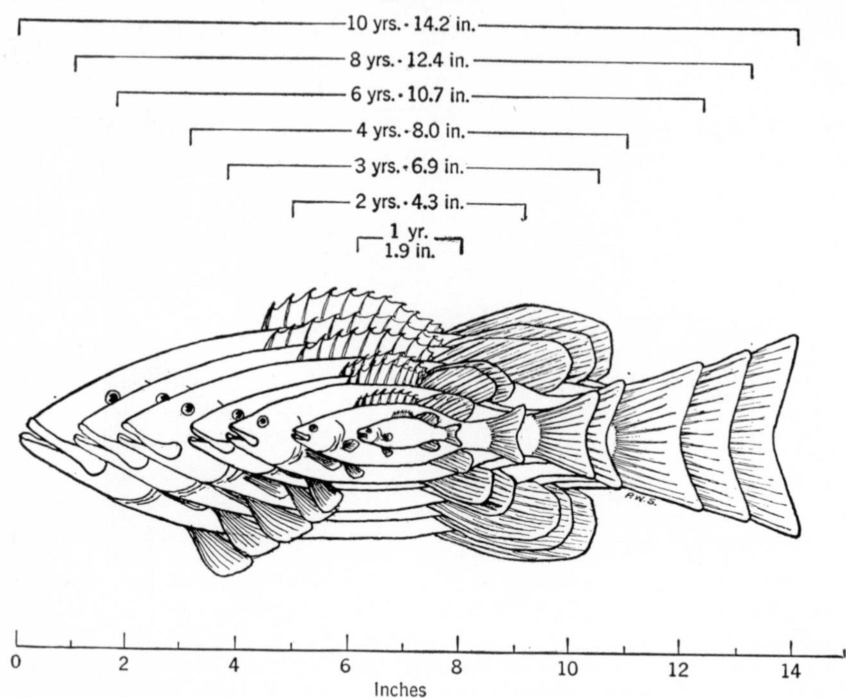

FIG. 24-3. Length and age relationship of the smallmouth black bass from northern waters (63).

Smallmouth black bass from the southern part of their range grow larger in a shorter time than the above figures indicate. Stroud (56) reported the following age-size for smallmouth bass from Norris Reservoir, Tennessee:

Age, years	1	2	3	4	5	6	7
Length, in.	3.1	8.9	13.3	15.8	17.4	18.0	18.6

Thus it seems the growth is about triple in Tennessee what it is in Ontario, or nearly proportional to the differences in the length of the growing season.

Habits. The activities of smallmouth bass vary according to the season of the year and the age of the fish. Young bass as they are hatched seek the protection of rocks and debris or take shelter in any place they can find. As they begin to feed they penetrate bush shelters or other cover but seem to avoid thick weed beds. Older bass in flowing water lie on the downstream side of a rock or boulder out of the force of the current but in a position to catch insects or fish as they are swept past by the current. They are more likely to be found at the head of a pool than in the pool or at the lower end.

Feeding seems to be done more at night than during the day, and this is probably a direct reaction to sunlight and fear of enemies. According to Hubbs and Bailey (36), adults remain in fairly deep water during the daylight hours where they may be in groups of five or more under a shelving rock. They may feed during the day, as is indicated when fisherman catch bass with hook and line during daylight hours. At dusk they become more active and move about, often feeding near the surface far from shore. Outside of these daily movements and the general movement to spawning beds, there is little evidence to indicate smallmouth bass move very far (28).

Spawning. The male selects the site of the nest and helps to prepare it for the placing of the eggs. He stays on guard to prevent other animals from eating the eggs. The nest or redd is made in coarse sand, gravel, rubble, or rock bottoms. The nest is so placed as to be protected from currents or wave action in a depth of water from 3 to 6 feet. The male sweeps the pebbles in the nest clean of silt and soil by taking a position in the water, head up, and sweeping the pebbles clean with its tail. The nose and mouth are used to dislodge materials not suited for the nest. The nest is usually circular and of a diameter about twice the length of the male. The stones are polished clean and it is to these that the eggs adhere. Spawning takes place soon after the nest is ready if the water temperature is 59 to 65°F. As spawning time approaches, a female comes out of deep water and approaches the male. He tries to drive her to the nest he has prepared, but like other species, the female assumes a coy attitude and has to be coaxed to the redd by repeated attention of the male. Any strange male that approaches is driven away by the attending male. After one female has deposited her eggs, the male may seek another female to spawn on the same nest if he still retains milt.

After spawning is completed, the male continues to guard the nest and keeps the eggs clean and aerated by a gentle fanning of the water above the eggs. The eggs hatch in from 2 to 3 days (62). Temperatures as low as 50°F. or as high as 75°F. do not affect the eggs adversely. At 75°F. the incubation time is about 2 days, and at 55°F. it is 10 days (68). The young drop down among the rocks after hatching and emerge about 12 days later.

Food. The food of smallmouth bass is entirely animal in nature. The young feed on small invertebrate animals, including water fleas or daphnia and other small water forms (40). Insects are eaten until the small bass are able to eat small fish, which may include its own brothers and sisters. Adult bass feed on insects, crayfish, earthworms, and other fish (63). The favorite bait in Lake Huron is minnows. Surber (58) studied the food of fingerlings, fry, and adults from river habitats in Virginia and found that adults eat mostly minnows.

The food of Maine smallmouth bass is about as follows:

Small fish	80%
Crayfish	12
Insects (mayflies, nymphs, caddis fly larvae, ants, and beetles)	8
Total	100%

A study of the food of Maine streams shows the food grade of pools is higher than that of riffles.

Hibernation. Hubbs and Bailey (36) describe a condition of inactivity for smallmouth bass during the colder part of the northern winter which is called hibernation. This condition is not one of sleep or stupor, but rather one where activity is suspended. From about December when the water reaches 50°F. until the ice goes out in the spring, the fish seek deep water and sheltered spots under logs or rock ledges. They move very little and cease feeding during this period.

Habitat. The favorite habitat of the smallmouth bass is cool, flowing streams and large, clear lakes. Smallmouth bass are most abundant in lakes over the northern part of the range and in streams over the southern part. Hubbs and Bailey (36) say this is a temperature effect. In the north the streams do not warm sufficiently for bass but are populated by trout. In nearby lakes, however, the water temperature gets sufficiently high for bass. Based on the conclusions of Belding (8) in Massachusetts and the fisheries workers in Michigan, excellent waters for smallmouth bass can be described as follows:

1. Lakes or ponds of large size, preferably over 100 acres
2. A depth of 30 feet or more with thermal stratification
3. Water clear and not colored
4. Vegetation present but scanty
5. Large shoal areas of rock, gravel, or sand with patches of gravel
6. An ample supply of food organisms such as small fishes, crayfish, or insects
7. Moderate summer temperatures, neither very cold nor excessively warm

These conclusions are borne out for Ontario by Doan (19).

In lakes where bass seldom or never spawn because of a dearth of gravel or spawning beds, the addition of gravel piles at water depths of 3 to 5 feet often provides for normal reproduction. Also the construction of brush shelters in shallow water affords protection for minnows and small fish in sufficient numbers to increase the forage possibilities for bass. These shelters may reduce effective predation and lead to stunted populations, however.

In streams, bass prefer clear, cool water, gravel and rock bottom and a good current. Bass are seldom found in streams less than 35 feet wide, but the young live in smaller streams (36). Smallmouth fry and fingerlings use rocks for protection rather than weed beds to escape other predaceous fish.

Physical and Chemical Limits. Optimum temperatures are hard to define, as good smallmouth fishing is found in both the north where the winters are long and in the south where they are short. Better production is found where the growing season is long. Nest-building temperatures are 59 to 65°F. Hoover (35) gives the pH range as 6 to 9. Oxygen should be at least 3 ppm and carbon dioxide not over 20 ppm. Production of bass is greater in ponds where the water contains sufficient amounts of organic nitrogen. Variations in ammonia, nitrate, and nitrite-nitrogen content made little difference in fish production (59).

Game Status. There are few finer game fish than the smallmouth bass. Whether you seek it with bait in Ontario or Missouri or with artificial flies in the St. Croix River of Maine, it displays the same fighting spirit when hooked and gives the fisherman an exciting time until it is landed. It has beautiful colors of yellow, green, and bronze and furnishes a type of flesh hard to beat when served from the frying pan. Fried bass is an article of food which has no peer.

LARGEMOUTH BLACK BASS *Micropterus salmoides*

Description. No greater contrast could be found in the habitat of two closely related fish than between the smallmouth and largemouth black bass. While the former lives with a minimum of cover and water vegetation, the other seeks fertile muddy bottoms and the protection of weeds.

The largemouth bass has its favorite loitering places, especially during the daytime, and these are usually in a deep pocket of water with bulrushes or water lilies nearby. Here it will rest through the summer days waiting for a frog or some other hapless animal to show itself.

Suitable loitering places are recognized by the bass if not always by the fisherman. Lay your surface plug on a certain area of water and a bass will take it. Return to the same spot a week later, and another bass will strike in the identical spot.

The largemouth bass is much the same in appearance as the smallmouth. The mouth of this species is larger and in the adult the maxillary or jaw extends back of the center of the eye. The young have dark spots along the lateral line, but the tail lacks all color markings in contrast to the dark spots on the caudal fin of the smallmouth (36).

FIG. 24-4. The largemouth black bass, an excellent food and game fish of shallow muddy rivers and lakes.

Age, Size, and Growth. Great variation exists in the size and rate of growth of this fish in the northern and southern parts of the range. In the north 5- to 8-pound bass are considered exceptionally good, but in the south those from 8 to 15 pounds are not exceptional.

Table 24-2. Age and Length of Largemouth Black Bass from Norris Reservoir, Tennessee (56)
(Basis 1,589 fish)

Age, years	*Length, in.*
1	6.9
2	12.4
3	14.7
4	16.1
5	17.5
6	19.3
7	20.8

It has been generally accepted that the mild climate of the central southern states, as Kentucky and Tennessee, is reflected in a shorter winter period and faster growth of fish. Usually this is referred to as a longer growing season. With fish, however, the growing season can be determined by the markings on the scales. A study of fish growth in Tennessee showed the growing season of the largemouth to be from late May to early October, a season of possibly 4½ months. Study of the length of fish of the same group taken in the fall and again in the spring indicates little or no growth during the intervening time. In the same general locality the agricultural growing season is about 7 months. The difference is probably caused by the relative slowness of water to change temperature as compared to the land.

Habits. The movements and general habits of the largemouth bass are much the same as the smallmouth. During the winter it is semidormant, but as spring approaches it seeks suitable spawning beds and goes through the activities related to reproduction. In the winter the fish seeks deep parts of the pond where it waits for the temperature to warm up and the breeding season to begin. Because of the tendency of the largemouth bass to inhabit more fertile waters, it is likely to be heavy-bodied and perhaps a little less active than the smallmouth.

Many fishermen as well as fisheries technicians have wondered about the extent of the movements of bass and whether they follow any definite pattern of migration. In a series of connected Florida lakes, Dequine and Hall (18) tagged 1,600 largemouth bass and released them in several adjacent ponds. About 40 per cent were caught within a mile of the spot where released and 84 per cent within a 5-mile radius. Two of the tagged fish traveled more than 12 miles.

Spawning. The time of spawning of largemouth bass is March to July, depending on the latitude. In Minnesota, Eddy and Surber (22 *g.r.*) give the time as May to July when the water is 60 to 65°F. A sudden drop of 10 to 12° in the temperature is sufficient to kill both the eggs and newly hatched fry. The spawning beds are in 2 to 6 feet of water, and the parents will desert the nest if silt covers the eggs. As already indicated, the largemouth is not so particular in the selection of a nest site as the smallmouth. Dead vegetation or a mass of roots are desirable as an anchorage for the eggs, but bass will spawn on nearly any firm bottom. The male clears a depression 2 to 3 feet across and 6 inches deep. The male also defends the nest, eggs, and fry as long as the fry stay together. Nests may be made 30 feet apart, so this is about the limit of the territory defended. According to Eddy and Surber (22 *g.r.*), the bass male will not drive off other bass performing similar duties.

The female largemouth is capable of laying 2,000 to 26,000 eggs or even more. The time of hatching depends on the temperature of the water. Carbine (12) found the average number of eggs per nest was about 5,000.

Food. Bass, including largemouth, eat very little during the colder parts of the year. As warm weather approaches, however, they begin to feed. All types of small living animals become victims to the feeding bass, including insects, small fish, frogs, and even birds and small land mammals (16). Largemouth bass will be found at the edge of the lily pads or among some bulrushes waiting for small animals to pass nearby.

Fishermen take advantage of this type of feeding by presenting all kinds of lures, both natural and artificial, to the bass during the summer period. Angle worms, live minnows, frogs, and a multitude of artificial baits, both floating and submerged, are used. Floating bait to be most successful must be allowed to lie still and then moved intermittently. If placed near a bass it is usually successful in getting a strike.

Food found in the stomachs of largemouth bass is as follows (25):

Food item	Lake Erie (25), per cent	Massachusetts (42), per cent
Crustacea	87.10	24.8
Fishes	11.40	66.8
Insects	1.38	5.4
Miscellaneous	0.12	3.7
Total	100.00	100.7*

* Sum of percentages as given by the investigator do not total 100.

Habitat. The largemouth bass is found in ponds and streams from New England to the Great Plains, as well as in the South from Florida to Texas.

The most common habitat of the largemouth is the weedy lake or pond of eastern United States. Even in small impoundments it does well and reaches good size. The bottom may be a deep black mud or composed of sand or gravel. The water may be deep or shallow, so long as it does not freeze to the bottom during the winter. The common border weeds, including white and yellow water lilies, pickerelweeds, and river bulrushes are suitable for cover.

The largemouth black bass selects deep locations among the vegetation to wait for its prey and to rest during the bright part of the day. At night it moves inshore to feed on the minnows and animal life that live in the protected shallows near the shore line. It prefers spots near large boulders or fallen tree trunks to rest and occupies these sites day after day if not disturbed. During the winter, it moves to deeper parts of the stream or pond to wait out the coming of warmer weather.

Physical and Chemical Limits. These are the same as for smallmouth bass except perhaps higher carbon dioxide content.

Game Status. Few species of fish are so generally popular as the largemouth bass. They have a broad range and are found in a wide variety of habitats, both streams and lakes. They strike at both natural and artificial lures and are still not so easily caught as to make bass fishing commonplace. In general the bass fisherman specializes in the kind of tackle and lures he uses and even the time of day he fishes. The largemouth bass is large enough to be prized for its flesh and is a strong and violent fighter. Anyone who has mastered the art of taking largemouth bass consistently has a right to be proud of his prowess.

PUMPKINSEED SUNFISH *Lepomis gibbosus*

Description. The sunfish or "punkie" is a favorite item of game for a host of fishermen including the small boy with the willow pole and the cotton line. The sunfish will bite on garden worms and seems to have little fear of a sharp hook. It seldom grows to large size, but pumpkinseeds 6 to 8 inches long provide a morsel of solid, fine-flavored flesh that makes tasty eating if properly prepared.

FIG. 24-5. The sunfish, or pumpkinseed, one of the three most popular pan fish in the Middle West. (*New York Zoological Society.*)

The shape of the pumpkinseed is well described by its common name. Its body is deep horizontally but compressed laterally. The color of the sides is dark green or bronze above, and the belly is a bright orange. During the spring and early summer it takes on breeding colors and is very beautiful. The eyes are bright and prominent, and the fins, especially along the dorsal side, are long and held aloft with stiff spines.

Age, Size, and Growth. The pumpkinseed never grows very large. Table 24-3 gives the age and total length of more than 3,000 sunfish from Michigan lakes.

The sunfish seldom weighs as much as ½ pound. In Beckman's studies (7) the largest fish was a female that was 9 years old, 8.4 inches long, and weighed 8.11 ounces. Males of this same age class were about an inch shorter and weighed 5.43 ounces.

Table 24-3. Age and Length of Sunfish from 182 Michigan Lakes (7)
(Basis 3,534 specimens)

Age in growing seasons, Jan. 1	*Total length, in.*
1	2.8
2	4.2
3	4.8
4	5.7
5	6.3
6	6.7
7	7.3
8	7.7

Distribution. The distribution of the pumpkinseed extends in Canada from the Red River of the North to the Maritime Provinces, south to Georgia and possibly Florida, and west to Ohio and Missouri in the Mississippi River system (36).

Habits. *Spawning.* The male builds the nest and protects the eggs and young. Nest sites are in water from 1 to 5 feet deep and may be in combination with nests of bluegills or rock bass. The spawning beds may be placed where bottom materials are coarse or fine gravel, sand, muck, weeds, roots, or any combination of the above. The nests are about 20 inches across and several inches deep, with roots and sticks exposed by sweeping away the mud and silt (12).

The breeding season is long, extending from May to August or possibly longer farther south. Thorpe (64) gives the spawning temperatures as varying from 62 to 68°F. in one lake and 71 to 80°F. in another. The female leaves the nest as soon as she has finished spawning, and the male remains to protect the nest and young fish. Carbine (12) counted 1,500 and 14,000 fry from 2 sunfish nests. The young sunfish live among the weeds more than the older fish.

Food. Sunfish feed on small crustaceans, water insects, and snails. Fosburgh (27) says the favorite food of the "punkie" is the snail. It does not feed on other fish (64).

Food-habit studies of sunfish from the western end of Lake Erie show the food to be mayfly larvae, caddis worms, and some plant fragments (9).

In Third Sister Lake near Ann Arbor, Michigan, Ball (5) found the food of sunfish to be as follows:

Food	*Per cent by volume*
Mollusks (snails)	67.50
Insects	16.63
Annelid worms	5.48
Plants	0.47
Unaccounted for	9.92
Total	100.00

Habitat. The favorite habitat of the sunfish is a shallow, warm-water pond that has deep black bottom soil with many weedy borders and a deep hole or two for escape cover. It is found in the pools of intermittent streams in the middle west and can also be raised in farm fish ponds. In Connecticut, Thorpe (64) says that sunfish live in both weedy and rocky habitats but seem to prefer the latter.

Game Status. In Minnesota the pumpkinseed is rated along with the bluegill, which is considered the most frequently taken fish in the state. In the Lake states it is no doubt the most frequently taken fish if not the most important one. It has a long breeding season and high tolerance for warm temperatures.

The "punkie" is well able to take a heavy pounding by the "one-gallus" fisherman. Its lack of size is against it as a game fish, however.

BLUEGILL *Lepomis macrochirus*

Description. Taking bluegills with artificial flies and light tackle equals trout fishing in thrills. Where bluegills grow to good size—8 to 10 inches long and a pound in weight—they will test the strength of a light fly rod.

FIG. 24-6. The bluegill, or bream, is a common fish in warm-water lakes, and many consider it to be a good game fish. (*Wisconsin Conservation Department.*)

Bluegills will take a dry or wet fly readily or will bite on earthworms or small minnows.

Michigan calls the bluegill the "kingfish" because it tops all others in the total catch of sport fish. The reasons for this high take are: it is widely distributed, easy to catch, and able to stand up under heavy fishing.

The bluegill is a typical pumpkinseed shape, being deep and thin. In color it is a deep blue or dark green with a spot at the base of the soft part of the dorsal fin. The "ear" or posterior part of the gill cover is blue or deep green, giving it the name "bluegill."

Age, Size, and Growth. The size and rate of growth of bluegills varies from South to North as well as with the condition and the fertility of the water. Overcrowding often causes them to remain small. Table 24-4 gives the age and length of this fish from Michigan waters.

Table 24-4. Age and Length of Bluegills from 153 Michigan Lakes (7) (Basis 8,159 fish)

Age in growing seasons, Jan. 1	*Total length, in.*
1	1.7
2	3.1
3	4.3
4	5.4
5	6.6
6	7.4
7	7.7
8	8.2
9	8.4
10	8.7
11	8.9

The legal size at which bluegills may be taken in Michigan is 6 inches from nose to end of tail. A 6-inch fish is slightly over 5 years old and weighs about 2½ ounces. Bluegills seldom grow to very large size, probably not more than 15 to 16 inches. A fish that weighs a pound is worth talking about. Many states have no legal limit on bluegills because of the prolific nature of their breeding habits.

Distribution. Hubbs and Lagler (34 *g.r.*) give the range of bluegills from Minnesota to Lake Champlain, southward to the Chattahoochee River in Georgia and westward to the Arkansas and Red River systems in Arkansas and Louisiana. It has been stocked in many waters outside this range. Much emphasis has been given to bluegill culture because of their use in combination with largemouth bass in farm fish ponds.

Habits. The bluegill is not much of a traveler. Apparently it feeds all year long, as it can be caught both summer and fall and through the ice during the winter (44). It is somewhat sensitive to light and becomes active only during the early morning and evening.

Spawning. The spawning beds are prepared by the male in colonies and often adjacent to other beds; bluegills spawn from June to August or perhaps longer. The spawning season varies with latitude, being more delayed farther north. It is thought that the eggs of a female do not all ripen at the same time, so that the spawning is an intermittent process. The nest is circular, about 18 to 24 inches in diameter, and swept clear by the workings of the male. It is in water 1 to 5 feet deep and may be over sand or gravel or in mud. The female stays on the nest only until the eggs are laid, but the male guards and aerates them and later protects the young. Carbine (12) counted from 5,000 to 62,000 fry from a single nest, but the average was about 18,000. Eddy and Surber (22 *g.r.*) give the number of eggs from a half-pound fish as varying from 15,000 to 58,000 with a high of 67,000 from a single female. The length of the incubation period is not given.

Food. Beckman (6) gives the food of bluegills as plankton, insects, mainly dragonflies, mayflies, midges, damsel flies, caddis flies, and their larvae. Crayfish, snails, fresh-water shrimp, and land-dwelling insects are also included. Earthworms are taken readily.

Habitat. The bluegill is a lake and pond fish rather than a river dweller, although it may be found in the slow-moving weedy margins of many streams. It likes warm water and prefers muddy and weedy bottoms to clean sand or rock. A typical type of lake for bluegill would be one such as is found in the agricultural lands of southern Michigan. It is not more than 100 acres in size and 20 feet or less in depth, with deep fertile soil in the bottom and emergent vegetation along the borders. Such a lake would have considerable aquatic vegetation and dark-colored soil over most of the bottom.

Game Status. The bluegill is a popular sport fish with both high-brow and low-brow fishermen. It will take a baited hook both winter and summer and is an excellent food item. It will take earthworms and grasshoppers readily and will rise to either a wet or a dry fly cast in its vicinity. It provides excellent sport for dry-fly fishing during the periods when mayflies are hatching. Once on the hook it is a strong and courageous fighter and will test the strength of any light tackle.

CRAPPIE *Promoxis* spp.

Description. The black crappie (*P. nigro-maculatus*) or "calico bass" of New England and the eastern states has a counterpart in the white crappie of the Middle West and prairie regions. In form it is intermediate between the true bass and the pumpkinseed, being thick-bodied from top to bottom but not so round as the bluegill or sunfish. It is compressed laterally and has spiny dorsal and anal fins. The forehead is slightly dished, with an upturned nose and a protruding lower jaw.

In color the white crappie has a more over-all pattern and fewer dark-colored markings than its cousin the black crappie. In the former the markings are vague and less intense, while in the latter the general appearance is dark with some white showing through. For the common fisherman both of these fish are "calico bass."

Age, Size, and Growth. "Calico bass" grow to fairly large size with an extreme of 15 to 18 inches, but for their length are heavy, weighing 1 to 2 pounds (56) at this length. Eddy and Surber (22 *g.r.*) give the extreme weights as about 4 pounds. Most "calico bass" caught on hook and line are much smaller than these extreme sizes, being 6 to 8 inches long and weighing half a pound or less. It has been introduced widely in ponds

FIG. 24-7. The crappie, or calico bass, is a fish similar to the sunfish and bluegill but less highly regarded. (*Wisconsin Conservation Department.*)

of the East including New York and New England, but there are no records of this fish at present in New England waters.

The age and length of 1,323 specimens of black crappies from 84 lakes in Michigan are given in the table below.

Table 24-5. Age and Length of Black Crappies from 84 Michigan Lakes (6)
(Basis 1,323 fish)

Age in growing seasons, Jan. 1	*Total length, in.*
3	5.9
4	8.0
5	9.0
6	9.9
7	10.7
8	11.3
9	11.6

Distribution. The black crappie is found in the clear, weedy lakes and ponds and larger streams from Manitoba to Quebec in Canada, south from western New York and Pennsylvania to Florida, and west to Texas.

From Florida the range extends northward along the Atlantic Coast to North Carolina.

The white crappie is a middle-western fish having a range from Minnesota and Nebraska through the lower Great Lakes region east to the Lake Ontario drainage, south along the Mississippi drainage to Alabama and Texas, east to northern Florida, and north along the Atlantic Coast to North Carolina (34 *g.r.*). It has been introduced widely in the ponds of the East, including New England and New York, and is now found in nearly all the waters of the eastern United States.

Habits. See description of streams suitable for sunfish and ponds for bluegills.

Spawning. Crappies are known to spawn when they are 2 years old and may spawn at 1 year of age. Large numbers of eggs are produced, the greater numbers being produced by the heaviest females. Huber and Binkley (37) found an average of 7,120 eggs per fish in 3- and 4-year-old females.

Crappies spawn in early summer, May in Connecticut and May or June in Minnesota. Spawning sites are either sand or gravel bottoms and may be in aquatic vegetation. The eggs are adhesive and stick to the bottom or to the weeds in the immediate vicinity. Water temperature suitable for spawning is 68°F. in southern Wisconsin (37, 46). Time of hatching is not available.

Food. The young of the "calico bass" are weed lovers and are found among the aquatic plants near the nests. In Wisconsin the young feed on all kinds of plankton of suitable size. Fish from 7 to 13½ inches long from Connecticut lakes were found to have eaten plankton, crustacea, insects, and fish. The insects were beetles, dragonflies, damsel flies, mayflies, and two-winged flies (*Diptera*). In Wisconsin specimens examined throughout the year fed chiefly on insects (largely on immature stages), water fleas, amphipods, and fishes. Food of black crappies from Massachusetts consists of 51 to 67 per cent fishes, 32 to 46 per cent insects, and the remainder miscellaneous materials (42).

In Florida the most important year-round food of the black crappie is the gizzard shad (50).

Habitat. The habitat of the crappie may be considered identical with that of the sunfish and the bluegills. It avoids the very large, very cold, and rocky types of lakes but gets along well in mud-bottomed streams that have wide shallow borders and are generally weedy. It also is found in the streams of the mid-continent where warm water and muddy bottoms are the rule. Hubbs and Lagler (34 *g.r.*) say the white crappie is found more often in turbid rivers, while the black prefers clear weedy lakes and the larger clear streams farther south. Its similarity of habitat with the other members of the pan-fish group is indicated in a study of

112 southern Minnesota lakes, where crappies of both kinds were taken to the extent of 25 pounds per acre with the sunfish also producing 25.9 pounds per acre (45).

It would appear that the hard-water lakes of the Middle West are better habitats for the crappie than are the New England ponds. In Massachusetts the black crappies were only 6.39 per cent of the catch of over 1,600 anglers although, next to the bullhead, the black crappie was once the most heavily stocked fish in the natural great ponds of that state (42).

Game Status. The "calico bass" is a very important fish in the over-all picture of hook-and-line fishing. It never gets very large, and the flesh is somewhat soft, but it seems to fit the aquatic environment of many waters of the flat lands of the central part of the continent. It will take an artificial fly but it is not so much of a fighter as the bluegill.

CHAIN PICKEREL *Esox niger*

Description. The chain pickerel is the eastern counterpart of the northern pike of the Middle West. These two fish resemble each other in form, but the pickerel is usually much the smaller of the two. The chain pickerel is more easterly in its distribution than the northern pike and is caught on many kinds of tackle and a variety of lures. As a table item its flesh is soft if taken from warm waters and contains a great many small

FIG. 24-8. The chain pickerel, the eastern game representative of the pike genus. (*New York Zoological Society.*)

bones. Its flesh also usually has a muddy or grassy flavor unless the skin is separated from the meat.

The chain pickerel has a long streamlined body and a long bony head and prominent eyes. The tail fin is broad and both anal and dorsal fins are near the tail. The color is a mottled dark green and white with dark markings joined into connecting spots on a light background. The color on the dorsal side (back) is darker and that on the ventral (belly) side is nearly pure white with the gradation from darker to light from top to bottom.

Age, Size, and Growth. The chain pickerel never reaches the enormous size or weight of the northern pike. Underhill (66) speaks of two chain pickerel presumably from New York waters that weighed 6½ pounds apiece. He indicates these are probably record fish.

Table 24-6. Age and Length of Chain Pickerel Taken in Three Central New York State Waters (66)
(Basis 269 fish)

Age in growing seasons, Jan. 1	*Total length, in.*
1	7.1
2	11.7
3	14.7
4	16.6
5	18.2
6	19.3
7	21.0

The length-weight relationships of pickerel from a Connecticut pond are given by Foote and Blake (26) as follows:

Table 24-7. Length and Weight of Chain Pickerel in Relation to Sex

No.	Standard length, cm.	Female		Male	
		No.	Weight, g.	No.	Weight, g.
2	15.8	1	33.5	1	33.5
15	20.3	4	69.5	11	72.4
32	25.9	18	141.4	14	137.9
18	29.8	8	212.7	10	193.3
11	35.6	7	407.7	4	331.5
4	40.2	4	621.8		
5	42.0	3	737.8	2	597.2
3	49.5	3	1,176.8		

Pickerel mature to breeding size during the third growing season in New York State (66). Underhill says the females had spawned once and many of the males had spawned twice before they reached 12 inches in length, which is the legal size. Underhill indicates that in most situations a legal size limit of 12 inches is too small; 14 inches is probably better.

Distribution. The distribution of the chain pickerel is given by Hubbs and Lagler (34 *g.r.*) as extending from New Brunswick and the St.

Lawrence River and the Lake Ontario drainage southward to Florida, and in the Mississippi Valley to Texas, southern Missouri, and the Tennessee River system in Alabama. It was introduced into the Lake Erie drainage of New York. In New England it is one of the common fish and is held in high esteem by many fisherman (60, 64).

Habits. Young pickerel stay in shallow water, where they have the protection of numerous weeds, until they are several inches long. Seldom are young pickerel found in water beyond the 2-foot depth (47). Adult and mature pickerel come into the shallows to feed at night, and some are found along the shallow weedy borders during the daytime. Apparently the movements of these fish are related to light, as they are more active as the sun begins to recede.

Pickerel feed during the winter time. The author has caught them through the ice in central New England from December to February, sometimes with large tagged trout in their stomachs.

Spawning. The time of spawning of chain pickerel occurs as soon as the ice goes out. This is April for New York State and late April or May farther north. In Massachusetts spawning takes place in April and May.

Chain pickerel do not build nests but scatter their eggs in long gelatinous strings in shallow waters among the submerged roots of vegetation. The number of eggs is large, being recorded as 30,000 eggs for a 2-pound female (16 *g.r.*). The eggs require from 6 to 12 days to hatch, the length of time depending on the water temperature (66). The pickerel fry lie on their sides on the muddy bottom after hatching, and some at least attach themselves to the vegetation. Feeding begins in from 6 to 8 days. The spawning sites are usually fertile with numerous related aquatic animals that are available as food, so the growth of the young is rapid. The fry soon take on the manner of the adult by lying quietly waiting for a victim and then rushing out to capture it (66).

Food. The most popular bait used by fishermen for the chain pickerel is a live minnow impaled on a hook so it moves around. This is effective because the pickerel diet is almost entirely small fish. Foote and Blake (26) give the diet of young pickerel from 15 to 20 centimeters (5.9 to 7.9 inches) as 100 per cent insects, gradually changing from insects to small fish. The diet becomes 100 per cent fish at about 3 inches.

Of the insects eaten, dragonfly larvae, water striders, and beetles are the most conspicuous forms. Of the fishes, golden shiners, bullheads, sunfish, yellow perch, chain pickerel, and no doubt others are the standard food items. Crayfish are almost as important as fish in terms of volume consumed. Frogs and other vertebrates also become food of pickerel where available.

Habitat. The chain pickerel has a broad environmental tolerance, being found in any type of shallow water in its range. While its most usual type of habitat is the relatively shallow mud-bottomed and weed-clogged ponds or river borders, it is not unusual to find it in deep cold ponds where forage fish are abundant (42). Underhill (66) collected and studied pickerel from three habitats in New York State: Papish Pond, Skaneateles Lake, and Wilseyville Creek. Papish Pond is a brown-water pond of 35 acres in area with mud bottom and with woody vegetation along the shore. It is spring-fed and has a depth of no greater than 20 feet. Skaneateles Lake is 30 miles long and 2 miles wide. The pickerel habitat is the shallow south end of the lake where the bottom is silted and the depth varies from 15 inches to 20 feet. The shallow portion contains many weed beds. Wilseyville Creek is a branch of Susquehanna River and is fed by springs and contains many beaver flowages. The banks are often swampy and flood during the spring runoff.

Physical and Chemical Limits. There is probably no temperature limit under conditions that prevail in natural waters in the eastern part of the continent. The pickerel seems able to adjust itself and to thrive in the naturally warm waters found in the shallow, mud-bottomed ponds of the East. It feeds under the ice when the ponds are frozen over. For the New Hampshire pickerel (*Esox reticulatus*) Hoover (35) gives the pH range as 6 to 9 and the oxygen minimum, 3 ppm.

Along with the yellow perch and bullhead the chain pickerel is the fish of the "one-gallus" Nimrod. It often strikes at the lures of a bass fisherman and give life to the sport of fishing when the bass refuse to strike.

Game Status. The catching of chain pickerel gives pleasure to millions of fishermen who cast in the waters of the eastern part of the United States. One never knows when a fish hits his lure whether it is a pickerel or bass. Almost any type of bait may be taken, but success is more likely to result if the fisherman uses a live minnow or some moving lure. The streamer fly on a light fly rod is ideal because of the size and weight of the fish and its lively antics after being hooked.

NORTHERN PIKE *Esox lucius*

Description. The northern pike has always been a favorite of many fishermen in the north central part of the country. You can catch northerns, and frequently large ones 4 to 10 pounds, by merely hooking a sucker through the back and allowing it to swim around. If you fish with a bamboo pole you probably use a float and leisurely watch the bobber disappear under water as the pike plays with the bait and finally proceeds to swallow it, head first.

Other methods of fishing for pike are plug casting from a boat or trolling behind a boat. All of the methods will pay off in northern pike. You may even spear them through the ice during the winter time.

This fish is dark green on the back and sides and lighter in color on the underside. The head is long, the eyes prominent, and the mouth is large with conspicuous teeth. The upper part of the body is marked with characteristic light spots giving it a mottled effect. The northern pike has light spots, as compared with dark spots or bars on a light background for the muskellunge. The dorsal fin is far back on the body and has 16 to 19 rays. The front and top of the head are without scales.

FIG. 24-9. The northern pike is the most common and widespread member of this group. (*Wisconsin Conservation Department.*)

A striking variation of the northern pike which lacks spots or other markings has been found in Minnesota in Lake Belletaine near Nevis. This is a true northern pike but because of variation has lost the light markings (22 *g.r.*).

Age, Size, and Growth. The growth and size of northern pike depend on the fertility of the water in which it grows. In the north, in shallow

Table 24-8. Age and Length of Northern Pike from Minnesota (22)
(Basis 557 fish)

Age in growing seasons, Jan. 1	*Total length, in.*
1	6.6
2	12.0
3	16.6
4	20.3
5	23.9
6	27.4
7	30.4
8	32.8
9	35.2
10	36.8
11	39.2
12	41.5

lakes with bottoms and surroundings of very fertile soil, the size may be large, but because of short growing seasons, it may take longer to produce a large fish.

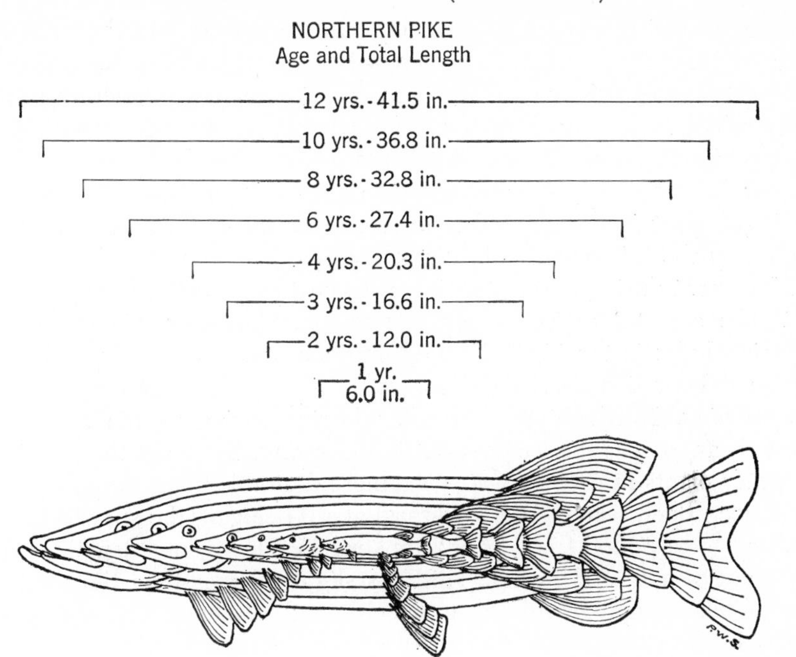

FIG. 24-10. Length and age relationship of the northern pike (22).

The weight of large fish is always interesting to fishermen. According to Eddy and Surber (22 *g.r.*), northern pike weighing over 50 pounds have been reported from Minnesota. The New York State record for a northern pike is 46 pounds 2 ounces taken in Sacondaga Reservoir.

Habits. As soon as the ice goes out in the spring, the mature northern breeders move into their spawning grounds. The spawning habitat may be a weed-choked ditch, a marsh, overflowed lands, or a small side branch of a stream. The breeding fish apparently stay in large holes in the river until the water level rises during the next freshet. Perhaps the larger holes in the creeks are their permanent homes.

After the fish are hatched they remain in the protected waters of the nursery stream throughout the summer (10). The favorite site of mature fish appears to be protected spots near a tree that has fallen into the water or behind a boulder or near some aquatic vegetation. Here they spend part of their time resting or waiting for food organisms to move into striking distance. They also cruise along a lake shore or among the water lilies seeking food. In the hottest part of the summer they seek cooler parts of the lake and appear not to feed, or at least they do not take bait and lures readily. This has led to the claim by fishermen that pike get sore mouths or lose their teeth during August. Trautman and Hubbs (65) in a study of the teeth of northern pike, "muskies," and chain pickerel found no foundation for the lost- or sore-tooth theory. Eddy and Surber (22 *g.r.*) suggest the reason for the poor fishing for northern pike during August is that natural foods are plentiful so that the lures presented by the fishermen hold little attraction for these well-fed fish.

Movement during the winter time is less extensive than in the summer, but pike are still active during this season. Northerns will appear at spearing holes in the ice if decoy minnows are allowed to move around on the end of a line under the openings.

Spawning. Northern pike breeders begin moving to the spawning grounds as soon as the ice goes out in the spring. No doubt the presence of water plants in shallow water is a more desirable place for young fish than deep open water. At Houghton Lake, Michigan, the spawning run is listed for a period from April 2 to April 25. The average length of the spawning fish is 21.8 inches. This was slightly larger than the average size of pike caught by fishermen, which was 21.2 inches. The number of males in the run is about twice that of females. In capturing spawning pike the second year, it was discovered that several were yearlings 13 to 15 inches long. The majority of the spawning fish returned downstream over a period of about 3 months (13).

Northern pike eggs hatch in about 14 days (10). The young fish remain in the vicinity of their spawning beds for an indefinite period, then move downstream to the adjoining waters. Thus in this one study of natural reproduction in a single spawning area, more than 7,000 young returned to the parent body of water as the result of the spawning of 125 females and 280 males, or an average of more than 56 young per female.

Food. The food of young northern pike is small water animals. Those examined by Hankinson had eaten mostly insect larvae (43).

The adult appears always to be hungry and is constantly looking for food. It feeds on almost anything that is small enough to be swallowed, including songbirds, ducklings, mice, and shrews. Its main food is of aquatic origin, however, and includes leeches, suckers, perch, bluegills, and sunfish and minnows of several kinds.

Habitat. The northern pike is found in a wide variety of waters through the central part of the continent and Alaska. Slow-moving rivers, lakes with weedy or shallow borders, reservoirs created by dams, and all variety of other warm waters are the home of this fish. Usually these waters are quite shallow and may get excessively warm during the summer. They must have large quantities of food and suitable spawning grounds.

Game Status. Fishing for northern pike is a popular pastime although less specialized than is bass or "musky" fishing. The pike is so widely distributed and so eager to strike that large numbers are taken each year. Yet the sport holds up well if the habitat remains favorable.

The flesh of northern pike is excellent if taken from cold water. The fish has natural mucous secretions that make it slimy, and the flesh often has a strong grassy flavor if taken where it is weedy or where the lake has a muddy bottom.

MUSKELLUNGE *Esox masquinongy*

Description. A muskellunge fisherman will pursue a particular fish for one or several summers, possibly making contact only once during the fishing season. Once a particularly large one is caught it is usually dis-

FIG. 24-11. The muskellunge, the tiger of the pike genus, is the largest of the warm-water game fish and one of the gamiest. (*New York Zoological Society.*)

played in the window of a sport shop and spurs on other fishermen. The "musky" is a true tackle buster, and because of its size and strength is hard to catch.

The muskellunge is the largest of the pike family and in shape and general appearance resembles a northern pike. In fact the layman would have difficulty in telling it from a pike. Eddy and Surber (22 *g.r.*) describe the Wisconsin muskellunge as having a silvery body with dark markings on a lighter background. Likewise the muskellunge is supposed to have the lower part of the cheek (gill covers) naked or without scales. Hubbs and Lagler (34 *g.r.*) do not use this character to distinguish the muskellunge, and it is said that Minnesota specimens have scales on the lower cheek (22 *g.r.*).

Age, Size, and Growth. Muskellunge eggs are small in size, as a quart jar will hold about 55,000. At 2 weeks after hatching the young fish will be between 1 and 3 inches long; at 9 weeks 3 or 4 inches long; in 100 days they will be 8 or 9 inches long. Males grow more slowly than females, as, according to Seagers (51), a 14-year-old male may be 34 inches long and a female the same age 47 inches or nearly 4 feet long. A 40-pound "tiger" musky may be 25 years old.

Table 24-9. Age and Length of Minnesota and Wisconsin "Muskies" (22)
(Basis 83 fish)

Age in growing seasons, Jan. 1	*Total length, in.*
1	6.4
2	12.6
3	17.4
4	21.7
5	25.5
6	28.4
7	31.0
8	35.6
9	37.7
10	39.3
11	40.8

The weight of any fish in relation to length will vary according to its condition, which in turn depends on the amount of food available and the competition for that food. A rough compilation of length-weight data recorded from "muskies" taken from Lake St. Clair is as follows:

Table 24-10. Approximate Length-Weight Relationship of Lake St. Clair "Muskies" (39)

Length, in. (approx.)	*Weight, lb. (approx.)*
10	0.2
15	0.5
20	2.0
25	3+
30	6+
35	10+
40	13.5
45	21
50	34

Distribution. The range of the "musky" centers in the Great Lakes region but extends east along the St. Lawrence watershed, south into New York, Ohio, and West Virginia, west to Wisconsin and Minnesota, and in Canada to the Lake of the Woods.

Habits. The activities of muskellunge are little known. Records of tagged fish and knowledge of experienced "musky" fishermen would probably yield excellent material, but these are not available. In Chautauqua Lake, New York, there is, or was, a huge female tagged on April 19, 1930, called Queen Minnie Methuselah, that showed up in 1950 in the conservation department nets and was stripped of her eggs.

The feeding tactics of muskellunge are to cruise around until within range of smaller fish, then to wait until they are near enough to strike. The final action is a slashing rush that either consumes the victim or gives it a blow that stuns it or cuts it into pieces. For a large fish with a huge food capacity this means covering many acres of water and the pursuit of many schools of fish.

Changes of season and changes in the temperature of the water also regulate the activities of both the "musky" and its food supply. The thawing of the ponds and ripening of the eggs bring on the activities in connection with reproduction.

Spawning. In Minnesota the spawning of "muskies" occurs during the first part of May. This is later than for the northern pike, according to Eddy and Surber (22 *g.r.*). A pair of fish, female and male, moves into a narrow channel or weed bed and lies side by side with bodies touching. The deposition of the eggs and milt on the bottom then occurs, and fertilization takes place. Seagears (51) gives the egg output of one large muskellunge female as 165,000 eggs or about 3 quarts.

Hatching time under artificial conditions is 10 to 20 days. MacKay and Werner (41) give the water temperature for spawning as varying from 49 to 79°F. and the incubation period as 6 to 12 days.

Food. The "musky" is called the "eating machine" by Clayt Seagears of New York State. He describes it as follows:

> The muskalonge has one chief wish:
> Combine in one all smaller fish.

Fry, when planted in a good feeding area, will remain suspended quietly among the swarms of water animals and occasionally will dart at one of the larger plankton organisms and capture it. When 4 or 5 weeks old they begin to feed on small minnow fry as well as the smaller water plankton. By 7 weeks of age, the fish are quite proficient in catching other small fish. From the middle of June to November, fish of all kinds become increasingly important in the diet (23). Cannibalism is common and is a problem where "muskies" are being raised. Providing sufficient food is another problem where rearing is carried out under artificial conditions. Williamson (73) gives the food of the muskellunge in Wisconsin as insects, small animals of all kinds, minnows, and other fishes.

Habitat. The favorite haunt of the muskellunge is a deep body of water with sandy or rocky bottom and a current that moves slowly.

Lake St. Clair, a body of water of 180 square miles in area within sight of the city of Detroit, produces a heavy crop of "muskies" (2,500 speared in 1937–1938) of near-record sizes. Percy Hover of Detroit took a 62½-pound fish here and also holds the world record for five fish taken in one day, weighing a total of 187 pounds (72). They are found in many large lakes and connecting waters of the Great Lakes as well as in the St. Lawrence River. Large river flowages created by power dams are also favorite spots for this fish. Lake of the Woods in Ontario and Lake Chautauqua in New York are famous "musky" waters. Lake Chautauqua is long and narrow with a narrow belt of water connecting two larger arms of the lake (31). One arm has a maximum depth of 77 feet and considerable sand and gravel bottom, while the other has a maximum depth of 19 feet and has a muck bottom and extensive weed beds (54).

One spawning and rearing ground in Ontario is described by Elson (23) as a sheltered bay in Stony Lake, one of the chain of Kawartha Lakes. The bay consists of about 10 acres of water and is fronted by a large island. The depth of the water is uniformly 3 to 5 feet and the bottom consists of soft muck 2 to 6 feet deep. Vegetation is very abundant, especially in summer, and consists of water lilies, pickerelweed, potamegetons, wild rice, bladderwort, water-milfoil, cat-tails, and shrubs. There are some floating islands of plant debris. The animal inhabitants consist of suckers, bullheads, yellow perch, sunfish, rock bass, smallmouth and largemouth black bass, golden shiners, blunt-nosed minnows, black-chinned shiners, northern black-nosed shiners, mud minnows, Iowa darter tadpoles, leopard frogs and bullfrogs, four species of turtles, and water snakes. Various forms of phytoplankton, zooplankton, and water insects are plentiful. The highest water temperature recorded was 89°F. in July.

The muskellunge grows to a large size and needs plenty of room and a rich supply of forage fish. This would require extensive borders of fertile waters. Eddy and Surber (22 *g.r.*) say the spawning sites in Minnesota are in tributary streams and shallow lake channels, rather than in weed beds.

Fishing Methods and Game Status. "Muskies" are caught by numerous methods, one of the most common being to sit with a line and hook baited with a live minnow or a gob of night crawlers and wait for the fish to take the bait. In Lake St. Clair area more than five times more fish are caught by trolling than by still fishing. When the still fisherman catches one, however, it is usually a big one. For trolling, all kinds of lures are used including plugs, spinners, minnows (live and dead) and enough hardware to almost sink a boat. The black-and-white daredevil is one of the most consistent lures (72).

As to size, the "muskies" run to various lengths and weights. Williams (72) speaks of the granddaddy of all "muskies" as weighing 110 pounds and being more than 7 feet long. It was caught in Intermediate Lake in Antrim County, Michigan, in 1919. Many are speared through the ice during the winter period.

New York State has adopted the following policies for muskellunge fishing on Chautauqua lake:

1. Limit fishing to a season from July 1 to October 15
2. Limit the number of fish per fisherman to one fish a day and five fish during a season
3. Use of a metal line (except a 6-foot leader) is prohibited
4. Maximum number of hook points is limited to six
5. Limit legal length to 32 inches or above
6. Prohibit the use of a gaff
7. A special 25-cent "muskie" license is required in Chautauqua and Cattaraugus Counties (except Lake Erie)

YELLOW PERCH *Perca flavescens*

Description. The yellow perch is the best known of the pan fish. It lives in almost any permanent water either stream or lake and will eagerly bite on almost any type of natural bait. The night crawler is one

FIG. 24-12. The yellow perch, both a game and commercial fish, is well known for its fine eating qualities. (*New York Zoological Society.*)

of its favorite foods. It is big game to the youthful fisherman wetting a line for the first time and is a standard item for the experienced fisherman. Where yellow perch have room and food enough to grow to large size, they provide excellent sport for any fisherman and supply some of the finest flesh of all the finny tribe. In large lakes, including the Great

Lakes, it is an item of prime importance to the commercial fishermen. The fact that it feeds during the winter makes it a favorite of the ice fisherman as well. Even with a heavy fishing take, its numbers have held up well and it has diminished only where pollution or destruction of its spawning places and crowding of too many fish into a small space has occurred.

The yellow perch is dark bronze on the back, grading to a white or bright-yellow color on the sides and lower parts. The pectoral fins are likely to be a very bright orange color. The head is pointed, the eyes prominent, and the sides have alternating vertical bars of dark and lighter color. The anterior dorsal fin has spiny rays.

Age, Size, and Growth. The growth and size of the yellow perch depends on the extent of the food supply (34). Table 24-11 gives the age and total length of a sample of 7,314 fish.

Distribution. Hubbs and Lagler (34 *g.r.*) give the distribution of yellow perch as extending from Nova Scotia to South Carolina, going west to southern Kansas, and north across Missouri, Wisconsin, and the Great Lakes to the Hudson Bay drainage of eastern Canada. It has been introduced into many waters. In New England it is found in most of the rivers and lakes, and except where infested with grubs, is an excellent pan fish. Grubs appear to develop to a greater degree in excessively warm waters and cause the perch so infested to be shunned by fishermen.

Habits. Young perch are hatched in shallow water either along sandy beaches or among the weeds of a bay or pond border. They stay in schools and often forage very close to shore. As they grow larger they move into deeper or more open waters and take on a regular pattern of feeding and moving about. In Lake Mendota, Wisconsin, it was found that perch form in schools and make daily migrations at sunrise and sunset from May to October. The fish move shoreward just before sunset and cruise along the shore in 18 to 20 feet of water until the sun goes down (29).

The most conspicuous seasonal movement of yellow perch takes place during the spring spawning migration during April or May. At this time in the Great Lakes and other large bodies of water, spawning fish move shoreward and cruise along the shores in search of suitable spawning sites. They also move about and feed freely during the winter.

Spawning. Hoover (35) gives the age at which yellow perch spawn as 3 to 4 years. The spawning fish move to sandy shallow waters and spawn at a temperature of 44 to 49°F. (42). The eggs are laid in long accordionlike strings that absorb water as they are laid and settle to the bottom. A female weighing ½ pound may spawn 10,000 to 15,000 eggs and larger ones up to 48,000 (22 *g.r.*). The eggs hatch in 27 days in

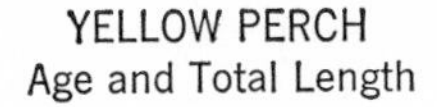

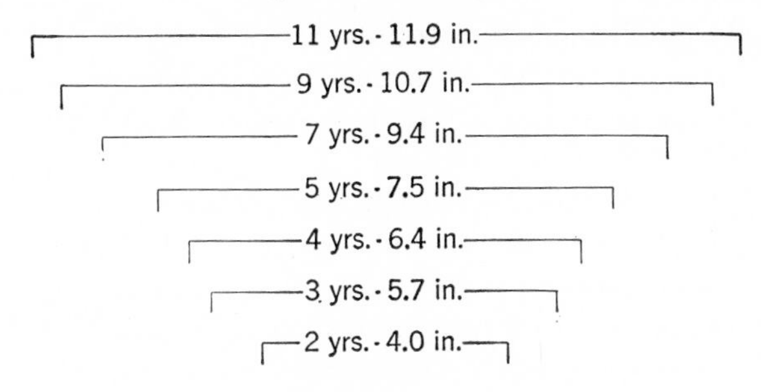

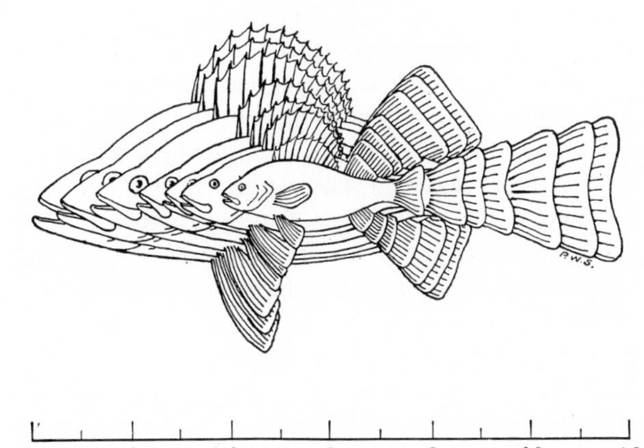

FIG. 24-13. Length and age relationship of the yellow perch (7).

water of 47°F. (64). Many of the eggs are eaten or destroyed, but the numbers are so prodigious that plenty are left. The limitation of most waters is that there is not enough food to allow the fish that survive to

Table 24-11. Age and Length of Yellow Perch from 198 Michigan Lakes (7) (Basis 7,314)

Age in growing seasons, Jan. 1	*Total length, in.*
1	2.0
2	4.0
3	5.7
4	6.4
5	7.5
6	8.4
7	9.4
8	10.3
9	10.7
10	11.2
11	11.9

grow to good size, or inadequate predation or harvest does not limit the numbers sufficiently.

Food. Young perch begin feeding on plankton crustaceans soon after they are hatched. As they grow larger they take larger aquatic forms including crustacea, copepods, mollusks, crayfish, insects and many species of fish including their own kind. Ewers (25) gives the food taken from Lake Erie as copepods, cladocera insects, and fish. They will feed on large mayflies as they emerge and also any kind of small animal life. Perch are caught on artificial flies, minnows, perch eyes, grasshoppers, and night crawlers. The usual bait for fishing through the ice is minnows, or just a bright spoon with a hook attached and operated with a sharp up-and-down movement to give a flashing display.

Habitat. The habitat of yellow perch varies widely and indicates the extreme tolerance of this fish for its surroundings. It may be found in large rivers, small streams, weedy ponds and flowages, and in large bays and lakes including Lake Champlain and the Great Lakes.

In the larger bodies of water large perch are often caught several miles offshore among the weed beds that find anchorage in the sandy bottom. The channels of rivers are favorite places and appear to be particularly attractive to the older and larger fish. The channels between islands along the shores of Georgian Bay and Lake Huron and connecting the various lakes are favorite places for this fish.

Physical and Chemical Limits. The temperature tolerance of the yellow perch is high. It seems to do well in shallow and warm as well as in deep, cold lakes. In the latter it is quite free from parasites, and its flesh is solid and fine-flavored. Oxygen demands are apparently not great.

Game Status. The yellow perch is one of the best of our game fish. It is easily caught and so abundant that even the most clumsy fisherman can catch it. Its flesh is of the highest quality. As a forage fish it is the bread and butter for many other game fish, including the northern pike and black bass.

The one drawback to yellow perch is its tendency to be too successful and take over a water by sheer numbers. Such fish fail to grow to large size because of lack of food.

YELLOW PIKE-PERCH OR WALLEYED PIKE

Stizostedion vitreum vitreum

Description. The pike-perch or walleyed pike is both a sport and a commercial fish. It is not a hard fighter on the end of a line, but its flesh is of such fine quality that it is always popular with the sport fisherman. It is very prolific so stands heavy utilization without loss of numbers (3).

The pike-perch is an elongated fish with a broad caudal fin and dark mottled spots on the back and sides. It belongs to the spiny-rayed group and has sharp barbs in the rays of the anterior dorsal fin. The background color may appear yellow, white, or blue, depending on the type of habitat.

FIG. 24-14. The pike-perch, or walleyed pike. Gravid female, weighing 10 pounds 15 ounces, from Saginaw Bay. (*Institute of Fisheries Research, Michigan Conservation Department.*)

Age, Size, and Growth. The walleyed pike may attain lengths of 3 feet and weights of 15 to 18 pounds (22 *g.r.*) but seldom grows longer than 28 inches. Fish of heavy weight are usually deep in girth. The record walleyed pike for New York State was taken in 1945 in Butterfield Lake, Saratoga County, and weighed 14 pounds (1). An age-length table for fish from Lake of the Woods, Minnesota, is given below.

Table 24-12. Age and Length of Walleyed Pike from Lake of the Woods, Minnesota (14)
(Basis 2,898 fish)

Age in growing seasons, Jan. 1	*Total length, in.*
1	6.4
2	9.3
3	11.5
4	13.4
5	14.8
6	16.7
7	18.2
8	19.9
9	21.6
10	22.7
11	23.9
12	24.3
13	25.6
14	26.4

The age and size of mature fish, ready to produce young, will of course vary with the latitude, coldness of the water, and amount of food available (21). The following conditions of age and size of maturity are given for Lake of the Woods, Minnesota, Clear Lake, Iowa, and Lake Erie (14, 15):

Water	Age at maturity, years		Size at maturity, total length, in.	
	Male	Female	Male	Female
Lake of the Woods	4	5–6	11.4–13.7	17.3
Lake Erie	. .	. . .	13.0–13.5	14.0–14.5
Clear Lake	2	3	12.0	13.0–14.0

Habits. Perhaps the most conspicuous movements of walleyed pike are their attempts to move up a river tributary where it is blocked by a dam. Here in the limited pools below such dams the fish accumulate in unbelievable numbers and often leave huge quantities of spawn on the dam apron and rocks.

Young walleyed pike are hatched in shallow water and remain in these locations where their natural food supply is found. As they gain in size they move to deeper water and are found in water up to 2 feet deep during midsummer. Raney and Lachner (48) reported them still in schools in September, but they had moved to water 10 to 12 feet deep by that time. There seemed to be no particular choice of bottom selected by the young fish, as they were found over sand and gravel, rock or silt. They were consistently found near rooted plants, however.

The adults make their way back to deeper water after the spawning runs. During the summer they are found in water from 6 to 20 feet deep (48). Usually in both lakes and rivers they will be found in the deepest holes and grouped near rocky ledges and crevices during the daytime. At night they move to the shallow parts of their habitat to feed (15).

In a study of tagged fish in a large lake in Minnesota, it was found that after spawning the mature fish moved around freely and distributed themselves over the entire lake. One of the interesting points of the study was the estimate of 15 to 20 adult walleyed pike per acre of water. Spawning fish tend to return to the same spawning ground each year (55).

The all-time record movement by tagged walleyed pike has come from Ohio where a fish of unknown origin moved 435 miles downstream. The maximum upstream movement was 25 miles. Native walleyed pike in this experiment moved an average of 13 miles, while introduced ones moved 43 miles. Seventy-nine per cent moved downstream (70).

Spawning. The spawning run starts soon after the ice goes out and may occur in the North during April or May. The spawning temperature is 38 to 44°F. Spawning beds include ripples in tributary streams or gravel reefs in shallow waters of lakes. According to Eddy and Surber (22 *g.r.*), the males precede the females on the spawning beds by a few days. Spawning females are usually much larger than males and may produce as many as 388,000 eggs for a large individual (22 *g.r.*). The number of eggs produced by 3 to 3½-pound fish is from 72,000 to 110,000. On the average, 2 males spawn with 1 female. The eggs are scattered promiscuously in the waters of the hatchery stream. Where spawning occurs in the headwaters of a stream, the adults stay in the vicinity of the spawning grounds for a period of several weeks.

Food. The food of adult walleyed pike is mostly fish. Forbes and Richardson estimated that it would take between 1,800 and 3,000 forage fish to produce a 3-pound walleyed pike. When we consider that some females weigh from 8 to 15 pounds and may produce 300,000 eggs, the amount of food needed is prodigious. Unlike many fish, the walleyed pike feeds through the winter, so the rate of growth and the amount of food consumed are increased to this extent.

The tendency of walleyed pike to eat each other is apparent soon after the fish hatch. As a result of this cannibalistic tendency the usual practice of hatcherymen is to plant walleyed fry soon after they are hatched.

The natural food of young walleyed pike consists of the following groups (53): rotifers, copopods, cladocerans, insects, and fishes. As the fish develop in size, the tendency is to feed less on the upper members of the list and to take more of the larger forms. Finally the young fish begin to feed almost exclusively on fish, although not entirely so. Food of young walleyed pike collected during the summer from Oneida Lake, New York, showed that these middle-sized pike lived on a diet of 92 per cent fish and the remaining 8 per cent insects, crustaceans, and mollusks. The fishes eaten included perch, darters, bass, sunfish, and minnows (five species), killifish and suckers. Other food organisms are caddis flies, mayflies, midges, copopods, water fleas, and scuds; the mollusks eaten were snails (48).

Food of larger walleyed pike in Michigan waters is 40 to 99 per cent fish, mostly yellow perch (30). Aquatic insects, especially mayflies, were found to be second in importance. The walleyed pike feeds in late afternoon or after dark and mostly close to the bottom except when mayflies are emerging; then it may follow the emerging nymphs to the surface. Hazzard calls attention to the fact that the streamer fly is an effective bait when the mayflies are hatching.

In the food predilection of the walleyed pike feeding on yellow perch, we have the phenomena of two fish living together where one is the predator of the other. The yellow perch is so versatile in its environmental relations and its prolific breeding habits that it is well able to keep ahead of its larger relative, even though it furnishes as much as 99 per cent of the food for the walleyed pike.

Habitat. The walleyed pike is often referred to as a fish of mystery. It is widespread in its distribution and high in popularity with fishermen everywhere. It is sought eagerly by commercial fishermen because of its large size and fine table qualities.

The habitat of the walleyed pike is the larger lakes and rivers of central eastern United States and Canada. It tends to move considerable distances, so a lake must be large or have connecting links with other lakes or large rivers to suit its needs.

No one seems to be quite sure about the details of a suitable habitat. Walleyed pike live in such large bodies of water and move about so freely that it is difficult to discover their exact requirements. In the east they are found in the Connecticut River and the St. Lawrence waterway but not in great abundance. Their center of abundance appears to be the Great Lakes, particularly the bays and large rivers such as the Detroit and St. Clair Rivers and the larger lakes in Minnesota and the central Canadian provinces. They are recommended for lakes with medium to hard water, but not soft-water lakes. This may be related to the type of organism needed to support the young until they reach a size where they feed on other fishes. In addition they are found in waters with sandy or rocky bottoms as well as near weed beds. It is probably this association with perch or some other prolific fish that provides a food supply of sufficient proportions to support a vigorous feeder like the walleyed pike.

In summary, the walleyed pike needs a body of water advanced in the ecological scale beyond the trout stage, but not so advanced as that needed by largemouth black bass and bullheads. Lakes with cold water, deep holes, sandy beaches, and some weed beds, and rivers with rocky ledges and a swift flow of cold pure water are necessary for ideal conditions. Man-controlled operations also seem to fit the needs of the walleyed pike. Each year walleyed spawners run up to the Hardy and Newaygo dams of the Muskegon River in Michigan and are lifted over by the conservation department. The fish spawn in the reservoirs, and the young move out of the river in their first or second year, many going through the power turbines unharmed. Thus the reservoir provides a nursery spot for the walleyed pike but also supplies both sport and commercial fishing in the reservoir, the river, and Lake Michigan (30).

Green Bay along northern Lake Michigan is a locality of special interest for walleyed pike fishermen. Here the production of walleyed pike rose from a 14-year average of 51,000 pounds to a high of over a million pounds in a short period of 6 years. It is thought the big increase in 1947 was due to an exceptionally good survival of young fish hatched in 1943. Green Bay is a typical sandy- and rock-bottomed arm of Lake Michigan large enough to be suitable for walleyed pike, yellow perch, and other lake fish life (30, 32).

Saginaw Bay, another high producer of walleyed pike, is an arm of Lake Huron. It, too, has sandy shores and sandy and rocky bottom and a large river feeding into it. Eschmeyer (24) says walleyed pike also do well in a lake with a stony, wave-washed shore line.

Game Status. The walleyed pike fisherman is no specialist as a rule. When walleyed pike are biting, almost anyone with a line, sinker, hook, and a few minnows can obtain a string of these fish. At other times walleyed pike angling is not so easy, and the fisherman has to use his best talents to obtain a satisfactory return for his efforts. Trolling slowly with bait near the bottom is a common way to obtain these fish. The bait may be a spinner and night crawlers or a minnow impaled on the hook. Casting with a spinning outfit or fly fishing with a streamer fly also brings results. Fishing through the ice with live bait is successful in many northern lakes in the United States and Canada. Commercial fishing with nets is practiced in many parts of the Great Lakes and the larger lakes of Minnesota and Canada.

The results of walleyed pike fishing are usually most satisfactory. The walleyed pike lives in such a desirable habitat and has such tasty flesh that it provides an excellent product both on the end of the line and in the skillet. No one who has tasted crisp golden-brown walleyed pike will ever speak disparagingly of its quality. Its universal distribution makes the species available to a wide segment of fishermen.

NORTHERN BROWN BULLHEAD *Ameiurus nebulosus*

Description. There are several species and subspecies of the catfishes and bullheads, but only the northern brown bullhead will be considered here.

The color of the bullhead is solid brown or black above and lighter below, either yellow or light brown. The tail fin is only slightly forked, and the anal fin is rounding in outline. It has a smooth skin rather than scales and appears to be able to obtain oxygen from moist air as well as from water. If the water dries up or freezes over, it buries itself in the mud. Its sensibilities are not very sharp, as it will bite again after being once caught or with a hook in its mouth. The mouth is large and ringed with soft barbels. A sharp spear adorns both the pectoral fins and the front ray of the dorsal fin. No one who has had experience with these poisoned spears will ever mistake the bullhead for any other fish. These consist of sharp spines in the forward edge of its dorsal as well as the pectoral fins. You may take a firm hold of the fish to remove the hook, and at just the right instant these poisoned spears will be erected with the result that several punctures are made in your hand. These will be painful for several hours after the wound is inflicted.

The flesh of the bullhead is sweet and nutritious. In order to be edible, however, the very tough skin must be removed. This process can be accomplished by dipping the "critter" in boiling water for a few seconds. An eightpenny nail through the head and a pair of pliers will help in the operation.

Age, Size, and Growth. The bullhead seldom exceeds a foot in total length or a pound in weight. Eight to ten inches is the ordinary length. Whether the condition of fertility is high or low, the size and condition of the bullheads present appear to be related to the total number of fish the pond is supporting.

Distribution. Hubbs and Lagler (34 *g.r.*) give the distribution of the brown bullhead as southern Canada from North Dakota to the Great Lakes and St. Lawrence basin south to Virginia, the Ohio Valley, southern Illinois, and eastern Arkansas. Bullheads have been widely scattered through artificial planting, so this range may not be entirely accurate.

Habits. The bullhead has a mode of family life not duplicated in many of the fish families. The young stay in schools throughout their first summer and are herded into tightly grouped masses soon after hatching. Their nursery is the shallow water along a shore and is usually associated with plenty of vegetation (64).

Both young and adults are more active at night than in the daytime. Because of the advantage of sense organs in the end of the feelers they are able to select suitable food and find their way about with the aid of these feelers which extend out in all directions around their enormous mouths. Apparently feeding is reduced during the breeding season from May to July.

The adults, both male and female, may guard the eggs and the young after the eggs hatch. They fan the eggs to keep them aerated and clean of silt and after hatching herd the young together and keep other fish away from them. Thorpe (64) says the bullhead often feeds near the surface of the water on emerging mayflies. Otherwise it stays near the bottom and probably does not move very far from a choice location.

Spawning. Spawning may occur any time between May and late July (1). The mature adults make circular shallow nests in the mud of the bottom. Depth of water may vary from 6 inches to 4 feet. Thorpe (64) says the nests are usually sheltered by logs, rocks, or vegetation. The eggs are arranged in cream-colored strings. One female may produce as many as 6,000 to 13,000 (22 *g.r.*). The eggs hatch in from 7 to 14 days in water with a temperature of 77°F. (35, 64).

Food. Water fleas form the first food of young bullheads. Midge larvae, larvae of aquatic insects, ostracods, and crustaceans are eaten as the fish grow larger (49, 64). A study of stomachs of bullheads from lakes in eastern South Dakota showed that bullheads eat both plant and animal foods and, rarely, the eggs and young of other fish. Other foods include bivalve mollusks, snails, etc. (11). Mayflies are eaten as the latter hatch and emerge from the bottom of a stream or pond. Earthworms are also eaten (64).

Analysis of the food of 170 young bullheads taken from Cayuga Lake, New York, showed the staple foods to be crustacea, 60 per cent; insects (*Diptera*), 25 per cent. Almost all the diptera were chironomid larvae, while 80 per cent of the crustacea were ostracods and cladocerans (49).

Habitat. The bullhead has great versatility in its choice of habitats. Where waters are extensive, as in Lake Champlain, it finds suitable locations in deep muddy holes where the fine mud accumulates in deep pockets. In general, bullheads like deep water, and in muddy river tributaries they will be found in the deepest holes.

Game Status. Bullhead fishing is the choice sport of many fishermen and is usually enjoyed at night from May to October. The hook may be baited with night crawlers (or even red string) and allowed to rest on the bottom. Feeding bullheads are not frightened readily and many may be caught from a very small area. Bullhead fishermen are so numerous as to outnumber all others. When cleaned and fried to a crisp brown, bullheads will tempt an epicure.

WHITE PERCH *Morone americana*

Description. The white perch is classified as a marine river bass. Another member of the same group is the striped bass that is so popular in New England coastal waters during the summer period and migrates up some of the rivers along the Atlantic Coast to spawn. The white perch has become landlocked in many New England ponds and lakes and biologically is one of the least known of our fresh-water fishes. It is about the same size as the yellow perch in suitable inland waters, having a form much like the bass and a very desirable type of flesh. It has a tolerance for both shallow warm waters and deep cold lakes and a tendency like its namesake, the yellow perch, to overpopulate its environment.

The color of the white perch is an over-all white or silver with scales that are large and conspicuous. The lateral line is dark-colored and shows up prominently against the lighter background. The head is pointed and the eyes bright.

Age, Size, and Growth. White perch grow to a good size in some ponds but remain small and stunted in others. Cooper (17) gives the age and body length of different ages from measurements taken from 43 lakes and ponds in Maine.

Table 24-13. Age and Length of White Perch Taken from 43 Lakes in Maine (17)

Age in growing seasons, Jan. 1	Total length, in.	Weight, oz.
1		
2		
3	6.1	
4	7.0	3.0
5	9.2	2.4
6	9.3	4.3
7	9.8	4.7
8	9.8	6.0
9	10.6	7.3
10	11.5	7.6
11	....	8.5
12	....	9.6
13	....	12.9
14	....	13.8

White perch grow to good size in suitable waters, as is indicated for some fish from ponds in the Connecticut watershed of New Hampshire. Warfel (67) took a white perch 13½ inches long from Lary Pond, Canaan, New Hampshire. Such a fish, if in good condition, would weigh a pound or more.

The growing season for this species as far north as northern Maine extends from about the first of July to the middle of September.

Distribution. The white perch is found in the coastal waters of eastern North America from Nova Scotia to Florida. It is not found to any extent far from the coast, but has probably been stocked in most of the ponds in New England and New York State.

Habits. Little is known of the daily or seasonal movements of the white perch. Thorpe (64) says the young have a nocturnal inshore movement and are found over sandy shoals in some Connecticut lakes. Large individuals also move inshore to feed at night. In the daytime the adults are taken in nets in 10 to 20 feet of water, particularly in locations where there is a scarcity of aquatic weeds. Apparently these fish feed any time of day or night.

Spawning. The spawning period occurs in the spring and early summer from June to August. In Connecticut white perch spawn from the middle of June to August 1. Spawning occurs on sand and gravel bars in tributary streams and also on sand or gravel along the shorelines of ponds. The eggs are small and sticky. They hatch in 48 to 52 hours in water temperatures of 60°F. (64). Hoover (35) estimates the fish reach sexual maturity at 3 years of age.

Food. Few data on the food of immature perch are available. It is believed the fry feed on plankton. The summer diet of fish over 6 inches in length is as follows (17):

Groups of organisms	*Per cent of volume*
Crustaceans	12.00
Aquatic insects	60.29
Fish	26.27
Other	1.44
Total	100.00

Of the fish taken, only smelt, yellow, and white perch were found. Of the insects, mayfly nymphs were the most abundant.

In Massachusetts the food of adult white perch collected from 12 lakes during the summer period consists of 42.1 per cent insects, 37.6 per cent crustaceans, 13.3 per cent fish, and 7 per cent plants and unidentified materials (42).

Habitat. The white perch is a versatile fish, being found in deep, cold-water lakes as well as in shallow, warm ponds. Lakes suitable for white perch may be large or small. For example, Sabbathday Lake in Cumberland County at the headwaters of the Royal River, Maine, where white perch are abundant, is 1½ miles long, ½ mile wide, and has an area of approximately 400 acres. Maximum depth of the lake is 73 feet and three-fourths of the lake is 40 feet deep. The bottom is mostly rubble and boulders, with a thin mud deposit in the deep part of the lake. The water is clear. There is practically no aquatic vegetation. Sandy Pond is only 107 acres and is mostly 10 to 20 feet deep. Both have white perch.

Physical and Chemical Limits. Hoover (35) gives the temperature and chemical requirements for white perch as follows: over 75°F. in summer; pH range, 6 to 9 ppm; oxygen minimum, 3 ppm; carbon dioxide, not over 20 ppm. The fish enter brackish waters freely and will live in either fresh- or salt-water habitats.

Game Status. The white perch along the Atlantic Coast hold about the same economic place as do the yellow perch farther inland. They are nearly always present and keep the angler employed, and sometimes annoyed, by forcing him to take perch from his hook and replace his bait. In Connecticut anglers take tons of this fish from lakes and ponds, and no doubt this condition prevails during the summer fishing season in other New England waters (64). Frequently white perch are of small size, indicating the tendency of overpopulations.

Where white perch grow to good size, many fishermen consider them an excellent fish both to catch and to eat. While the food habits of this species does not indicate undue competition with more desirable species, it is a foregone conclusion that a lake overcrowded with white perch probably interferes with the development of other and perhaps better fish. Thorpe (64) suggests that white perch should not be planted in lakes or ponds where they are not already present.

REFERENCES

1. Adams, Charles C., and Thomas L. Hankison. 1928. The ecology and economics of Oneida Lake fish. *N.Y. State Col. Forestry, Syracuse Univ., Bul.* **1**(3–4):235–548.
2. Anonymous. 1941. Muskie catches. *Wis. Conserv. Bul.* **6**(9):43.
3. ———. 1941. Ways of the walleye. *Ohio Dept. Agr. Div. Conserv. and Nat. Resources, News Release,* January 22, 1941.
4. ———. 1946. Just a matter of record. *New York Conserv.* **1**(1):26.
5. Ball, Robert C. 1948. Relationship between available fish food, feeding habits of fish and total fish production in a Michigan lake. *Mich. Agr. Expt. Sta. Tech. Bul.* 206.
6. Beckman, William C. 1941. Meet Mr. Bluegill. *Mich. Conserv.* **10**(7): 6–7, 11.
7. ———. 1946. The rate of growth and sex ratio of seven Michigan fishes. *Trans. Amer. Fisheries Soc.* **76**:63–81.
8. Belding, David L. 1925. A new method of studying fish environment and determining the suitability of waters for stocking. *Trans. Amer. Fisheries Soc.* **55**:79–82.
9. Boesel, M. W. 1937. The food of nine species of fish from the western end of lake Erie. *Trans. Amer. Fisheries Soc.* **67**:215–223.
10. Bordner, John S. 1942. Inventory of northern Wisconsin Lakes. *Wis. Dept. Agr., Div. Land Economic Survey, Bul.* 228.
11. Cable, Louella E. 1928. Food of bullheads. *U.S. Bur. Fisheries Doc.* 1037.
12. Carbine, W. F. 1939. Observations on the spawning habits of *Centrarchid* fishes in Deep Lake, Oakland County, Michigan. *Trans. 4th* North *Amer. Wildlife Conf.* Pp. 275–87.
13. ———. 1941. Observations on the life history of the northern pike, *Esox lucius* L., in Houghton Lake, Michigan. *Trans. Amer. Fisheries Soc.* **71**:149–164.
14. Carlander, Kenneth D. 1943. Age, growth, sexual maturity and population fluctuations of yellow pike-perch, *Stizostedion vitreum vitreum* (Mitchill), with reference to commercial fisheries, Lake of the Woods, Minnesota. *Trans. Amer. Fisheries Soc.* **73**:90–107.
15. ——— and Robert E. Cleary. 1949. The daily activity pattern of some freshwater fishes. *Amer. Midland Nat.* **41**(2):447–452.
16. Cooper, Gerald P. 1936. Food habits, rate of growth and cannibalism of young largemouth bass (*Aplites salmoides*) in state-operated rearing ponds in Michigan during 1935. *Trans. Amer. Fisheries Soc.* **66**:242–266.
17. ———. 1941. A biological survey of lakes and ponds of the Androscoggin

and Kennebec river drainage systems in Maine. *Dept. Inland Fisheries and Game Survey Rpt.* 4.
18. Dequine, John F., and Charles E. Hall, Jr. 1949. Results of some tagging studies of the Florida largemouth bass *Micropterus salmoides floridanus* (LeSueur). *Trans. Amer. Fisheries Soc.* **79**:155–166.
19. Doan, Kenneth H. 1940. Studies of smallmouth bass. *Jour. Wildlife Mangt.* **4**(3):241–266.
20. Douchette, Earle. (No date). The fisherman's guide to Maine, Random House, New York.
21. Eddy, Samuel, and Kenneth Carlander. 1939. The growth rate of wall-eye pike (*Stizostedion vitreum* [Mitchill]) in various lakes of Minnesota. *Proc. Minn. Acad. Sci.* **7**:44–48.
22. ———. 1942. Growth rate studies of Minnesota fish. *Minn. Conserv. Dept., Div. Inland Fisheries and Game, Bur. Fisheries Res. Investigational Rpt.* 28.
23. Elson, Paul F. 1940. Rearing maskinonge in a protected area. *Trans. Amer. Fisheries Soc.* **70**:421–429.
24. Eschmeyer, Paul H. 1948. The life history of the walleye, *Stizostedion vitreum vitreum* (Mitchill), in Michigan. *Institute of Fisheries Res. Bul.* 3.
25. Ewers, Lela A. 1933. Summary report of crustacea used as food by the fishes of the western end of Lake Erie. *Trans. Amer. Fisheries Soc.* **63**:379–390.
26. Foote, Leonard E., and Bradford P. Blake. 1945. Life history of the eastern pickerel in Babcock Pond, Connecticut. *Jour. Wildlife Mangt.* **9**(2):89–99.
27. Fosburgh, Pete. 1947. The punkie. *New York Conserv.* **1**(6):21.
28. Fry, F. E. J. 1947. South Bay Experiment. Advance report on smallmouth bass (*Micropterus dolomieu*). *Ontario Dept. Lands and Forests, Advance Rpt.* 1.
29. Hasler, Arthur D., and John E. Bardack. 1949. Daily migrations of perch in Lake Mendota, Wisconsin. *Jour. Wildlife Mangt.* **13**(1):40–51.
30. Hazzard, Albert S. 1951. The walleye—fish of mystery. *Michigan Conserv.* **20**(4):6–8, 28–29.
31. Heacox, Cecil. 1946. The Chautauqua Lake muskellunge: research and management applied to a sport fishery. *Trans. 11th North Amer. Wildlife Conf.* Pp. 419–425.
32. Hile, Ralph. 1936. The increase in the abundance of the yellow pike-perch, *Stizostedion vitreum* (Mitchill), in Lakes Huron and Michigan, in relation to the artificial propagation of the species. *Trans. Amer. Fisheries Soc.* **66**:143–159.
33. ———. 1950. Green Bay walleyes. *The Fisherman.*
34. ——— and Frank W. Jobes. 1940. Age, growth and production of yellow perch. *Perca flavescens* (Mitchill), of Saginaw Bay. *Trans. Amer. Fisheries Soc.* **70**:102–122.
35. Hoover, Earl E. (No date). Preliminary biological survey of some New Hampshire lakes. *N.H. Fish and Game Dept. Survey Bul.* 1.
36. Hubbs, Carl L., and Reeve M. Bailey. 1938. The smallmouthed bass. *Cranbrook Inst. Sci. Bul.* 10.
37. Huber, W. B., and L. E. Binkley. (No date). Reproduction and growth of the white crappie (*Pomoxis annularis*) in Meander Lake. *U.S. Dept. Agr., Div. of Conserv., Bur. Sci. Res. Bul.* 91.

38. Jones, Alden M. 1940. Length of the growing season of largemouth and smallmouth black bass in Norris reservoir, Tennessee. *Trans. Amer. Fisheries Soc.* **70**:183–187.
39. Krumholz, Louis A. 1947. Length-weight relationship of the muskellunge, *Esox m. masquinongy*, in Lake St. Clair. *Trans. Amer. Fisheries Soc.* **77**:42–48.
40. Lachner, Ernest A. 1950. Food, growth and habits of fingerling northern smallmouth bass, *Micropterus dolomieu dolomieu* Lacepede, in trout waters of western New York. *Jour. Wildlife Mangt.* **14**(1):50–56.
41. MacKay, H. H., and W. H. R. Werner. 1934. Some observations on the culture of maskinonge. *Trans. Amer. Fisheries Soc.* **64**:313–317.
42. McCabe, Britton C. 1946. Fisheries report for lakes of central Massachusetts, 1944–1945, Department of Conservation, Division of Fisheries and Game.
43. McNamara, Fred. 1936. Breeding and food habits of the pikes, (*Esox lucius* and *Esox vermiculatus*). *Trans. Amer. Fisheries Soc.* **66**:372–373.
44. Moffett, James W., and Burton P. Hunt. 1943. Winter feeding habits of bluegills, *Lepomis machrochirus* Rafinesque and yellow perch, *Perca flavescens* (Mitchill), in Cedar Lake, Washtenaw County, Michigan. *Trans. Amer. Fisheries Soc.* **73**:231–242.
45. Moyle, John B., Jerome H. Kuehn, and Charles R. Burrows. 1948. Fish population and catch data from Minnesota lakes. *Trans. Amer. Fisheries Soc.* **78**:163–175.
46. Pearse, A. S. 1919. Habits of the black crappie in inland lakes of Wisconsin. *U.S. Bur. Fisheries Doc.* 867, pp. 5–16.
47. Raney, Edward C. 1942. The summer food and habits of the chain pickerel (*Esox niger*) of a small New York pond. *Jour. Wildlife Mangt.* **6**(1):58–66.
48. ——— and Ernest A. Lachner. 1942. Studies of the summer food, growth and movements of young yellow pike-perch, *Stizostedion v. vitreum*, in Oneida Lake, New York. *Jour. Wildlife Mangt.* **6**(1):1–16.
49. ——— and Dwight A. Webster. 1939. The food and growth of the young of the common bullhead, *Ameiurus nebulosus nebulosus* (LeSueur), in Cayuga Lake, New York. *Trans. Amer. Fisheries Soc.* **69**:205–209.
50. Reid, George K., Jr. 1949. Food of the black crappie, *Poxomis nigromaculatus* (LeSueur), in Orange Lake, Florida. *Trans. Amer. Fisheries Soc.* **79**:145–154.
51. Seagears, Clayt. 1947. Making muskies. *New York Conserv.* **1**(6):10.
52. ———. 1947. The inside on the outdoors. *New York Conserv.* **1**(6):11.
53. Smith, Lloyd L., and John B. Moyle. 1943. Factors influencing production of yellow pike-perch, *Stizostedion vitreum vitreum*, in Minnesota rearing ponds. *Trans. Amer. Fisheries Soc.* **73**:243–261.
54. Stone, Urdell B. 1947. Chautauqua. *New York Conserv.* **1**(6):8–9.
55. Stout, Jerome H., and Samuel Eddy. 1939. Walleye pike study, 1937–1938, Chippewa National Forest. *Trans. 4th North Amer. Wildlife Conf.* Pp. 305–310.
56. Stroud, Richard H. 1948. Growth of the basses and black crappie in Norris Reservoir, Tennessee. *Tenn. Acad. Sci. Jour.* **23**(1):31–99.
57. ———. 1949. Growth of Norris Reservoir walleye during the first twelve years of impoundment. *Jour. Wildlife Mangt.* **13**(2):157–177.

58. Surber, Eugene W. 1940. A quantitative study of the food of small-mouth black bass, *Micropterus dolomieu,* in three eastern streams. *Trans. Amer. Fisheries Soc.* **70**:311–334.
59. ———. 1944. Variations in nitrogen content and fish production in small-mouth black bass ponds. *Trans. Amer. Fisheries Soc.* **74**:338–349.
60. Swartz, Albert H. 1942. Fisheries survey report, Department of Conservation, Division of Fisheries and Game.
61. Swingle, H. S., and E. V. Smith. 1942. Management of farm fish ponds. *Ala. Agr. Expt. Sta. Bul.* 254.
62. Tester, Albert L. 1930. Spawning habits of the small-mouthed bass in Ontario waters. *Trans. Amer. Fisheries Soc.* **60**:53–61.
63. ———. 1932. Food of the small-mouthed black bass (*Micropterus dolomieu*) in some Ontario waters. *Toronto Univ. Ontario Fisheries Res. Lab. Pub.* 46.
64. Thorpe, Lyle. 1942. A fisheries survey of important Connecticut Lakes. *State Bd. Fisheries and Game Bul.* 63.
65. Trautman, Milton B., and Carl L. Hubbs. 1948. When do pike shed their teeth? *Michigan Conserv.* **17**(8):4–5, 10.
66. Underhill, A. H. 1949. Studies of the development, growth and maturity of the chain pickerel, *Esox niger* LeSueur. *Jour. Wildlife Mangt.* **13**(4): 377–391.
67. Warfel, Herbert E. 1939. Biological survey of the Connecticut watershed. *N.H. Fish and Game Comn. Survey Rpt.* 4.
68. Webster, Dwight A. 1945. Relation of temperature to survival and incubation of the eggs of smallmouth bass (*Micropterus dolomieu*). *Trans. Amer. Fisheries Soc.* **75**:43–47.
69. Westman, James R., and Charlotte B. Westman. 1949. Population phenomena in certain game fishes of Lake Simcoe, Ontario, and some effects upon angling returns. Part 1. The smallmouth bass, *Micropterus dolomieu* Lacepede. *Canad. Jour. Res. Sect. D, Zool. Sci.* **27**:7–29.
70. Wickliff, Edward L. 1933. Returns from fish tagged in Ohio. *Trans. Amer. Fisheries Soc.* **63**:326–331.
71. ——— and M. B. Trautman. 1931. Some food and game fishes of Ohio. *Ohio Dept. Agr. Bur. Sci. Res. Bul.* 7.
72. Williams, John E. 1948. The muskellunge in Michigan. *Mich. Conserv.* **17**(10):10–11, 15.
73. Williamson, Lyman O. 1941. Muskie food. *Wis. Conserv. Bul.* **6**(2):14–18.

General References

1. Adams, Harry, and R. E. Trippensee. (No date). Wildlife handbook. U.S. Department of Agriculture, Forest Service, Region 9, Milwaukee.
2. Addy, C. A., and L. G. MacNamara. 1948. Waterfowl management on small areas. Wildlife Management Institute, Washington, D.C.
3. Aldrich, John W., *et al.* 1949. Migration of some North American waterfowl. *U.S. Fish and Wildlife Serv. Spec. Sci. Wildlife Rpt.: Wildlife* 1.
4. Anthony, H. E. 1928. Field book of North American mammals, G. P. Putnam's Sons, New York.
5. Ashbrook, Frank G. 1948. Fur—an important wildlife crop. *Fish and Wildlife Service, U. S. Department of the Interior.*
6. ———. 1951. Annual fur catch of the United States. *U.S. Fish and Wildlife Serv., Wildlife Leaflet* 315.
7. Bachrach, Max. 1946. Fur, Prentice-Hall, Inc., New York.
8. Beard, Daniel B., *et al.* 1942. Fading trails, The Macmillan Company, New York.
9. Bellrose, Frank C., Jr. 1944. Waterfowl hunting in Illinois: Its status and problems. *Ill. Nat. Hist. Survey Biol. Notes.* No. 7.
10. Bennett, Hugh Hammond. 1939. Soil conservation, McGraw-Hill Book Company, Inc., New York.
11. ———. 1950. The value of water resources. *The Saturday Evening Post.* **222**(May 13):32–33.
12. Bennitt, Rudolph, and Werner O. Nagel. 1937. A survey of the resident game and furbearers of Missouri. *Univ. Mo. Studies.* Vol. 12, No. 2.
13. Bent, Arthur Cleveland. 1951. Life histories of North American wild fowl order *Anseres,* Dover Publications, New York.
14. Burt, William H. 1948. The mammals of Michigan, University of Michigan Press, Ann Arbor.
15. Cahalane, Victor H. 1947. Mammals of North America, The Macmillan Company, New York.
16. Carlander, Kenneth D. 1950. Handbook of freshwater fishery biology, Iowa Cooperative Reservation Unit, Ames.
17. Cottam, Clarence. 1949. Limiting factors of present waterfowl knowledge. *Trans. 14th North Amer. Wildlife Conf.* Pp. 42–57.
18. Day, Albert M. 1949. North American waterfowl, Stackpole Co., Harrisburg, Pa.
19. ———. 1950. North American waterfowl. *Trans. 15th North Amer. Wildlife Conf.* Pp. 99–104.
20. Dearborn, Ned. 1932. Foods of some predatory fur-bearing animals in Michigan. *Univ. Mich. School Forestry and Conserv. Bul.* 1.
21. Dufrense, Frank. 1942. Mammals and birds of Alaska. *U.S. Fish and Wildlife Serv. Cir.* 3.

22. Eddy, Samuel, and Thaddeus Surber. 1943. Northern fishes, University of Minnesota Press, Minneapolis.
23. Farrington, S. Kip, Jr. 1945. The ducks came back, Coward-McCann, Inc., New York.
24. Gabrielson, Ira N. 1943. Wildlife refuges, The Macmillan Company, New York.
25. Graham, Edward H. 1947. The land and wildlife, Oxford University Press, New York.
26. Grange, Wallace Byron. 1949. The way to game abundance, Charles Scribner's Sons, New York.
27. Grimm, William C., and Harvey A. Roberts. 1950. Mammal survey of southwestern Pennsylvania, Pennsylvania Game Commission, Harrisburg.
28. Grinnell, Joseph, Joseph S. Dixon, and Jean M. Linsdale. 1937. Fur-bearing mammals of California, University of California Press, Berkeley.
29. Hamilton, W. J., Jr. 1939. American mammals, McGraw-Hill Book Company, Inc., New York.
30. Harshberger, John W. 1911. Phyto geographic survey of North America, G. E. Stechert & Company, New York.
31. Hochbaum, H. Albert. 1944. The canvasback on a prairie marsh, Wildlife Management Institute, Washington, D.C.
32. Hosley, N. W. 1938. Woody plants used by wildlife in the northeastern United States. Unpublished Ph.D. thesis, University of Michigan, Ann Arbor.
33. Hubbs, Carl L., and R. W. Eschmeyer. 1938. The improvement of lakes for fishing. *Univ. Mich. Inst. Fisheries Res. Bul.* 2.
34. —— and Karl F. Lagler. 1941. Guide to the fishes of the Great Lakes and tributary waters. *Cranbrook Inst. Sci. Bul.* 18.
35. Jordan, James S., and Frank C. Bellrose. 1951. Lead poisoning in wild waterfowl. *Ill. Nat. Hist. Surv. Biol. Notes* No. 26.
36. Kellogg, Charles E. 1939. Nutrition of fur animals. *U.S. Dept. Agr. Yearbook.*
37. ———. 1950*a*. Chinchilla raising. *U.S. Dept. Agr. Leaflet* 266.
38. ———. 1950*b*. Fur farming possibilities. *U.S. Dept. Agr. Leaflet* 267.
39. ———, Charles F. Bassett, and Robert K. Enders. 1948. Mink raising. *U.S. Dept. Agr. Cir.* 801.
40. Knight, H. G., *et al.* 1938. Soils and men. *U.S. Dept. Agr. Yearbook.*
41. Kortright, Francis H. 1943. The ducks, geese and swans of North America, Wildlife Management Institute, Washington, D.C.
42. Lane, Guy W. 1951. Trapping licenses sold in the United States July 1, 1950, to June 30, 1951, U.S. Fish and Wildlife Service, Department of the Interior.
43. Latham, Roger M. 1950. Food of predaceous animals in the northeastern United States. *Pa. Game Comn. Pittman-Robertson Proj.* 36-R. *Rpt.* 1.
44. Leitch, William G. 1951. Saving, maintaining and developing waterfowl habitat in western Canada. *Trans. 16th North Amer. Wildlife Conf.* Pp. 94–99.
45. Leopold, Aldo. 1933. Game management, Charles Scribner's Sons, New York.
46. Lincoln, Frederick C. 1950. Migration of birds. *U.S. Fish and Wildlife Serv., Cir.* 16.

47. McHugh, Tom. 1950. Underwater slaughter. *Hunting & Fishing.* **27**(2): 18–20.
48. Miller, Gerrit S., Jr. 1924. List of North American recent mammals, 1923. *U.S. Natl. Mus. Bul.* 128.
49. Miller, J. Paul, and Burwell B. Powell. 1942. Game and wild-fur production and utilization on agricultural land. *U.S. Dept. Agr. Cir.* 636.
50. Munro, David A. 1950. Review of waterfowl conditions in Canada. *Trans. 15th North Amer. Wildlife Conf.* Pp. 94–98.
51. Needham, Paul R. 1938. Trout streams, Comstock Publishing Co., Inc., Ithaca.
52. Newell, Frederick Haynes. 1920. Water resources present and future uses, Yale University Press, New Haven.
53. Petrides, George A. 1950. Determination of sex and age ratios in fur animals. *Amer. Midland Nat.* **43**(2):355–382.
54. Phillips, John C. 1923. A natural history of the ducks, Vol. 2, Houghton Mifflin Company, Boston.
55. ———. 1925. A natural history of the ducks, Vol. 3, Houghton Mifflin Company, Boston.
56. ———. 1926. A natural history of the ducks, Vol. 4, Houghton Mifflin Company, Boston.
57. ——— and Frederick C. Lincoln. 1930. American waterfowl, Houghton Mifflin Company, Boston.
58. Quick, H. F. 1950. Fur resources of a wilderness region in northern British Columbia. U.S. Office of Naval Research, Project ONR5.
59. Richmond, Neil D., and Harry R. Rosland. 1949. Mammal survey of northwestern Pennsylvania, Pennsylvania Game Commission and U.S. Fish and Wildlife Service, Harrisburg.
60. Schoonmaker, W. J. 1929. Weights of some New York mammals. *Jour. Mammal.* **10**(2):149–152.
61. Seton, Ernest Thompson. 1929. Lives of game animals, Doubleday & Company, Inc., New York.
62. Shortt and Cartwright. 1948. Sports Afield collection of know your ducks and geese, Sports Afield Publishing Company, Minneapolis.
63. Smith, G. Ennis. 1935. Experimental fox farming. *Rpts. Supt. Canad. Expt. Farms, 1931, 1932, 1933 and 1934, Summerside, Prince Edward Isle.*
64. Williams, Cecil S., and William H. Marshall. 1938. Duck nesting studies, Bear River Migratory Bird Refuge, Utah, 1937. *Jour. Wildlife Mangt.* **2**(2):29–48.
65. Wing, Leonard W. 1951. Practice of wildlife conservation, John Wiley & Sons, Inc., New York.
66. Wright, Bruce S. 1948. Waterfowl as a forest product in eastern Canada. *Forestry Chron.* **24**(4):266–269.
67. Yeager, Lee E. 1941. Contribution toward a bibliography on North American fur animals. *Ill. Nat. Hist. Survey Biol. Notes.* No. 16.
68. Yocom, Charles F. 1950. Weather and its effects on hatching of waterfowl in eastern Washington. *Trans. 15th North Amer. Wildlife Conf.* Pp. 309–318.
69. ———. 1951. Waterfowl and their food plants in Washington, University of Washington Press, Seattle.

Index

Boldface numerals indicate main discussion of the topic and references

H

I

J

K

L

N

O

P

T

U

V

W